ENGINEERING SOCIETIES MONOGRAPHS

Harrison W. Craver, *Consulting Editor*

THEORY OF
ELASTIC STABILITY

The quality of the materials used in the manufacture of this book is governed by continued postwar shortages.

˙ ENGINEERING SOCIETIES MONOGRAPHS

F͟OUR national engineering societies, the American Society of Civil Engineers, American Institute of Mining and Metallurgical Engineers, The American Society of Mechanical Engineers, and American Institute of Electrical Engineers, have made arrangements with the McGraw-Hill Book Company, Inc., for the production of selected books adjudged to possess usefulness for engineers or industry, but not likely to be published commercially because of too limited sale without special introduction. The societies assume no responsibility for any statements made in these books. Each book before publication has, however, been examined by one or more representatives of the societies competent to express an opinion on the merits of the manuscript.

ENGINEERING SOCIETIES MONOGRAPHS COMMITTEE

·Engineering Societies Library,
New York

THEORY OF
ELASTIC STABILITY

BY

S. TIMOSHENKO

Professor of Theoretical and Applied Mechanics
Stanford University

FIRST EDITION
SEVENTH IMPRESSION

McGRAW-HILL BOOK COMPANY, INC.
NEW YORK AND LONDON
1936

THE MAPLE PRESS COMPANY, YORK, PA.

ENGINEERING SOCIETIES MONOGRAPHS

For many years those who have been interested in the publication of papers, articles, and books devoted to engineering topics have been impressed with the number of important technical manuscripts which have proved too extensive, on the one hand, for publication in the periodicals or proceedings of engineering societies or in other journals, and of too specialized a character, on the other hand, to justify ordinary commercial publication in book form.

No adequate funds or other means of publication have been provided in the engineering field for making these works available. In other branches of science, certain outlets for comparable treatises have been available, and besides, the presses of several universities have been able to take care of a considerable number of scholarly publications in the various branches of pure and applied science.

Experience has demonstrated the value of proper introduction and sponsorship for such books. To this end, four national engineering societies, the American Society of Civil Engineers, American Institute of Mining and Metallurgical Engineers, The American Society of Mechanical Engineers, and American Institute of Electrical Engineers, have made arrangements with the McGraw-Hill Book Company, Inc., for the production of a series of selected books adjudged to possess usefulness for engineers or industry but of limited possibilities of distribution without special introduction.

The series is to be known as "Engineering Societies Monographs." It will be produced under the editorial supervision of a Committee consisting of the Director of the Engineering Societies Library, Chairman, and two representatives appointed by each of the four societies named above.

Engineering Societies Library will share in any profits made from publishing the Monographs; but the main interest of the societies is service to their members and the public. With their aid the publisher is willing to adventure the production and distribution of selected books that would otherwise be commercially unpractical.

Engineering Societies Monographs will not be a series in the common use of that term. Physically the volumes will have similarity, but there will be no regular interval in publication, nor relation or continuity in subject matter. What books are printed and when will, by the nature of the enterprise, depend upon the manuscripts that are offered and the Committee's estimation of their usefulness. The aim is to make accessible to many users of engineering books information which otherwise would be long delayed in reaching more than a few in the wide domains of engineering.

ENGINEERING SOCIETIES MONOGRAPHS COMMITTEE
Harrison W. Craver, Chairman.

PREFACE

The modern use of steel and high-strength alloys in engineering structures, especially in bridges, ships, and aircraft, has made elastic instability a problem of great importance. Urgent practical requirements have given rise in recent years to extensive investigations, both theoretical and experimental, of the conditions governing the stability of such structural elements as bars, plates, and shells. It seems that the time has come when this work, recorded in various places and languages, often difficult of access to engineers who need it for guidance in design, should be brought together and put in the form of a book.

The first problems of elastic instability, concerning lateral buckling of compressed members, were solved about 200 years ago by L. Euler.* At that time the principal structural materials were wood and stone. The relatively low strength of these materials necessitated stout structural members for which the question of elastic stability is not of primary importance. Thus Euler's theoretical solution, developed for slender bars, remained for a long time without practical application. Only with the beginning of extensive construction of steel railway bridges during the latter half of the past century did the question of buckling of compression members become of practical importance. The use of steel led naturally to types of structures embodying slender compression members, thin plates, and thin shells. Experience showed that such structures may fail in some cases not on account of high stresses, surpassing the strength of material, but owing to insufficient elastic stability of slender or thin-walled members.

Under pressure of practical requirements, the problem of lateral buckling of columns, originated by Euler, has been extensively investigated theoretically and experimentally and the limits within which the theoretical formulas can be applied have been established. However, lateral buckling of compressed members is only a particular case of elastic instability. In the modern

* Leonard Euler's "Elastic Curves," translated and annotated by W. A. Oldfather, C. A. Ellis, and D. M. Brown, 1933.

design of bridges, ships, and aircraft we are confronted by a variety of stability problems.   We encounter there not only solid struts, but built-up or "lattice-work" columns, and tubular members, where there is the possibility of local buckling, as well as buckling as a whole.   In the use of thin sheet material, as in plate girders and airplane structures, we have to keep in mind that thin plates may prove unstable under the action of forces in their own planes, and fail by buckling sideways.   Thin cylindrical shells, such as vacuum vessels, which have to withstand uniform external pressure, may exhibit instability and collapse at a relatively low stress if the thickness of the shell is too small in comparison with the diameter.   The thin cylindrical shell may buckle also under axial compression, bending, torsion, or combinations of these.   All such problems are of the utmost importance in the design of airplanes of the modern monocoque type.

In the discussion of these problems and their solutions, it has not been deemed necessary to include an account of the general theory of elastic stability, which finds its appropriate place in books on the theory of elasticity.   This book proceeds directly to particular problems showing in each case under what conditions the question of stability calls for consideration.   The various methods of solution are presented in connection with the types of problem to which they are best suited.   The solutions have in most cases been supplemented by tables and diagrams which furnish values of critical loads and stresses for each particular case.   While all available information relevant to a prescribed problem has been given, no attempt has been made to go beyond this into actual design, since it is a field in which other considerations besides rational theory and testing play their parts.

The preliminary knowledge of mathematics and strength of materials taken for granted is that usually covered by our schools of engineering.   Where additional mathematical equipment has been found necessary, it is given in the book with the appropriate explanations.   To simplify the reading of the book, problems which, although of practical importance, are such that they can be omitted during a first reading are put in small type.   The reader may return to the study of such problems after finishing the more essential portions of the book.

Numerous references to papers and books treating stability problems are given in the book.   These references may be of interest to engineers who wish to study some special problems in more detail. They give also a picture of the modern development of the theory of elastic stability and may be of some use to graduate students who are planning to take their work in this field.

In the preparation of this book the contents of a previous book* dealing with stability problems and representing a course of lectures on the theory of thin plates and shells, as given in several Russian engineering schools, have been freely drawn upon.

To the University of Michigan the author is grateful for financial support obtained from a research fund and used in the preparation of numerical tables and diagrams for this book. He also takes this opportunity to extend thanks to Dr. D. H. Young who read over the complete manuscript and made many valuable suggestions and corrections, to Professors G. H. MacCullough and H. R. Lloyd who read some portions of the manuscript, to Dr. I. A. Wojtaszak and Mr. S. H. Fillion for the checking of equations and numerical tables, to Dr. Wojtaszak for reading proofs, to Miss Reta Morden for the typing of the manuscript, and to Mr. L. S. Veenstra for the preparation of the drawings.

S. TIMOSHENKO.

ANN ARBOR, MICHIGAN,
  May, 1936.

* "Theory of Elasticity," Vol. II, St. Petersburg, Russia, 1916.

CONTENTS

xiv CONTENTS

NOTATIONS

x, y, z	Rectangular coordinates
l	Length of a bar
L	Reduced length of a strut
h	Depth of a beam. Thickness of a plate or shell
r	Radius of gyration. Radius
s	Core radius
l/r	Slenderness ratio of a strut
$1/\rho, 1/r$	Curvature of a deflection curve
e	Eccentricity
A	Cross-sectional area
P	Axial load
Q	Shearing force. Lateral load
q	Intensity of distributed load
P_{cr}	Critical load for a strut
P_e	Euler load for a strut
M	Bending moment
M_t	Torque
E	Modulus of elasticity in tension and compression
G	Modulus of elasticity in shear
ν	Poisson's ratio
E_r	Reduced modulus
$B = EI$	Flexural rigidity of a beam
$D = Eh^3/12(1 - \nu^2)$	Flexural rigidity of plates and shells
C	Torsional rigidity
$k^2 = P/EI$	For struts
$u = kl/2$	For struts
σ	Normal stress
τ	Shearing stress
σ_{cr}	Critical normal stress
τ_{cr}	Critical shearing stress
$\sigma_{Y.P.}$	Yield point stress
σ_c	Average compressive stress for columns
u, v, w	Components of displacements in x, y and z directions
ϵ	Unit elongation
γ	Unit shear
$\epsilon_x, \epsilon_y, \epsilon_{xy}$	Components of strain
$\chi_x, \chi_y, \chi_{xy}$	Changes of curvature
N_x, N_y, N_{xy}	Resultant forces in middle plane of a plate or in middle surface of a shell
Q_x, Q_y	Resultant shearing forces in a plate or shell, normal to middle surface
M_x, M_y, M_{xy}	Resultant bending and twisting moments in plates or shells
V	Strain energy
T	Work produced by external forces

THEORY OF
ELASTIC STABILITY

CHAPTER I

BENDING OF PRISMATIC BARS UNDER THE SIMULTANEOUS ACTION OF AXIAL AND LATERAL LOADS

From the elementary theory of bending it is known that, if a beam is submitted to the action of lateral loads alone, the deflection of the beam and the stress produced are proportional to the magnitudes of the loads. Small changes in the positions of the loads have only small effect on deflections and stresses. Small deflections do not affect materially the bending moments and shearing forces in the beam, and in the calculation of these quantities it is usual practice to neglect entirely the deflections and determine all necessary distances from the initial straight form of the beam.

In the case of the simultaneous action on the beam of axial and lateral loads, conditions are entirely different. The stresses and deflections are not proportional to the magnitude of the longitudinal force. The slightest eccentricity in application of the axial load and the slightest deviation of the beam from a straight form may have a substantial effect on the deflection of the beam and on the stresses produced. The effect of small deflections of the beam is no longer negligible and must be considered in the calculation of bending moments and shearing forces. When the magnitude of the axial compressive force approaches a certain limiting value, usually called the *critical load*, the deflections become very sensitive to the slightest change in the position of the point of application or in the magnitude of the axial load, and the bending of the beam becomes a characteristic sudden lateral buckling.

1

For a satisfactory understanding of stability problems, it is advantageous to begin with a discussion of the above characteristics in connection with prismatical bars simultaneously subjected to axial and lateral loads. The results obtained in a discussion of this problem may be used later in the study of various stability problems.

1. A Single Lateral Load Acting on a Compressed Bar.—If an axial compressive force acts on an ideal prismatical bar, it produces only uniform compression. However, if there is also a lateral load acting on the bar, the axial force produces a certain effect on the bending of the bar. This effect can be investigated only by considering the deflection curve of the bar. We begin

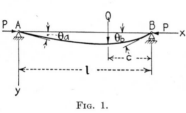

Fig. 1.

with the simplest case of a single lateral force Q acting on a compressed bar with hinged ends (Fig. 1). Assuming that bending occurs in one of the two *principal planes* of the bar,[1] and denoting by EI the corresponding *flexural rigidity* and by P the axial compressive force, the differential equations of the deflection curve for the left and the right portions of the bar are, respectively,

$$EI \frac{d^2y}{dx^2} = -\frac{Qc}{l}x - Py; \qquad (a)$$

$$EI \frac{d^2y}{dx^2} = -\frac{Q(l - c)(l - x)}{l} - Py, \qquad (b)$$

in which l is the span and c the distance of the load Q from the right support B. For simplification we denote

$$\frac{P}{EI} = k^2. \qquad (1)$$

Then Eq. (a) becomes

$$\frac{d^2y}{dx^2} + k^2y = -\frac{Qc}{EIl}x.$$

[1] If the forces are not in a principal plane, they can always be resolved each into two components acting in the principal planes. Thus the problem can be reduced to that of bending of a bar in a principal plane.

The general solution of this equation is

$$y = A \cos kx + B \sin kx - \frac{Qc}{Pl}x. \qquad (c)$$

In the same manner the general solution of Eq. (b) is

$$y = C \cos kx + D \sin kx - \frac{Q(l - c)(l - x)}{Pl}. \qquad (d)$$

The constants of integration $A, \ldots, D$ will now be determined from the conditions at the ends of the bar and at the point of application of the load Q. Since the deflections at the ends of the bar are zero, we conclude:

$$A = 0; \qquad C = -D \tan kl. \qquad (e)$$

At the point of application of the load Q the two portions of the deflection curve, as given by Eqs. (c) and (d), have the same deflection and a common tangent. Then

$$B \sin k(l - c) - \frac{Qc}{Pl}(l - c) =$$

$$D[\sin k(l - c) - \tan kl \cos k(l - c)] - \frac{Qc}{Pl}(l - c);$$

$$Bk \cos k(l - c) - \frac{Qc}{Pl} =$$

$$Dk[\cos k(l - c) + \tan kl \sin k(l - c)] + \frac{Q(l - c)}{Pl},$$

from which

$$B = \frac{Q \sin kc}{Pk \sin kl}; \qquad D = -\frac{Q \sin k(l - c)}{Pk \tan kl} \qquad (f)$$

Substituting in (c) and (d) the values of the constants from (e) and (f), we obtain the following equations for the two portions of the deflection curve:

$$y = \frac{Q \sin kc}{Pk \sin kl} \sin kx - \frac{Qc}{Pl}x, \qquad \text{for} \qquad x < (l - c); \qquad (2)$$

$$y = \frac{Q \sin k(l - c)}{Pk \sin kl} \sin k(l - x) - \frac{Q(l - c)(l - x)}{Pl},$$

$$\text{for} \qquad x > (l - c). \qquad (3)$$

It is seen that Eq. (3) may be obtained from Eq. (2) by substituting $l - c$ for c and $l - x$ for x.

By differentiation of (2) and (3) the following formulas, useful in future calculations, are obtained:

$$y' = \frac{Q \sin kc}{P \sin kl} \cos kx - \frac{Qc}{Pl}, \qquad \text{for} \quad x < (l - c); \quad (4)$$

$$y' = -\frac{Q \sin k(l - c)}{P \sin kl} \cos k(l - x) + \frac{Q(l - c)}{Pl},$$
$$\text{for} \quad x > (l - c); \quad (5)$$

$$y'' = -\frac{Qk \sin kc}{P \sin kl} \sin kx, \qquad \text{for} \quad x < (l - c); \quad (6)$$

$$y'' = -\frac{Qk \sin k(l - c)}{P \sin kl} \sin k(l - x), \quad \text{for} \quad x > (l - c). \quad (7)$$

In the particular case of a load applied at the middle, the deflection curve is symmetrical and it is necessary to consider only the portion to the left of the load. To get the maximum deflection in this particular case, we substitute $x = c = l/2$ in Eq. (2), obtaining

$$\delta = (y)_{x=\frac{l}{2}} = \frac{Q \tan \frac{kl}{2}}{2Pk} - \frac{Ql}{4P}.$$

To simplify this equation the following notation will be used:

$$\frac{kl}{2} = \frac{l}{2}\sqrt{\frac{P}{EI}} = u. \qquad (8)$$

Then, from above,

$$\delta = \frac{Q}{2Pk}\left(\tan \frac{kl}{2} - \frac{kl}{2}\right) = \frac{Ql^3}{48EI}\frac{3(\tan u - u)}{u^3}. \qquad (9)$$

The first factor on the right side of this equation represents the deflection which is obtained if only lateral load Q is acting. By the second factor, the influence of the longitudinal force P on the deflection δ, is given.[1] When P is small, the quantity u

[1] The numerical values of this factor for various values of the quantity u are given in Table I in Appendix, p. 499. By using this table, the deflections of the bar can be easily calculated in each particular case from Eq. (9).

is also small [see Eq. (8)] and the above factor approaches unity. This can be shown by using the series

$$\tan u = u + \frac{u^3}{3} + \frac{2u^5}{3 \cdot 5} + \cdots$$

and retaining only the first two terms of this series. With the increase of u the factor also increases, and approaches infinity as u approaches the value $\pi/2$. When $u = \pi/2$, we find from Eq. (8)

$$P = \frac{\pi^2 EI}{l^2}. \tag{10}$$

Thus it can be concluded that, when the axial compressive force approaches the *limiting value* (10), the smallest lateral load may produce considerable lateral deflection. This limiting value of the compressive force will be called the *critical load*, denoted by P_{cr}. By using the critical value (10) of the longitudinal force, the quantity u [(see Eq. (8)] can be represented in the following form:

$$u = \frac{\pi}{2}\sqrt{\frac{P}{P_{cr}}}. \tag{8'}$$

Thus u depends only on the magnitude of the ratio $P:P_{cr}$.

To get the slope of the deflection curve at the end, we substitute in Eq. (4) $c = l/2$, $x = 0$. Then

$$(y')_{x=0} = \frac{Q}{2P}\left(\frac{1}{\cos\dfrac{kl}{2}} - 1\right) = \frac{Ql^2}{16EI}\frac{2(1 - \cos u)}{u^2 \cos u}. \tag{11}$$

By using Eq. (6) we obtain the maximum bending moment:

$$M_{\text{max.}} = -EI(y'')_{x=\frac{l}{2}} = \frac{EIQk}{2P}\tan\frac{kl}{2} = \frac{Ql}{4}\frac{\tan u}{u}. \tag{12}$$

We see that, in the case of simultaneous action of lateral and axial loads, the maximum bending moment is obtained by multiplying the bending moment produced by lateral load alone by a certain trigonometrical factor. The value of this factor approaches unity when the compressive force becomes smaller and smaller, and the same factor increases indefinitely when the quantity u approaches $\pi/2$, *i.e.*, when the compressive force approaches its *critical value* (10).

2. Several Lateral Loads Acting on a Compressed Bar.—The results of the previous article will now be used in a more general case of several lateral loads acting on the beam together with an axial compressive force. Equations (2) and (3) show that for a given longitudinal force the deflections of the bar are proportional to the lateral load Q. At the same time the relation between deflections and the magnitude of the longitudinal force P is more complicated, since this force enters in the trigonometrical functions containing k. The fact that deflections are linear functions of Q indicates that the method of superposition, which is widely used in the case when lateral loads alone are acting on a beam, can also be applied, in a somewhat modified form, in the case of the combined action of lateral loading with an axial force. It is seen from Eqs. (2) and (3) that, when we add to the lateral load Q some load Q_1, the resultant deflection is obtained by superposing on the deflections produced by the load Q the deflections produced by the load Q_1, if in each case we assume that the same axial force is acting on the bar.

It can be shown that the same method of superposition can also be used if several lateral loads are acting on the compressed bar. The resultant deflection is obtained by using Eqs. (2) and (3) and superposing deflections produced by each lateral load separately combined with the total axial force. Take, for instance, the case of two lateral loads Q_1 and Q_2 at the distances c_1 and c_2 from the right support B (Fig. 2). Proceeding as in the previous article, it will be found that the differential equation

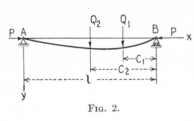

Fig. 2.

of the deflection curve for the left portion of the beam $[x < (l - c_2)]$ is

$$EIy'' = -\frac{Q_1c_1}{l}x - \frac{Q_2c_2}{l}x - Py. \qquad (a)$$

If we consider now separately the load Q_1 and the load Q_2 acting on the compressed bar and denote deflections by y_1 when the load Q_1 is acting and by y_2 when the load Q_2 is acting, there will be found for these two cases the following equations for the deflection curve for the left portion of the beam:

$$EIy''_1 = -\frac{Q_1 c_1}{l}x - Py_1;$$

$$EIy''_2 = -\frac{Q_2 c_2}{l}x - Py_2.$$

By adding these two equations together we find

$$EI(y''_1 + y''_2) = -\frac{Q_1 c_1}{l}x - \frac{Q_2 c_2}{l}x - P(y_1 + y_2).$$

It is seen that this equation for the sum of the deflections $(y_1 + y_2)$ is the same as Eq. (*a*) for the deflections obtained when the loads Q_1 and Q_2 were acting simultaneously. The same conclusion can be made also for the middle and for the right portions of the bar. From this it can be concluded that, in the case of several loads acting on a compressed bar, the resultant deflections can be obtained by *superposition* of the deflections produced by each separate lateral load acting together with the longitudinal force P.

On the basis of this statement we can now write the equation of the deflection curve for any portion of the bar and for any number of lateral loads. Assume that there are n lateral forces $Q_1, Q_2, \ldots, Q_n$ and that their distances from the right support of the beam are $c_1, c_2, \ldots, c_n (c_1 < c_2 < c_3 \ldots)$. Then, by using Eqs. (2) and (3) for a single lateral load, the deflection curve between the loads Q_m and Q_{m+1} is given by the equation

$$y = \frac{\sin kx}{Pk \sin kl}\sum_{i=1}^{i=m} Q_i \sin kc_i - \frac{x}{Pl}\sum_{i=1}^{i=m} Q_i c_i + \frac{\sin k(l-x)}{Pk \sin kl}\sum_{i=m+1}^{i=n} Q_i \sin k(l-c_i) - \frac{l-x}{Pl}\sum_{i=m+1}^{i=n} Q_i(l-c_i). \quad (13)$$

In the same manner, by using Eqs. (4), (5), (6) and (7), we can obtain the slope of the deflection curve and bending moment at any cross section of the beam. Thus, by using the method of superposition in its modified form, the general problem of calculating deflections for a beam submitted to the action of several lateral loads together with an axial force is solved.

It was assumed at the beginning that the transverse load Q acts in one of the two principal planes of flexure of the beam.

If the force is acting in any other axial plane of the beam, we resolve it into two components, each acting in a principal plane. Then for each component the deflection curve and the maximum bending moment are obtained by using the equations previously derived. The resultant deflections and the resultant stresses are obtained in the usual way by superposition of deflections and stresses calculated separately for each of the two principal planes.

3. Uniform Lateral Load Acting on a Compressed Bar.—The *method of superposition*, described in the previous article, can be used also in the case of continuous loads, it being necessary only to replace summations by integrations. Take the case of a uniform lateral load on a compressed bar with hinged ends. If q denotes the intensity of the lateral load and c the variable distance from the right support of an element qdc of the continuous load, this element can be considered as an infinitesimally small concentrated force and the uniform load can be replaced by a system of such infinitesimally small concentrated forces.

Then, using Eq. (13) and replacing the summation $\sum\limits_{i=1}^{i=m}$ by the integration $\int_0^{l-x}$ and the summation $\sum\limits_{i=m+1}^{i=n}$ by the integration $\int_{l-x}^{l}$, we obtain

$$y = \frac{\sin kx}{Pk \sin kl}\int_0^{l-x} q \sin kc \, dc - \frac{x}{Pl}\int_0^{l-x} qc \, dc +$$
$$\frac{\sin k(l-x)}{Pk \sin kl}\int_{l-x}^{l} q \sin k(l-c)dc - \frac{l-x}{Pl}\int_{l-x}^{l} q(l-c)dc. \quad (a)$$

After integration and using notation (8), we obtain the following equation of the deflection curve:

$$y = \frac{ql^4}{16EIu^4}\left[\frac{\cos u\left(1 - \dfrac{2x}{l}\right)}{\cos u} - 1\right] - \frac{ql^2}{8EIu^2}x(l-x). \quad (14)$$

Substituting in this equation $x = l/2$, the deflection at the middle, after simple transformations, is found to be

$$\delta = (y)_{x=\frac{l}{2}} = \frac{5}{384}\frac{ql^4}{EI}\frac{24(\sec u - 1 - \frac{1}{2}u^2)}{5u^4}. \quad (15)$$

The first factor on the right side of this equation represents the deflection produced by the lateral load alone. The second factor shows the effect of the longitudinal compressive force P on the deflection at the middle. By expanding sec u in the form of a series, it can be shown that the second factor approaches unity when u approaches zero and that it increases indefinitely as u approaches $\pi/2$, *i.e.*, when P approaches the critical value (10). Thus the effect of the axial load P on the deflection depends on the value of u, *i.e.*, on the value of P/P_{cr} [see Eq. (8′), p. 5]. If this ratio is small, the effect of P on the deflection is also small but increases rapidly when the above ratio approaches unity. The same conclusion can be obtained also for other kinds of lateral loading

By differentiation of Eq. (14) we can find the expression for the slope of the deflection curve. In our further investigations we shall need to have the slopes at the ends of the bar. Substituting x equal to zero in the above-mentioned expression for the slope, it can be easily shown that the slope at the left end of the bar, equal to the small angle of rotation θ of the end, is

$$(y')_{x=0} = \theta = \frac{ql^3}{24EI} \frac{3(\tan u - u)}{u^3}. \tag{16}$$

The first factor on the right side is the known formula for the slope at the end for the case when the uniform load alone is acting on the beam. The second factor represents the effect on the slope of the longitudinal force P. It can be shown, as before, by expanding tan u into a series, that the above factor approaches unity when u is approaching zero and that it increases indefinitely when u approaches $\pi/2$, *i.e.*, as P approaches its critical value.

For calculating the maximum bending moment, we differentiate twice Eq. (14) for the deflection curve. Then the maximum bending moment, which is evidently at the middle of the span, is

$$M_{\text{max.}} = -EI(y'')_{x=\frac{l}{2}} = \frac{ql^2}{8} \frac{2(1 - \cos u)}{u^2 \cos u}. \tag{17}$$

The same result can be obtained by adding to the moment $ql^2/8$ the moment $P\delta$ due to longitudinal force. Substituting for δ its value from expression (15), we obtain

$$M_{max.} = \frac{ql^2}{8} + \frac{5}{384}\frac{ql^4}{EI}\frac{24(\sec u - 1 - \frac{1}{2}u^2)}{5u^4}P.$$

Substituting in this expression $P = k^2 EI$ and using notation (8), we can easily bring this result into coincidence with formula (17).

The first factor in formula (17) represents the bending moment produced by the uniform load alone. The second factor gives the effect of the longitudinal force P on the maximum bending moment. It can be shown again that this effect is small for small values of the ratio P/P_{cr} and that it increases indefinitely as P approaches P_{cr}.

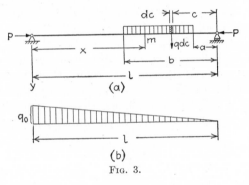

FIG. 3.

The method of superposition in the calculation of deflections can be applied also in the case where the load q is distributed along only a portion of the span (Fig. 3a). To get, for instance, the deflection curve for the portion of the beam to the left of the load, we use Eq. (2). The deflection produced by one element qdc of the load is obtained by substituting qdc for Q in Eq. (2). To get the deflection produced by the total load, it is necessary to make the integration by varying c from $c = a$ to $c = b$. In this way we obtain the deflection curve for the left portion of the beam in the following form:

$$y = \int_a^b \frac{qdc \sin kc}{Pk \sin kl} \sin kx - x\int_a^b \frac{qc\,dc}{Pl}. \tag{b}$$

If it is necessary to find the deflection at any point m under the load (Fig. 3a), we use Eq. (2) for the load to the right of m and Eq. (3) for the load to the left of m. Then the required deflection is

$$y = \int_a^{l-x} \frac{qdc \sin kc}{Pk \sin kl} \sin kx - x \int_a^{l-x} \frac{qc\ dc}{Pl} +$$
$$\int_{l-x}^b \frac{qdc \sin k(l-c)}{Pk \sin kl} \sin k(l-x) - \int_{l-x}^b \frac{qdc(l-c)(l-x)}{Pl}. \quad (c)$$

By making the integration as indicated and taking $a = 0$ and $b = l$, we obtain Eq. (14) for a uniformly loaded beam.

If q is not constant but is a certain function of c, we can obtain the deflection curve from such equations as (b) and (c) by substituting for q the given function of c. For instance, in the case shown in Fig. 3b, the deflection curve is obtained by substituting in Eq. (c) $q = q_0 c/l$ and making $a = 0$; $b = l$.

The problem of applying the equations of the deflection curve in calculating maximum stress and the question of allowable stresses in the case of combined action of lateral load and axial force P will be discussed later (see Art. 9).

4. Bending of a Compressed Bar by Couples.—Having the solution for a single concentrated force Q (Fig. 1), it is easy to obtain the equation of the deflection curve for the case when a couple is applied, say at the right end of the beam. For this purpose assume that the distance c in Fig. 1 is indefinitely decreasing and that at the same time Q is increasing, so as to have the product Qc finite and equal to M_b. At the limit we obtain in this way the bending of the bar by a couple M_b (Fig. 4). The deflection curve is then obtained from Eq. (2) by substituting in this equation $\sin kc = kc$ and $Qc = M_b$, giving

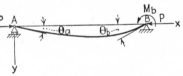

Fig. 4.

$$y = \frac{M_b}{P}\left(\frac{\sin kx}{\sin kl} - \frac{x}{l}\right). \quad (18)$$

In our further discussion it will be necessary to have the formulas giving the small angles of rotation θ_a and θ_b of the ends of the bar.[1] These angles are found by using the derivative of expression (18):

---

[1] Those angles are considered as positive where the ends rotate in the directions of the positive bending moments as shown in Fig. 4.

$$\theta_a = (y')_{x=0} = \frac{M_b}{P}\left(\frac{k}{\sin\,kl} - \frac{1}{l}\right) = \frac{M_b l}{6EI}\frac{3}{u}\left(\frac{1}{\sin\,2u} - \frac{1}{2u}\right) \quad (19)$$

$$\theta_b = -(y')_{x=l} = -\frac{M_b}{P}\left(\frac{k\,\cos\,kl}{\sin\,kl} - \frac{1}{l}\right) = \frac{M_b l}{3EI}\frac{3}{2u}\left(\frac{1}{2u} - \frac{1}{\tan\,2u}\right).$$
$$(20)$$

We see that the known expressions $M_b l/6EI$ and $M_b l/3EI$, for the angles produced by the couple M_b acting alone, are multiplied by trigonometric factors representing the influence of the axial force P on the angles of rotation of the ends of the bar.   By representing the trigonometric functions in the forms of series and retaining only the first few terms of these series, it can be shown that the above factors approach unity when u approaches zero.   As u approaches $\pi/2$, the same factors increase indefinitely, since they have terms with $\sin\,2u$ and $\tan\,2u$ in the denominator and these functions approach zero when u approaches $\pi/2$.

Since, in the discussion of stability problems, we shall have frequent use for formulas (19) and (20), the following notation is introduced in order to simplify the equations:

$$\frac{3}{u}\left(\frac{1}{\sin\,2u} - \frac{1}{2u}\right) = \phi(u); \quad (21)$$

$$\frac{3}{2u}\left(\frac{1}{2u} - \frac{1}{\tan\,2u}\right) = \psi(u). \quad (22)$$

The numerical values of these functions for various values of $2u$ are given in Table I in the Appendix (p. 499).

If two couples M_a and M_b are applied at the ends A and B of the bar (Fig. 5a), the deflection curve is obtained by superposition.   From Eq. (18) we obtain the deflections produced by the couple M_b.   Substituting in the same equation M_a for M_b and $(l - x)$ for x, we find the deflections produced by the couple M_a.   Then the deflection curve for the case represented in Fig. 5a is

$$y = \frac{M_b}{P}\left(\frac{\sin\,kx}{\sin\,kl} - \frac{x}{l}\right) + \frac{M_a}{P}\left[\frac{\sin\,k(l-x)}{\sin\,kl} - \frac{l-x}{l}\right]. \quad (23)$$

We have this kind of loading where two eccentrically applied compressive forces P act as shown in Fig. 5b.   Substituting $M_a = e_a P$ and $M_b = e_b P$ in Eq. (23), we obtain

$$y = e_b\left(\frac{\sin kx}{\sin kl} - \frac{x}{l}\right) + e_a\left[\frac{\sin k(l - x)}{\sin kl} - \frac{l - x}{l}\right]. \quad (24)$$

The angles θ_a and θ_b giving the rotation of the ends (Fig. 5a) are obtained by using Eqs. (19) and (20) and notations (21) and (22). Then, by superposition,

$$\left.\begin{array}{l} \theta_a = \dfrac{M_a l}{3EI}\psi(u) + \dfrac{M_b l}{6EI}\phi(u); \\[2mm] \theta_b = \dfrac{M_b l}{3EI}\psi(u) + \dfrac{M_a l}{6EI}\phi(u). \end{array}\right\} \quad (25)$$

Using for $\phi(u)$ and $\psi(u)$ their values from Table I (p. 499), the angles θ_a and θ_b can be readily obtained from these equations.

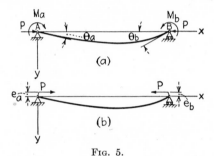

(a)

(b)

Fig. 5.

Equations (25) will be used often in discussing various cases of statically indeterminate beams with redundant constraints at the ends.

In the case of two equal couples $M_a = M_b = M$, we obtain from Eq. (23)

$$y = \frac{M}{P\cos\dfrac{kl}{2}}\left[\cos\frac{kl}{2}\left(1 - \frac{2x}{l}\right) - \cos\frac{kl}{2}\right] =$$

$$\frac{Ml^2}{8EI}\frac{2}{u^2\cos u}\left[\cos u\left(1 - \frac{2x}{l}\right) - \cos u\right]. \quad (26)$$

The deflection at the center of the bar is obtained by substituting $x = l/2$; then

$$\delta = (y)_{x=\frac{l}{2}} = \frac{Ml^2}{8EI}\frac{2(1 - \cos u)}{u^2\cos u}. \quad (27)$$

The angles at the ends are obtained by using the derivative of expression (26), giving

$$\theta_a = \theta_b = (y')_{x=0} = \frac{Ml}{2EI} \frac{\tan u}{u}. \tag{28}$$

The maximum bending moment, which occurs at the middle of the bar, is obtained by using the second derivative of expression (26), from which

$$M_{max.} = -EI(y'')_{x=\frac{l}{2}} = M \sec u. \tag{29}$$

This formula may be used in calculating the maximum bending moment in a bar with eccentrically applied compressive forces (Fig. 5b) when both eccentricities are equal. When the longitudinal force P is small in comparison with its critical value (10), the quantity u is small and the trigonometrical factor in formula (29) can be taken equal to unity, i.e., the bending moment can be assumed constant along the length of the bar. As u approaches $\pi/2$ (P approaches P_{cr}), sec u increases indefinitely. At such values of P the slightest eccentricity in the application of the load produces a considerable bending moment at the middle of the bar. The discussion of working stresses for such cases will be given in Art. 9.

5. Longitudinally Compressed Beams with Built-in Ends.—By using the results of the previous articles and the method of superposition (see Art. 2), various statically indeterminate problems, in which one or both ends of the beam are built in, can be easily solved. Take, for instance, the case represented in Fig. 6, that of a uniformly loaded compressed beam, simply supported at the end A and built in at the end B. The statically indeterminate bending moment M_b at the support B is obtained from the condition that the tangent to the deflection curve at the built-in end must remain horizontal. Therefore, the rotation of the end B produced by the uniform load [Eq. (16)] must be eliminated by the action of the moment M_b [Eq. (20)]. In this way we obtain

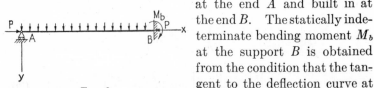

Fig. 6.

$$\frac{ql^3}{24EI} \frac{3(\tan u - u)}{u^3} = -\frac{M_b l}{3EI} \frac{3}{2u}\left(\frac{1}{2u} - \frac{1}{\tan 2u}\right),$$

from which

$$M_b = -\frac{ql^2}{8}\frac{4(\tan u - u)\tan 2u}{u(\tan 2u - 2u)}. \tag{30}$$

The calculation of the moment M_b can easily be made by using the table on page 499. The negative sign of this moment indicates that it is directed as shown in Fig. 6 and produces bending convex upwards. Having the moment (30), the deflection curve is obtained by superposing on the deflection produced by uniform load [Eq. (14)] the deflection produced by the moment M_b [Eq. (18)].

If both ends of the uniformly loaded beam are built in, the deflection curve is symmetrical and the moments at the built-in ends are equal: $M_a = M_b = M$. The magnitude of these moments is obtained from the condition that the rotation of the ends produced by the uniform load is eliminated by the moments acting at the ends [Eq. (28)]. Then

$$\frac{ql^3}{24EI}\frac{3(\tan u - u)}{u^3} = -\frac{Ml}{2EI}\frac{\tan u}{u},$$

from which

$$M = -\frac{ql^2}{12}\frac{3(\tan u - u)}{u^2 \tan u}. \tag{31}$$

Having this moment, the deflection curve is obtained by superposing on the deflections produced by uniform load [Eq. (14)] the deflections produced by the two equal moments applied at the ends [Eq. (26)]. The bending moment at the middle is obtained by superposing on the moment (17) the moment (29). Then

$$(M)_{x=\frac{l}{2}} = \frac{ql^2}{8}\frac{2(1 - \cos u)}{u^2 \cos u} - \frac{ql^2}{12}\frac{3(\tan u - u)}{u^2 \sin u} = \frac{ql^2}{24}\frac{6(u - \sin u)}{u^2 \sin u}. \tag{32}$$

As a more general case of a statically indeterminate problem, let us consider a bar with elastically built-in ends. An example of such end conditions is represented in Fig. 7. A laterally loaded beam AB is rigidly connected with vertical bars at A and B and is compressed axially by the forces P. If θ_a and θ_b

are the angles of rotation of the ends, there will be couples, resisting these rotations, with magnitudes

$$M_a = -\alpha\theta_a; \qquad M_b = -\beta\theta_b. \qquad (a)$$

The negative signs in these expressions indicate that the couples have directions opposite to the directions of rotation. The factors α and β are coefficients defining the degree of fixity existing at the ends of the member, each being equal to the reactive moment at its end which is produced when the angle of rotation of that end is equal to unity. Such coefficients will

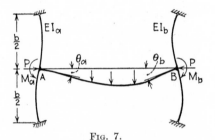

Fig. 7.

be called *coefficients of end restraint*. If, for instance, EI_a is the flexural rigidity of the vertical bar at A, the relation between the angle of rotation θ_a and the moment M_a is

$$\theta_a = -\frac{M_a b}{12EI_a};$$

thus

$$\alpha = \frac{12EI_a}{b}.$$

The angles θ_a and θ_b can now be determined from a consideration of the bending of the bar AB. Denoting by θ_{0a} and θ_{0b} the angles calculated for hinged ends and determining the angles produced by the couples M_a and M_b from Eqs. (25), we obtain

$$\left.\begin{aligned}
\theta_a &= \theta_{0a} + \frac{M_a l}{3EI}\psi(u) + \frac{M_b l}{6EI}\phi(u); \\
\theta_b &= \theta_{0b} + \frac{M_b l}{3EI}\psi(u) + \frac{M_a l}{6EI}\phi(u).
\end{aligned}\right\} \qquad (b)$$

Now, from (a) and (b), the following equations for determining the moments at the ends are obtained:

$$-\frac{M_a}{\alpha} = \frac{M_a l}{3EI}\psi(u) + \frac{M_b l}{6EI}\phi(u) + \theta_{0a};$$
$$-\frac{M_b}{\beta} = \frac{M_b l}{3EI}\psi(u) + \frac{M_a l}{6EI}\phi(u) + \theta_{0b}.$$

(33)

By using these equations various conditions at the ends of the bar AB can be considered. Taking, for instance, $\alpha = 0$, $\beta = \infty$, we obtain the case represented in Fig. 6, in which the left end of the bar is free to rotate and the right end is rigidly built in. In this case $M_a = 0$ and the moment at the end B, from the second of Eqs. (33), is

$$M_b = -\frac{3EI\theta_{0b}}{l\psi(u)}.$$

(c)

Assuming, for instance, that the bar AB is uniformly loaded and using for θ_{0b} Eq. (16), formula (30) will be obtained from (c). By taking $\alpha = \beta = \infty$, we obtain the case of a bar with rigidly built-in ends.

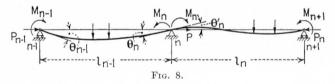

Fig. 8.

Several applications of Eqs. (33) will be given later in discussing stability problems (see Arts. 17 and 18).

6. Continuous Beams Longitudinally Compressed.—*Continuous Beams on Rigid Supports.*—In the case of a continuous beam on rigid supports submitted to the simultaneous action of lateral and axial loads, we consider as statically indeterminate quantities the bending moments at the supports. Let $1, 2, \ldots, m$ denote the consecutive supports; $M_1, M_2, \ldots, M_m$ the corresponding bending moments; $l_1, l_2, \ldots, l_{m-1}$ the spans and $u_1, u_2, \ldots, u_{m-1}$ the corresponding values of the quantity u calculated for each span [from Eq. (8)]. The compressive force and the flexural rigidity may vary from one span to the other but along one span these quantities are assumed constant.

Let us consider the two consecutive spans with the supports $n - 1$, n and $n + 1$ (Fig. 8). The relation between the corresponding bending moments M_{n-1}, M_n and M_{n+1} is obtained from the condition that at the intermediate support n the deflection curves of the two spans have the same tangent. Denoting by θ_n the angle of rotation of the right end of the span $n - 1$ and by θ'_n the angle of rotation of the left end of the span n, and taking, as before, these angles positive, if the rotation is in the direction of the positive bending moment, we conclude from the continuity of the deflection curve at the support n that

$$\theta_n = -\theta'_n. \tag{a}$$

Now, considering the span $n - 1$ as a beam simply supported at the ends, the expression for the angle θ_n will consist of two parts, one depending on the action of the lateral load on the span, which we denote by θ_{0n}, and the second, corresponding to the action of the couples M_{n-1} and M_n, which can be obtained by using Eqs. (25). Thus

$$\theta_n = \theta_{0n} + \frac{M_{n-1}l_{n-1}}{6EI_{n-1}}\phi(u_{n-1}) + \frac{M_n l_{n-1}}{3EI_{n-1}}\psi(u_{n-1}).$$

We can also write a similar expression for the angle θ'_n. When this is done, Eq. (a) becomes

$$\theta_{0n} + \frac{M_{n-1}l_{n-1}}{6EI_{n-1}}\phi(u_{n-1}) + \frac{M_n l_{n-1}}{3EI_{n-1}}\psi(u_{n-1}) =$$
$$-\left[\theta'_{0n} + \frac{M_n l_n}{3EI_n}\psi(u_n) + \frac{M_{n+1}l_n}{6EI_n}\phi(u_n) \right],$$

from which

$$M_{n-1}\phi(u_{n-1}) + 2M_n\left[\psi(u_{n-1}) + \frac{l_n}{l_{n-1}}\frac{I_{n-1}}{I_n}\psi(u_n) \right] +$$
$$M_{n+1}\frac{l_n}{l_{n-1}}\frac{I_{n-1}}{I_n}\phi(u_n) = -\frac{6EI_{n-1}}{l_{n-1}}(\theta_{0n} + \theta'_{0n}). \tag{34}$$

The angles θ_{0n} and θ'_{0n} for any kind of lateral loading can be calculated by the methods which were explained in Arts. 1, 2 and 3. Thus Eq. (34) contains only three unknown moments M_{n-1}, M_n and M_{n+1}. Writing Eq. (34) for each intermediate support of the continuous beam and using also the conditions at the first and the last supports, we obtain a sufficient number of equations for calculating all statically indeterminate quantities.

If uniformly distributed loads of intensities q_{n-1} and q_n are acting on the spans $n-1$ and n, respectively, we have, from Eq. (16),

$$\theta_{0n} = \frac{q_{n-1}l^3_{n-1}}{24EI_{n-1}}\frac{3(\tan u_{n-1} - u_{n-1})}{u^3_{n-1}};$$

$$\theta'_{0n} = \frac{q_n l^3_n}{24EI_n}\frac{3(\tan u_n - u_n)}{u^3_n}.$$

Then by using the notation

$$\chi(u_n) = \frac{3(\tan u_n - u_n)}{u^3_n},$$

we can write Eq. (34) in the following form:

$$M_{n-1}\phi(u_{n-1}) + 2M_n\left[\psi(u_{n-1}) + \frac{l_n}{l_{n-1}}\frac{I_{n-1}}{I_n}\psi(u_n)\right] +$$
$$M_{n+1}\frac{l_n}{l_{n-1}}\frac{I_{n-1}}{I_n}\phi(u_n) = -\frac{q_{n-1}l^2_{n-1}}{4}\chi(u_{n-1}) -$$
$$\frac{q_n l^2_n}{4}\frac{I_{n-1}}{I_n}\frac{l_n}{l_{n-1}}\chi(u_n). \quad (34')$$

The numerical calculation of bending moments from these equations is greatly simplified by using the table of functions $\phi(u)$, $\psi(u)$ and $\chi(u)$ (see p. 499).

In the particular case where there is no lateral loading on the spans $n-1$ and n, Eq. (34) becomes

$$M_{n-1}\phi(u_{n-1}) + 2M_n\left[\psi(u_{n-1}) + \frac{l_n}{l_{n-1}}\frac{I_{n-1}}{I_n}\psi(u_n)\right] +$$
$$M_{n+1}\frac{l_n}{l_{n-1}}\frac{I_{n-1}}{I_n}\phi(u_n) = 0. \quad (35)$$

Continuous Beams with Supports Not on a Straight Line.—If an initially straight compressed bar is held on rigid supports which are not on a straight line, additional bending is introduced. Let $n-1$, n and $n+1$ be three consecutive supports of the continuous beam (Fig. 9); h_{n-1}, h_n and h_{n+1} are the corresponding ordinates to the supports. We assume that the differences between these ordinates are small so that the angle β_n between the two consecutive spans is given with sufficient accuracy by the equation

$$\beta_n = \frac{h_n - h_{n-1}}{l_{n-1}} - \frac{h_{n+1} - h_n}{l_n}. \tag{b}$$

The bending moments M_{n-1}, M_n and M_{n+1}, owing to the irregularities in placing the supports, are now found from the conditions of continuity.

Considering the spans $n - 1$ and n as two simple beams, we conclude that the rotation of the ends of these two beams on the common support n must be such as to eliminate the angle β_n. Then by using Eqs. (25) we find

$$\frac{M_n l_{n-1}}{3EI_{n-1}}\psi(u_{n-1}) + \frac{M_{n-1}l_{n-1}}{6EI_{n-1}}\phi(u_{n-1}) + \frac{M_n l_n}{3EI_n}\psi(u_n) + \frac{M_{n+1}l_n}{6EI_n}\phi(u_n) = \beta_n;$$

from which

$$M_{n-1}\phi(u_{n-1}) + 2M_n\left[\psi(u_{n-1}) + \frac{l_n}{l_{n-1}}\frac{I_{n-1}}{I_n}\psi(u_n)\right] +$$
$$M_{n+1}\frac{l_n}{l_{n-1}}\frac{I_{n-1}}{I_n}\phi(u_n) = \frac{6EI_{n-1}}{l_{n-1}}\beta_n. \quad (36)$$

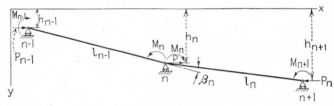

Fig. 9.

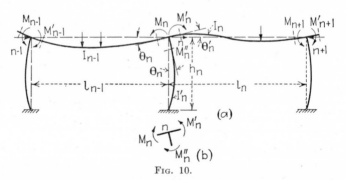

Fig. 10.

This equation is analogous to Eq. (34) and, if the positions of all supports are given,[1] β_n is easily determined for each intermediate support and then the moments at these supports are obtained from Eqs. (36).

Continuous Beams Rigidly Connected to Columns.—If the cross sections at the supports of a continuous beam are not free to rotate, being rigidly attached to columns as shown in Fig. 10, the bending moments M_n and M'_n at the two adjacent cross sections to the left and to the right of the support n are not equal. The relation between them is then given by the equation of equilibrium of the joint n (Fig. 10b):

$$M_n - M'_n + M''_n = 0. \quad (c)$$

[1] This method can be used also when the supports are elastic and deflect in proportion to pressures on the support. See papers by H. Zimmermann, *Sitzungsb., Akad. Wiss., Berlin,* 1907 and 1909.

Proceeding now as before, and using Eq. (a), we obtain:[1]

$$\theta_{0n} + \frac{M'_{n-1}l_{n-1}}{6EI_{n-1}}\phi(u_{n-1}) + \frac{M_n l_{n-1}}{3EI_{n-1}}\psi(u_{n-1}) =$$
$$-\left[\theta'_{0n} + \frac{M'_n l_n}{3EI_n}\psi(u_n) + \frac{M_{n+1}l_n}{6EI_n}\phi(u_n) \right];$$

or

$$M'_{n-1}\phi(u_{n-1}) + 2M_n\psi(u_{n-1}) + 2M'_n\frac{l_n}{l_{n-1}}\frac{I_{n-1}}{I_n}\psi(u_n) +$$
$$M_{n+1}\frac{l_n}{l_{n-1}}\frac{I_{n-1}}{I_n}\phi(u_n) = -\frac{6EI_{n-1}}{l_{n-1}}(\theta_{0n} + \theta'_{0n}). \quad (37)$$

Another equation for the same joint is obtained from a consideration of bending of the column. Assuming that the joint n has no lateral displacement, the moment M''_n, representing the action of the column on the joint n, can be represented by the equation

$$M''_n = \alpha_n\theta_n, \quad (d)$$

where α_n is the coefficient of restraint (see page 16) for the support n. For instance, in the case of a column hinged at the bottom and having a flexural rigidity EI'_n and a length h_n, we obtain[2]

$$\theta_n = \frac{M''_n h_n}{3EI'_n}; \qquad M''_n = \frac{3EI'_n\theta_n}{h_n}; \qquad \text{and} \qquad \alpha_n = \frac{3EI'_n}{h_n}.$$

Substituting in Eq. (d) the above values α_n, θ_n and the value of M''_n from Eq. (c), we obtain

$$\frac{1}{\alpha_n}(M'_n - M_n) = \theta_{0n} + \frac{M'_{n-1}l_{n-1}}{6EI_{n-1}}\phi(u_{n-1}) + \frac{M_n l_{n-1}}{3EI_{n-1}}\psi(u_{n-1}). \quad (38)$$

For each intermediate support we can write two equations such as Eqs. (37) and (38). Thus we have sufficient equations to determine all statically indeterminate moments if the ends of the beam are simply supported. If they are built in, the two additional equations expressing the conditions of fixity of the ends should be added.[3] The solution of these equations is greatly simplified by using the tables of functions $\phi(u)$ and $\psi(u)$ (see p. 499). Some applications of these equations will be shown later (see p. 99).

[1] The change in axial forces of the beam due to horizontal reactions of the pillars at the supports $n - 1$, n and $n + 1$ is neglected in this derivation.

[2] The effect of the axial force acting on the pillar is neglected in this calculation. It is also assumed that there are no lateral displacements at the tops of the pillars.

[3] A very complete discussion of this problem can be found in the book by F. Bleich and J. Melan: "Die gewönlichen und partiellen Differenzengleichungen der Baustatic," Berlin, 1927. See also F. Bleich, "Die Berechnung statisch unbestimmter Tragwerke nach der Methode des Viermomenten satzes," 2d ed., Berlin, 1925.

Continuous Beams on Elastic Supports.—If the intermediate supports of the beam are elastic, *i.e.*, such that they deflect in proportion to the acting pressures, Eqs. (36) can still be used. However, if the compressive force P is constant along the length of the beam and the ends are rigidly supported, it is sometimes advantageous to take the intermediate reactions as the statically indeterminate quantities. For determining these reactions we use Eq. (13) and change the previous notations accordingly. The distances of the intermediate supports from the right end of the continuous beam we denote by $c_1, c_2, \ldots, c_n$ ($c_1 < c_2 < c_3 \ldots$) and the corresponding reactions by $R_1, R_2, \ldots, R_n$ (Fig. 11). The deflection of the continuous beam at any point can be calculated as for a simple beam AB of length l on which are acting a given lateral loading and the unknown reactions $R_1, R_2, \ldots$. Assume that we have found in this way the deflection for any support m. The same deflection can be found in another way, by considering the elasticity of the support. Let α_m be the load necessary to produce a unit deflection of the support m. Then under the action of the pressure R_m, equal to the reaction of the support m, the deflection will be R_m/α_m. Putting this deflection equal to the above calculated deflection, we obtain an equation

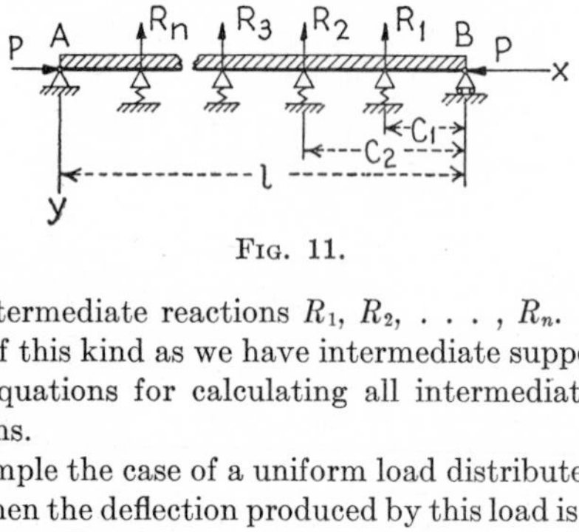

FIG. 11.

containing the intermediate reactions $R_1, R_2, \ldots, R_n$. We can write as many equations of this kind as we have intermediate supports, so that there will be enough equations for calculating all intermediate statically indeterminate reactions.

Take as an example the case of a uniform load distributed along the beam AB (Fig. 11). Then the deflection produced by this load is given by Eq. (14) and the deflection produced by the reactions $R_1, R_2, \ldots$ is calculated by using Eq. (13). Using the notation $x_m = l - c_m$, we obtain then for any support m

$$\frac{ql^4}{16EIu^4}\left[\frac{\cos\left(1 - \frac{2x_m}{l}\right)u}{\cos u} - 1\right] - \frac{ql^2}{8EIu^2}x_m(l - x_m) -$$

$$\frac{\sin kx_m}{Pk\sin kl}\sum_{i=1}^{i=m} R_i \sin kc_i + \frac{x_m}{Pl}\sum_{i=1}^{i=m} R_i c_i -$$

$$\frac{\sin k(l - x_m)}{Pk\sin kl}\sum_{i=m+1}^{i=n} R_i \sin k(l - c_i) + \frac{l - x_m}{Pl}\sum_{i=m+1}^{i=n} R_i(l - c_i) = \frac{R_m}{\alpha_m}. \quad (39)$$

There will be as many equations of this kind as we have intermediate supports and all statically indeterminate reactions at these supports can be calculated. Application of this equation will be shown later in discussing the stability of an elastically supported compressed bar.

7. Application of Trigonometric Series.—In studying deflections of a prismatical bar, it is advantageous sometimes to represent the deflection curve in the form of a trigonometric series.[1] In such a case a single mathematical expression holds for the entire length of the beam and it is not necessary to discuss separately each portion of the deflection curve between consecutive loads as was explained in Arts. 1 and 2. This method of analysis is especially useful in the case of a beam with simply supported ends (Fig. 12). The deflection curve in this case can be represented in the form of a sine series:

$$y = a_1 \sin \frac{\pi x}{l} + a_2 \sin \frac{2\pi x}{l} + a_3 \sin \frac{3\pi x}{l} + \cdots . \quad (40)$$

Each term of the series satisfies the end conditions, since each term, together with its second derivative, becomes zero at the ends of the beam. Thus the deflections of the beam and the bending moments at the ends are equal to zero. Geometrically the series (40) means that the deflection curve of the beam AB can be obtained by superposing simple sinusoidal curves such as shown in Fig. 12 (*b*), (*c*) and (*d*). The first term of the series (40) is represented by the curve (*b*), the second by the curve (*c*), etc.

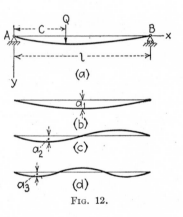

Fig. 12.

The coefficients a_1, a_2, . . . of the series are the maximum ordinates of the consecutive sine curves and the numbers 1, 2, 3, . . . , with which π is multiplied, indicate the number of half waves in the same curves.

It can be rigorously proved that, by properly determining the coefficients a_1, a_2, a_3, . . . , the series (40) can be made to repre-

---

[1] See the author's paper, Application of Generalized Coordinates to Solution of Problems on Bending of Bars and Plates, *Bull. Polytech. Inst., Kiev.*, 1909 (Russian).

sent any deflection curve[1] with a degree of accuracy which depends upon the number of terms taken. In the following discussion, the coefficients $a_1, a_2, a_3, \ldots$ are obtained by using the general expression for the strain energy of bending, which is given by the equation[2]

$$V = \frac{EI}{2} \int_0^l \left(\frac{d^2y}{dx^2}\right)^2 dx. \tag{a}$$

The second derivative of y with respect to x, from (40), is

$$\frac{d^2y}{dx^2} = -a_1\frac{\pi^2}{l^2}\sin\frac{\pi x}{l} - 2^2 a_2\frac{\pi^2}{l^2}\sin\frac{2\pi x}{l} - 3^2 a_3\frac{\pi^2}{l^2}\sin\frac{3\pi x}{l} - \cdots.$$

Substituting in Eq. (a), we find that the expression under the integral sign contains terms of two kinds:

$$a^2_n\frac{n^4\pi^4}{l^4}\sin^2\frac{n\pi x}{l} \quad \text{and} \quad 2a_n a_m\frac{n^2m^2\pi^4}{l^4}\sin\frac{n\pi x}{l}\sin\frac{m\pi x}{l}.$$

By direct integration it can be shown that

$$\int_0^l \sin^2\frac{n\pi x}{l}\, dx = \frac{l}{2}, \quad \text{and} \quad \int_0^l \sin\frac{n\pi x}{l}\sin\frac{m\pi x}{l}\, dx = 0.$$

Hence in expression (a) all terms containing the products of coefficients such as $a_m a_n$ disappear and only the terms with squares of those coefficients remain. The expression for strain energy then becomes

$$V = \frac{\pi^4 EI}{4l^3}(a^2_1 + 2^4 a^2_2 + 3^4 a^2_3 + \cdots) = \frac{\pi^4 EI}{4l^3}\sum_{n=1}^{n=\infty} n^4 a^2_n. \tag{41}$$

If we give to the beam (Fig. 12a) a very small displacement from the position of equilibrium, the change in the potential energy of the beam is equal to the work done by the external load during such a displacement. This follows from the principle of virtual displacements, and we shall use it in determining the coefficients of the series (40). Small displacements of the beam from the position of equilibrium can be obtained by small

[1] See W. E. Byerly, "Fourier's Series and Spherical Harmonics," §§19–24, 1893, and W. F. Osgood, "Advanced Calculus," p. 391, 1928.

[2] See author's "Strength of Materials," vol. 1, p. 306, 1930.

variations of the coefficients a_1, a_2, a_3, ... If any coefficient a_n is given an increase da_n, we have the term $(a_n + da_n) \sin \frac{n\pi x}{l}$ in series (40), instead of the term $a_n \sin \frac{n\pi x}{l}$, the other terms remaining unchanged. Thus the increase da_n in the coefficient a_n represents an additional small deflection of the beam given by the sine curve $da_n \sin (n\pi x/l)$ superposed upon the original deflection curve. The work done by the external load during this additional deflection can now be calculated. In the case of a single load Q, applied at the distance c from the left support (Fig. 12a), the point of application of the load undergoes a vertical displacement $da_n \sin \frac{n\pi c}{l}$ and the load produces the work

$$Q \, da_n \sin \frac{n\pi c}{l}. \qquad (b)$$

The change in strain energy (41) of the beam, due to the increase da_n in a_n, is

$$\frac{\partial V}{\partial a_n} \, da_n = \frac{\pi^4 EI}{2l^3} n^4 a_n \, da_n. \qquad (c)$$

Equating this to the work done (b), we obtain an equation for determining the coefficient a_n:

$$\frac{\pi^4 EI}{2l^3} n^4 a_n = Q \sin \frac{n\pi c}{l},$$

from which

$$a_n = \frac{2Ql^3}{\pi^4 EI n^4} \sin \frac{n\pi c}{l}. \qquad (d)$$

Substituting such expressions for the coefficients in the series (40), we obtain

$$y = \frac{2Ql^3}{\pi^4 EI} \left(\sin \frac{\pi c}{l} \sin \frac{\pi x}{l} + \frac{1}{2^4} \sin \frac{2\pi c}{l} \sin \frac{2\pi x}{l} + \cdots \right) =$$

$$\frac{2Ql^3}{\pi^4 EI} \sum_{n=1}^{n=\infty} \frac{1}{n^4} \sin \frac{n\pi c}{l} \sin \frac{n\pi x}{l}. \qquad (42)$$

Using this series, the deflection for any value of x can be calculated. Take, for instance, the case in which the load is applied at the middle of the span and calculate the deflection under the load. Substituting in the series (42) $x = c = l/2$, we obtain

$$\delta = (y)_{x=\frac{l}{2}} = \frac{2Ql^3}{\pi^4 EI}\left(1 + \frac{1}{3^4} + \frac{1}{5^4} + \cdots \right).$$

The series is rapidly converging and the first few terms give the deflection with a high degree of accuracy. Using, only the first term of the series, we obtain

$$\delta = \frac{2Ql^3}{\pi^4 EI} = \frac{Ql^3}{48.7EI}.$$

Comparison with the exact solution shows that we obtained 48.7 instead of 48. Thus the error made in using only the first term instead of the whole series is about $1\frac{1}{2}$ per cent. Such accuracy is sufficient in many practical cases.

Having the solution for a single load (42), other cases of loading can be solved by using the method of superposition. Consider, for instance, a beam carrying a uniformly distributed load of intensity q. Each increment of load, qdc, at distance c from the left support can be considered as a concentrated load, and the corresponding deflections, which we denote by dy, are obtained from series (42) by substituting qdc for Q. Then

$$dy = \frac{2qdcl^3}{\pi^4 EI}\sum_{n=1}^{n=\infty} \frac{1}{n^4} \sin \frac{n\pi c}{l} \sin \frac{n\pi x}{l}.$$

Integrating this expression with respect to c, between the limits $c = 0$ and $c = l$, we obtain the deflection curve for the case when the uniform load is distributed along the entire span:

$$y = \frac{4ql^4}{n^5 EI} \sum_{n=1,3,5,\ldots}^{n=\infty} \frac{1}{n^5} \sin \frac{n\pi x}{l}.$$

Again we obtain a very rapidly converging series. Taking, for instance, only the first term, the deflection at the middle is

$$\delta = \frac{4ql^4}{\pi^5 EI} = \frac{ql^4}{76.5EI}.$$

The exact solution for this case gives

$$\delta = \frac{5ql^4}{384EI} = \frac{ql^4}{76.8EI}.$$

Thus the error in taking only the first term is less than one-half of 1 per cent in this case.

The representation of the deflection curve in the form of the trigonometric series (40) is especially useful in the case in which the beam is submitted to the simultaneous action of a lateral load and an axial force. Consider, for example, the beam represented in Fig. 13. In determining the coefficients $a_1, a_2, \ldots$ of the series (40), we consider as before an infinitely small displacement $da_n \sin \frac{n\pi x}{l}$ from the deflection curve of equilibrium of the beam. The corresponding change in the strain energy of bending is the

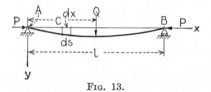

Fig. 13.

same as in the previous case. In calculating the work done by the external forces during this displacement, we must consider not only the work $Q\, da_n \sin \frac{n\pi c}{l}$, produced by the lateral load, but also the work done by the longitudinal forces P. Any change in the shape of the deflection curve usually results in some displacement of the movable hinge B, and the force P acting on this hinge produces work. Let us consider first the displacement of the hinge B which occurs during the deformation of the bar from its initial straight form to the equilibrium curve, shown in Fig. 13. This displacement is equal to the difference between the length of the deflection curve and the length of the chord AB. Denoting this displacement by λ and observing that the difference between the length of an element ds of the curve and the corresponding element dx of the chord is equal to

$$ds - dx = dx\sqrt{1 + \left(\frac{dy}{dx}\right)^2} - dx \approx \frac{1}{2}\left(\frac{dy}{dx}\right)^2 dx,$$

we obtain

$$\lambda = \frac{1}{2} \int_0^l \left(\frac{dy}{dx}\right)^2 dx. \tag{43}$$

Substituting in this expression the series (40) for y and taking into account that

$$\int_0^l \cos^2 \frac{n\pi x}{l} \, dx = \frac{l}{2}, \qquad \int_0^l \cos \frac{n\pi x}{l} \cos \frac{m\pi x}{l} \, dx = 0,$$

we find

$$\lambda = \frac{\pi^2}{4l} \sum_{n=1}^{n=\infty} n^2 a^2_n. \tag{44}$$

If we take now a small displacement from the position of equilibrium by giving to a coefficient a_n an increase da_n, the corresponding small displacement of the hinge B is

$$d\lambda = \frac{\partial \lambda}{\partial a_n} \, da_n = \frac{\pi^2 n^2}{2l} a_n da_n.$$

Equating the change in strain energy of bending to the work done by the external forces during the small displacement $da_n \sin \frac{n\pi x}{l}$, we obtain the following equation for determining any coefficient a_n of the series (40):

$$\frac{\pi^4 EI}{2l^3} n^4 a_n da_n = Q da_n \sin \frac{n\pi c}{l} + P \frac{\pi^2 n^2}{2l} a_n da_n,$$

from which

$$a_n = \frac{2Ql^3}{\pi^4 EI} \sin \frac{n\pi c}{l} \frac{1}{n^2 \left(n^2 - \dfrac{Pl^2}{\pi^2 EI}\right)}. \tag{e}$$

To simplify the equations, we denote by α the ratio of the longitudinal force P to its critical value (10); then

$$a_n = \frac{2Ql^3}{\pi^4 EI} \sin \frac{n\pi c}{l} \frac{1}{n^2(n^2 - \alpha)}.$$

Substituting in the series (40), we obtain

$$y = \frac{2Ql^3}{\pi^4 EI} \left[\frac{1}{1-\alpha} \sin \frac{\pi c}{l} \sin \frac{\pi x}{l} + \frac{1}{2^2(2^2 - \alpha)} \sin \frac{2\pi c}{l} \sin \frac{2\pi x}{l} + \cdots \right] =$$

$$\frac{2Ql^3}{\pi^4 EI} \sum_{n=1}^{n=\infty} \frac{1}{n^2(n^2 - \alpha)} \sin \frac{n\pi c}{l} \sin \frac{n\pi x}{l}. \tag{45}$$

Comparing this with the series (42) for the case when only a lateral load Q is acting, we conclude that, owing to the action of the longitudinal compressive force P, all the coefficients of the series (42) increase. It may be seen also that, when the force P approaches its critical value and α approaches unity, the first term in the series (45) increases indefinitely.

It was shown before that the first term of the series (40) gives a satisfactory approximation for the deflections of the bar when only lateral load is acting. Then, denoting by δ_0 the maximum deflection of the bar produced by lateral load Q alone, we conclude from the comparison of series (42) and (45) that, in the case of simultaneous action of lateral load Q and longitudinal compressive force P, the maximum deflection is approximately

$$\delta = \frac{\delta_0}{1 - \alpha}. \tag{46}$$

Having the deflection curve (45) for the case of one lateral load Q, we can, without difficulty, obtain the deflections for any kind of lateral loading by using the principle of superposition. In the case of a uniform lateral load on a compressed bar, we substitute qdc instead of Q in the series (45) and integrate this series by varying c within the limits of the loaded portion of the beam. If the load covers the entire span, the integration limits are 0 and l and we obtain

$$y = \frac{4ql^4}{\pi^5 EI} \sum_{n=1,3,5,\ldots}^{n=\infty} \frac{1}{n^3(n^2 - \alpha)} \sin \frac{n\pi x}{l}. \tag{f}$$

Again we have a rapidly converging series, and the first term gives a satisfactory approximation so that a formula analogous to formula (46) can also be used in this case and the deflection can be calculated by multiplying the deflection δ_0, produced by lateral load alone, by the factor $1/(1 - \alpha)$. This formula is very accurate for small values of α. With the increase of α, the error of the approximate formula increases also and approaches one-half of 1 per cent when P approaches its critical value.

By moving the load Q to the left support (Fig. 13) and making c infinitesimally small, we approach the condition of bending of the bar by a couple Qc applied at the left end. Substituting for this case in Eq. (45) $\sin \frac{n\pi c}{l} = \frac{n\pi c}{l}$ and using the notation

$Qc = M_a$, we obtain the following series giving the deflection curve of a compressed bar bent by a couple at the end:

$$y = \frac{2M_a l^2}{\pi^3 EI} \sum_{n=1}^{n=\infty} \frac{1}{n(n^2 - \alpha)} \sin \frac{n\pi x}{l}. \tag{g}$$

If there are two moments M_a and M_b applied at the ends, the deflection curve is obtained by superposing deflections produced by each of the moments. Assuming, for instance, $M_a = M_b = M$ and using Eq. (g), we obtain, for the case of two equal moments, the deflection curve

$$y = \frac{2M l^2}{\pi^3 EI} \sum_{n=1}^{n=\infty} \frac{1}{n(n^2 - \alpha)} \sin \frac{n\pi x}{l} +$$

$$\frac{2M l^2}{\pi^3 EI} \sum_{n=1}^{n=\infty} \frac{1}{n(n^2 - \alpha)} \sin \frac{n\pi(l - x)}{l} =$$

$$\frac{4M l^2}{\pi^3 EI} \sum_{n=1, 3, 5, \ldots}^{n=\infty} \frac{1}{n(n^2 - \alpha)} \sin \frac{n\pi x}{l}. \tag{h}$$

Since the curve in this case is symmetrical with respect to the middle of the beam, the terms with even values of n do not appear in the series (h). The deflection at the middle is

$$\delta = (y)_{x=\frac{l}{2}} = \frac{4M l^2}{\pi^3 EI}\left[\frac{1}{1 - \alpha} - \frac{1}{3(9 - \alpha)} + \cdots \right]. \tag{i}$$

If the couples at the ends are produced by compressive forces P applied at both ends with the same eccentricity e, we put Pe instead of M in Eq. (i); then

$$\delta = \frac{4e\alpha}{\pi}\left[\frac{1}{1 - \alpha} - \frac{1}{3(9 - \alpha)} + \cdots \right].$$

Again the series is a rapidly converging one and we can obtain the deflection δ with sufficient accuracy by taking only the first term of the series. Thus

$$\delta = \frac{4e\alpha}{\pi(1 - \alpha)}. \tag{j}$$

In the general case where M_a and M_b are not equal, we can always replace them by two equal moments M' of the same sign, equal to $\frac{1}{2}(M_a + M_b)$, and two equal moments M'' of the opposite sign, equal to $\frac{1}{2}(M_a - M_b)$. Only the first two moments produce deflection at the middle. Hence, if compressive forces P are applied at the ends with the eccentricities e_1 and e_2, the deflection at the middle is obtained from Eq. (j) by substituting $\frac{1}{2}(e_1 + e_2)^1$ for e.

8. The Effect of Initial Curvature on Deflections.—When a bar is submitted to the action of lateral load only, a small initial curvature of the bar has no effect on the bending and the final

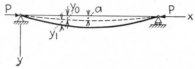

Fig. 14.

deflection curve is obtained by superposing the ordinates due to initial curvature on the deflections calculated as for a straight bar. However, if there is an axial force acting on the bar, the deflections produced by this force will be substantially influenced by the initial curvature.

Let us consider, as an example, the case in which the initial shape of the axis of the bar is given by the equation (see Fig. 14)

$$y_0 = a \sin \frac{\pi x}{l}. \qquad (a)$$

Thus the axis of the bar has initially the form of a sine curve with a maximum ordinate at the middle equal to a. If this bar is submitted to the action of a longitudinal compressive force P, additional deflections y_1 will be produced so that the final ordinates of the deflection curve are

$$y = y_0 + y_1, \qquad (b)$$

and the bending moment at any cross section is
$$M = P(y_0 + y_1).$$

Then the deflections y_1 due to deformation are determined in the usual way from the differential equation

$$EI\frac{d^2y_1}{dx^2} = -P(y_0 + y_1), \qquad (c)$$

---

[1] The eccentricities should be taken positive when they result in positive bending moments at the ends, and negative in the reversed case.

or, by substituting expression (a) for y_0 and using notation (1) (p. 2), we obtain

$$\frac{d^2 y_1}{dx^2} + k^2 y_1 = -k^2 a \sin \frac{\pi x}{l}.$$

The general solution of this equation is

$$y_1 = A \sin kx + B \cos kx + \frac{1}{\dfrac{\pi^2}{k^2 l^2} - 1} a \sin \frac{\pi x}{l}. \qquad (d)$$

To satisfy the end conditions ($y_1 = 0$, for $x = 0$ and for $x = l$) for any value of k, we must put $A = B = 0$. Then, by using the previous notation α for the ratio of the longitudinal force to its critical value, we obtain

$$\frac{\pi^2}{k^2 l^2} = \frac{1}{\alpha},$$

and

$$y_1 = \frac{\alpha}{1 - \alpha} a \sin \frac{\pi x}{l}. \qquad (47)$$

The final ordinates of the deflection curve are

$$y = y_0 + y_1 = a \sin \frac{\pi x}{l} + \frac{\alpha}{1 - \alpha} a \sin \frac{\pi x}{l} = \frac{a}{1 - \alpha} \sin \frac{\pi x}{l}. \qquad (48)$$

It is seen that, owing to the action of the longitudinal compressive force, the initial deflection a at the middle of the bar is magnified in the ratio $1/(1 - \alpha)$. The final ordinates increase with α and increase indefinitely as α approaches unity, i.e., when the compressive force approaches its critical value.

If the initial shape of the bar is given by a series[1]

$$y_0 = a_1 \sin \frac{\pi x}{l} + a_2 \sin \frac{2\pi x}{l} + \cdots,$$

we substitute this expression for y_0 in Eq. (c); then, proceeding as before with each term of the series, we obtain

$$y_1 = \alpha \left(\frac{a_1}{1 - \alpha} \sin \frac{\pi x}{l} + \frac{a_2}{2^2 - \alpha} \sin \frac{2\pi x}{l} + \cdots \right). \qquad (49)$$

Since α is always less than one and approaches unity when P approaches P_{cr}, the first term in this expression usually has

[1] See author's paper in *Bull. Soc. Eng. Tech.*, St. Petersburg, 1913 (Russian).

predominant importance and is seen to coincide with expression (47).

The problem of bending of an initially curved bar can be approached in a different way by replacing the effect of an initial curvature on deflections with the effect of an *equivalent lateral load*. An equivalent lateral load, then, will be one which will produce the same bending-moment diagram as the longitudinal forces produce if initial deflections only are taken. Take, for instance, the case in which the initial curvature is given by Eq. (*a*). The effect of this curvature on deflections of the compressed bar is the same as the effect of a distributed lateral load producing in the bar bending moments $M = Pa \sin \dfrac{\pi x}{l}$, since the differential equations of the elastic curve (*c*) are identical for both cases. Then the expression for the intensity q of the equivalent lateral load is obtained by using the known relation between q and M, namely,

$$q = -\frac{d^2M}{dx^2} = \frac{\pi^2 aP}{l^2} \sin \frac{\pi x}{l}.$$

The deflections produced by this lateral load are obtained by using the general method of the previous article.

Substituting in the general expression (45) $\dfrac{\pi^2 aP}{l^2} \sin \dfrac{\pi c}{l} \, dc$ for Q, and integrating from $c = 0$ to $c = l$, we obtain

$$y_1 = \frac{2l^3}{\pi^4 EI} \frac{\pi^2 aP}{l^2} \int_0^l \sin \frac{\pi c}{l} \, dc \sum_{n=1}^{n=\infty} \frac{1}{n^2(n^2 - \alpha)} \sin \frac{n\pi c}{l} \sin \frac{n\pi x}{l}.$$

Since

$$\int_0^l \sin \frac{\pi c}{l} \sin \frac{n\pi c}{l} \, dc = 0, \quad \text{when } n \neq 1, \quad \text{and} \quad \int_0^l \sin^2 \frac{\pi c}{l} \, dc = \frac{l}{2},$$

all the terms of the above integral, except the first, disappear and we finally obtain

$$y_1 = \frac{\alpha}{1 - \alpha} a \sin \frac{\pi x}{l}. \tag{e}$$

This expression coincides with the expression (47) previously derived.

As another example, take the case in which the initial deflection curve of the bar (Fig. 14) is a parabola

$$y_0 = \frac{4a}{l^2}x(l - x). \qquad (f)$$

The corresponding equivalent lateral load is

$$q = -\frac{d^2(Py_0)}{dx^2} = \frac{8aP}{l^2}.$$

Substituting this for q in Eq. (14), the deflection curve becomes

$$y_1 = \frac{2a}{u^2}\left[\frac{\cos\left(1 - \frac{2x}{l}\right)u}{\cos u} - 1\right] - \frac{4a}{l^2}x(l - x), \qquad (g)$$

in which [see Eq. (8)]

$$u^2 = \frac{Pl^2}{4EI}.$$

Superposing on these deflections the initial deflections (f), the total ordinates of the bent bar are

$$y = y_0 + y_1 = \frac{2a}{u^2}\left[\frac{\cos\left(1 - \frac{2x}{l}\right)u}{\cos u} - 1\right].$$

If the initial shape of the bar consists of two rectilinear portions making an angle with each other (Fig. 15), the equivalent lateral

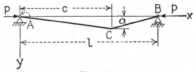

Fig. 15.

load becomes a concentrated load Q at C, since this gives the same shape of bending-moment diagram as that produced by P in Fig. 15. The magnitude of the equivalent load is obtained from the equality of the moments

$$Pa = \frac{Qc(l - c)}{l},$$

from which

$$Q = \frac{Pal}{c(l - c)}.$$

Substituting this in Eqs. (2) and (3) (Art. 1), the deflections y_1 for this case are obtained.

It is interesting to note that, owing to the non-linear relation between the compressive force and the deflections produced in an initially curved bar, it may happen that, during a continuous increase of the force P, the direction of deflections in some portions of the bar may be reversed. To explain this phenomenon, let us consider the initial curvature

$$y_0 = a_1 \sin \frac{\pi x}{l} + a_2 \sin \frac{2\pi x}{l}$$

and assume that a_1 is small in comparison with a_2 so that the initial curvature has substantially the shape shown in Fig. 16.

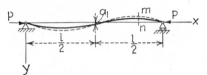

Fig. 16.

The deflections produced by the force P, from (49), are

$$y_1 = \frac{\alpha a_1}{1 - \alpha} \sin \frac{\pi x}{l} + \frac{\alpha a_2}{2^2 - \alpha} \sin \frac{2\pi x}{l}. \qquad (h)$$

If the compressive force P is small in comparison with the critical load, the quantity α is also small; since a_1 is small in comparison with a_2, it can be concluded that the second term in expression (h) is of a greater importance and that deflections are such as indicated by the dotted line. In a cross section such as mn, the direction of the deflection is upward. Assume now that the force P is gradually increased until it begins to approach the critical value. Then α approaches unity and the first term in Eq. (h) becomes predominant. Thus, the direction of the deflection at mn is now downward.

If a compressed bar, having an initial curvature, carries in addition certain lateral loading, the total deflection is obtained by superposing on the deflections due to curvature, discussed above, the deflections due to lateral loading calculated as for a straight compressed bar. That such a superposition is justified we can see from the fact that the effect of initial curvature can be replaced by the effect of an equivalent lateral load, and it was proved before (see Art. 2) that for all kinds of lateral loading the principle of superposition holds. It is necessary, however, in calculating deflections produced by each kind of lateral loading, to assume that the compressive force P is acting with each.

If the ends of the compressed bar are fixed, bending moments at the ends will be produced during compression; the magnitude of these can be readily obtained from the condition of fixity of the ends. Assume, for example, the case in which the initial curvature of the bar is given by the equation

$$y_0 = a \sin \frac{\pi x}{l}.$$

The deflection of the bar due to compressive forces is given then by Eq. (47) and the magnitude of the angle of rotation of the ends is

$$\left(\frac{dy_1}{dx}\right)_{x=0} = \frac{\alpha}{1-\alpha} \frac{\pi a}{l}. \qquad (i)$$

To counteract these rotations, moments must be applied at the ends, and their magnitude can be found [see Eq. (28)] from the following equation:

$$\frac{\alpha}{1-\alpha} \frac{\pi a}{l} = \frac{Ml}{2EI} \frac{\tan u}{u},$$

from which

$$M = \frac{\alpha}{1-\alpha} \frac{2\pi a EI}{l^2} \frac{u}{\tan u}. \qquad (j)$$

The resultant deflection of the bar is obtained by superposing on the deflection due to curvature [Eq. (48)] the deflection due to moments M [Eq. (26)]. In this manner we obtain the deflection at the middle equal to

$$\delta = \frac{a}{1-\alpha} - \frac{Ml^2}{8EI} \frac{2(1-\cos u)}{u^2 \cos u},$$

or, by using Eq. (j),

$$\delta = \frac{a}{1-\alpha}\left(1 - \frac{\pi\alpha}{2} \frac{1-\cos u}{u \sin u}\right). \qquad (k)$$

The bending moment at the middle is now obtained by subtracting from the moment $P\delta$ the moment M acting at the end.

9. Determination of Allowable Stresses.—In designing steel beams submitted to the action of lateral loads, it is usual practice to choose the working stress as a certain portion of the yield-point stress. Thus

$$\sigma_w = \frac{1}{n}\sigma_{\text{Y.P.}} \qquad (a)$$

where n is the factor of safety.

The cross-sectional dimensions of a beam should be so chosen that the maximum stress will not exceed the working stress determined from (a).

The same procedure can also be used in the case of the simultaneous action of lateral loads and a longitudinal compressive force, if the conditions are such that the longitudinal force always remains constant and only the possibility of increase of lateral loads must be considered. From the principle of super-position discussed in Art. 2, it follows at once that, by taking the working stress from Eq. (a), we obtain such proportions of the beam that the maximum stress becomes equal to the yield-point stress when all lateral loads become n times greater.[1]

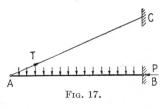

Fig. 17.

There are cases, however, in which the longitudinal force increases simultaneously with the lateral loads. The structure shown in Fig. 17 is an example of such a case. It is seen that the tensile force T in the wire AC and the corresponding compressive force P in the bar AB are increasing in the same proportion as the lateral load acting on the beam. In such cases the deflections and maximum stresses will increase at a greater rate than the lateral loads, and this fact must be considered in choosing the working stress in order to assure the desired factor of safety. To make the factor of safety equal to n, it is necessary to determine the cross-sectional dimensions of the beam in such a manner that the maximum fiber stress will become equal to the yield-point stress when all loads (including the longitudinal force P) acting on the beam are taken n times greater. This requires the use of a smaller working stress than that obtained from Eq. (a).

To illustrate the procedure of selecting the cross-sectional dimensions of such beams, let us consider the case of a column

---

[1] It is assumed that up to the yield point the usual beam formula for stresses holds with sufficient accuracy. For such material as structural steel this assumption is justifiable.

compressed by eccentrically applied loads P (Fig. 5b) and assume that both eccentricities are equal to e and are in one of the principal planes of the beam. The maximum bending moment is then, from Eq. (29),

$$M_{\text{max.}} = Pe \sec \frac{l}{2}\sqrt{\frac{P}{EI}}. \tag{b}$$

Denoting by r the radius of gyration of the cross section, we find the maximum stress at the middle cross section to be

$$\sigma_{\text{max.}} = \frac{P}{A}\left(1 + \frac{e}{s} \sec \frac{l}{2r}\sqrt{\frac{P}{AE}}\right), \tag{50}$$

where s is the ratio of the section modulus of the cross section to the cross-sectional area. Sometimes this is called the *core radius* since it marks out a certain core in the cross section within which a compressive force may act without causing tensile stress in any extreme fiber. In the case of a rectangular cross section, for instance,

$$s = \frac{bh^2/6}{bh} = \frac{h}{6}.$$

For given dimensions of a column and for a given eccentricity e, the ratios l/r and e/s are known and Eq. (50) represents the relation between the maximum fiber stress and the average compressive stress $\sigma_c = P/A$. For a given value of the modulus E, this relation can be represented in the form of a curve by taking Pl^2/Ar^2 as the abscissa and $\sigma_{\text{max.}}l^2/r^2$ as the ordinates. In Fig. 18, three curves of this kind are given, calculated for the three different eccentricity ratios,[1] $e/s = 1$, $e/s = 0.5$ and $e/s = 0.1$. The modulus of elasticity is taken equal to $30 \cdot 10^6$ lb. per square inch. There is shown also a straight line $0A$, giving the maximum fiber stress for the case where the load is centrally applied, *i.e.*, for $e/s = 0$. This line gives the maximum fiber stresses up to the critical value of the average compressive stress. The critical value is indicated in the figure by the vertical line CAB. All curves similar to the three shown in the figure will have this vertical line as their asymptote, since $\sec (l/2r)\sqrt{P/AE}$ in Eq. (50) becomes infinitely large when $P = P_{cr}$. As the eccentricity e becomes smaller and smaller, the corresponding curves come closer and closer to the straight lines $0A$ and AB.

[1] In this figure the scale for $\sigma_{\text{max.}}l^2/r^2$ is one-half the scale for Pl^2/Ar^2.

Having a series of curves like those in Fig. 18, we can easily find, for a given column, the maximum fiber stress produced by a given compressive force applied with a known eccentricity.

The same curves can also be used to determine, for a given column and a given eccentricity, the amount of compressive load which can be applied with a given factor of safety. Assume, for instance, that the yield-point stress for the material of the column is 40,000 lb. per square inch, that the desired factor of safety is 2.5, that $e/s = 0.1$, and that the slenderness ratio $l/r = 100$.

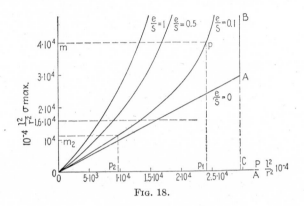

Fig. 18.

Then the numbers marked on the coordinate axes in Fig. 18 will give directly the stresses σ_c and $\sigma_{max.}$. Drawing the horizontal line mp for $\sigma_{max.} = 40,000$ lb. per square inch to the intersection at p with the corresponding curve in Fig. 18, we find on the abscissa axis point p_1, which gives the value of the average stress σ_c, which will produce a maximum fiber stress equal to the yield-point stress. We shall denote this value of average stress by $(\sigma_c)_{\text{Y.P.}}$. To have the factor of safety equal to 2.5, the allowable average stress should be only 0.4 of that given by point p_1. In Fig. 18 this is indicated by point p_2 (equal to 9,700 lb. per square inch), and the corresponding ordinate of the curve $e/s = 0.1$, equal to $0m_2$, gives the maximum fiber stress $\sigma_{max.}$ (equal to 11,400 lb. per square inch), which must be taken as a working stress in order to have the desired factor of safety. It is seen that the value of the working stress so obtained is much less than the stress 16,000 lb. per square inch, which would be obtained by using Eq. (a).

In designing an eccentrically loaded column, we begin by assuming probable cross-sectional dimensions. Then, proceeding as explained above, we obtain the safe value of the load that the column can carry. If this load differs substantially from the actual load, the assumed cross-sectional dimensions should be changed and the calculations repeated. Thus, by using the trial-and-error method we can always find satisfactory cross-sectional dimensions for the column.

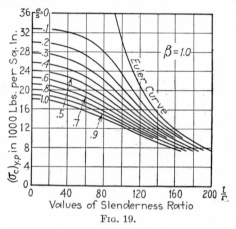

Fig. 19.

Instead of the above curves, we can use Eq. (50) directly in designing eccentrically loaded columns. If P denotes the safe load on the column and n is the factor of safety, then nP is the load at which the maximum fiber stress should become equal to the yield-point stresses. Equation (50) for this load becomes

$$\sigma_{\text{Y.P.}} = \frac{nP}{A}\left(1 + \frac{e}{s}\sec\frac{l}{2r}\sqrt{\frac{nP}{AE}}\right). \qquad (50')$$

We can always solve this equation for P/A by using the trial-and-error method and in this way obtain the safe average stress P/A for a given column. Assuming certain values for $\sigma_{\text{Y.P.}}$, n and e/s and using Eq. (50'), we can calculate a table of safe values of the average compressive stress $\sigma_c = P/A$ for various values of the slenderness ratio l/r. This relation between σ_c and l/r can be represented graphically in the form of a family of curves.

To make these curves independent of the factor of safety n, values of $nP/A = (\sigma_c)_{\text{Y.P.}}$ can be plotted against l/r so that the values of the average compressive stress $(\sigma_c)_{\text{Y.P.}}$, at which yielding begins, may be taken directly from the curves, and any desired factor of safety may be obtained simply by dividing the ordinates of the curve by the desired value of n. Figure 19 represents such curves[1] for structural steel, assuming $E = 30 \cdot 10^6$ lb. per square inch, $\sigma_{\text{Y.P.}} = 36,000$ lb. per square inch and $e/s = 0.1, 0.2, \ldots, 1.0$. Having such curves, no difficulty is encountered in determining by the trial-and-error method the necessary cross section for an eccentrically compressed bar.

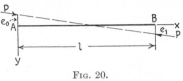

Similar curves can also be calculated for other kinds of lateral loading acting simultaneously with the compressive

Fig. 20.

force.[2] For instance, in the case of uniformly loaded beams it will be necessary to use Eq. (17) in the same manner as Eq. (29) was used above.

In the case of compressive forces applied with two different eccentricities e_0 and e_1 (Fig. 20), we use Eq. (24) of Art. 4. This case is of practical importance in discussing stresses in compressed members of a truss. Owing to the rigidity of the joints, secondary stresses are always present and each compressed member is submitted to the simultaneous action of compression and bending by the moments at the ends. If the magnitudes of the bending moments are known from the analysis of secondary stresses,[3] the maximum stresses in each particular case can be obtained in a manner analogous to that discussed above for the case of two equal moments.[4]

Assuming that e_0 is the numerically larger eccentricity, we use the notation $\beta = e_1/e_0$. Thus β varies from $+1$, when the

[1] These curves were calculated by D. H. Young. See his paper, *Rational Design of Steel Columns*, presented at the joint meeting of A.S.M.E. and A.S.C.E., Chicago, June, 1933.

[2] Several tables of this kind were prepared by S. Zavriev; see *Mémoirs of the Institute of Engineers of Ways of Communication*, St. Petersburg, 1913.

[3] The analysis of secondary stresses can always be made with sufficient accuracy by a method of successive approximations (see Waddell, "Bridge Engineering," vol. 1, p. 178). Such an analysis should be required in all important cases since a rational design of compressed members is impossible without a knowledge of the secondary stresses.

[4] This problem is fully discussed in D. H. Young's paper in *Pub. Intern. Assoc. Bridge and Structural Eng.*, vol. 1, p. 507, 1932.

eccentricities are equal and in the same direction, to -1 when the eccentricities are equal and in opposite directions.

In the case of comparatively short bars, the maximum fiber stress will occur at the end A, where the eccentricity is larger. The magnitude of this stress is easily calculated from the usual formula for combined compression and bending, and the average compressive stress at which yielding begins is given by the equation

$$(\sigma_c)_{\text{Y.P.}} = \frac{\sigma_{\text{Y.P.}}}{1 + \dfrac{e_0}{s}}. \tag{c}$$

In the case of slender bars, the maximum stress occurs at an

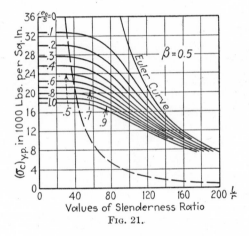

Fig. 21.

intermediate cross section and the value of the average compressive stress at which yielding begins is given by the equation[1]

$$(\sigma_c)_{\text{Y.P.}} = \frac{\sigma_{\text{Y.P.}}}{1 + \dfrac{e_0}{s}\psi \cos ec\, 2u}, \tag{d}$$

in which

$$2u = kl = l\sqrt{\frac{P_{\text{Y.P.}}}{EI}} \quad \text{and} \quad \psi = \sqrt{\beta^2 - 2\beta \cos 2u + 1}.$$

The limiting value of the slenderness ratio l/r, up to which Eq. (c) should be used, is found in each particular case by using

[1] See D. H. Young, *loc. cit.*, p. 41.

the equation

$$\cos^{-1} \beta = \frac{l}{r}\sqrt{\frac{(\sigma_c)_{\text{Y.P.}}}{E}}, \qquad (e)$$

which is obtained by equating (c) and (d).

The results of calculations made with Eqs. (c), (d) and (e) are represented by the curves in Figs. 21 to 24. These calcula-

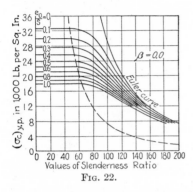

Fig. 22.

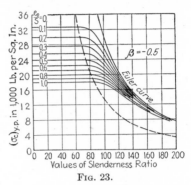

Fig. 23.

tions are made for structural steel, assuming $E = 30 \cdot 10^6$ lb. per square inch and $\sigma_{\text{Y.P.}} = 36{,}000$ lb. per square inch, and for the ratios $e_0/s = 0.1, 0.2, \ldots, 1$. By using these curves, the value of the average compressive stress $(\sigma_c)_{\text{Y.P.}}$ at which yielding begins can easily be obtained in each particular case by interpolation. The dotted curve in Figs. 21, 22, and 23 is obtained from Eq. (e) and is the dividing line between the ranges of application of Eqs. (c) and (d). When the eccentricity e_0 approaches zero, the average stress $(\sigma_c)_{\text{Y.P.}}$ for a short column is equal to $\sigma_{\text{Y.P.}}$. For slender columns $(l/r$ a large number), the

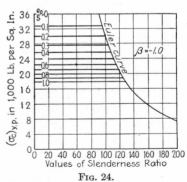

Fig. 24.

value of $(\sigma_c)_{\text{Y.P.}}$ approaches the value P_{cr}/A, where P_{cr} is the critical load given by Eq. (10).

In a similar manner we can determine the safe load for the case of an initially curved and compressed column. Take, for instance, the case in which the initial deflection of the column is a flat sine curve $y = a \sin \dfrac{\pi x}{l}$ (Fig. 13). If a compressive force P is centrally applied at the ends, the total deflection at the middle is [see Eq. (48)]

$$\delta = \frac{a}{1 - \dfrac{P}{P_{cr}}},$$

and the maximum compressive stress will be

$$\sigma_{\text{max.}} = \frac{P}{A}\left(1 + \frac{a}{s}\,\frac{1}{1 - \dfrac{P}{P_{cr}}}\right), \tag{51}$$

in which s denotes the core radius of the cross section.

Denoting as before by $(\sigma_c)_{\text{Y.P.}}$ the average compressive stress, which produces a maximum fiber stress equal to the yield-point stress, the equation for determining $(\sigma_c)_{\text{Y.P.}}$, from Eq. (51), becomes

$$\sigma_{\text{Y.P.}} = (\sigma_c)_{\text{Y.P.}}\left[1 + \frac{a}{s}\,\frac{1}{1 - \dfrac{(\sigma_c)_{\text{Y.P.}}}{\pi^2 E}\,\dfrac{l^2}{r^2}}\right]. \tag{52}$$

This is a quadratic equation for $(\sigma_c)_{\text{Y.P.}}$ which can be solved for any values of the ratios a/s and l/r.

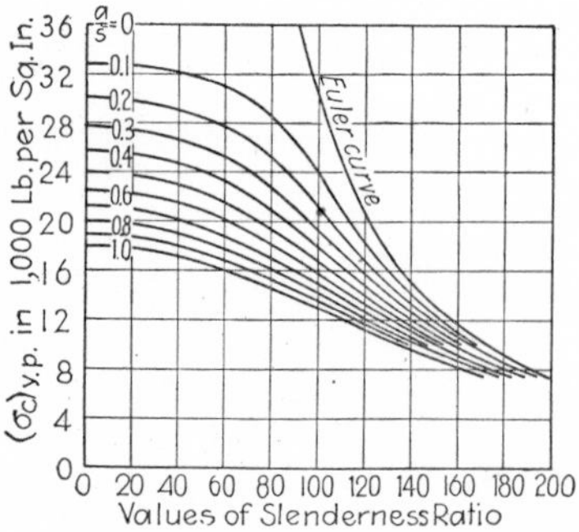

FIG. 25.

Having the average compressive stress at which yielding begins, the allowable average compressive stress for an initially curved column can be obtained simply by dividing this $(\sigma_c)_{\text{Y.P.}}$, stress by the desired factor of safety. In Fig. 25 are represented curves[1] giving the average compressive stress at which yielding begins, calculated for structural steel having $\sigma_{\text{Y.P.}} = 36{,}000$ lb. per square inch, $E = 30 \cdot 10^6$ lb. per square inch and $a/s = 0.1, 0.2, \ldots , 1$. Using these curves and any desired factor of safety, the allowable compressive load for a column with a given initial curvature

[1] These curves are taken from the paper by D. H. Young, *loc. cit.*, p. 41.

can be calculated by the trial-and-error method. It will be noted that these curves are very similar to the curves in Fig. 19 which have values of the ratio e/s corresponding to a/s.

10. Bending beyond Proportional Limit.—In the discussion of the previous article, the beginning of yielding of the material at the most stressed point has been taken as a basis for the determination of the allowable stress. The beginning of yielding usually does not mean complete failure of a beam or column, although at this stress a permanent set is often produced which is too large to be permitted in permanent structures.

It is sometimes of practical interest to know how much additional load a structure can carry after yielding has started before complete failure occurs. To answer this question it is necessary to go into an investigation of the deformations of beams and columns beyond the elastic range. The theory of bending of beams beyond the proportional limit is developed on two assumptions: (1) that the cross sections of the beam during bending beyond the proportional limit remain plane,

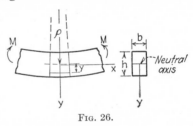

Fig. 26.

and (2) that for the longitudinal fibers of the beam there exists during bending the same relation between stress and strain as in the case of simple tension and compression.[1]

Let us begin with pure bending of a beam of rectangular cross section (Fig. 26) and assume that for tension and compression the material has the same stress-strain diagram (Fig. 27). This condition is practically fulfilled in the case of structural steel. Under this assumption the neutral axis is at the middle of the depth h of the beam. If y (positive as shown in Fig. 26) denotes the distance from this axis to any fiber, then the unit elongation of this fiber is

$$\epsilon = \frac{y}{\rho}, \qquad (a)$$

---

[1] This theory has been developed by B. de Saint Venant in his notes to the famous Navier's book: "Résumé des leçons," 3d ed., p. 173, 1864. See also E. Meyer, *Z. Ver. deut. Ing.*, 1908, p. 167. Th. v. Kármán, *Forschungsarbeiten*, no. 81, 1910, Berlin. E. Chwalla, *Sitzungsb. Akad. Wiss., Wien.*, vol. 137, IIa, p. 469, 1928.

where ρ is the radius of curvature of the deflection curve. The maximum elongation and the maximum compression[1] are obtained from Eq. (a) by substituting in it $y = h/2$ and $y = -h/2$ respectively. Denoting by Δ the difference between the unit elongations of the two extreme fibers, one on the convex and the other on the concave side, we obtain

$$\Delta = \frac{h}{\rho}. \tag{53}$$

Assuming a certain value for Δ, we obtain, from (53), the corresponding radius of curvature ρ for a given depth of the beam. The distribution of stresses over the depth of the beam is then obtained from Fig. 27. The verticals drawn at the distances $\Delta/2$ from the origin give us the stresses in the outermost fibers. For any fiber at a distance y from the neutral surface the elongation is obtained from Eq. (a). Then the corresponding ordinate of Fig. 27 gives the stress σ in this fiber.

The moment of internal forces distributed over a cross section of the beam is

$$M = b \int_{-\frac{h}{2}}^{+\frac{h}{2}} \sigma y \, dy. \tag{b}$$

This moment can be calculated by using Fig. 27. From Eq. (a) we have $y = \epsilon\rho$ and $dy = \rho \, d\epsilon$. Substituting in Eq. (b) and observing that the ordinates in the compression portion of Fig. 27 are the same as in the tension portion, we obtain

$$M = 2b\rho^2 \int_0^{\frac{\Delta}{2}} \sigma\epsilon \, d\epsilon. \tag{c}$$

The integral on the right side of this equation represents the moment with respect to the σ axis of the area $0AB$ in Fig. 27; since ϵ is a dimensionless number, the moment of this area has the same dimensions as σ and can be measured in pounds per square inch. By using Eq. (53) we can also represent Eq. (c) in the following form:

$$M = \frac{2bh^3}{\Delta^3 \rho} \int_0^{\frac{\Delta}{2}} \sigma\epsilon \, d\epsilon = \frac{I}{\rho} \frac{24}{\Delta^3} \int_0^{\frac{\Delta}{2}} \sigma\epsilon \, d\epsilon, \tag{d}$$

in which I is the moment of inertia of the cross section.

[1] Compression is considered as negative elongation in the following discussion.

Within the elastic limit $\sigma = E\epsilon$, and we obtain from (d) the usual equation

$$M = \frac{EI}{\rho}. \tag{54}$$

Beyond the elastic limit σ is given by Fig. 27. Then substituting in (d) for any value of Δ the moment of the area $0AB$ for the

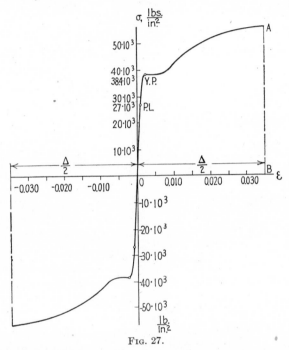

Fig. 27.

integral, we obtain finally, instead of E in Eq. (54), some other quantity which will be called the *reduced modulus* and denoted with E_r. Thus Eq. (d) becomes

$$M = \frac{E_rI}{\rho}. \tag{55}$$

This equation has the same form as Eq. (54) but we must keep in mind that E_r is no longer a constant; it depends on the magnitude of Δ and becomes smaller and smaller as Δ increases.

Having the stress-strain diagram for a given material, such as shown in Fig. 27, E_r can be calculated for any value of Δ, as was explained above; the relation between E_r and Δ can be represented by a curve such as the one shown in Fig. 28.   Using this curve and Eqs. (53) and (55), we can calculate for the given

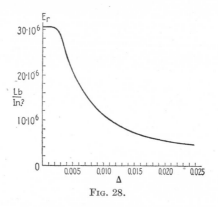

FIG. 28.

cross-sectional dimensions of the beam the bending moment M for any value of Δ and represent the relation between M and Δ

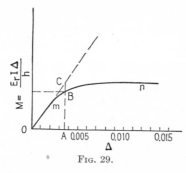

FIG. 29.

by a curve such as the one shown in Fig. 29. For small values of Δ Hooke's law holds and the moment M increases in proportion to Δ. Beyond the proportional limit the moment is no longer increasing in proportion to Δ, and we obtain the curve mn. For any value of M the ratio of the ordinate AB of the curve to the ordinate AC of the dotted straight line gives the ratio of the moments calculated from Eqs. (55) and (54), respectively.   This ratio we call β, so that

$$\beta = \frac{E_r I}{\rho} \div \frac{EI}{\rho} = \frac{E_r}{E}. \qquad (e)$$

The ratio β gives for the chosen value of the bending moment M the proportion by which the flexural rigidity of the beam is diminished owing to plastic deformation of the material.   The relation between β and M can be represented by a curve (Fig. 30).   Having this curve, the deflection of the beam when stressed beyond the proportional limit can be calculated without difficulty.

The simplest case is represented by pure bending. The deflection curve is then the arc of a circle. The radius of this arc [calculated from Eq. (55)] is smaller than we get from Eq. (54)

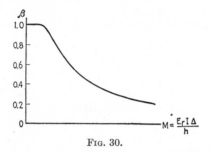

FIG. 30.

in the ratio β. Thus, to get deflections of the beam beyond the proportional limit for any value of M, we need only to divide the deflections calculated on the basis of Hooke's law by the ratio β.

In the case of a beam loaded transversely (Fig. 31), we can use the area-moment method in calculating deflections. To take into account the diminishing of flexural rigidity of the beam beyond the proportional limit, it is necessary only to multiply each ordinate of the bending-moment

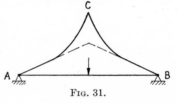

FIG. 31.

diagram by $1/\beta$ taken from Fig. 30. In this way the area ACB is obtained. This area, instead of the true bending-moment area, should now be used in calculating deflections of the beam.

From the above discussion it may be seen that, in the case of a rectangular beam, an increase of the load beyond the point that first produces yielding of the material does not mean immediate failure of the beam. At the beginning yielding occurs only in the outermost fibers of the cross section with the maximum bending moment and a large portion of the material continues to work elastically. By plotting a load-deflection diagram for such a beam, we find that the shape of this diagram is quite different from the stress-strain diagram (Fig. 27) for simple tension. When yielding of the material begins, we obtain in the load-deflection diagram only a slight deviation from a straight line, and a considerable flattening of the curve occurs only at a much higher load when yielding spreads over a large portion

of the material of the beam. The amount of this flattening
of the load-deflection diagram and the magnitude of the corresponding permanent deflection of the beam depend upon the
percentage of plastic flow at the yield point in the tension-com-
pression stress-strain diagram for the material (Fig. 27).

Assume, for instance, that plastic flow at the yield point is
$1\frac{1}{2}$ per cent, *i.e.*, about fifteen times larger than the elastic

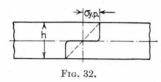

FIG. 32.

elongation at the proportional limit
of structural steel. If the outermost
fibers of the beam undergo this much
plastic flow, the stress distribution
will approach the condition represented in Fig. 32. The correspond-
ing bending moment then is seen to approach a value one and
one-half times greater than the moment $M_{\text{Y.P.}}$ at which yielding first begins. The radius of curvature at this condition, from
Eq. (53), is

$$\rho = \frac{h}{\Delta} = \frac{100}{3}h.$$

This large curvature will occur only in portions of the beam
where the bending moment approaches the above high value of
$1\frac{1}{2}M_{\text{Y.P.}}$. That is, there will be a tendency for the bending
to concentrate at the section of maximum bending moment, and
the deflection curve beyond the yield point will have a different
shape from that below the elastic limit. In the bending of a
beam by a force at the middle, yielding will occur principally
at the middle, where a considerable curvature will result,
while the remaining portions of the beam will be only slightly
bent.

With further loading of the beam the strain hardening of the
material begins to affect the deflection; nevertheless the deformation increases rapidly with the load and soon reaches proportions
at which further service of the beams becomes out of the question.
The shape of the corresponding portion of the load-deflection
curve evidently depends on the shape of the bending-moment
diagram and also on the ratio between the yield-point stress and
the ultimate strength of the material.

If, instead of a solid rectangular cross section, we take an
I-section, the effect of plastic flow at the yield-point stress on

the load-deflection diagram will be much more pronounced.[1] This is obvious since most of the material is concentrated in the flanges of the beam and consequently all fibers at the section of maximum bending moment begin to yield at about the same time. This yielding of material results finally in buckling of the flanges; thus the maximum load that an I-beam may carry is very little larger than the load that first produces yield-point stress in the flanges.

From this discussion it may be seen that, when we take the loading which first produces a yield-point stress as the basis for determining the allowable stress in a beam, the factor of safety for loading which produces unpermissible damage depends on the shape of the cross section. In the case of a rectangular beam, this extra safety factor is considerably higher than in the case of an I-beam. The difference between these two safety factors can be determined in each particular case only on the basis of the above-discussed analysis in which the stress-strain diagram of the material is used. In structural design this difference is usually disregarded and beams of any cross section are designed on the basis of yield-point stresses. It is also usually assumed that up to this point our elementary formulas for calculating stresses, based on Hooke's law, are sufficiently accurate.

11. Combined Bending and Compression beyond Proportional Limit.—Let us consider now the case of simultaneous bending and compression of a rectangular beam. In the solution of this problem the same semi-graphical method of the previous discussion can be used. If ϵ_1 and ϵ_2 denote the strain in the outermost fibers on the convex and the concave sides of the beam, respectively, and $\Delta = \epsilon_1 - \epsilon_2$, we can again use Eq. (53) in calculating the radius of curvature ρ. The neutral axis is no longer at the middle of the depth of the beam, its position now being determined by the values of ϵ_1 and ϵ_2 (Fig. 33). The internal forces over a cross section of the beam can be reduced in this case to a compressive force P applied at the centroid of the cross section and to a couple M. The values of P and M can be calculated in each particular case from the stress-strain dia-

---

[1] It is assumed that there is a sufficient lateral constraint preventing the beam from lateral buckling so that bending proceeds in the plane of the web of the beam.

gram (Fig. 33).   Measuring y (positive as explained in Art. 10, see p. 45), the distance of any fiber from the axis through the centroid of the cross section, and denoting by ϵ_0 the strain at the centroid, the strain at any other point is

$$\epsilon = \epsilon_0 + \frac{y}{\rho},$$

and we obtain $y = \rho(\epsilon - \epsilon_0)$, from which $dy = \rho\, d\epsilon$.

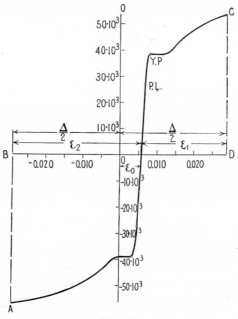

FIG. 33.

The magnitude of the compressive force is then

$$P = -b \int_{-\frac{h}{2}}^{+\frac{h}{2}} \sigma\, dy = -b\rho \int_{\epsilon_2}^{\epsilon_1} \sigma\, d\epsilon = -\frac{bh}{\Delta} \int_{\epsilon_2}^{\epsilon_1} \sigma\, d\epsilon.$$

Dividing this by the cross-sectional area bh, we obtain the average compressive stress

$$\sigma_c = \frac{P}{bh} = -\frac{1}{\Delta} \int_{\epsilon_2}^{\epsilon_1} \sigma\, d\epsilon. \tag{56}$$

The integral in this expression represents the area bounded by the stress-strain diagram and the ordinates AB and CD (Fig.

33). The area corresponding to compression should be taken negative and that corresponding to tension taken positive.

The bending moment is

$$M = b \int_{-\frac{h}{2}}^{+\frac{h}{2}} \sigma y \, dy = b\rho^2 \int_{\epsilon_2}^{\epsilon_1} \sigma(\epsilon - \epsilon_0)d\epsilon,$$

or, by using Eq. (53),

$$M = \frac{I}{\rho} \frac{12}{\Delta^3} \int_{\epsilon_2}^{\epsilon_1} \sigma(\epsilon - \epsilon_0)d\epsilon. \qquad (a)$$

The integral in this expression represents the moment of the area bounded by the stress-strain diagram and the ordinates AB

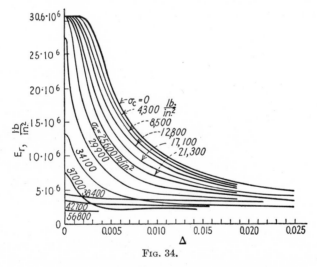

FIG. 34.

and CD with respect to the vertical axis 00 (Fig. 33). For any given values of ϵ_1 and ϵ_2 we can calculate this moment and represent Eq. (a) in the following form:

$$M = \frac{E_r I}{\rho}. \qquad (55')$$

This equation has the same form as Eq. (55) for the case of pure bending, but the reduced modulus E_r depends now on ϵ_1 and ϵ_2 and therefore not only on Δ but also on the direct compressive stress σ_c Eq. (56). By varying ϵ_1 and ϵ_2 in such a manner that σ_c always remains constant, we obtain E_r as a function of

Δ for a given σ_c. This relation can be represented by a curve. Several curves of this kind for various values of σ_c and for the material given by the stress-strain curve shown in Fig. 33 are

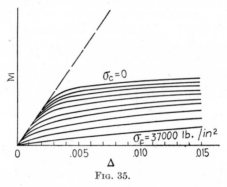

$\sigma_c = 0$

$\sigma_c = 37000$ lb. $/in^2$

0   .005   .010   .015

Δ

FIG. 35.

represented in Fig. 34.[1] By using these curves and Eqs. (53) and (55'), the bending moment M can be represented as a function of Δ for each value of σ_c as shown in Fig. 35.

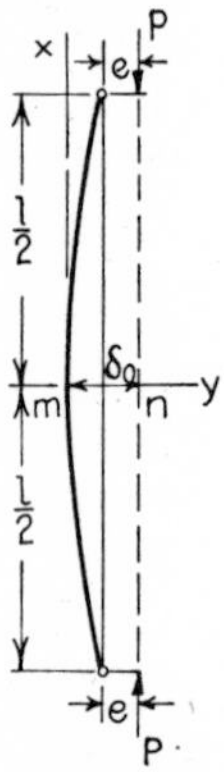

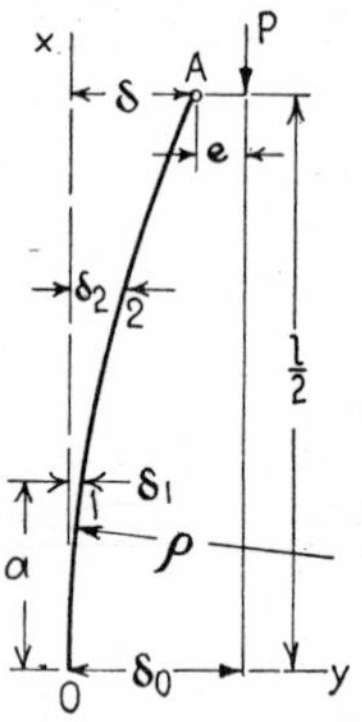

By using the curves of this figure, the deflection curve for an eccentrically loaded bar (Fig. 36) can be obtained by applying approximate methods of graphical or numerical integration.[2] Considering the middle plane mn as a plane of symmetry, we assume definite values of ϵ_1 and ϵ_2; then, from Eq. (56), we find the corresponding values of σ_c and P. Next, using the curves of Fig. 35, we find M corresponding to the above value of σ_c and of $\Delta = \epsilon_1 - \epsilon_2$. Thus the compressive force and the bending moment for the middle cross section mn are determined. The distance $\delta_0 = M/P$ determines the line of action of the com-

FIG. 36.   FIG. 37.

---

[1] These curves are taken from the paper by M. Roš, *Proc. 2d Intern. Cong. Appl. Mech., Zurich*, p. 368, 1926. The curves with $\sigma_c > 37,000$ are obtained assuming that bending occurs after yielding is produced by the compressive force.

[2] Several methods of integration are discussed in the paper by Th. v. Kármán, *loc. cit.*, p. 45.

pressive force (Fig. 37). Next we construct an element 01
of the deflection curve of small length a by using the radius
$\rho = h/\Delta$ calculated for the middle of the bar. The deflection
at the cross section 1 is approximately for a flat circular arc
$\delta_1 = a^2/2\rho$ and the bending moment is $M_1 = P(\delta_0 - \delta_1)$. With
this moment we find from Fig. 35 the corresponding value of Δ
equal to Δ_1 and $\rho_1 = h/\Delta_1$.[1] Using this new radius, we construct
the second portion 1-2 of the curve and calculate the deflec-
tion δ_2. Continuing these calculations, we arrive finally at the
end A of the compressed bar and determine the deflection δ
at this end and the eccentricity e of the load P corresponding to
the assumed values of ϵ_1 and ϵ_2. Making such calculations for
several values of ϵ_1 and ϵ_2 and selecting these values in each case
so as to make P always the same, we finally obtain for P the deflection δ as a function of the eccentricity e.

The above calculations can be generalized and made independent of the particular cross-sectional dimensions b and h
of the column. First of all, it may be seen that the force P,
producing certain deflections in a column, is proportional to
the width b of the cross section; if this width is changed, the force
P must be changed in the same proportion in order to have the
deflection curve unchanged. To make our results independent
of the particular values of the depth h, we make the calculations
by using the ratios ρ/h, δ/h and l/h instead of the quantities
ρ, δ, and l themselves, i.e., we take h as the unit for measuring
distances and lengths.

Assuming certain values for ϵ_1 and ϵ_2, we determine

$$\Delta = \epsilon_1 - \epsilon_2 = \frac{h}{\rho},$$

and find σ_c from Eq. (56). The bending moment is determined
now from Eq. (55') and is equal to

$$M = \frac{E_r}{12} \frac{h}{\rho} bh^2.$$

The position of the line of action of the force P (Fig. 37) is
defined by the distance δ_0, for which we have

[1] A better approximation is obtained if we repeat the calculation for the
first interval by taking the radius $(\rho + \rho_1)/2$ before going to the second
interval.

$$\delta_0 = \frac{M}{P} = \frac{E_r}{12\sigma_c} \frac{h}{\rho} h,$$

or

$$\frac{\delta_0}{h} = \frac{E_r}{12\sigma_c} \frac{h}{\rho}.$$

For the deflection δ_1 at the end of the small interval a (Fig. 37), we have

$$\delta_1 = \frac{a^2}{2\rho} = \frac{a^2}{h^2} h \div \left(2\frac{\rho}{h}\right),$$

or

$$\frac{\delta_1}{h} = \frac{a^2}{h^2} \div \left(2\frac{\rho}{h}\right).$$

Thus, all our calculations are made independent of the particular values of b and h, if we use h as the unit of length. For

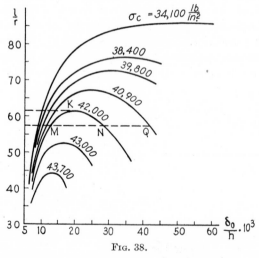

FIG. 38.

a certain value of σ_c and a given eccentricity e/h, we find the deflection δ/h as a function of the length l/h of the column. This function can be represented graphically by a curve. Several curves of this kind, calculated[1] for various values of σ_c and for $e = 0.005h$, are shown in Fig. 38. Instead of values of l/h, values of the slenderness ratio l/r are taken as ordinates in this

---

[1] These curves were calculated by Th. v. Kármán, *loc. cit.*, p. 45, for steel having a yield-point stress equal to about 45,000 lb. per square inch.

figure. It is seen that each of the curves has a certain maximum value of l/r. For values of l/r below this maximum, we obtain two different values for the deflection, such as shown in the figure, by the two points M and N on the curve $\sigma_c = 42,000$ lb. per square inch. The point M, corresponding to the smaller deflection, represents the deflection which actually will be reached by a gradual increase of the load P from zero up to the final value equal to $bh\sigma_c$.

To obtain the deflection corresponding to the point N, we must apply some additional forces. If by using such forces we bring the bent column to the shape defined by the point N, we arrive again at a position of equilibrium between the external load and the internal forces of elasticity; but this equilibrium is unstable, since, as is seen from the figure, any further increase of deflection does not require an increase of the load and the deflection proceeds with diminishing of the load. To obtain, for instance, the deflection corresponding to the point Q, only 40,900 lb. per square inch average compressive stress is required instead of 42,000 lb. per square inch. For each of the maximum points, such as point K, the two possible forms of equilibrium, discussed above, coincide and the corresponding value of l/r is the maximum slenderness ratio at which the column can carry the compressive load $P = bh\sigma_c$, with an eccentricity equal to $0.005h$. Thus, by using curves like those in Fig. 38, the relation between the slenderness of the column and the maximum load which it can carry can be established for a definite value of eccentricity.

The same limiting values of the compressive loads can be obtained in another way. It is seen that the points of intersection of the horizontal lines, such as the line MNQ, with the curves in Fig. 38 give us, for a given slenderness ratio of the column and an assumed eccentricity e, the relation between the direct compressive stress σ_c and the deflection δ. This relation can be represented by a curve. Several curves of this kind, calculated[1] for various values of the initial eccentricity and for a slenderness ratio $l/r = 75$, are given in Fig. 39. It is seen that for any initial eccentricity it is necessary to increase the load at the beginning in order to produce an increase of deflection, while beyond a certain limit, given by the maximum point of the

---

[1] KÁRMÁN, TH. V., *loc. cit.*, p. 45.

corresponding curve in Fig. 39, further deflection may proceed with a diminishing of the load. Thus the maximum points of the curves in Fig. 39 give us, for the given slenderness ratio and assumed eccentricity, the limiting value of the load which the column can carry.

An approximate determination of the limiting values of the load can be accomplished by assuming[1] that the deflection curve is given by the equation (Fig. 37)

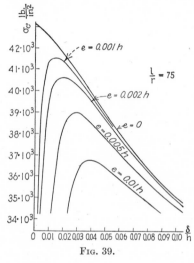

FIG. 39.

$$y = \delta\left(1 - \cos\frac{\pi x}{l}\right).$$

Then, from the usual approximate expression for the curvature of the deflection curve,[2] we find for the curvature at the middle:

$$\frac{1}{\rho} = \left(\frac{d^2y}{dx^2}\right)_{x=0} = \frac{\pi^2\delta}{l^2},$$

from which

$$\delta = \frac{l^2}{\pi^2\rho} = \frac{l^2\Delta}{\pi^2h}. \qquad (57)$$

For any value of ϵ_1 and ϵ_2 at the middle, we next obtain the value of the compressive force from Eq. (56) and the deflection δ from Eq. (57).

Assume, now, that ϵ_1 and ϵ_2 are always chosen in such a manner that the compressive force P remains constant and that at the same time $\Delta = \epsilon_1 - \epsilon_2$ is increasing. Then M and $\delta_0 = M/P$ (Fig. 37) are increasing also. If the rate of increase of δ_0 is greater than the rate of increase of δ, the assumed deflection curve can be produced only by increasing the eccentricity e of the load

---

[1] Such an approximate solution was proposed by M. Roš and J. Brunner, *loc. cit.*, p. 54.

[2] More accurate calculations, made by E. Chwalla (*loc. cit.*, p. 45), show that in the case of comparatively small eccentricities ($e/h < 1/6$), the limiting compressive force producing failure is attained at a maximum deflection of less than $0.5h$. At such a deflection the elastic line is a flat curve and the usual approximate expression for the curvature can be applied with sufficient accuracy.

(Fig. 36). If we have a reversed condition, the assumed deflection curve will be a curve of equilibrium only if we reduce the eccentricity e; otherwise the column will continue to deflect under the constant load P. Thus the limiting value of the eccentricity e for a given value of the compressive force P is that value at which the rates of change of δ and of δ_0 are the same. This means that

$$\frac{d\delta_0}{d\Delta} = \frac{d\delta}{d\Delta}.$$

Substituting $\delta_0 = M/P$ and using formula (57), we obtain

$$\frac{dM}{d\Delta} = \frac{l^2 P}{\pi^2 h}. \tag{58}$$

Thus, to determine the limiting value of e, we need only to find on the corresponding curve in Fig. 35 a point, the slope of which is given by the right side of Eq. (58). Knowing the abscissa Δ of this point, the values of δ_0, δ and $e = \delta_0 - \delta$ are easily obtained as has been explained before.

This approximate solution, based on the assumption that the deflection curve is a cosine curve with a half-wave length l, gives satisfactory results only in the case of very small eccentricities when the moment at the end approaches zero. For larger eccentricities it gives somewhat exaggerated values[1] for the load producing failure, and more elaborate calculations are necessary in order to obtain this load with sufficient accuracy. Such calculations, based on the assumption that the deflection curve is a cosine curve the wave length of which can be varied, have been made by H. M. Westergaard and W. R. Osgood.[2] As a result of these calculations, the curves given in Fig. 40 were obtained. These curves, calculated for columns of solid rectangular cross section and for various values of the eccentricity ratio e/s, give the limiting values of the direct compressive stress σ_c as a function of the ratio l/r. The properties of the material are given by the stress-strain diagram shown in Fig. 40.[3] For

---

[1] See paper by E. Chwalla, *loc. cit.*, p. 45.

[2] *Trans. Am. Soc. Mech. Eng.*, vol. 50, 1928.

[3] In these calculations the assumption was made that at the beginning the load was centrally applied, it being allowed to have the eccentricity e only after having reached its final value. This differs from our assumption that

comparison there are shown also, by dotted lines, the curves
for the same material giving the average compressive stress that
will produce a maximum fiber stress equal to the yield point.
It may be seen that, in designing a column on the basis of yield-
point stress, as was explained in Art. 9, we are, in all practical cases,

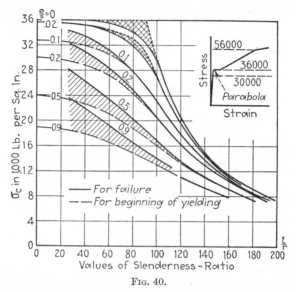

Fig. 40.

on the safe side.[1] The difference between the load producing
yield-point stress and the load producing failure of the column
is small for small eccentricities and diminishes with the increase
of the ratio l/r for the column.

The approximate method for determining the compressive
load producing failure can be used also in the case of a column
having a certain initial curvature. Assume, for instance, that
the initial shape of the center line of the column (Fig. 41) is
given by the equation

---

the compressive load is acting eccentrically from the beginning of loading.
Beyond the proportional limit, the manner in which the final condition of
eccentric loading is arrived at has a certain effect on the bending. This
effect can, however, be considered as of no practical importance.

[1] For values of e/s less than 0.1, the load obtained on the basis of yield-
point stress may be somewhat greater than the load producing failure.
This discrepancy on the side of danger for very nearly perfect columns is of
no consequence since in the practical design of columns larger values for
e/s should be assumed.

$$y_1 = a \cos \frac{\pi x}{l}, \qquad (b)$$

and that, under the action of the compressive forces P, an additional deflection,

$$y_2 = \delta \cos \frac{\pi x}{l}, \qquad (c)$$

is produced.

Then the change of curvature at the middle of the beam is

$$\frac{1}{\rho} - \frac{1}{\rho_0} = -\left(\frac{d^2 y_2}{dx^2}\right)_{x=0} = \delta \frac{\pi^2}{l^2}. \qquad (d)$$

Assuming that the strains in the outermost fibers at the middle of the column are ϵ_1 and ϵ_2, we obtain $\Delta = \epsilon_1 - \epsilon_2$; the corresponding change in curvature is equal to

$$\frac{1}{\rho} - \frac{1}{\rho_0} = \frac{\Delta}{h}. \qquad (e)$$

From Eqs. (d) and (e) an equation, equivalent to Eq. (57), for the calculation of δ may be obtained. The corresponding compressive force is obtained from Eq. (56) and the bending moment M at the middle from the curves in Fig. 35. Then the initial deflection a, which the column should have in order that the assumed bending may be actually produced by forces P, is obtained from the equation

$$P(a + \delta) = M.$$

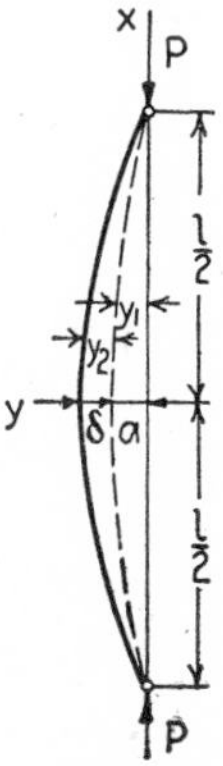

Fig. 41.

In order to obtain the limiting condition at which the load P brings the column to failure, we must proceed in exactly the same manner as in the case of an eccentrically loaded column and use Eq. (58). The results obtained in this way can be presented in the form of curves, each of which corresponds to a given initial deflection a and gives the values of the direct compressive stress σ_c, producing failure, as functions of the slenderness ratio l/r of the column.

A more elaborate approximate solution can be worked out[1] by taking, instead of simple cosine curves (b) and (c), two or more terms of the Fourier series

[1] See the paper by H. M. Westergaard and W. R. Osgood, *loc. cit.*, footnote 2, p. 59.

$$y = a \cos \frac{\pi x}{l} + b \cos \frac{3\pi x}{l} + \cdots.$$

The curves obtained in this way give the limiting values of the average compressive stresses σ_c producing failure; they are shown in Fig. 42. For comparison there are given also the values of σ_c corresponding to the beginning of yielding. The relation between these two sets of curves is the same as in Fig. 40.

The comparison of loads producing in columns the yield-point stress with loads producing failure, Figs. (40) and (42),

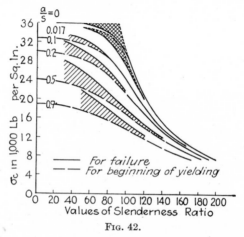

Fig. 42.

shows that, in the case of combined bending and compression and especially for small eccentricities, these two sets of loads are much nearer to each other than in the case of bending by transverse loading. Since, in the latter case, it is usual practice not to go into the investigation of bending beyond the yield point, but to base the working stresses on the yield-point stress, it seems logical to proceed in the same manner in the case of combined bending and compression and to take as a basis for determining the allowable stresses the load that first produces the yield-point stress in the column (see Art. 9). This method of procedure will eliminate the necessity of making the laborious computations required in the investigation of bending beyond the proportional limit when the load producing complete failure of the column is required.[1]   Bars submitted to the simultaneous

[1] It should be noted also that this laborious exact method is based on the use of the stress-strain diagram, the characteristic points (such as propor-

action of bending and compression will be designed in exactly the same way as beams submitted to the action of lateral loads only, and there will be no need to introduce new criteria for the selection of working stresses for those cases in which longitudinal compression becomes an important factor. We shall return to this question again in Chap. 3, when the design of centrally loaded columns will be discussed.

---

tional limit and yield point) of which may vary their positions considerably for different specimens. The variation of yield point, for example, can be as much as ±10 per cent of the average value. Under such conditions the necessity of such calculations in practical applications seems questionable.

CHAPTER II

BUCKLING OF CENTRALLY COMPRESSED BARS

12. Euler's Formula.—In the previous chapter the value of
the critical load on a compressed bar was obtained by considering
the simultaneous action of compressive and bending forces or
by assuming an initial curvature. The same result may be
obtained by assuming initially that the bar is perfectly straight
and simply compressed by a centrally applied load. Let us

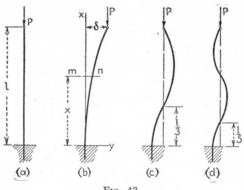

Fig. 43.

consider the case of a slender prismatical bar built in vertically
at the bottom and loaded axially at the top (Fig. 43a). In this
form the problem of buckling of columns was first discussed by
L. Euler.[1] If the load P is less than its critical value, the bar
remains straight and undergoes only axial compression. This
straight form of elastic equilibrium is *stable, i.e.,* if a lateral force
is applied and a small deflection produced, this deflection dis-
appears when the lateral force is removed and the bar becomes
straight again.[2] By gradually increasing P a condition is

[1] See Additamentum, "De curvis elasticis," in the "Methodus inveniendi
lineas curvas maximi minimive proprietate gaudentes," Lausanne, 1744, and
also *Histoire de l'Académie*, Berlin, vol. 13, pp. 252–282, 1757.

[2] It is assumed that the material is perfectly elastic and that no stresses
beyond the proportional limit are produced.

obtained in which the straight form of equilibrium becomes unstable and a slight lateral force may produce a lateral deflection which does not disappear when the lateral force is removed. The *critical load* is then defined as the axial load, which is sufficient to keep the bar in a slightly bent form (Fig. 43b).

This load can be calculated by using the differential equation of the deflection curve. Taking the coordinate axes as indicated in Fig. 43b, the bending moment at any cross section mn is $P(\delta - y)$ and the differential equation of the deflection curve becomes

$$EI \frac{d^2y}{dx^2} = P(\delta - y). \qquad (a)$$

It is clear that, with the upper end free, buckling of the bar will occur in the plane of *smallest flexural rigidity*. This smallest rigidity EI is used in the above Eq. (a). Using the previously defined notation (see p. 2):

$$k^2 = \frac{P}{EI}, \qquad (b)$$

Eq. (a) becomes

$$\frac{d^2y}{dx^2} + k^2y = k^2\delta. \qquad (c)$$

The general solution of this equation is

$$y = \delta + A \cos kx + B \sin kx, \qquad (d)$$

in which A and B are constants of integration which must be adjusted to satisfy the conditions at the built-in end:

$$(y)_{x=0} = 0; \qquad \left(\frac{dy}{dx}\right)_{x=0} = 0.$$

These conditions are fulfilled if

$$A = -\delta, \qquad \text{and} \qquad B = 0.$$

Then

$$y = \delta(1 - \cos kx). \qquad (e)$$

The condition at the upper end requires

$$(y)_{x=l} = \delta.$$

This will be satisfied if $\delta \cos kl = 0$, which requires either $\delta = 0$, in which case there is no deflection, or $\cos kl = 0$, *i.e.*,

$$kl = (2n + 1)\frac{\pi}{2}, \tag{f}$$

where n is any integer.   In this case δ is apparently indeterminate (see Art. 13).

The smallest value of kl, and therefore of P [see Eq. (b)], which satisfies Eq. (f), is obtained by taking $n = 0$.   Then, by using Eq. (b),

$$kl = l\sqrt{\frac{P}{EI}} = \frac{\pi}{2},$$

from which

$$P_{cr} = \frac{\pi^2 EI}{4l^2}. \tag{59}$$

This is the *critical load* for the bar represented in Fig. 43a, *i.e.*, it is the smallest axial load that can keep the bar in a slightly bent shape.   The angle kx in Eq. (e) varies in this case from zero to $\pi/2$ and the shape of the deflection curve is that shown in Fig. 43b.

Substituting $n = 1$, $n = 2$, $\cdots$ in Eq. (f), we obtain for the corresponding values of the compressive force

$$P = \frac{9\pi^2 EI}{4l^2}; \qquad P = \frac{25\pi^2 EI}{4l^2}, \cdots$$

The angle kx in Eq. (e) varies, then, from 0 to $3\pi/2$ and from 0 to $5\pi/2$, respectively, and the corresponding deflection curves are shown in Figs. 43c and 43d.

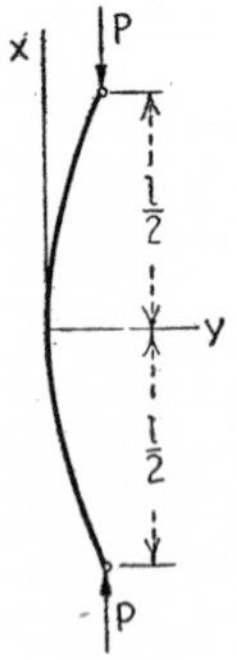

For the shape shown in Fig. 43c a force nine times larger than critical is necessary, and for that in Fig. 43d a force twenty-five times larger is required.   Such forms can be produced by using a very slender bar and by applying constraints at the inflection points. Otherwise these forms of buckling are unstable and have no practical meaning because the structure fails as the load reaches the value given in Eq. (59).

Fig. 44.

The critical loads for other cases can be obtained from the solution of the foregoing case.   For example, in the case of a bar with hinged ends, Fig. 44, it is evident from symmetry that each half of the bar is in the same condition as the entire bar of Fig. 43.   Hence, the critical load for this case is obtained by using $l/2$, instead of l, in Eq. (59).   Then,

$$P_{cr} = \frac{\pi^2 EI}{l^2}.$$ (60)

This case is very often encountered in the design of compression members of trusses and will be called in subsequent discussions the *fundamental* case of buckling of a prismatical bar, and the critical load (60) will sometimes be called *Euler's load* and will be denoted by P_e.

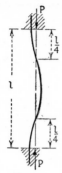

In the case of a bar with both ends built in (Fig. 45), there are reactive moments that keep the ends from rotating during buckling. The combination of the axial compressive forces with these moments is equivalent to the compressive forces P applied eccentrically. There are inflection points where the line of action of P intersects the deflection curve, because the bending moments at these points are zero. These points and the mid-point of the span divide the bar into four equal portions, each of which is in the same condition as the bar represented in

Fig. 45.

Fig. 43*b*. Hence, the critical load for a bar with built-in ends is found from Eq. (59) by using $l/4$ instead of l, which gives

$$P_{cr} = \frac{4\pi^2 EI}{l^2}.$$ (61)

It was assumed in the previous discussion that the bar was very slender so that the bending stress, which occurred during buckling, remained within the proportional limit. Only with this condition fulfilled can Eq. (*a*) be used and only under such conditions will formulas (59), (60) and (61) give the true critical values of the compressive force P. To establish the limit of applicability of these formulas for critical loads, let us consider the fundamental case (Fig. 44). Dividing formula (60) by the cross-sectional area A of the bar, and letting $r = \sqrt{I/A}$ be the smallest radius of gyration,[1] the critical value of the compressive stress, before bending occurs, will be

$$\sigma_{cr} = \frac{P_{cr}}{A} = \pi^2 E \left(\frac{r}{l}\right)^2.$$ (62)

[1] It is assumed that the column is free to buckle in any direction. Then buckling will, of course, occur in the plane of the smallest flexural rigidity.

This stress is seen to depend only on the modulus E of the material and on the *slenderness ratio* l/r. Formula (62) is applicable as long as the stress σ_{cr} remains within the proportional limit. With this limit and the modulus E known for a given material, the limiting value of the slenderness ratio l/r can be easily obtained from Eq. (62) for each particular case. For structural steel with a proportional limit of 30,000 lb. per square inch and $E = 30 \cdot 10^6$ lb. per square inch, we find $l/r \approx 100$. Consequently the critical load for steel bars hinged at the ends,

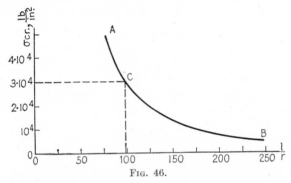

Fig. 46.

having $l/r \gtreqless 100$, is to be calculated from Eq. (62). When $l/r < 100$, the compressive stress reaches the limit of proportionality before buckling can occur, and this equation, derived on the basis of perfect elasticity, is no longer applicable. The question of buckling of bars compressed beyond proportional limit will be discussed later (see Art. 29).

Equation (62) may be represented graphically by the curve ACB in Fig. 46, using values of l/r as abscissas and σ_{cr} as ordinates. The curve approaches the l/r axis asymptotically, *i.e.*, the critical stress diminishes indefinitely with the increase of the slenderness ratio of the bar. The curve also approaches the vertical axis asymptotically, but is here applicable only so long as the stress σ_{cr} is below the proportional limit of the material. In the case of the above structural steel, for instance, point C is the upper limit of the curve.

Referring to the cases represented in Figs. 43a and 45, and proceeding as above, we find that

$$\sigma_{cr} = \pi^2 E \left(\frac{r}{2l}\right)^2, \quad \text{and} \quad \sigma_{cr} = \pi^2 E \left(\frac{r}{\frac{1}{2}l}\right)^2.$$

It is seen that in these two cases equations analogous to Eq. (62) for the fundamental case (Fig. 44) can be used in calculating critical stress by taking, instead of the actual length of the bar l, a modified length L, called the *reduced length*.[1] Equation (62) can then be written

$$\sigma_{cr} = \pi^2 E \left(\frac{r}{L} \right)^2. \tag{63}$$

In the case of a prismatical bar with one end built in and the other end free, the reduced length is twice as great as the actual length, *i.e.*, $L = 2l$. In the case of a prismatical bar with both ends built in, the reduced length is half the actual length, $L = \frac{1}{2}l$. Thus the results obtained for the fundamental case may be used for other cases of buckling of bars by using the reduced length instead of the actual length of the bar; some of these will be discussed later.

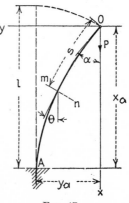

FIG. 47.

13. Large Deflections of Buckled Slender Bars.—In the discussion of the previous article the maximum deflection δ [see Eq. (*e*), Art. 12] remained indeterminate, indicating that, at the critical load, the bar may have any small deflection. Such a result is obtained because we used in the derivation the approximate expression d^2y/dx^2 for the curvature in place of the exact expression. To get a definite solution for the deflection of a buckled bar, it is necessary to refine our calculations by using the exact expression for the curvature.

Experiments show that, by taking a load P somewhat larger than the critical value [Eq. (59)], a large deflection of a bar will be produced (Fig. 47). Taking the coordinate axes as shown in the figure, the exact differential equation of the deflection curve is

$$EI\frac{d\theta}{ds} = -Py, \tag{a}$$

[1] This notion of reduced length was introduced by F. S. Jasinsky, *Bull. Society of Engineers of Ways of Communication*, St. Petersburg, 1892. See also his paper in *Ann. ponts chaussées*, Paris, 1894.

in which s is the length of the curve measured from the top 0 of the bent bar and θ the angle between the tangent to the curve and the vertical; thus $-d\theta/ds$[1] is the exact expression for the curvature of the bar at any cross section mn.

Differentiating Eq. (*a*) with respect to s and using the relation $dy/ds = \sin\,\theta$, we obtain

$$EI\frac{d^2\theta}{ds^2} = -P \sin\,\theta. \qquad (b)$$

Thus the differential equation of the deflection curve is seen to be of the same form as the differential equation for the oscillations of a pendulum.[2] In the case of a pendulum, EI will be replaced by the moment of inertia of the pendulum with respect to the axis of rotation, s by the time, and P by the weight of the pendulum multiplied by the distance of the center of gravity from the axis of rotation. To carry the analogy further, let α be the initial angular displacement of the pendulum from the vertical. Then this angle varies with the time in exactly the same way as the angle θ of the tangent to the deflection curve (Fig. 47), if we assume that the point of tangency is moving along the curve with a constant velocity v such that l/v is equal to one-quarter of the period of the pendulum.

In integrating Eq. (*b*) we proceed as is usually done in the case of a pendulum. We multiply both sides with $d\theta/ds$ and integrate. Then

$$EI \int d\left(\frac{d\theta}{ds}\right) \frac{d\theta}{ds} = -P \int \sin\,\theta d\theta.$$

By integrating and taking into account the end conditions, namely, that the curvature at the upper end of the bar is zero and $\theta = \alpha$, we obtain

$$\frac{EI}{2}\left(\frac{d\theta}{ds}\right)^2 = P(\cos\,\theta - \cos\,\alpha).$$

---

[1] The minus sign is placed before the derivative $d\theta/ds$ since this derivative is negative, *i.e.*, θ decreases with the increase of s.

[2] The analogy between the problem of rotation of a rigid body about a fixed point and the problem of the equilibrium of a slender bar deformed by forces applied at the ends was discovered by Kirchhoff, *J. Math.*, *Crelle*, vol. 56, 1859. See also W. Hess, *Math. Annalen*, vol. 25, 1885.

Now, with $k^2 = P/EI$,

$$ds = -\frac{d\theta}{k\sqrt{2}\sqrt{\cos\theta - \cos\alpha}}.^1$$

The total length of the bar is obtained by integration:

$$l = \int_0^\alpha \frac{d\theta}{k\sqrt{2}\sqrt{\cos\theta - \cos\alpha}} = \frac{1}{2k}\int_0^\alpha \frac{d\theta}{\sqrt{\sin^2\frac{\alpha}{2} - \sin^2\frac{\theta}{2}}}. \quad (c)$$

This integral can be simplified by using the notation $p = \sin\frac{\alpha}{2}$ and by introducing a new variable ϕ in such a manner that

$$\sin\frac{\theta}{2} = p\sin\phi = \sin\frac{\alpha}{2}\sin\phi. \quad (d)$$

It is seen from this that when θ is varying from 0 to α, $\sin\phi$ is varying from zero to one and ϕ from zero to $\pi/2$. We find also, from (d), that

$$d\theta = \frac{2p\cos\phi d\phi}{\sqrt{1 - p^2\sin^2\phi}}.$$

Substituting in (c) we obtain

$$l = \frac{1}{k}\int_0^{\frac{\pi}{2}} \frac{d\phi}{\sqrt{1 - p^2\sin^2\phi}}. \quad (e)$$

The integral on the right side is a known elliptic integral the numerical values of which, for various values of p, can be found in tabulated form.[2] Having such tables, we obtain at once, from (e), for any value of the angle α at the top of the bar (Fig. 47), the corresponding value of k and hence the value of the load P. When the deflection is very small, α and p are also small and the term $p^2\sin^2\phi$ can be neglected in comparison with 1 in expression (e). Then

$$l = \frac{\pi}{2k} = \frac{\pi}{2}\sqrt{\frac{EI}{P}}$$

---

[1] The negative sign is taken here, since, as is seen from Fig. 47, a negative $d\theta$ corresponds to a positive ds.

[2] The tables of elliptic integrals were published first by Legendre (1826). A new edition of these tables was recently published in Germany by F. Emde and K. Wittwer, Stuttgart, 1931. Condensed tables of the same integrals can be found in many places such as "Funktionentafeln" by E. Jahnke and F. Emde, Hütte, vol. 1; B. O. Peirce, "A Short Table of Integrals," 1929.

and we obtain for P the value given by formula (59).   With the increase of α, the integral (e) and the load P increase also.   Take, for instance, $\alpha = 60°$.   Then $p = \sin \dfrac{\alpha}{2} = \dfrac{1}{2}$.   From the table of elliptic integrals we find that the integral in Eq. (e), for $p = \frac{1}{2}$, is equal to 1.686.   Thus

$$l = 1.686\sqrt{\frac{EI}{P}}; \qquad P = 2.842\frac{EI}{l^2},$$

and

$$\frac{P}{P_{cr}} = \frac{4 \cdot 2.842}{\pi^2} = 1.152.$$

To produce a deflection of a compressed bar such that the tangent at the top (Fig. 47) has an angle of 60° with the vertical, it is necessary to apply a load only about 15 per cent larger than Euler's load at which lateral buckling first began. Several values of the ratio P/P_{cr} for various values of the angle α are given in the table below.

TABLE 2.—LOAD-DEFLECTION DATA FOR A BUCKLED COLUMN (FIG. 47)

α	20°	40°	60°	80°	100°	120°	140°	160°	176°
P/P_{cr}	1.015	1.063	1.152	1.293	1.518	1.884	2.541	4.029	9.116
x_a/l	0.970	0.881	0.741	0.560	0.349	0.123	−0.107	−0.340	−0.577
y_a/l	0.220	0.422	0.593	0.719	0.792	0.803	0.750	0.625	0.421

In calculating deflections of the bar we note that

$$dy = ds \sin \theta = -\frac{\sin \theta d\theta}{k\sqrt{2}\sqrt{\cos \theta - \cos \alpha}}.$$

Then the total deflection of the top of the bar in the horizontal direction (Fig. 47) is

$$y_a = \frac{1}{2k} \int_0^\alpha \frac{\sin \theta d\theta}{\sqrt{\sin^2 \dfrac{\alpha}{2} - \sin^2 \dfrac{\theta}{2}}}. \tag{f}$$

From Eq. (d) we find

$$\sin \theta = 2p \sin \phi \sqrt{1 - p^2 \sin^2 \phi}.$$

Substituting this and also the expression for $d\theta$ in (f), we obtain

$$y_a = \frac{2p}{k} \int_0^{\frac{\pi}{2}} \sin \phi\, d\phi = \frac{2p}{k}. \tag{g}$$

Thus, the deflection y_a can be easily obtained provided k is calculated from Eq. (e). For the case considered above, in which $\alpha = 60°$, we found $2p = 1$ and $1/k = l/1.686$. Thus

$$y_a = \frac{l}{1.686} = 0.593l.$$

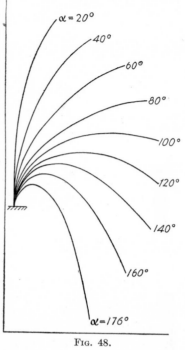

Numerical results obtained in this way are given in the last line of Table 2.

The coordinate x_a can also be calculated without difficulty by using tables of elliptic integrals. Numerical results are given in the third line of Table 2. In the same way the coordinates of the intermediate points of the deflection curve can also be calculated.[1] The shapes of the deflection curves for the cases given in Table 2 are represented in Fig. 48. It is seen that a slight increase of the load above

Fig. 48.

critical is sufficient to produce a considerable deflection of the bar.

In the case of small deflections and hinged ends (Fig. 44), the relation between the deflection and the load can be represented by the following approximate formula,[2]

---

[1] The first investigation of the shape of the curve of a buckled slender bar was made by Lagrange; see his paper "Sur les figures des colonnes," "Oeuvres," vol. 2, and also "Sur la force des ressorts pliés," "Oeuvres," vol. 3. See also Clebsch, "Theorie d'élasticité des corps solides," tr. by S. Venant, p. 864, 1883. Several cases of large deflections of compressed bars are discussed with great detail in the book by L. Saalschütz, "Der belastete Stab," Leipzig, 1880. See also E. Collignon, *Ann. ponts chaussées*, vol. 17, p. 98, 1889; C. Kriemler, "Labile und stabile Gleichgewichtsfiguren," Karlsruhe, 1902; and M. Born, Dissertation, Göttingen, 1909. Recently the same problem was discussed by A. N. Krylov, "Sur les formes d'équilibre des pièces chargées debout," *Bull. acad. sci. U.R.S.S.*, p. 963, 1931.

[2] See R. v. Mises, *Z. angew. Math. Mech.*, vol. 4, p. 435, 1924, and also O. Domke, "Die Bautechnik," vol. 4, p. 747, 1926.

$$y_a = \frac{2\sqrt{2}}{\pi}l\sqrt{\frac{P}{P_{cr}} - 1}\left[1 - \frac{1}{8}\left(\frac{P}{P_{cr}} - 1\right)\right].$$

This formula can be represented graphically by a curve AB as in Fig. 49. This curve has a horizontal tangent at A. Thus the

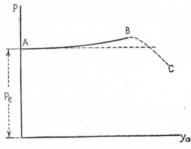

FIG. 49.

increase in load, corresponding to a small deflection, is a small quantity of the second order. This explains why, by using an approximate expression for curvature, the deflection remains indefinite. It should be noted that the curve AB can be used only up to the proportional limit of the material. Beyond this limit the resistance of the bar to bending diminishes and a curve similar to that indicated by the dotted line BC will be obtained.

In the above discussion it was assumed that the bar is built in at one end and free at the other. The results obtained can be

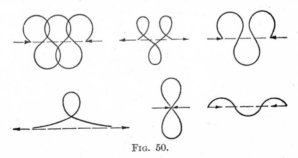

FIG. 50.

used also in the case of a bar with hinged ends. In this case the curves of Fig. 48 represent only half of the length of the bar. The curves shown in Fig. 50, representing possible forms of equilibrium of a thin wire, can all be obtained by combining curves of Fig. 48. Thus, the forces necessary to produce such bending can be found from Table 2 (p. 72).

14. Stable and Unstable Equilibrium.—From the previous discussions it is seen that, if the centrally applied compressive force is smaller than its critical value, a compressed bar remains straight and this straight form of equilibrium is stable. If we increase the load slightly above its critical value, there are, theoretically, two forms of equilibrium possible: the bar may be compressed uniformly and remain straight, or it may buckle sideways. Experiments show that the straight form is unstable and that a bar, under the action of a load greater than the critical value, will always buckle sideways.

The question of the stability of various forms of equilibrium of a compressed bar can be investigated by using the same methods as are used in investigating the stability of equilibrium of rigid-body systems.   Consider, for instance, the three cases of equilibrium of a ball, shown in Fig. 51.   It can be concluded at once that the

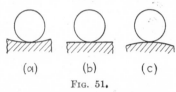

(*a*)   (*b*)   (*c*)

Fig. 51.

ball on the concave spherical surface (*a*) is in *stable equilibrium*, while the ball on the convex spherical surface (*c*) is in *unstable equilibrium*.   The ball on the horizontal plane (*b*) is said to be in *indifferent equilibrium*.   These conclusions can be arrived at by considering the energy of the system.   In the first case (Fig. 51*a*) any displacement of the ball from its position of equilibrium will raise the center of gravity.   A certain amount of work is required to produce such a displacement; thus the potential energy of the system increases for any displacement from the position of equilibrium.   In the second case (Fig. 51*c*) any displacement from the position of equilibrium will lower the center of gravity of the ball, *i.e.*, will decrease the potential energy of the system. Thus in the case of stable equilibrium the energy of the system is a *minimum* and in the case of unstable equilibrium it is a *maximum*.   In the case of indifferent equilibrium (Fig. 51*b*) there is no change in energy with displacement.

For each of the above systems (Fig. 51) stability depends only on the shape of the supporting surface and does not depend on the weight of the ball.   Considering a compressed column (see **Art. 12**), we find that the same system may be stable or unstable, depending on the magnitude of the load. A rigid-body model representing such a condition is shown[1] in Fig. 52. A ball of weight Q and radius r is in equilibrium at the lowest point of a spherical seat of radius R. A vertical load P is transmitted by a pin to the ball acting along its vertical diameter. It is assumed that the bodies are absolutely rigid and that there is no friction. If P is very small in comparison with the weight of the ball Q, the conditions of equilibrium will approach those shown in Fig. 51a and the equilibrium will be stable. If P is large in comparison

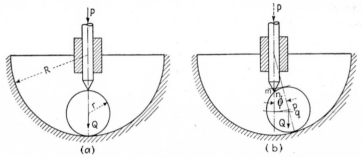

Fig. 52.

with Q, the equilibrium will be unstable and the ball will move to one side as shown in Fig. 52b. To determine the magnitude of the load P at which stable equilibrium changes to unstable equilibrium, it is necessary to consider the change in the potential energy of the system during a small lateral movement of the ball (Fig. 52b). Defining this displacement by the angle ϕ, the lowering of the load P is given by the vertical distance $\overline{mn}$ between the circles of radii r and $R - 2r$. The rising of the center of gravity of the ball is given by the distance $\overline{pq}$. Thus, applying the energy method, just discussed, we conclude that the system is stable if

$$Q\overline{pq} > P\overline{mn},$$

and unstable if

$$Q\overline{pq} < P\overline{mn}.$$

The critical value of the load P is that value at which the equilibrium changes from stable to unstable, *i.e.*, at which

$$Q\overline{pq} = P\overline{mn}. \tag{a}$$

[1] This model was proposed by R. V. Southwell, *Phil. Trans. Roy. Soc., London*, series A, vol. 213, p. 187, 1913.

The distance $\overline{pq}$ between the circle of radius $R - r$ and the horizontal tangent for a small angle ϕ is

$$\overline{pq} = \frac{\phi^2}{2}(R - r). \tag{b}$$

The distance $\overline{mn}$ between the circles of radii $R - 2r$ and r, at the points corresponding to the central angles ϕ and $\phi\dfrac{R - 2r}{r}$, respectively, is

$$\overline{mn} = \frac{\phi^2}{2}(R - 2r) + \frac{\phi^2}{2}\frac{(R - 2r)^2}{r} = \frac{\phi^2}{2r}(R - 2r)(R - r). \tag{c}$$

Substituting (b) and (c) in Eq. (a), we obtain

$$P_{cr} = \frac{Qr}{R - 2r}.$$

For any load P below this critical value, the system represented in Fig. 52 is stable. If a disturbing force produces a small lateral displacement of the ball, the system returns to its initial position of equilibrium as soon as the disturbing force is removed. For a load P above the critical value, the system is unstable.

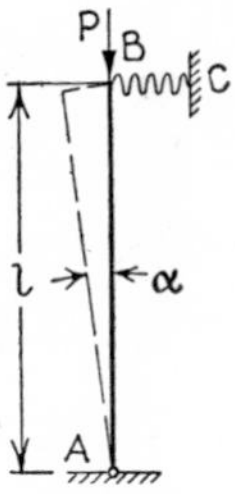

Another example of the same kind is represented in Fig. 53. A vertical bar AB, considered to be infinitely rigid in itself, is hinged at the bottom and supported by a spring BC at the top, and carries a centrally applied load P. For small values of this load the vertical position of the bar is stable; if a disturbing force produces some lateral displacement at B, the bar comes back to its vertical position under the action of the spring BC. The critical value of the load P can be found from a consideration of the energy of the system. Assume a small lateral displacement at B such that the bar becomes inclined to the vertical by a small angle α. Owing to this displacement, the load P is lowered by the amount

Fig. 53.

$$l(1 - \cos \alpha) \approx \frac{l\alpha^2}{2}.$$

At the same time the spring BC elongates by the amount $l\alpha$. The decrease in the potential energy of the load P is $Pl\alpha^2/2$. The increase in the energy of the spring, if β is the spring constant,[1] is $\beta(\alpha l)^2/2$. If

$$\frac{\beta(\alpha l)^2}{2} > \frac{Pl\alpha^2}{2},$$

the system is stable, and, if

$$\frac{\beta(\alpha l)^2}{2} < \frac{Pl\alpha^2}{2},$$

the system is unstable. The critical value of the load P is found from the condition that

$$\frac{\beta(\alpha l)^2}{2} = \frac{Pl\alpha^2}{2},$$

from which $P_{cr} = \beta l$.

The same reasoning can be applied also in the case of lateral buckling of a compressed column (Fig. 43). Assume that some lateral deflection is produced in the compressed bar shown in Fig. 43a. Then the strain energy of deformation increases, since to the energy of compression some energy of bending of the bar is added.[2] At the same time the potential energy of the load diminishes, owing to the lowering of its point of application. This decrease in potential energy is simply the work done by the load during the lowering of the top of the bar. If ΔV denotes the strain energy of bending of the bar and ΔT the work done by the load during bending, then, applying the same reasoning as in the case of the above models, the straight form of the compressed bar will be stable if $\Delta V - \Delta T > 0$. It is unstable if $\Delta V - \Delta T < 0$. The critical value of the load at which the straight form of equilibrium changes from stable to unstable is determined from the equation

$$\Delta V = \Delta T. \tag{64}$$

This equation is very often useful in calculating critical loads. Several applications will be shown in the next article.

15. Energy Method of Calculating Critical Loads.—As a first application of the energy method, let us consider the case repre-

---

[1] The spring constant is the force required to produce a unit elongation of the spring.

[2] There is also some change in the energy of compression, but a more detailed investigation (see author's paper in *Z. Math. Physik.*, vol. 58, p. 337, 1910) shows that this small change of energy can be neglected.

sented in Fig. 43b. The deflection curve of the slightly buckled bar is given by the equation (see Art. 12)

$$y = \delta\left(1 - \cos\frac{\pi x}{2l}\right). \tag{a}$$

The bending moment at any cross section is

$$M = P(\delta - y) = P\delta\cos\frac{\pi x}{2l},$$

and the corresponding energy of bending is

$$\Delta V = \int_0^l \frac{M^2\,dx}{2EI} = \frac{P^2\delta^2 l}{4EI}. \tag{b}$$

The vertical movement of the load P during buckling is equal to [see Eq. (43), p. 28].

$$\lambda = \frac{1}{2}\int_0^l\left(\frac{dy}{dx}\right)^2 dx = \frac{\delta^2\pi^2}{16l}, \tag{c}$$

and the corresponding work produced by P is

$$\Delta T = \frac{P\delta^2\pi^2}{16l}. \tag{d}$$

Substituting (b) and (d) in Eq. (64) of the previous article, we obtain for the critical load the same value as given by Eq. (59) (see p. 66). Here we obtain the exact value for the critical load, since we use the correct expression for the deflection curve obtained previously by integration of the differential equation.

The energy method can be used also for approximate calculations of critical loads in the cases in which the deflection curves are unknown. We will take again the above example, for which the exact solution is known, so that the accuracy of the approximate solution can be readily seen. Assuming that the correct expression for the deflection curve is unknown,[1] we begin, in applying the energy method, with some assumed shape for the deflection curve. The assumed curve must be chosen so as to satisfy the conditions at the ends of the bar. We may take, as the deflec-

Fig. 54.

---

[1] Sometimes the integration of the differential equation of the deflection curve presents difficulties that cannot be easily overcome.

tion curve of the buckled bar represented in Fig. 43b, the deflection curve of a cantilever beam loaded at the end (Fig. 54). The equation of this curve is

$$y = \frac{Qx^2}{6EI}(3l - x) = \frac{\delta x^2}{2l^3}(3l - x). \tag{e}$$

This curve is different from the actual curve, given by Eq. (a), but it satisfies the required end conditions, i.e., it has a vertical tangent at the bottom and zero curvature at the top.

The strain energy of bending of the buckled bar is then

$$\Delta V = \int_0^l \frac{M^2\, dx}{2EI} = \frac{P^2}{2EI}\int_0^l (\delta - y)^2 dx.$$

Substituting the above expression (e) for y, we find

$$\Delta V = \frac{P^2 \delta^2}{2EI}\frac{17l}{35}.$$

The vertical displacement of the load P is

$$\lambda = \frac{1}{2}\int_0^l \left(\frac{dy}{dx}\right)^2 dx = \frac{3}{5}\frac{\delta^2}{l}.$$

Equation (64) then becomes

$$\frac{P^2 \delta^2}{2EI}\frac{17l}{35} = \frac{3P\delta^2}{5l}$$

from which

$$P_{cr} = \frac{42}{17}\frac{EI}{l^2} = 2.4706\frac{EI}{l^2}.$$

The correct value of the critical load is

$$P_{cr} = \frac{\pi^2}{4}\frac{EI}{l^2} = 2.4674\frac{EI}{l^2}.$$

Hence the error of the approximate solution is only 0.13 per cent.

The energy method usually gives a satisfactory approximation provided the assumed curve is properly chosen. Sometimes we can make a very rough assumption for the shape of the curve and still obtain a satisfactory result. That is, we might assume the deflection curve in the above example to be a parabola given by the equation

$$y = \frac{\delta x^2}{l^2}. \tag{f}$$

Then

$$\Delta V = \int^l \frac{M^2\,dx}{2EI} = \frac{P^2\delta^2}{2EI}\int_0^l \left(1 - \frac{x^2}{l^2}\right)^2 dx = \frac{P^2\delta^2}{2EI}\frac{8}{15}l.$$

The vertical displacement of the upper end of the buckled bar in this case is

$$\lambda = \frac{1}{2}\int_0^l \left(\frac{dy}{dx}\right)^2 dx = \frac{2}{3}\frac{\delta^2}{l}.$$

Now Eq. (64) gives

$$\frac{P^2\delta^2}{2EI}\frac{8}{15}l = \frac{2}{3}\frac{P\delta^2}{l},$$

from which

$$P_{cr} = 2.50\frac{EI}{l^2}.$$

The error of this approximate solution is about $1\frac{1}{3}$ per cent. A satisfactory approximation is thus obtained although the parabolic curve, which we assumed, cannot be considered as a very satisfactory one. It has an approximately constant curvature along the length while in the actual curve the curvature is proportional to the bending moment. It is zero at the top of the bar and a maximum at the bottom.

In calculating the strain energy of bending we used the expression

$$\Delta V = \int_0^l \frac{M^2\,dx}{2EI} = \int_0^l \frac{P^2(\delta - y)^2 dx}{2EI} \qquad (g)$$

in the above discussion. Sometimes the expression

$$\Delta V = \frac{EI}{2}\int_0^l \left(\frac{d^2y}{dx^2}\right)^2 dx \qquad (h)$$

is used. Both are exact so long as we are working with the true expression for the deflection curve. However, when we are using an assumed curve, expression (g) is preferable since by its use the accuracy of our approximate solution will depend on the accuracy of y; if expression (h) is used, the accuracy of our solution will depend on the accuracy of d^2y/dx^2. In selecting any deflection curve, y will usually be obtained with a better approximation than d^2y/dx^2.

By using the energy method with an assumed curve satisfying the end conditions, we always obtain a value for the critical load which is higher than the true value. This follows from the fact that the actual deflection curve of a buckled bar is always the one that corresponds to the least resistance of the bar. Only by the merest chance will an assumed curve be the true curve of least resistance. Generally the assumed curve will be different from this curve of least resistance, thus giving values too high for the calculated critical loads. Working with an assumed curve is equivalent to introducing into the system some additional constraints which prevent the buckled bar from taking any other shape except that prescribed by the assumed curve. By introducing such additional constraints both the rigidity of the system and the critical loads can only be made larger.

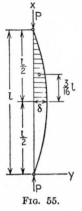

FIG. 55.

It may be seen from this discussion that the energy method can be improved and that better approximations for critical loads can be obtained if we take expressions for assumed curves with several parameters by the variation of which the shape of the curve may be changed. The critical load, as determined from Eq. (64), will then depend on these parameters, and the next step will be to adjust the parameters to make the expression for the critical load a minimum.[1]

Let us take a prismatical bar with hinged ends buckled under the action of the compressive forces P (Fig. 55). Any shape of the deflection curve of such a bar can be represented by the trigonometric series (see Art. 7)

$$y = a_1 \sin \frac{\pi x}{l} + a_2 \sin \frac{2\pi x}{l} + a_3 \sin \frac{3\pi x}{l} + \cdots . \qquad (i)$$

By varying the parameters $a_1, a_2, \ldots$, we can obtain various shapes of the deflection curve. The energy of bending of the buckled bar is

$$\Delta V = \int_0^l \frac{M^2 \, dx}{2EI} = \frac{P^2}{2EI} \int_0^l y^2 \, dx$$

or, by substituting the series (i) for y and performing the integration (see Art. 7),

---

[1] This method has proved very useful for the approximate determination of critical loads. See author's paper in *Bull. Polytech. Inst.*, Kiev, 1910, and *Ann. ponts chaussées*, 1913, Paris.

$$\Delta V = \frac{P^2 l}{4EI} \sum_{n=1}^{n=\infty} a^2{}_n.$$

The forces P produce during buckling the work (see **Art. 7**)

$$P\lambda = \frac{P}{2} \int_0^l \left(\frac{dy}{dx}\right)^2 dx = \frac{\pi^2 P}{4l} \sum_{n=1}^{n=\infty} n^2 a^2{}_n.$$

Then Eq. (64) becomes

$$\frac{P^2 l}{4EI} \sum_{n=1}^{n=\infty} a^2{}_n = \frac{\pi^2 P}{4l} \sum_{n=1}^{n=\infty} n^2 a^2{}_n$$

and we obtain

$$P = \frac{\pi^2 EI}{l^2} \frac{\displaystyle\sum_{n=1}^{n=\infty} n^2 a^2{}_n}{\displaystyle\sum_{n=1}^{n=\infty} a^2{}_n}. \qquad (j)$$

To find the critical value of the compressive force P we must adjust the parameters $a_1, a_2, \ldots$ in such a manner as to make expression (j) a minimum. This is easy to do in this case on the basis of the following discussion. Imagine a series of fractions:

$$\frac{a}{b}, \quad \frac{c}{d}, \quad \frac{e}{f}, \quad \cdots \qquad (k)$$

If we add the numerators together and likewise the denominators,[1] we obtain the fraction

$$\frac{a + c + e + \cdots}{b + d + f + \cdots}. \qquad (l)$$

This fraction is evidently of some intermediate value between the largest and the smallest of the fractions (k). From this it follows that, if we wish to make expression (j), which may be considered analogous to fraction (l), a minimum, we must take only one term of the series in each numerator and denominator, *i.e.*, we must take all parameters $a_1, a_2, a_3, \ldots$, except one,

[1] Numbers $a, b, c, \ldots$ are assumed positive.

equal to zero. It is seen also that the parameter different from zero must be a_1. Then Eq. (j) gives

$$P_{cr} = \frac{\pi^2 EI}{l^2}$$

and the corresponding deflection curve is

$$y = a_1 \sin \frac{\pi x}{l}.$$

In this way we arrive at the same result as was obtained before by integration (see Art. 12).

Expression (i) for the deflection curve of a buckled bar with hinged ends can be used in more complicated cases when the cross section of the bar is variable, or when the compressive forces are distributed along its length. Then the deflection curve is no longer a sine curve, and by taking the first few terms in series (i) a satisfactory approximate solution can be obtained. The calculation of the parameters a_1, a_2, a_3, . . . for such problems will be shown later (see Art. 23).

16. The Method of Successive Approximations in Calculating Critical Loads.—In the previous article it was shown that the energy method makes it possible to obtain an approximate solution for the critical load and that this solution always gives too large a value. The method of successive approximations, which we will now discuss, makes it possible to establish, for the critical load, both the upper and lower limits. Having these two limits, a better conclusion regarding the accuracy of approximate solutions can be established.

We begin with the simple case of a prismatical bar with hinged ends (Fig. 55), for which an exact solution is known, so that the accuracy of the successive approximations can be readily seen. The bending moment at any cross section of the buckled bar is Py. Thus, the deflection curve of the bar may be considered as the bending-moment diagram to some scale. To get an approximate solution we assume a certain shape for the deflection curve, which satisfies the conditions at the ends. This curve gives us the bending-moment diagram and we can calculate the deflections by using the area-moment method. Comparing this calculated deflection curve with the assumed one, an equation for determining the critical value of the load is obtained.

As an example, assume that the deflection curve of the buckled bar in Fig. 55 is a parabola:

$$y_1 = \frac{4\delta_1}{l^2}x(l - x). \tag{a}$$

The area of the bending-moment diagram is then

$$A = \tfrac{2}{3}P\delta_1 l.$$

Considering this bending-moment area as a fictitious load, the bending moment at the middle of the bar produced by this load is

$$\frac{A}{2}\left(\frac{l}{2} - \frac{3l}{16}\right) = \frac{5}{32}Al = \frac{5}{48}P\delta_1 l^2$$

and the corresponding deflection is $\dfrac{5}{48EI}P\delta_1 l^2$. Putting this deflection equal to the assumed deflection δ_1 at the middle, and solving for the load, we obtain

$$P_{cr} = \frac{48}{5}\frac{EI}{l^2} = 9.6\frac{EI}{l^2}.$$

In this way we obtain a value of P_{cr} which is about 2.7 per cent smaller than the true critical load [Eq. (60)].

To get a better approximation we take the deflection curve, produced by the fictitious parabolic load considered above, as a new approximation for the curve of the buckled bar and repeat the above calculations. The intensity of the fictitious lateral load is then given by the expression

$$q_1 = \frac{4\delta_1 P}{l^2}x(l - x).$$

The deflection curve produced by this distributed load is

$$y_2 = \frac{P\delta_1 lx}{3EI}\left(1 - \frac{2x^2}{l^2} + \frac{x^3}{l^3}\right),$$

or, denoting the deflection at the middle by δ_2,

$$y_2 = \frac{16\delta_2 x}{5l}\left(1 - \frac{2x^2}{l^2} + \frac{x^3}{l^3}\right). \tag{b}$$

Taking this as a second approximation for the deflection curve of the buckled bar, the new expression for the fictitious load is

$$q_2 = Py_2 = \frac{16\delta_2 Px}{5l}\left(1 - \frac{2x^2}{l^2} + \frac{x^3}{l^3}\right). \tag{c}$$

The bending moment at the middle produced by this load is $\frac{61}{600}\delta_2 l^2 P$, and the corresponding center deflection is $61\delta_2 l^2 P/(600EI)$. The critical value of the load P is now obtained from the equation

$$\delta_2 = \frac{61}{600}\frac{\delta_2 l^2 P}{EI},$$

from which

$$P_{cr} = \frac{600}{61}\frac{EI}{l^2} = 9.836\frac{EI}{l^2}.$$

This is lower than the true value of the critical load by about one-third of 1 per cent. A further approximation y_3 can be obtained by taking for the deflection curve of the buckled bar the one produced by the fictitious load (c). In this way we find

$$y_3 = \frac{16P\delta_2 l^2}{5EI}\left(\frac{x}{10l} - \frac{x^3}{6l^3} + \frac{x^5}{10l^5} - \frac{x^6}{30l^6}\right).$$

Mathematically, the above method of determining the critical load is equivalent to an integration, by successive approximations, of the differential equation of the deflection curve for a centrally compressed bar:

$$\frac{d^2 y}{dx^2} + \frac{P}{EI}y = 0. \tag{d}$$

We take for y an approximate expression y_1 [Eq. (a)] which satisfies the end conditions. Substituting this expression for y in Eq. (d), we obtain by double integration[1] a more accurate expression for y, namely, y_2 [Eq. (b)]. Substituting this in Eq. (d) for y, a better approximation is obtained, and so on.

If y_1, y_2, y_3, . . . are the consecutive approximations for the deflection curve obtained in this way, it can be shown[2] that for any approximation y_n the following inequality holds:

$$\left(\frac{y_n}{y_{n+1}}\right)_{min.} < \frac{P_{cr}}{P} < \left(\frac{y_n}{y_{n+1}}\right)_{max.} \tag{65}$$

Take, for instance, expressions y_1 and y_2 calculated above; then

$$\frac{y_1}{y_2} = \frac{12EI}{Pl^2}\frac{l^2 x(l-x)}{x(l^3 - 2lx^2 + x^3)}.$$

[1] The above use of the area-moment method is equivalent to such a double integration.

[2] This method of successive approximations in the integration of differential equations was originated by H. A. Schwarz, "Gesammelte Werke," vol. 1, pp. 241–265. See also P. Funk, *Mitt. Hauptvereines deut. Ing. Tschechoslowaki*, Heft 21 and 22, Brünn, 1931. The method of successive approximations in calculating critical loads as described in the beginning of the article has been used by several engineers. See, for instance, F. Engesser, *Z. oesterr. Ing. Arch. Vereines*, 1893, and L. Vianello, *Z. Ver. deut. Ing.*, 1898, p. 1436.

Calculating the maximum and minimum of this ratio as a function of x and substituting in (65), we find

$$\frac{9.6EI}{l^2} < P_{cr} < \frac{12EI}{l^2}.$$

Taking the second and the third approximations, we have

$$\frac{y_2}{y_3} = \frac{10EI}{Pl^2} \frac{1 - \frac{2x^2}{l^2} + \frac{x^3}{l^3}}{1 - \frac{10x^2}{6l^2} + \frac{x^4}{l^4} - \frac{x^5}{3l^5}}.$$

Substituting in (65), we obtain

$$\frac{9.836EI}{l^2} < P_{cr} < \frac{10EI}{l^2}.$$

Thus, by successive approximations, we obtain not only the upper but also the lower limit for P_{cr}.

Instead of an analytical calculation of the deflections, a graphical method can be used. In this method we assume a certain deflection curve for the buckled bar such that the end conditions are satisfied. Then, by multiplying the deflections by some assumed value of the compressive load P, the bending moments M are obtained. Now, considering the bending-moment diagram as a fictitious lateral load and constructing the corresponding funicular curve, the new deflection curve is obtained. If, by adjusting the value of P, the new curve can be brought into complete coincidence with the assumed curve, this will indicate that the assumed curve is the true deflection curve and that the corresponding P is the correct value of the critical load. Usually the above two curves will be different; by adjusting the value of P we can make the deflections equal at only one point, say at the middle of the span, as was done in the calculations at the beginning of this article. In this way we obtain an approximate value for the critical load. To get a better approximation, we take the constructed funicular curve as a second approximation for the deflection curve and repeat again the same constructions as above.

Instead of calculating the critical load from the condition that the deflections of the two consecutive curves at a certain point are equal, we can use the average values of the deflections and calculate the critical load from the condition

$$P_{cr} = \frac{\int_0^l M \, dx}{\int_0^l y \, dx}. \tag{e}$$

In this expression the integral in the numerator, if divided by the span l, gives the average ordinate of the assumed bending-moment diagram and in the same way the integral in the denominator gives the average value of deflections as obtained from the funicular curve. Proceeding with the construction of the consecutive funicular curves as explained before and using Eq. (*e*) each time, we can approximate the critical load more and more closely.[1]   An example of this graphical solution is given in Art. **25.**

17. Buckling of a Bar with One End Hinged and the Other Built In.

Fig. 56.

—So far only the simplest end conditions for a compressed prismatical bar have been considered, namely, the fundamental case in which the ends are hinged, the case of built-in ends and the case in which one end is built in and the other is free.   Other end conditions can also be treated, however, without any difficulty.   Take, as a first example, the case of a bar built in at the lower end and hinged at the top (Fig. 56).   Assuming that the bar is buckled slightly under the action of the compressive force *P*, there must be some lateral reaction[2] *Q*.   Thus the differential equation of the deflection curve is

$$EI \frac{d^2y}{dx^2} = -Py + Q\,(l - x). \tag{a}$$

Using the previous notation $k^2 = P/EI$, the general solution of Eq. (*a*) is

$$y = A \cos kx + B \sin kx + \frac{Q}{P}(l - x). \tag{b}$$

The end conditions in this case are:

$$(y)_{x=0} = 0; \qquad \left(\frac{dy}{dx}\right)_{x=0} = 0; \qquad (y)_{x=l} = 0.$$

Substituting expression (*b*) for *y* in these equations, we obtain

$$A + \frac{Ql}{P} = 0; \qquad kB - \frac{Q}{P} = 0;$$

$$A \cos kl + B \sin kl = 0.$$

Determining *A* and *B* from the first two equations and substituting in the third one, we obtain the following transcendental equation

$$\tan kl = kl, \tag{66}$$

[1] The mathematical proof of this statement is discussed by R. v. Mises. *Monatsschr. Math. Physik*, vol. 22, p. 33, 1911, and by E. Trefftz, *Z. angew, Math. Mech.*, vol. 3, p. 272, 1923.

[2] The direction of this reaction is determined from the direction of curvature at the built-in end.

from which the value of k, and therefore the value of the critical load, is obtained.

The graphical method is useful in solving Eq. (66). The curves in Fig. 57 represent $\tan kl$ as a function of kl. These curves have the verticals $kl = \pi/2,\ 3\pi/2,\ \cdot\ \cdot\ \cdot$ as asymptotes, since for these values of kl, $\tan kl$ becomes infinity. The roots of Eq. (66) are now obtained as the intersection points of the above curves with the straight line $y = kl$. The smallest root, obtained in this way, is

$$kl = 4.493.$$

Then

$$P_{cr} = k^2 EI =$$
$$\frac{20.16EI}{l^2} \approx \frac{\pi^2 EI}{(0.7l)^2} \quad (67)$$

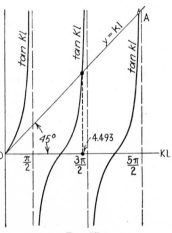

Fig. 57.

Thus the critical load is the same as for a bar with hinged ends having a reduced length equal to $0.7l$.

Equation (66), from which the critical load has been determined, can be obtained in another way by using the results of the previous chapter. In discussing bending of a compressed bar with one end built in and the other simply supported (Art. 5), expression (30) for the bending moment at the built-in end has been obtained in the following form

$$M_b = -\frac{ql^2}{8}\frac{4(\tan u - u)\tan 2u}{u(\tan 2u - 2u)}.$$

It is seen that this moment increases indefinitely when the denominator of the expression approaches zero. Putting this denominator equal to zero and remembering that $2u = kl$ (see p. 4), Eq. (66), given above, is obtained. Thus the critical value of the compressive force is that value for which the expression for the reactive bending moment produced by a slight lateral load becomes infinitely large. Such a conclusion is reached because we are using an approximate expression for the curvature. By taking the exact equation for the deflection curve (Art. 13), it may be shown that the deflection always remains finite, but with the slightest increase of the compressive load above its critical value this deflection increases very rapidly, so that the critical load, calculated above, is practically the load that will produce complete failure of the bar.

This method of calculating critical loads by using formulas for combined bending and compression, and by determining the value of the compressive load at which the expressions for the deflections or bending moments become infinitely large, is very useful and will be illustrated by several examples in the following article.

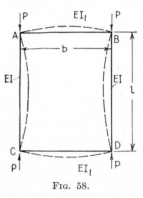

FIG. 58.

18. Buckling of Bars with Elastically Built-in Ends. Frames.—As an illustration of a practical problem in which we have columns with elastically built-in ends, consider the bars AC and BD of the symmetrical rectangular frame (Fig. 58), the joints of which are not free to move laterally. When the load P reaches its critical value, the vertical bars begin to buckle as indicated by the dotted lines. This buckling must be accompanied by bending of the horizontal bars AB and CD, which resist buckling with reactive moments at the ends proportional to the angle of rotation of the joints. Hence the vertical members of the frame are examples of bars with elastically built-in ends. Considering the simplest case in which the frame is symmetrical with respect to both vertical and horizontal axes, the conditions at both ends of each buckled vertical member are identical.

In calculating the value of the critical load we can use the results of the previous chapter (see Art. 5) and consider bending of a compressed bar with elastically built-in ends. The end moments in this case are determined by Eqs. (33). In the case of symmetry these moments are equal ($M_a = M_b$) and we have to consider only one equation:

$$-\frac{M_a}{\alpha} = \frac{M_a l}{3EI}\psi(u) + \frac{M_a l}{6EI}\phi(u) + \theta_0, \qquad (a)$$

in which M_a denotes the end moments, θ_0 the rotation of the ends of the compressed bar if some lateral load is acting and if the ends are hinged, l the length of the bar, EI its flexural rigidity and α the coefficient of end restraint defined on page 16. In the case under consideration, if b is the length of the horizontal bars and if EI_1 is their flexural rigidity, a simple consideration of bending of horizontal bars by equal couples at the ends gives

$$\alpha = \frac{2EI_1}{b}. \tag{b}$$

The functions $\psi(u)$ and $\phi(u)$ are given by Eqs. (21) and (22) (see p. 12). Substituting the values of α, $\psi(u)$ and $\phi(u)$ from Eqs. (b), (21) and (22), respectively, in Eq. (a) and using notation (8) (see p. 4), we obtain the following equation for determining the end moments:

$$M_a\left(\frac{b}{2EI_1} + \frac{1}{kEI}\tan\frac{kl}{2}\right) = -\theta_0,$$

from which

$$M_a = -\frac{kEI\theta_0}{\dfrac{bI}{lI_1}\dfrac{kl}{2} + \tan\dfrac{kl}{2}}.$$

The critical value of the compressive force is obtained from the condition that the expression for the moment M_a becomes infinitely large. This condition requires that

$$\tan\frac{kl}{2} + \frac{kl}{2}\frac{b}{l}\frac{I}{I_1} = 0. \tag{68}$$

In the particular case of a square frame with equal rigidity of all four members, we obtain from Eq. (68)

$$\tan\frac{kl}{2} + \frac{kl}{2} = 0. \tag{c}$$

The smallest root of this equation is

$$\frac{kl}{2} = 2.029,$$

making

$$P_{cr} = \frac{16.47EI}{l^2}. \tag{d}$$

If the horizontal bars of the frame are absolutely rigid, we put $I_1 = \infty$ in Eq. (68). Then

$$\tan\frac{kl}{2} = 0.$$

The smallest root of this equation, different from zero, is

$$kl = 2\pi,$$

from which

$$P_{cr} = \frac{4\pi^2 EI}{l^2}.$$

This checks the value previously obtained for a bar with built-in ends.

Taking $I_1 = 0$ in Eq. (68), we obtain

$$\tan \frac{kl}{2} = \infty,$$

from which

$$P_{cr} = \frac{\pi^2 EI}{l^2}.$$

This checks the value previously obtained for a bar with hinged ends.

In each particular case Eq. (68) can be represented in the form

$$-\frac{\tan \dfrac{kl}{2}}{kl/2} = \frac{bI}{lI_1},$$

and can be easily solved by using a curve representing the numerical values of the ratio $-\dfrac{\left(\tan \dfrac{kl}{2}\right)}{kl/2}$ as a function of the angle $\dfrac{kl}{2}$. Several values of the ratio $-\dfrac{\tan (kl/2)}{kl/2}$ are given in Table 3 below.[1]

$$\text{TABLE 3.—VALUES OF } \frac{\tan \dfrac{kl}{2}}{kl/2}$$

$\dfrac{kl}{2}$	$\dfrac{\pi}{2}$	$1.1\dfrac{\pi}{2}$	$1.2\dfrac{\pi}{2}$	$1.3\dfrac{\pi}{2}$	$1.4\dfrac{\pi}{2}$	$1.5\dfrac{\pi}{2}$	$1.6\dfrac{\pi}{2}$	$1.7\dfrac{\pi}{2}$	$1.8\dfrac{\pi}{2}$	$1.9\dfrac{\pi}{2}$	π
$-\dfrac{\tan \dfrac{kl}{2}}{kl/2}$	∞	3.65	1.63	0.961	0.626	0.424	0.289	0.191	0.115	0.053	0

[1] The first discussions of problems on stability of members of a rectangular frame were given by F. Engesser in his book: "Die Zusatzkräfte und Nebenspannungen eiserner Fachwerkbrücken," 1893, Berlin. See also H. Zimmermann's "Knickfestigkeit der Stabverbindungen," Berlin, 1925.

It may be seen that the *reduced length* (see p. 69) of the compressed vertical members of the frame, which must be taken in calculating the critical value of the compressive force, depends on the rigidity of the horizontal members of the frame and varies from $L = 0.5l$ for $I_1 = \infty$ to $L = l$ for $I_1 = 0$.

If the horizontal members of the frame are submitted to the action of compressive forces Q, as shown in Fig. 59, the coefficients of end restraint α will be diminished; instead of Eq. (b) we must use the equation [see Eq. (28), p. 14]

$$\alpha = \frac{2EI_1}{b} \frac{u}{\tan u}$$

in which

$$u = \frac{b}{2}\sqrt{\frac{Q}{EI_1}}.$$

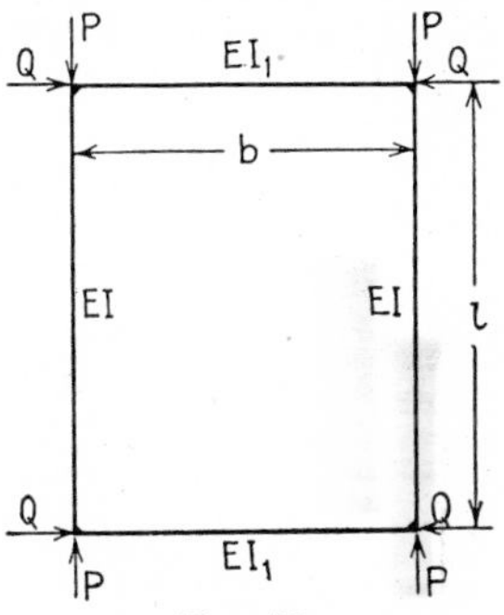

In calculating the critical value of the compressive force P, we can again use Eq. (68), it being only necessary to substitute $\dfrac{I_1 u}{\tan u}$ for I_1.[1]

Fig. 59.

If the flexural rigidities of the two horizontal members of the frame (Fig. 58) are different, the end conditions for the compressed vertical members are no longer the same for both ends and in calculating the critical value of the compressive force P we have to use the two Eqs. (33). The critical value of P is that value at which the end moments as calculated from Eqs. (33) become infinite, *i.e.*, the determinant of Eqs. (33) becomes zero. Thus the equation for determining the critical value of P is:[2]

$$\left[\frac{1}{\alpha} + \frac{l\psi(u)}{3EI}\right]\left[\frac{1}{\beta} + \frac{l\psi(u)}{3EI}\right] - \left[\frac{l\phi(u)}{6EI}\right]^2 = 0, \qquad (69)$$

[1] It is assumed in this discussion that the critical condition is first reached for the vertical bars and that the horizontal bars, although compressed, continue to resist buckling of the vertical bars.

[2] Small changes in the lengths of horizontal bars, due to axial forces produced at buckling, are neglected in this derivation. The justification of this is discussed later (see Art. 28).

where $u = \dfrac{kl}{2} = \dfrac{l}{2}\sqrt{\dfrac{P}{EI}}$. In the particular case where $\alpha = \beta$, we obtain, from (69),

$$\frac{1}{\alpha} + \frac{l\psi(u)}{3EI} = \pm \frac{l\phi(u)}{6EI}.$$

By taking the sign minus on the right side of this equation, we obtain Eq. (68). By taking the sign plus, the equation becomes

$$2\psi(u) - \phi(u) = -\frac{6EI}{l\alpha}.$$

This equation corresponds to the case in which $M_b = -M_a$ in

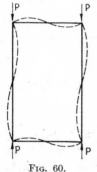

FIG. 60.

Eqs. (33) and gives values for the force P at which the buckled vertical members of the frame have inflection points at the middle (Fig. 60). These values are higher than those obtained from Eq. (68) and are of no practical significance.

If we put $\alpha = 0$ and $\beta = \infty$ in Eq. (69), we obtain

$$\psi(u) = 0,$$

which is equivalent to Eq. (66) above and which gives the same critical value of the load as for the bar shown in Fig. 56.

In the case shown in Fig. 61a, the vertical bar is rigidly built in at the bottom and elastically built in at the top. Then, $\beta = \infty$ and α is finite.[1] Equation (69) becomes

$$\left[\frac{3EI}{\alpha l} + \psi(u)\right]\psi(u) = \frac{1}{4}[\phi(u)]^2 \tag{70}$$

This equation can be solved easily for each particular case by the trial-and-error method, using the table of functions $\phi(u)$ and $\psi(u)$ (see p. 499).

[1] To make this discussion exact, it must be assumed that the compressive force P is applied to the vertical bar before the rigid joint of the two bars is made so that there is no bending in the horizontal bar before buckling. The small changes in the length of the bars produced at buckling are also neglected as before.

For the case represented in Fig. 61b, $\beta = 0$ and α is finite. When β is approaching zero in Eq. (69), the factor $\left[\dfrac{1}{\alpha} + \dfrac{l\psi(u)}{3EI}\right]$ must approach zero also and the equation for calculating the critical load becomes

$$\frac{1}{\alpha} + \frac{l\psi(u)}{3EI} = 0. \quad (71)$$

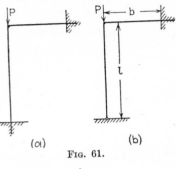

(a) (b)

Fig. 61.

Considering the horizontal member as a beam with one end built in and the other hinged, and denoting with EI_1 the flexural rigidity of this member, the magnitude of α in Eq. (71) is equal to $4EI_1/b$ and the equation gives

$$\psi(u) = -\frac{3}{4}\frac{bI}{lI_1}.$$

Assuming, for instance, $b = l$; $I = I_1$, we find, by using the table on page 499,

$$\psi(u) = -\frac{3}{4}, \qquad 2u = kl = 3.83, \qquad \text{and} \qquad P_{cr} = \frac{\overline{3.83}^2 EI}{l^2}.$$

For $\alpha = \infty$, Eq. (71) coincides with Eq. (66) and we obtain the solution for the case shown in Fig. 56.

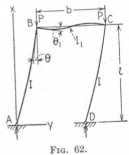

Fig. 62.

In the previous discussion it was always assumed that the ends of the compressed members have no lateral displacements. Let us consider now the case shown in Fig. 62 in which a frame with compressed vertical members is free at the top to move laterally. If the frame has a vertical axis of symmetry, each vertical member may be considered separately as a compressed bar free at the lower end and elastically built in at the upper end. Taking the coordinate axes as shown in the figure, the differential equation of the deflection curve of the bar AB is

$$EI\frac{d^2y}{dx^2} = -Py.$$

The solution of this equation, satisfying conditions at the lower end, is

$$y = A \sin kx. \qquad (e)$$

At the upper end the angles θ and θ_1 should be equal; since the horizontal bar BC is bent by two couples equal to $P(y)_{x=l}$, the condition at the upper end is

$$\left(\frac{dy}{dx}\right)_{x=l} = P(y)_{x=l}\frac{b}{6EI_1},$$

or, by using expression (e),

$$k \cos kl = \frac{Pb \sin kl}{6EI_1}. \qquad (f)$$

If the horizontal bar is absolutely rigid, $EI_1 = \infty$, and we obtain

$$\cos kl = 0; \qquad kl = \frac{\pi}{2}; \qquad P_{cr} = \frac{\pi^2 EI}{4l^2}.$$

In the general case, Eq. (f) can be represented in the following form:

$$kl \tan kl = 6\frac{I_1}{I}\frac{l}{b}, \qquad (g)$$

and the critical value of the load P can be easily found for any numerical value of the ratio I_1l/Ib. Assuming that all three bars of the frame are identical, we obtain

$$kl \tan kl = 6$$

from which

$$kl = 1.35 \qquad \text{and} \qquad P_{cr} = \frac{1.82EI}{l^2}.$$

19. Buckling of Continuous Bars on Rigid Supports.—In calculating critical compressive forces for continuous beams, the method of the previous article can be used. Here, continuous beams, subjected to longitudinal compression in addition to transverse bending loads, will be considered (see Art. 6, p. 17). We shall define the critical value of the compressive force as that force[1] at which a slight lateral load will produce an infinite deflection.

---

[1] The compressive forces are assumed constant along each span, but may vary from one span to the next.

Considering two consecutive spans of a bar on several supports (Fig. 8, p. 17), the relation between the three consecutive bending moments at the supports is given by Eq. (34) (see p. 18):

$$M_{n-1}\phi(u_{n-1}) + 2M_n\left[\psi(u_{n-1}) + \frac{l_n I_{n-1}}{l_{n-1} I_n}\psi(u_n)\right] +$$

$$M_{n+1}\frac{l_n}{l_{n-1}}\frac{I_{n-1}}{I_n}\phi(u_n) = -\frac{6EI_{n-1}}{l_{n-1}}(\theta_{0n} + \theta'_{0n}). \quad (a)$$

There will be as many equations of this kind as there are statically indeterminate moments.[1] The coefficients in these equations contain the functions $\phi(u)$ and $\psi(u)$ and depend on the magnitudes of the compressive forces P. The critical values of these forces are those values for which the bending moments, as solved from Eq. (a), become infinitely large.[2] This requires that the determinant of Eq. (a) be made

Fig. 63.

equal to zero. In this way an equation for calculating the critical values of the compressive forces is obtained.

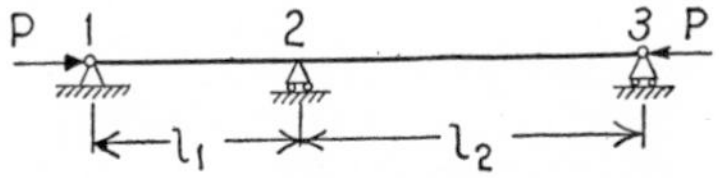

Let us consider a bar on three supports, with hinged ends, and compressed by forces P applied at the ends (Fig. 63). In this case there is only one unknown moment M_2 and Eq. (a) becomes

$$2M_2\left[\psi(u_1) + \frac{l_2 I_1}{l_1 I_2}\psi(u_2)\right] = -\frac{6EI_1}{l_1}(\theta_{02} + \theta'_{02}).$$

The critical value of the compressive force is now obtained from the condition (see p. 90) that

$$\psi(u_1) + \frac{l_2 I_1}{l_1 I_2}\psi(u_2) = 0. \quad (b)$$

Assuming that the cross section of the bar is the same for both spans, we have

[1] It is assumed that the ends of the bar are simply supported. In the case of built-in ends the two additional equations expressing the conditions of fixity should be taken in addition to Eqs. (a).

[2] There is an exceptional case in which buckling may occur with all bending moments at the supports equal to zero. This takes place when all spans of the bar have such proportions and such compressive forces that $u_1 = u_2 = u_3 = \cdots$. In this case buckling of each span is not influenced by the adjacent spans and the critical values of the forces are calculated for each span as for a bar with hinged ends.

$$u_1 = \frac{k_1 l_1}{2} = \frac{l_1}{2}\sqrt{\frac{P}{EI}}; \qquad u_2 = \frac{k_2 l_2}{2} = \frac{l_2}{2}\sqrt{\frac{P}{EI}};$$

$$\frac{u_1}{u_2} = \frac{l_1}{l_2}.$$

Equation (b) can now be put in the form

$$\frac{\psi(u_1)}{\psi(u_1 l_2/l_1)} = -\frac{l_2}{l_1}, \tag{b'}$$

which can be solved by using Table 1 for the function $\psi(u)$ (see p. 499). If we take $l_2 = 2l_1$, Eq. (b') becomes

$$\frac{\psi(u_1)}{\psi(2u_1)} = -2$$

and from Table 1 we find $2u_1 = 1.93$, whence

$$P_{cr} = \frac{(1.93)^2 EI}{l^2_1} = \frac{3.72EI}{l^2_1} = \frac{14.9EI}{l^2_2}.$$

It is seen that the value of the critical load lies between the two values $\pi^2 EI/l^2_1$ and $\pi^2 EI/l^2_2$, calculated for separate spans as if each were a bar with hinged ends. The stability of the shorter span is reduced, owing to the action of the longer span, while the stability of the longer span is increased.

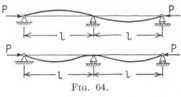

FIG. 64.

When the length l_2 approaches l_1, the quantity u_2 approaches u_1 and the root of Eq. (b') approaches the value $2u_1 = 2u_2 = \pi$. In this case the bending moment at the middle support is zero and each span can be considered as a bar with hinged ends (see footnote, p. 97). The next root of Eq. (b'), for u_2 approaching u_1, is (see Table 1) $2u_1 = 2u_2 = 4.492$. Then

$$P_{cr} = \frac{20.16EI}{l^2_1} \approx \frac{\pi^2 EI}{(0.7l_1)^2}.$$

The two forms of the buckled bar are shown in Fig. 64. Only the first form, corresponding to the smallest compressive force, is of practical significance.

As a second example, let us consider a bar on four supports (Fig. 65) and assume that $l_1 = l_3$ and $I_1 = I_3$. The first and last spans of this continuous beam may be considered as bars having one end hinged and the other end elastically built in. It may be seen that the shape of the buckled bar will be that shown in Fig. 65b. Then the bending moments at supports 2 and 3 are equal, from symmetry, and from Eq. (a), with $\phi(u_2) = \psi(u_2) = 1$ (since the compressive force in the second span is zero), we obtain

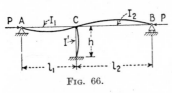

$$2\psi(u_1) + \frac{3l_2I_1}{l_1I_2} = 0. \qquad (c)$$

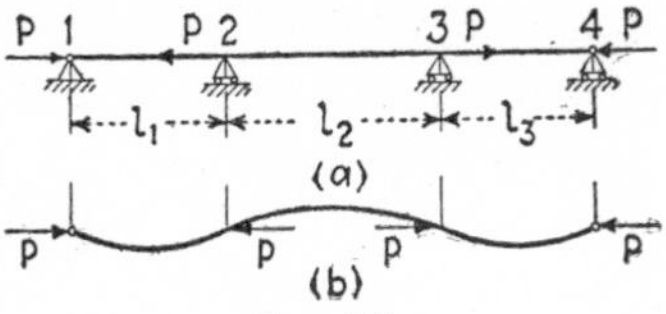

This equation coincides with Eq. (71) of the previous article (see p. 95) if we substitute in it $\alpha = 2EI_2/l_2$.

Fig. 65.

As a last example, let us consider the case shown in Fig. 66. A compressed bar AB is rigidly connected with a column at C, so that any lateral buckling of the bar must be accompanied by bending of the column. In the solution of this problem Eqs. (37) and (38) of Art. 6 (see p. 21) will be used. If M_c and M'_c are the values of the bending moments in the two adjacent cross sections to the left and to the right of support C, respectively, and if there is no lateral load, these equations become

Fig. 66.

$$2M_c\psi(u_1) + 2M'_c\frac{l_2}{l_1}\frac{I_1}{I_2}\psi(u_2) = 0,$$

and

$$\frac{h}{3EI'}(M'_c - M_c) = \frac{M_cl_1}{3EI_1}\psi(u_1),$$

$$\qquad (d)$$

in which EI' and h are the flexural rigidity and the length of the column. The critical value of the compressive force is found by setting the determinant of Eqs. (d) equal to zero. Thus we obtain

$$\psi(u_1) + \psi(u_2)\frac{l_2}{l_1}\frac{I_1}{I_2}\left[1 + \frac{l_1}{h}\frac{I'}{I_1}\psi(u_1)\right] = 0. \qquad (e)$$

This equation can be solved in each particular case by using Table 1 (p. 499). In the particular case where $l_1 = l_2$ and $I_1 = I_2$, Eq. (e) becomes

$$\psi(u_1)\left[2 + \frac{l_1}{h}\frac{I'}{I_1}\psi(u_1)\right] = 0$$

from which

$$\psi(u_1) = 0 \qquad \text{or} \qquad \psi(u_1) = -\frac{2hI_1}{l_1I'}.$$

The first of these two solutions gives us the same value for P_{cr} as that obtained for the bar shown in Fig. 56. It corresponds to a deflection curve symmetrical with respect to C, in which the column does not bend at all. The second solution, which gives a smaller value for P_{cr}, corresponds to a non-symmetrical shape of the buckled bar as shown in Fig. 66. Only this second solution has any practical significance. For any particular case it is readily obtained from Table 1 (p. 499). Taking, for example, $2hI_1/l_1I' = 1$, we find from the table, $2u_1 = kl_1 = 3.73$ and $P_{cr} = \overline{3.73}^2 EI/l^2{}_1$.

20. Buckling of a Bar on Elastic Supports.

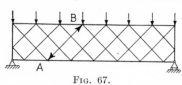

Fig. 67.

—The first problems of this kind were discussed by Jasinsky,[1] who considered the lateral buckling of compressed diagonals in trusses of the type shown in Fig. 67. It is seen that a compressed bar, such as AB, cannot buckle freely since it has lateral elastic support furnished by the diagonals which are in tension. The general method of solving such problems consists in using Eqs. (36) (see p. 20) for a continuous bar, the supports of which are not on a straight line. Let us consider, as a simple example, the

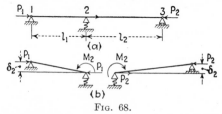

Fig. 68.

case of a bar on three supports, the middle one of which is elastic (Fig. 68). If the bar buckles under the action of the compressive forces, the middle reaction R_2 will be proportional to the deflection δ_2. Let α_2 be the *spring*

[1] See "Scientific Papers of F. S. Jasinsky," vol. 1, p. 145, St. Petersburg, 1902. This very important paper by Jasinsky on the buckling of columns app ared also in a French translation, see *Ann. ponts chaussées*, 1894. See also H. Zimmermann's, "Die Knickfestigkeit eines Stabes mit elastischer Querstützung," Wilhelm Ernst und Sohn, Berlin, 1906, and his papers in *Sitzungsb. Berl. Akad. Math. physik. Klasse*, 1905, p. 898; 1907, pp. 235 and 326; 1909, pp. 180 and 348.

constant of the support (see p. 22), *i.e.*, the load producing in it unit deflection. Then

$$R_2 = \alpha_2 \delta_2. \tag{a}$$

All the supports are such that the cross sections of the beam at the supports can rotate freely during bending. Considering the two spans as two simply supported beams acted upon by forces P_1, P_2, and couples M_2 (Fig. 68b), the reaction R_2, from statics, is

$$R_2 = \frac{P_1 \delta_2}{l_1} + \frac{P_2 \delta_2}{l_2} - \frac{M_2}{l_1} - \frac{M_2}{l_2}. \tag{b}$$

From (a) and (b) we obtain

$$\alpha_2 \delta_2 = \frac{P_1 \delta_2}{l_1} + \frac{P_2 \delta_2}{l_2} - \frac{M_2}{l_1} - \frac{M_2}{l_2}. \tag{c}$$

Another equation for support 2 is obtained from the general Eq. (36). Observing that, in this case, the ends of the bar are hinged, the moments M_1 and M_3 for the supports 1 and 3 are zero. The angle β_2 for the middle support (see Fig. 9) is

$$\beta_2 = \frac{\delta_2}{l_1} + \frac{\delta_2}{l_2}.$$

Then Eq. (36) becomes

$$2M_2 \left[\psi(u_1) + \frac{l_2}{l_1} \frac{I_1}{I_2} \psi(u_2) \right] = \frac{6EI_1}{l_1} \left(\frac{\delta_2}{l_1} + \frac{\delta_2}{l_2} \right). \tag{d}$$

Buckling of the bar becomes possible when Eqs. (c) and (d) yield a solution for M_2 and δ_2 different from zero. Hence the critical values of P_1 and P_2 are found by setting the determinant of these two equations equal to zero. Thus

$$2 \left[\alpha_2 - \frac{P_1}{l_1} - \frac{P_2}{l_2} \right] \left[\psi(u_1) + \frac{l_2}{l_1} \frac{I_1}{I_2} \psi(u_2) \right] = -\frac{6EI_1}{l_1} \frac{(l_1 + l_2)^2}{l^2_1 l^2_2}. \tag{e}$$

In this equation P_1 and P_2 are unknown; if the ratio between them is given, their values can be found by using Table 1 (see p. 499). In the particular case where $P_1 = P_2$ and $I_1 = I_2$, Eq. (e) can be simplified by using the expression for $\psi(u)$ (see p. 12) and finally represented in the following form:

$$\sin 2u_1 \sin 2u_2 = 2(u_1 + u_2) \sin 2(u_1 + u_2) \left[\frac{l_1 l_2}{(l_1 + l_2)^2} - \frac{P}{\alpha_2(l_1 + l_2)} \right]. \tag{f}$$

In a more general case where there are several intermediate elastic supports, we can write for each support two equations similar to (c) and (d); the critical values of the compressive forces are determined by equating the determinant of this system of equations to zero.

If the cross section is constant and the compressive force the same for all spans, it is advantageous to use Eqs. (39) (see p. 22) instead of Eqs. (36) in calculating the critical value of the compressive force. To illustrate this method of solution, let us consider again the beam on three supports (Fig. 68). Equation 39 for this case becomes

$$\frac{q(l_1 + l_2)^4}{16EIu^4}\left[\frac{\cos\left(1 - \dfrac{2l_1}{l_1 + l_2}\right)u}{\cos u} - 1\right] - \frac{q(l_1 + l_2)^2}{8EIu^2}l_1l_2 -$$

$$\frac{\sin kl_1}{Pk\sin k(l_1 + l_2)}R_2\sin kl_2 + \frac{l_1l_2}{P(l_1 + l_2)}R_2 = \frac{R_2}{\alpha_2}. \quad (g)$$

The critical value of the compressive force is that value at which the deflections and hence the reaction R_2 begin to increase indefinitely.[1] This requires that the coefficient of R_2 in Eq. (g) becomes zero. Thus in calculating the critical load, we obtain the following equation:

$$-\frac{\sin kl_1\sin kl_2}{Pk\sin k(l_1 + l_2)} + \frac{l_1l_2}{P(l_1 + l_2)} - \frac{1}{\alpha_2} = 0 \quad (h)$$

Observing that $kl_1 = 2u_1$ and $kl_2 = 2u_2$, we find that Eq. (h) coincides with Eq. (f) obtained before in another way.

In discussing solutions of Eq. (f), let us begin with several simple cases.

If $\alpha_2 = \infty$, Eq. (e), from which Eq. (f) is obtained as a particular case, coincides with Eq. (b) of the previous article (see p. 97), which was obtained for a bar on three rigid supports. Thus we can use the solution from that article.

If α_2 approaches zero, the second term in the parenthesis on the right side of Eq. (f) approaches infinity, and the equation can be satisfied only if, simultaneously, $\sin 2(u_1 + u_2)$ approaches zero. The critical load is then obtained from the equation

$$\sin 2(u_1 + u_2) = \sin k(l_1 + l_2) = 0$$

from which

$$P_{cr} = \frac{\pi^2 EI}{(l_1 + l_2)^2}.$$

This coincides with the critical load for a bar with hinged ends and of length $l = l_1 + l_2$.

If the two spans are equal, we have $u_1 = u_2$, $l_1 = l_2 = l/2$, and Eq. (f) can be put in a simpler form:

$$\sin 2u_1\left[-\sin 2u_1 + 8u_1\cos 2u_1\left(\frac{1}{4} - \frac{P}{\alpha_2 l}\right)\right] = 0. \quad (i)$$

The upper limit for the critical value of the compressive force is obtained by assuming that the intermediate support is absolutely rigid ($\alpha_2 = \infty$). In such case the shape of the buckled bar is that shown in Fig. 69a and the critical value of the compressive force is obtained from the equation

$$2u_1 = \pi,$$

which gives

$$P_{cr} = \frac{\pi^2 EI}{l^2_1} = \frac{4\pi^2 EI}{l^2}. \quad (j)$$

[1] If there are two equal spans, buckling may occur in such a way that $R_2 = 0$. In this case the buckling condition of each span is the same as that of a bar with hinged ends and it is not necessary to consider the continuous bar.

The lower limit for the critical load is obtained by assuming that the intermediate support is absolutely flexible ($\alpha_2 = 0$). The shape of the deflection curve of the buckled bar is then as in Fig. 69b, and we have

$$2u_1 = \frac{\pi}{2}, \qquad \text{giving} \qquad P_{cr} = \frac{\pi^2 EI}{l^2}. \tag{k}$$

For any intermediate value of the rigidity of the elastic support we have

$$\frac{\pi}{2} < 2u_1 \leqq \pi. \tag{l}$$

There are two possibilities for the left side of (i) to become zero; either $\sin 2u_1 = 0$, which gives for the critical load the value (j), or the expression in the brackets may become zero. From the inequality (l) it can be concluded that $\sin 2u_1$ is positive and $\cos 2u_1$ negative. Hence, the expression in brackets may become zero only if

$$\frac{P}{\alpha_2 l} \geqq \frac{1}{4},$$

and the corresponding smallest value of P is

$$P = \frac{\alpha_2 l}{4}. \tag{m}$$

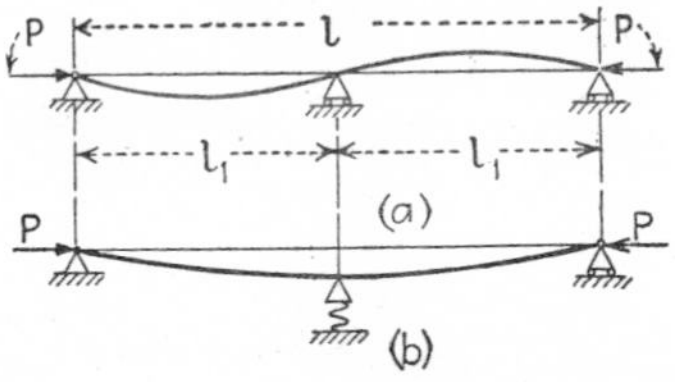

FIG. 69.

If this value is larger than (j), the condition $\sin 2u_1 = 0$ determines the critical value of the load and the shape of the buckled bar is that shown in Fig. 69a. The limiting value of the rigidity of the support at which this shape of buckling occurs is obtained from Eq. (m) by substituting for P the value (j). Then

$$\frac{4\pi^2 EI}{l^2} = \frac{\alpha_2 l}{4},$$

from which

$$\alpha_2 = \frac{16\pi^2 EI}{l^3}. \tag{n}$$

For smaller values of α_2, the flexibility of the intermediate support should be considered; the value of P_{cr} is obtained by determining the value of P at which the expression in the brackets of Eq. (i) becomes zero.

In Fig. 70 a curve is plotted which shows the variation of the critical load with the rigidity of the intermediate support. In this curve the ratios $P_{cr} : \pi^2 EI / l^2 = P_{cr} : P_e$ are taken as ordinates and the ratios

$$\alpha_2 l : \pi^2 EI / l^2 = \alpha_2 l / P_e$$

as abscissas. The curve deviates but very little from a straight line so that the critical load increases in approximately the same proportion as the rigidity of the support.

If the spans are not equal, the general Eq. (f) should be considered in calculating the critical load. The lower limit for P_{cr} is given, as before, by

Eq. (k). For determining the upper limit we assume $\alpha_2 = \infty$. Then the right side of Eq. (f) becomes zero when

$$2(u_1 + u_2) = 2\pi. \tag{o}$$

At the same time the left side is negative since one of the two angles $2u_1$ and $2u_2$ is larger and the other smaller than π. Both sides of Eq. (f) can be made equal (*i.e.*, the upper limit for P will be found) by taking for $2(u_1 + u_2)$ a quantity somewhat smaller than 2π. This indicates that in the case of rigid supports any lateral displacement of the intermediate support from the middle position diminishes the value of the critical load.

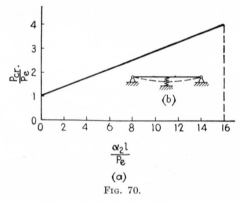

Fig. 70.

After the upper and lower limits for P are determined by taking $\alpha_2 = \infty$ and $\alpha_2 = 0$, the critical value of the compressive force for any intermediate value of α_2 is obtained by solving Eq. (f) by the trial-and-error method. This solution is simplified if we note that for

$$\alpha_2 = \frac{P(l_1 + l_2)}{l_1 l_2} \tag{p}$$

the right side of Eq. (f) is zero. Assuming $l_1 > l_2$, the smallest value of P which makes the left side of the equation equal to zero is obtained from the equation $\sin 2u_1 = 0$, from which $2u_1 = \pi$ and $2(u_1 + u_2) = \pi l/l_1$. If we take α_2 smaller than (p), the value of $2(u_1 + u_2)$ must be smaller than $\pi l/l_1$ found above; at the same time it must be larger than the value π found for $\alpha_2 = 0$. Hence, the root of Eq. (f) must lay within the limits

$$\pi < 2(u_1 + u_2) < \frac{\pi l}{l_1}. \tag{q}$$

For values of α_2 larger than that given by (p), the quantity $2(u_1 + u_2)$ will be larger than $\pi l/l_1$ and at the same time it must be smaller than 2π, as was explained before. Hence the limits for the root of Eq. (f) are

$$\frac{\pi l}{l_1} < 2(u_1 + u_2) < 2\pi. \tag{r}$$

By using (q) and (r), Eq. (f) can be solved by the trial-and-error method for any particular value of α_2.

As another problem of stability of a bar on elastic supports, let us consider a continuous beam of constant cross section simply supported at the ends on rigid supports and having several equally spaced intermediate elastic supports of equal rigidity. It is sometimes necessary to select the common rigidity of the intermediate supports so that they will not deflect when the bar buckles, and will, therefore, be equivalent to absolutely rigid supports.[1] We have already discussed the case of one intermediate support and obtained Eq. (*n*) for determining the value of α_2 at which the support behaves as though it were absolutely rigid.

The same problem can be solved with little difficulty in the general case of any number of intermediate supports by using Eqs. (39). Take a continuous beam with two intermediate supports each having a spring constant of α (Fig. 72*b*). Equations (39) for three equal spans, each of length $l/3$, are

$$-\frac{\sin \dfrac{2kl}{3}}{Pk \sin kl}R_3 \sin \frac{kl}{3} + \frac{2}{3P}R_3\frac{l}{3} - \frac{\sin \dfrac{kl}{3}}{Pk \sin kl}R_2 \sin \frac{kl}{3} + \frac{1}{3P}R_2\frac{l}{3} = \frac{R_3}{\alpha};$$

$$-\frac{\sin \dfrac{kl}{3}}{Pk \sin kl}R_3 \sin \frac{kl}{3} - \frac{\sin \dfrac{kl}{3}}{Pk \sin kl}R_2 \sin \frac{2kl}{3} + \frac{1}{3P}\left(R_3\frac{l}{3} + R_2\frac{2l}{3}\right) = \frac{R_2}{\alpha}.$$

$$(s)$$

If the supports are absolutely rigid, the bar buckles so that there will be inflection points at the supports and each span is in the same condition as a bar with hinged ends of length $l/3$. The critical value of the compressive force is then obtained from the equation

$$\frac{kl}{3} = \pi,$$

from which,

$$P_{cr} = \frac{9\pi^2 EI}{l^2}.$$

Assume now that the supports are elastic and that their rigidity approaches the limiting value at which the supports behave as though they were absolutely rigid. In this case the critical value of the compressive force approaches the value obtained above for absolutely rigid supports, and we can assume

$$\frac{kl}{3} = \pi - \Delta, \qquad (t)$$

where Δ is a small quantity. Substituting (*t*) in Eqs. (*s*) and neglecting small quantities, we finally obtain

$$\frac{l}{9P}R_2 + \left(\frac{2l}{9P} - \frac{1}{\alpha}\right)R_3 = 0;$$
$$\left(\frac{2l}{9P} - \frac{1}{\alpha}\right)R_2 + \frac{l}{9P}R_3 = 0. \qquad (u)$$

[1] This problem was first discussed by J. G. Boobnov, "Theory of Structure of Ships," vol. 1, p. 259, 1913, St. Petersburg. See also the recent paper by W. B. Klemperer and H. B. Gibbons in *Z. angew. Math. Mech.*, vol. 13, p. 251, 1933.

The value of α at which the critical load approaches that for absolutely rigid supports is obtained by equating the determinant of Eqs. (u) to zero. Then

$$\left(\frac{2l}{9P} - \frac{1}{\alpha}\right)^2 - \left(\frac{l}{9P}\right)^2 = 0,$$

from which,

$$\alpha = \frac{3P}{0.333l}, \tag{v}$$

where

$$P = \frac{9\pi^2 EI}{l^2}.$$

We can obtain solution (v) in a different way. Let us consider a system consisting of three equal bars of length $l/3$ (Fig. 71a), hinged at the ends

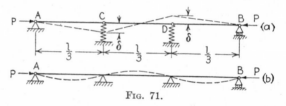

Fig. 71.

A and B to absolutely rigid supports and at C and D to elastic supports of equal rigidity defined by the spring constant α. If an axial compressive force P is applied, the system can buckle as shown in the figure by dashed lines. The critical value of the force P can be readily obtained by using the energy method. The small angle of inclination of the bars AC and BD to the horizontal axis after buckling is $3\delta/l$ and that of the bar CD is $6\delta/l$ where δ denotes the equal deflections of the elastic supports. Owing to this buckling, hinge B moves toward hinge A by the amount

$$\lambda = \frac{l}{3}\left(\frac{3\delta}{l}\right)^2 + \frac{l}{2\cdot3}\left(\frac{6\delta}{l}\right)^2.$$

The work done by the forces P during buckling is

$$P\left[\frac{l}{3}\left(\frac{3\delta}{l}\right)^2 + \frac{l}{2\cdot3}\left(\frac{6\delta}{l}\right)^2\right].$$

The strain energy stored in the elastic supports is $2\dfrac{\delta^2\alpha}{2}$, and the critical value of P is obtained from the equation

$$P\left[\frac{l}{3}\left(\frac{3\delta}{l}\right)^2 + \frac{l}{2\cdot3}\left(\frac{6\delta}{l}\right)^2\right] = \alpha\delta^2,$$

from which

$$\alpha = \frac{9P}{l}.$$

This result coincides with (v) and we can state that the minimum value of α at which the elastic supports behave during buckling as though absolutely rigid is that value at which P_{cr} is the same for the two cases shown in Figs. 71a and 71b.

The variation in the critical load due to an increase in the rigidity of the supports can be handled in the same manner as was explained for one elastic support. The results of such an investigation[1] are shown in Fig. 72a, in which the ratios $P_{cr}:P_e$ are plotted against $\alpha l/P_e$ where $P_e = \pi^2 EI/l^2$. When the rigidity of the supports is small, the deflection curve of the buckled bar has no inflection points (Fig. 72b). The curve AB in Fig. 72a corresponds to this condition. For greater rigidity of the supports an inflection

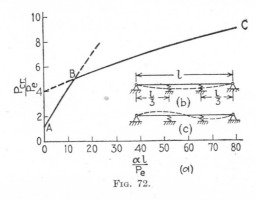

Fig. 72.

point occurs at the middle (Fig. 72c). This condition is represented in Fig. 72a by the curve BC. When α approaches the magnitude given by Eq. (v), the critical load approaches the value $9\pi^2 EI/l^2$ and the points of support become inflection points. A further increase in the rigidity of the supports has no effect on the buckling of the bar.

Proceeding in the same way for m equal spans of length l/m, we obtain for the necessary rigidity of the elastic supports, at which they behave as if absolutely rigid, the expression

$$\alpha = \frac{mP}{\beta l}, \tag{72}$$

in which m is the number of spans, β a numerical factor which depends on the number of spans, and $P = m^2\pi^2 EI/l^2$ is the critical load calculated for one span as for a bar of length l/m with hinged ends. Several values of the the factor β are given in the table below.

TABLE 4.—VALUES OF THE FACTOR β IN EQ. (72)

m	2	3	4	5	6	7	9	11
β	0.500	0.333	0.293	0.276	0.268	0.263	0.258	0.255

[1] See paper by Klemperer and Gibbons, *loc. cit.*, p. 105.

It is seen that β diminishes as the number of spans increases and approaches the value $\beta = 0.250$. This latter value can be obtained by considering one span as an absolutely rigid bar on two elastic supports (Fig. 73). Since each support serves for two consecutive spans, the value $\alpha/2$ should be taken for the spring constant here. Then, denoting with θ the small angle of rotation of the bar and applying the energy Eq. (64), we obtain

FIG. 73.

$$P\frac{l}{2m}\theta^2 = \frac{\alpha}{2}\left(\frac{l\theta}{2m}\right)^2,$$

from which

$$\alpha = \frac{mP}{\frac{1}{4}l}. \qquad (w)$$

21. Buckling of a Bar on an Elastic Foundation.—If there

are many equally spaced elastic supports of equal rigidity, their action on the buckled bar (Fig. 74), under certain conditions (see p. 112), can be replaced by the action of a continuous elastic medium, the reaction of which, at each cross section of the bar, is proportional to the deflection at that cross section. If α is the spring constant of the individual supports and a is the distance between them, the rigidity of the equivalent elastic medium is expressed by the quantity

$$\beta = \frac{\alpha}{a}. \qquad (a)$$

It is called the *modulus of foundation* and has the dimension of a force divided by the square of a length.

FIG. 74.

It represents the magnitude of the reaction of the foundation per unit length of the bar if the deflection is equal to unity.

In calculating the critical value of the compressive force, the energy method[1] will be most useful in this case. The general expression for the deflection curve of a bar with hinged ends can be represented by the series

---

[1] See author's paper in *Bull. Polytech. Inst., St. Petersburg*, 1907. Another method of solving the problem is given by H. Zimmermann, *Zentr. Bauver-waltung*, 1906. The case in which a bar is elastically supported along only a portion of its length has been discussed by Hjalmar Granholm, "On the Elastic Stability of Piles Surrounded by a Supporting Medium," Stockholm, 1929.

$$y = a_1 \sin \frac{\pi x}{l} + a_2 \sin \frac{2\pi x}{l} + a_3 \sin \frac{3\pi x}{l} + \cdots. \qquad (b)$$

The strain energy of bending of the bar is [Eq. (41), p. 24]

$$\Delta V_1 = \frac{EI}{2} \int_0^l \left(\frac{d^2 y}{dx^2}\right)^2 dx = \frac{\pi^4 EI}{4l^3} \sum_{n=1}^{n=\infty} n^4 a^2{}_n. \qquad (c)$$

In calculating the strain energy of the elastic medium, we note that the lateral reaction on an element dx of the bar is $\beta y \, dx$ and that the corresponding energy is $\frac{\beta y^2}{2} \, dx$. Then the total energy of deformation of the elastic medium is

$$\Delta V_2 = \frac{\beta}{2} \int_0^l y^2 \, dx$$

or, substituting series (b) for y,

$$\Delta V_2 = \frac{\beta l}{4} \sum_{n=1}^{n=\infty} a^2{}_n. \qquad (d)$$

The work done by the compressive forces P, from Eq. (44), is

$$\Delta T = \frac{P\pi^2}{4l} \sum_{n=1}^{n=\infty} n^2 a^2{}_n. \qquad (e)$$

Substituting (c), (d) and (e) in Eq. (64), we obtain

$$\frac{\pi^4 EI}{4l^3} \sum_{n=1}^{n=\infty} n^4 a^2{}_n + \frac{\beta l}{4} \sum_{n=1}^{n=\infty} a^2{}_n = \frac{P\pi^2}{4l} \sum_{n=1}^{n=\infty} n^2 a^2{}_n, \qquad (f)$$

from which

$$P = \frac{\pi^2 EI}{l^2} \frac{\displaystyle\sum_{n=1}^{n=\infty} n^4 a^2{}_n + \frac{\beta l^4}{\pi^4 EI} \sum_{n=1}^{n=\infty} a^2{}_n}{\displaystyle\sum_{n=1}^{n=\infty} n^2 a^2{}_n}. \qquad (73)$$

To determine the critical value of the load P, it is necessary to find such a relation between the coefficients a_1, a_2, . . . of series (b) as to make expression (73) a minimum. This result is obtained by making all coefficients, except one, equal to zero (see p. 83), which indicates that the deflection curve of the bar is a simple sine curve. If a_m is the coefficient, different from zero, we obtain

$$y = a_m \sin \frac{m\pi x}{l} \tag{g}$$

and

$$P = \frac{\pi^2 EI}{l^2}\left(m^2 + \frac{\beta l^4}{m^2\pi^4 EI}\right). \tag{74}$$

The number of half-waves m in which the bar subdivides at buckling will now be determined from the condition that expression (74) should be a minimum. When β is zero, there is no resisting elastic medium and m must be taken equal to 1. This is the familiar case of buckling of a bar with hinged ends. If β is very small we must again take $m = 1$ in expression (74). Thus, for a very flexible elastic medium, the bar buckles without inflection points. By gradually increasing β we finally arrive at a condition where expression (74) is smaller for $m = 2$ than for $m = 1$. This indicates that at such rigidity of the elastic medium the buckled bar will have an inflection point at the middle. The limiting value of the modulus β at which the transition from $m = 1$ to $m = 2$ occurs is found from the condition that at this limiting value of β expression (74) should give the same value for P independently of whether $m = 1$ or $m = 2$. Thus we obtain

$$1 + \frac{\beta l^4}{\pi^4 EI} = 4 + \frac{\beta l^4}{4\pi^4 EI},$$

from which

$$\frac{\beta l^4}{\pi^4 EI} = 4. \tag{h}$$

For values of β smaller than that given by Eq. (h), the deflection curve of the buckled bar has no inflection point. For β somewhat larger than that given by (h), there will be an inflection point at the middle and the bar will be subdivided into two half-waves.

By increasing β we can get conditions in which the number of half-waves is 3, 4, . . . and so on. To get the value of β at which the number of half-waves changes from m to $m + 1$, we proceed as above for one and two half-waves. In this way we obtain the equation

$$m^2 + \frac{\beta l^4}{m^2 \pi^4 EI} = (m + 1)^2 + \frac{\beta l^4}{(m + 1)^2 \pi^4 EI},$$

from which

$$\frac{\beta l^4}{\pi^4 EI} = m^2(m + 1)^2. \qquad (75)$$

For given dimensions of the bar and for a given value of β, this equation can be used for determining m, the number of half-waves. Substituting m in Eq. (74), the value of the critical load is obtained. It is seen that in all cases formula (74) can be represented in the form

$$P_{cr} = \frac{\pi^2 EI}{L^2}, \qquad (76)$$

where, for the actual length l of the bar, a reduced length L is substituted. A series of values of L/l, calculated from Eqs. (74) and (75), are given in Table 5 for various values of $\beta l^4/(16EI)$.

TABLE 5.—RATIOS OF L/l FOR A BAR IN AN ELASTIC MEDIUM[1]

$\beta l^4/(16EI)$	0	1	3	5	10	15	20	30	40	50	75	100
L/l	1	0.927	0.819	0.741	0.615	0.537	0.483	0.437	0.421	0.406	0.376	0.351

$\beta l^4/(16EI)$	200	300	500	700	1,000	1,500	2,000	3,000	4,000	5,000	8,000	10,000
L/l	0.286	0.263	0.235	0.214	0.195	0.179	0.165	0.149	0.140	0.132	0.117	0.110

As β increases, the number of half-waves also increases. Then, neglecting 1 in comparison with m, Eq. (75) becomes

$$\frac{\beta l^4}{\pi^4 EI} = m^4 \qquad \text{or} \qquad \frac{l}{m} = \sqrt[4]{\frac{\pi^4 EI}{\beta}}. \qquad (77)$$

Substituting this value of m in formula (74), we obtain

$$P_{cr} = \frac{2\pi^2 EI m^2}{l^2}. \qquad (78)$$

Thus the critical value of the compressive force is twice that for a hinged bar having the length l/m equal to the length of one half-wave. The length of half-waves is determined from Eq. (77). An example of a long bar elastically supported is found, for instance,

[1] Note that the table is calculated for values of $\beta l^4/(16EI)$ rather than for $\beta l^4/(\pi^4 EI)$.

in the case of welded rails. At high temperatures considerable compressive stress may be produced in such rails; since free lateral buckling is prevented by the pavement of the street, buckling of the rails in a wavy line may occur if lateral resistance is not sufficient.

In the above discussion a continuous distribution of lateral reactions was assumed. A satisfactory solution is also obtained from the above formulas in the case of isolated elastic supports, provided the proportions of the bar and the lateral rigidity of the supports are such that not less than three supports correspond to one half-wave of the buckled bar. If there are fewer than three supports per half-wave length, the critical value of the load should be calculated as explained in the preceding article.

Fig. 75.

22. Buckling of a Bar under the Action of Several Compressive Forces.—In practical design we sometimes encounter the case of a bar compressed by forces applied not only at the ends but also at some intermediate cross section. A simple example of this kind is shown[1] in Fig. 75, in which a bar with hinged ends is compressed by forces applied at the ends and also by a force P_2 applied at an intermediate cross section C. If the compressive forces exceed their critical value, the bar buckles as shown by the dashed line in Fig. 75. Let δ be the deflection at C; then the lateral reactions Q at the supports become

$$Q = \frac{\delta P_2}{l}.$$

Assuming, for generality, that the upper and lower parts of the bar have two different cross-sectional moments of inertia I_1 and I_2, the differential equations of the deflection curve for the two portions of the bar are

$$\left.\begin{aligned}
EI_1 \frac{d^2y_1}{dx^2} &= -P_1y_1 - Q(l-x) = -P_1y_1 - \frac{\delta P_2}{l}(l-x); \\
EI_2 \frac{d^2y_2}{dx^2} &= -P_1y_2 - Q(l-x) + P_2(\delta - y_2) = -P_1y_2 - \\
&\qquad \frac{\delta P_2}{l}(l-x) + P_2(\delta - y_2).
\end{aligned}\right\} \quad (a)$$

[1] This problem has been discussed by F. S. Jasinsky, *loc. cit.*, p. 100.

Using the following notations:

$$\frac{P_1}{EI_1} = k^2_1; \qquad \frac{P_2}{EI_2} = k^2_2; \qquad \frac{P_1 + P_2}{EI_2} = k^2_3; \qquad \frac{P_2}{EI_1} = k^2_4; \quad (b)$$

the general integrals of Eqs. (a) are

$$y_1 = C_1 \sin k_1 x + C_2 \cos k_1 x - \frac{\delta}{l} \frac{k^2_4}{k^2_1}(l - x), \quad \text{for} \quad l_2 \leqq x \leqq l;$$

$$y_2 = C_3 \sin k_3 x + C_4 \cos k_3 x + \frac{\delta}{l} \frac{k^2_2}{k^2_3} x, \quad \text{for} \quad 0 \leqq x \leqq l_2.$$

The constants of integration $C_1, \ldots, C_4$ are obtained from the following end conditions of the two portions of the buckled bar:

$$(y_1)_{x=l} = 0; \qquad (y_1)_{x=l_2} = \delta; \qquad (y_2)_{x=l_2} = \delta; \qquad (y_2)_{x=0} = 0.$$

From these,

$$C_1 = \frac{\delta(k^2_1 l + k^2_4 l_1)}{k^2_1 l(\sin k_1 l_2 - \tan k_1 l \cos k_1 l_2)}; \qquad C_2 = -C_1 \tan k_1 l;$$

$$C_3 = \frac{\delta(k^2_3 l - k^2_2 l_2)}{k^2_3 l \sin k_3 l_2}; \qquad C_4 = 0.$$

Substituting these in the additional condition

$$\left(\frac{dy_1}{dx}\right)_{x=l_2} = \left(\frac{dy_2}{dx}\right)_{x=l_2},$$

we obtain the following equation for calculating critical loads:

$$\frac{k^2_4}{k^2_1} - \frac{k^2_1 l + k^2_4 l_1}{k_1 \tan k_1 l_1} = \frac{k^2_2}{k^2_3} + \frac{k^2_3 l - k^2_2 l_2}{k_3 \tan k_3 l_2}. \qquad (79)$$

In each particular case, knowing the ratios

$$\frac{P_1 + P_2}{P_1} = m; \qquad \frac{I_2}{I_1} = n; \qquad \frac{l_2}{l_1} = p; \qquad (c)$$

we can find, by trial and error, the smallest value of the load $P_1 + P_2$ at which Eq. (79) is satisfied. This is the critical value of the compressive force. It can always be represented by the formula

$$(P_1 + P_2)_{cr} = \frac{\pi^2 EI_2}{L^2}, \qquad (80)$$

in which L is the *reduced length* of the bar. In the particular case where $l_1 = l_2$, which is commonly encountered in design, the values of L can be obtained from the following table.

TABLE 6.—VALUES OF L/l FOR THE COLUMN SHOWN IN FIG. 75, WITH $l_1 = l_2$

m	1.00	1.25	1.50	1.75	2.00	3.00	n
1.00	1.00	0.95	0.91	0.89	0.87	0.82	1.00
1.25	1.06	1.005	0.97	0.94	0.915	....	1.25
n { 1.50	1.12	1.06	1.02	0.99	0.96	....	1.50
1.75	1.18	1.11	1.07	0.99	1.04	....	1.75
2.00	1.24	1.16	1.12	1.08	1.05	....	2.00

The above method of calculating critical values of compressive loads can be used also where axial forces are applied at several intermediate cross sections. The differential equation for each portion of the deflection curve between any two consecutive forces can be easily set up, but the amount of calculation necessary to obtain the final criterion for determining critical loads, analogous to Eq. (79), increases rapidly with the increase in the number of intermediate loads. It is advantageous in such cases to use one of the approximate methods.

Applying the energy method to the above example (Fig. 75), and assuming as a first approximation that the deflection curve is a sine curve,

$$y = \delta \sin \frac{\pi x}{l},$$

the bending moments for the two portions of the curve are

$$M_1 = P_1 y + \frac{\delta P_2}{l}(l - x);$$

$$M_2 = (P_1 + P_2)y - \frac{\delta P_2 x}{l}.$$

Substituting in the expression for the strain energy of bending, we obtain, for $l_1 = l_2 = l/2$,

$$\Delta V = \int_{\frac{l}{2}}^{l} \frac{M^2_1 \, dx}{2EI_1} + \int_0^{\frac{l}{2}} \frac{M^2_2 \, dx}{2EI_2} = \frac{\delta^2}{2EI_1}\left(P^2{}_1 \frac{l}{4} + P^2{}_2 \frac{l}{24} + P_1 P_2 \frac{2l}{\pi^2}\right) +$$

$$\frac{\delta^2}{2EI_2}\left[(P_1 + P_2)^2 \frac{l}{4} + P^2{}_2 \frac{l}{24} - P_2(P_1 + P_2)\frac{2l}{\pi^2}\right]. \quad (d)$$

The work done by the forces P_1 and P_2 during buckling is

$$\Delta T = \frac{P_1}{2}\int_0^l \left(\frac{dy}{dx}\right)^2 dx + \frac{P_2}{2}\int_0^{\frac{l}{2}} \left(\frac{dy}{dx}\right)^2 dx = \frac{\delta^2 \pi^2}{4l}\left(P_1 + \frac{1}{2}P_2\right). \quad (e)$$

Substituting (d) and (e) in Eq. (64) (see p. 78) and using notations (c), we obtain

$$(P_1 + P_2)_{cr} = \frac{(\pi^2 E I_2/l^2)(m+1)}{m + \dfrac{m}{6}\left(\dfrac{m-1}{m}\right)^2 - \dfrac{8}{\pi^2}(m-1) + n\left[\dfrac{1}{m} + \dfrac{m}{6}\left(\dfrac{m-1}{m}\right)^2 + \dfrac{8}{\pi^2}\dfrac{m-1}{m}\right]}. \quad (81)$$

Substituting in this formula various values for m and n and comparing the results with those given in the table (see p. 114), we find that in all cases the formula gives errors less than 1 per cent, which accuracy is sufficient for all practical purposes.

23. Buckling of Prismatical Bars under the Action of Distributed Axial Loads.

—If longitudinal compressive forces are continuously distributed along a bar, the differential equation of the deflection curve of the buckled bar is no longer a simple equation with constant coefficients and its solution usually requires the application of infinite series or recourse to one of the approximate methods, as, for instance, the energy method. Both of these methods will now be illustrated in discussing the buckling of a prismatical bar under the action of its own weight[1] (Fig. 76). The lower end of the bar is assumed vertically built in and the upper end free. If, under the action of uniformly distributed weight, the bar buckles as shown by the dotted line, the differential equation of the deflection curve is

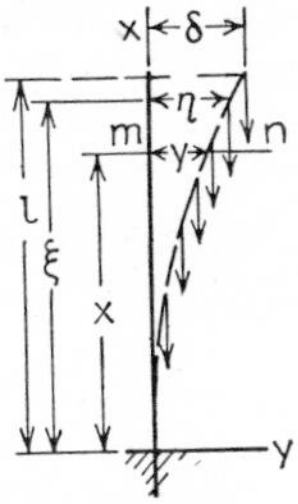

Fig. 76.

$$EI\frac{d^2y}{dx^2} = \int_x^l q(\eta - y)d\xi, \quad (a)$$

where the integral on the right side of the equation represents the bending moment at any cross section mn produced by a

---

[1] This problem was discussed first by Euler, but he did not succeed in obtaining a satisfactory solution. See J. Todhunter and K. Pearson, "History of Elasticity," vol. 1, pp. 39–50. The problem was finally solved by A. G. Greenhill, *Proc. Cambridge Phil. Soc.*, vol. 4, 1881. In his paper Greenhill indicates a variety of problems of buckling which can be solved by using Bessel's functions. Independently, the same problem was discussed in a very complete manner by F. S. Jasinsky, *loc. cit.*, p. 100. See also J. Dondorff, "Die Knickfestigkeit des geraden Stabes mit veränderlichem Querschnitt und veränderlichem Druck, ohne und mit Querstützen," Dissertation, Düsseldorf, 1907, and N. Grishcoff, *Bull. acad. sci.*, Kiev, 1930.

uniformly distributed load of intensity q. Differentiating Eq. (*a*) with respect to x, we obtain the equation

$$EI\frac{d^3y}{dx^3} = -q(l-x)\frac{dy}{dx},\tag{b}$$

in which the right side represents the shearing force at any cross section mn of the bar. To simplify the discussion, let us introduce, instead of x, a new independent variable z by taking

$$z = \frac{2}{3}\sqrt{\frac{q}{EI}(l-x)^3}.\tag{c}$$

Then, by differentiation, we obtain:

$$\left.\begin{aligned}
\frac{dy}{dx} &= -\frac{dy}{dz}\sqrt[3]{\frac{3}{2}\frac{qz}{EI}}; \qquad \frac{d^2y}{dx^2} = \left(\frac{3}{2}\frac{q}{EI}\right)^{\frac{2}{3}}\left(\frac{1}{3}z^{-\frac{1}{3}}\frac{dy}{dz} + z^{\frac{2}{3}}\frac{d^2y}{dz^2}\right); \\
\frac{d^3y}{dx^3} &= \frac{3}{2}\frac{q}{EI}\left(\frac{1}{9}z^{-1}\frac{dy}{dz} - \frac{d^2y}{dz^2} - z\frac{d^3y}{dz^3}\right).
\end{aligned}\right\}\tag{d}$$

Substituting in Eq. (*b*) and letting $dy/dz = u$, we obtain

$$\frac{d^2u}{dz^2} + \frac{1}{z}\frac{du}{dz} + \left(1 - \frac{1}{9z^2}\right)u = 0.\tag{e}$$

This is an equation the integral of which can be represented by Bessel's functions. We shall evaluate these functions[1] by taking the solution of the equation in the form of an infinite series:

$$u = a_1 z^{m_1} + a_2 z^{m_2} + a_3 z^{m_3} + \cdots .$$

Substituting this series in Eq. (*e*), we find that, in order to satisfy this equation, there must exist between the exponents $m_1, m_2, m_3, \ldots$ the relations

$$m_2 = m_1 + 2, \qquad m_3 = m_2 + 2, \cdots .$$

and between the coefficients $a_1, a_2, \ldots$ the relation

$$a_n = -\frac{a_{n-1}}{m^2{}_n - \frac{1}{9}}.$$

The exponent m_1 is determined from the equation

$$m^2{}_1 - \tfrac{1}{9} = 0,$$

from which,

$$m_1 = \pm\tfrac{1}{3}.$$

[1] A variety of problems of this kind can be found in Forsyth, "Treatise on Differential Equations."

In accordance with these two solutions for m_1, we obtain two series satisfying Eq. (*e*), and the general solution of this equation is

$$u = C_1 z^{-\frac{1}{3}}\left(1 - \frac{3z^2}{2 \cdot 4} + \frac{3^2 z^4}{2 \cdot 4 \cdot 4 \cdot 10} - \cdots\right) +$$
$$C_2 z^{\frac{1}{3}}\left(1 - \frac{3z^2}{2 \cdot 8} + \frac{3^2 z^4}{2 \cdot 8 \cdot 4 \cdot 14} - \cdots\right). \quad (f)$$

C_1 and C_2 are constants of integration and the series, multiplied by some constant factors, represent Bessel's functions of the orders $-\frac{1}{3}$ and $+\frac{1}{3}$. The constants C_1 and C_2 must now be determined to satisfy the conditions at the ends of the bar.

Since the upper end of the bar is free,

$$\left(\frac{d^2y}{dx^2}\right)_{x=l} = 0,$$

or, by using Eqs. (*c*) and (*d*),

$$(z)_{x=l} = 0; \qquad \left(\frac{1}{3}z^{-\frac{1}{3}}\frac{dy}{dz} + z^{\frac{2}{3}}\frac{d^2y}{dz^2}\right)_{z=0} = 0. \quad (g)$$

When z approaches zero, we retain in solution (*f*) only the first term in each series. Then for small values of z we obtain

$$u = \frac{dy}{dz} = C_1 z^{-\frac{1}{3}} + C_2 z^{\frac{1}{3}}$$

and

$$\frac{du}{dz} = \frac{d^2y}{dz^2} = -\frac{1}{3}C_1 z^{-\frac{4}{3}} + \frac{1}{3}C_2 z^{-\frac{2}{3}}.$$

Substituting in (*g*), we conclude that C_2 must be taken equal to zero. Then, from (*f*),

$$u = \frac{dy}{dz} = -z^{-\frac{1}{3}}\sqrt[3]{\frac{2EI}{3q}}\frac{dy}{dx} =$$
$$C_1 z^{-\frac{1}{3}}\left(1 - \frac{3z^2}{2 \cdot 4} + \frac{3^2 z^4}{2 \cdot 4 \cdot 4 \cdot 10} - \cdots\right). \quad (h)$$

At the lower end of the bar ($x = 0$), the conditions are:

$$(y)_{x=0} = 0; \qquad \left(\frac{dy}{dx}\right)_{x=0} = 0.$$

Hence, from (*c*) and (*d*),

$$u = \frac{dy}{dz} = 0 \qquad \text{when} \qquad z = \frac{2}{3}\sqrt{\frac{ql^3}{EI}}.$$

Substituting this value of z in expression (h), we obtain the following transcendental equation for determining the critical value of the weight ql of the bar, at which buckling begins:

$$\left(\frac{2}{3}\sqrt{\frac{ql^3}{EI}}\right)^{-\frac{1}{3}}\left[1 - \frac{3}{2\cdot4}\left(\frac{4}{9}\frac{ql^3}{EI}\right) + \right.$$

$$\left. \frac{3^2}{2\cdot4\cdot4\cdot10}\left(\frac{4}{9}\frac{ql^3}{EI}\right)^2 - \cdots \right] = 0. \quad (82)$$

By a trial-and-error method it can be shown that the smallest value of the weight ql of the bar at which the above equation is satisfied[1] is

$$(ql)_{cr} = \frac{7.83EI}{l^2} = \frac{\pi^2EI}{(1.122l)^2}. \quad (83)$$

This is the critical value of the uniform load for the bar shown in Fig. (76).

By using the same method, the case of the combined action of a uniform compressive load ql and a compressive force P applied at the ends can be studied. If the conditions at the ends are like those shown in Fig. 76 and if the uniformly distributed load q is absent, the critical value of the load P applied at the top is

$$P_{cr} = \frac{\pi^2EI}{4l^2}.$$

The uniform load ql reduces the critical value of the load P and we can put

$$P_{cr} = \frac{mEI}{l^2}, \quad (84)$$

where the factor m, smaller than $\pi^2/4$, gradually diminishes when the load ql increases, and approaches zero when ql approaches the value given by Eq. (83). Using the notation

$$n = ql \div \frac{\pi^2EI}{4l^2},$$

the values of the coefficient m in Eq. (84) for various values of n can be computed and are given in Table 7.[2]

[1] We can get the solution very easily by using the tables of Bessel's functions of the order $-\frac{1}{3}$. Such tables were calculated by A. N. Dinnik, *Bull. Don Polytech. Inst.*, 1925. See also "Tafeln der Besselschen Funktionen von der gebrochenen Ordnung" by A. N. Dinnik, published by the Ukrainian Academy of Science, Kiev, 1933.

[2] See paper by N. Grishcoff, *loc. cit.*, p. 115.

TABLE 7.—VALUES OF m IN EQ. (84)

n	0	0.25	0.50	0.75	1.0	2.0	3.0	3.18	4.0	5.0	10.0
m	$\pi^2/4$	2.28	2.08	1.91	1.72	0.96	0.15	0	-0.69	-1.56	-6.95

It may be seen from this table that in calculating the effect of ql on the magnitude of P_{cr} we get a satisfactory approximation by assuming that the effect of the uniform load ql is equivalent to a load $0.3ql$ applied at the top of the bar. When the uniform load is larger than that given by Eq. (83), P_{cr} becomes negative; in such cases a tensile force P must be applied in order to prevent the bar from buckling.

In calculating the critical value of the distributed compressive loads, the energy method can also be used to advantage. In the case represented in Fig. 76, for instance, we can take as a first approximation for the deflection curve

$$y = \delta\left(1 - \cos\frac{\pi x}{2l}\right). \tag{i}$$

This is the true curve for the case where buckling occurs under the action of a compressive load applied at the end (see p. 65). In the case of a uniformly distributed axial load, the true curve is more complicated, as was shown in the previous discussion; nevertheless, the curve (i) satisfies the actual end conditions and can be taken as a suitable curve in an approximate calculation. The bending moment at any cross section mn (Fig. 76) is

$$M = \int_x^l q(\eta - y)d\xi. \tag{j}$$

Substituting Eq. (i) for y in this expression and putting

$$\eta = \delta\left(1 - \cos\frac{\pi\xi}{2l}\right),$$

we obtain

$$M = \delta q\left[(l - x)\cos\frac{\pi x}{2l} - \frac{2l}{\pi}\left(1 - \sin\frac{\pi x}{2l}\right)\right].$$

Substituting this in the expression for the strain energy of bending, we obtain

$$\Delta V = \int_0^l \frac{M^2\,dx}{2EI} = \frac{\delta^2 q^2 l^3}{2EI}\left(\frac{1}{6} + \frac{9}{\pi^2} - \frac{32}{\pi^3}\right). \tag{k}$$

In calculating the work done by the distributed axial load during lateral buckling, we note that, owing to the inclination of an element ds of the deflection curve at the cross section mn (Fig. 76), the upper part of the load undergoes a downward displacement equal to

$$ds - dx \approx \frac{1}{2}\left(\frac{dy}{dx}\right)^2 dx,$$

and the corresponding work done by this load is

$$\frac{1}{2}q(l - x)\left(\frac{dy}{dx}\right)^2 dx.$$

Therefore, the total work produced by the load during buckling, by using Eq. (i), is

$$\Delta T = \frac{1}{2}q\int_0^l (l - x)\left(\frac{dy}{dx}\right)^2 dx = \frac{\pi^2 \delta^2 q}{8}\left(\frac{1}{4} - \frac{1}{\pi^2}\right). \qquad (l)$$

Substituting (k) and (l) in Eq. (64), we obtain as a first approximation for the critical value of the weight

$$(ql)_{cr} = \frac{7.89EI}{l^2}. \qquad (m)$$

Comparing this with formula (83), obtained by integration of the differential equation (a), it is seen that the error of the first approximation is less than 1 per cent. Thus it is accurate enough for any practical application.

A better approximation can be obtained, if necessary, by taking for y an expression with several parameters and then adjusting them so as to make $(ql)_{cr}$ a minimum. To illustrate this method, let us assume, for instance,

$$y = \delta_1\left(1 - \cos\frac{\pi x}{2l}\right) + \delta_2\left(1 - \cos\frac{3\pi x}{2l}\right). \qquad (n)$$

This equation satisfies the conditions at the ends of the bar and contains two parameters δ_1 and δ_2. Substituting in expression (j) for bending moment, we obtain

$$M = q\delta_1\left[(l - x)\cos\frac{\pi x}{2l} - \frac{2l}{\pi}\left(1 - \sin\frac{\pi x}{2l}\right)\right] +$$
$$q\delta_2\left[(l - x)\cos\frac{3\pi x}{2l} + \frac{2l}{3\pi}\left(1 + \sin\frac{3\pi x}{2l}\right)\right].$$

Substituting this in expression (k) for strain energy of bending and performing integration, we find that

$$\Delta V = \frac{q^2 l^3}{2EI}(\delta^2{}_1\alpha + 2\delta_1\delta_2\beta + \delta^2{}_2\gamma), \tag{o}$$

in which

$$\alpha = \frac{1}{6} + \frac{9}{\pi^2} - \frac{32}{\pi^3} = 0.04650; \qquad \beta = \frac{32}{9\pi^3} - \frac{1}{12\pi^2} = 0.10622;$$
$$\gamma = \frac{1}{6} + \frac{1}{\pi^2} + \frac{32}{27\pi^3} = 0.30621. \tag{p}$$

Substituting the new expression for y in expression (l) for the work done by the weight of the bar during buckling, we obtain

$$\Delta T = \frac{q\pi^2}{8}(\delta^2{}_1\alpha' + 2\delta_1\delta_2\beta' + \delta^2{}_2\gamma'), \tag{q}$$

where

$$\alpha' = \frac{1}{4} - \frac{1}{\pi^2} = 0.14868; \qquad \beta' = \frac{3}{\pi^2} = 0.30396;$$
$$\gamma' = \frac{9}{4} - \frac{1}{\pi^2} = 2.14868.$$

Substituting (o) and (q) in Eq. (64), we obtain

$$(ql)_{cr} = \frac{\pi^2 EI}{4l^2} \frac{\delta^2{}_1\alpha' + 2\delta_1\delta_2\beta' + \delta^2{}_2\gamma'}{\delta^2{}_1\alpha + 2\delta_1\delta_2\beta + \delta^2{}_2\gamma}. \tag{r}$$

The conditions for $(ql)_{cr}$ to be a minimum are:

$$\frac{\pi^2 EI}{4l^2}\frac{\partial}{\partial\delta_1}(\delta^2{}_1\alpha' + 2\delta_1\delta_2\beta' + \delta^2{}_2\gamma') - (ql)_{cr}\frac{\partial}{\partial\delta_1}(\delta^2{}_1\alpha + 2\delta_1\delta_2\beta + \delta^2{}_2\gamma) = 0;$$
$$\frac{\pi^2 EI}{4l^2}\frac{\partial}{\partial\delta_2}(\delta^2{}_1\alpha' + 2\delta_1\delta_2\beta' + \delta^2{}_2\gamma') - (ql)_{cr}\frac{\partial}{\partial\delta_2}(\delta^2{}_1\alpha + 2\delta_1\delta_2\beta + \delta^2{}_2\gamma) = 0.$$

After differentiation we obtain

$$\delta_1\left[\frac{\pi^2 EI}{2l^2}\alpha' - 2(ql)_{cr}\alpha\right] + \delta_2\left[\frac{\pi^2 EI}{2l^2}\beta' - 2(ql)_{cr}\beta\right] = 0;$$
$$\delta_1\left[\frac{\pi^2 EI}{2l^2}\beta' - 2(ql)_{cr}\beta\right] + \delta_2\left[\frac{\pi^2 EI}{2l^2}\gamma' - 2(ql)_{cr}\gamma\right] = 0.$$

The possibility of buckling occurs when these equations give for δ_1 and δ_2 solutions different from zero. This requires that the determinant of these equations must be equal to zero, $i.e.,$

$$\left[\frac{\pi^2 EI}{2l^2}\alpha' - 2(ql)_{cr}\alpha\right]\left[\frac{\pi^2 EI}{2l^2}\gamma' - 2(ql)_{cr}\gamma\right] - \left[\frac{\pi^2 EI}{2l^2}\beta' - 2(ql)_{cr}\beta\right]^2 = 0$$

or

$$4(ql)^2{}_{cr}(\alpha\gamma - \beta^2) - 2(ql)_{cr}\frac{\pi^2 EI}{2l^2}(\alpha\gamma' + \alpha'\gamma - 2\beta\beta') +$$
$$(\alpha'\gamma' - \beta'^2)\left(\frac{\pi^2 EI}{2l^2}\right)^2 = 0.$$

Solving this quadratic equation for $(ql)_{cr}$ and substituting for $\alpha, \ldots, \gamma'$ their numerical values, we obtain

$$(ql)_{cr} = \frac{7.84EI}{l^2}.$$

This value practically coincides with that given in (83).

By using the energy method we can consider also a vertical bar hinged at the ends and submitted to the action of its own weight ql in addition to compressive forces P applied at the ends (Fig. 77). The critical values of P can be represented by the equation

$$P_{cr} = \frac{mEI}{l^2}, \tag{85}$$

in which the numerical factor m depends on the value of the ratio

$$n = ql \div \frac{\pi^2EI}{l^2}.$$

Several values of the factor m are given in Table 8.

TABLE 8.—VALUES OF m IN EQ. (85)

n	0	0.25	0.50	0.75	1.0	2.0	3.0
m	π^2	8.63	7.36	6.08	4.77	$-.657$	-4.94

It is seen, from this table, that a satisfactory approximation for the critical load P is obtained by assuming that one-half of the weight ql of the bar is applied at the top, *i.e.*, by taking

FIG. 77.

$$P_{cr} = \frac{\pi^2EI}{l^2} - \frac{ql}{2}.$$

When n is 2 or larger, P_{cr} is negative, which indicates that in such cases tensile forces P should be applied at the ends to prevent the bar from lateral buckling.

The energy method can be applied advantageously in various cases of distributed compressive loads acting on a bar. In this way the integration of equations with variable coefficients, requiring the use of infinite series, is replaced by the simple problem of finding the minimum of a certain expression, such as the right side of Eq. (r) above. By increasing the number of terms in the expression for the deflection curve, as in Eq. (n) above, the accuracy of the solution can be increased, although the first approximation is usually sufficiently accurate for practical applications. Later, we shall apply this method to a discussion of the stability of the upper chord of a low-truss bridge.

24. Stability of the Upper Chord of a Low-truss Bridge.—In a low-truss bridge (sometimes called a pony truss), there is no bracing in the upper horizontal plane (Fig. 78) and the upper chord is in the condition of a compressed bar, the lateral buckling of which is resisted by the elastic reactions of the vertical and diagonal members. At the supports there are usually frames of considerable rigidity so that the ends of the chord may be considered as immovable in a lateral direction. Thus the upper chord may be considered as a bar with hinged ends compressed by forces distributed along its length and elastically supported at intermediate points. A general method of solving problems of this kind is discussed in Art. 20.

However, the amount of work necessary to obtain the critical value of the compressive force increases rapidly with the number of elastic supports.[1] The stability of the compressed chord can be increased by increasing the rigidity of the lateral supports. For a constant cross section of the chord and a constant compressive force, the minimum rigidity, at which the

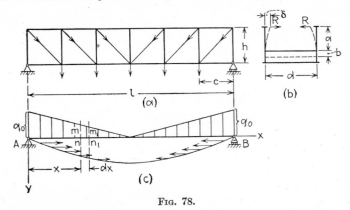

Fig. 78.

supports begin to behave as though they were absolutely rigid, is found from Eq. (72) of Art. 20 (see p. 107). If the proportions of the compressed chord and verticals of the bridge (Fig. 78) are such that the half-wave length of the buckled chord is large in comparison with one panel length of the bridge (say the half-wave length is not less than three panels), a great simplification of the problem can be obtained by replacing the elastic supports by an equivalent elastic foundation (see Art. 20) and replacing the concentrated compressive forces, applied at the joints, by a continuously distributed load. Assuming that the bridge is uniformly loaded, the compressive forces transmitted to the chord by the diagonals are proportional to the distances from the middle of the span, and the equivalent compressive load distribution is as shown in Fig. 78c by the shaded areas.

In calculating the modulus β of the elastic foundation, equivalent to the elastic resistance of the verticals,[2] it is necessary to establish the relation between the force R, applied at the top of a vertical (Fig. 78b) and the deflection that would be produced if the upper chord were removed. If

---

[1] Several numerical examples of calculations of the stability of a compressed chord as a bar on elastic supports can be found in the book by H. Müller-Breslau, "Graphische Statik," vol. 2, part 2, p. 336. See also a paper by A. Ostenfeld, *Beton und Eisen*, vol. 15, 1916.

[2] Since the diagonals are tension members, their rigidity is small in comparison with that of the struts and can be neglected.

only bending of the vertical is taken into account, then

$$\delta = \frac{Ra^3}{3EI_1},$$

where I_1 is the moment of inertia of one vertical. Taking into account the bending of the floor beam, and using notations indicated in the figure, we obtain

$$\delta = \frac{Ra^3}{3EI_1} + \frac{R(a+b)^2 d}{2EI_2},$$

where I_2 is the moment of inertia of the cross section of the floor beam. The force necessary to produce the deflection δ equal to unity is then

$$R_0 = \frac{1}{\dfrac{a^3}{3EI_1} + \dfrac{(a+b)^2 d}{2EI_2}}$$

and the modulus of the equivalent elastic foundation is

$$\beta = \frac{R_0}{c}$$

where c is the distance between verticals.

In this manner the problem of the stability of the compressed chord of the bridge is reduced to one of buckling of a bar with hinged ends, supported laterally by a continuous elastic medium and axially loaded by a continuous load, the intensity of which is proportional to the distance from the middle.[1]   The problem can be solved by taking the differential equation of the deflection curve of the buckled bar and integrating it by the use of infinite series as was explained in the previous article.   The same result can be obtained more easily by using the energy method.   The deflection curve of the buckled bar in the case of hinged ends can be represented by the series

$$y = a_1 \sin \frac{\pi x}{l} + a_2 \sin \frac{2\pi x}{l} + a_3 \sin \frac{3\pi x}{l} + \cdots . \qquad (a)$$

Assuming that the cross section of the bar is constant along its length, and denoting by β the modulus of elastic foundation, which is also considered as constant, the strain energy of bending of the bar,[2] together with the

---

[1] In this form the problem of the stability of low-truss bridges was first discussed by F. S. Jasinsky, *loc. cit.*, p. 100.   See also French translation. Some corrections of Jasinsky's results have been discussed by the writer by using the energy method, *loc. cit.*, p. 82.

[2] In applying the energy method, more accuracy in the approximate solution can be obtained by using for the strain energy of bending the expression $\int M^2 \, dx/2EI$ instead of $(EI/2)\int (d^2y/dx^2)^2 dx$ (see p. 81).   This is especially true in the case when only the first approximation is calculated. In the present problem, however, several consecutive approximations will be calculated.   The simple expression (b) for strain energy possesses certain advantages in making these calculations.

strain energy of the foundation, is (see Art. 20)

$$\Delta V = \frac{\pi^4 EI}{4l^3} \sum_{n=1}^{n=\infty} n^4 a^2{}_n + \frac{\beta l}{4} \sum_{n=1}^{n=\infty} a^2{}_n. \tag{b}$$

In calculating the work produced by the distributed compressive load during bending, we note that the intensity of this load at any cross section, distance x from the left support (Fig. 78c), is

$$q = q_0\left(1 - \frac{2x}{l}\right), \tag{c}$$

where q_0 is the intensity of load at the ends. For a truss with parallel chords and a large number of panels, it can be concluded from elementary statics that we can assume for the maximum intensity of the axial load (Fig. 78c)

$$q_0 = \frac{Q}{2h},$$

where Q is the total load on one truss and h the depth of the truss. Considering an element of the upper chord between the two consecutive cross sections mn and m_1n_1, the axial load to the right of the cross section mn will be displaced toward the immovable support A, owing to the small inclination of this element during buckling, by the amount $\frac{1}{2}(dy/dx)^2 dx$ and will produce the work

$$-\frac{1}{2}\left(\frac{dy}{dx}\right)^2 dx \int_x^l q_0\left(1 - \frac{2x}{l}\right)dx = \frac{q_0}{2l}x(l - x)\left(\frac{dy}{dx}\right)^2 dx.$$

The total work produced by the compressive load during bending is

$$\Delta T = \frac{q_0}{2l}\int_0^l x(l - x)\left(\frac{dy}{dx}\right)^2 dx.$$

Substituting in this expression the series (a) for y and using the formulas:

$$\int_0^l x \cos^2\frac{m\pi x}{l}\,dx = \frac{l^2}{4}; \qquad \int_0^l x^2 \cos^2\frac{m\pi x}{l}\,dx = \frac{l^3}{6} + \frac{l^3}{4m^2\pi^2};$$

$$\int_0^l x \cos\frac{n\pi x}{l} \cos\frac{m\pi x}{l}\,dx = 0, \qquad \text{when } m + n \text{ is an even number;}$$

$$\int_0^l x \cos\frac{n\pi x}{l} \cos\frac{m\pi x}{l}\,dx = -\frac{2l^2}{\pi^2}\frac{m^2 + n^2}{(m^2 - n^2)^2}, \text{ when } m + n \text{ is an odd number;}$$

$$\int_0^l x^2 \cos\frac{n\pi x}{l} \cos\frac{m\pi x}{l}\,dx = \frac{2l^3}{\pi^2}\frac{m^2 + n^2}{(m^2 - n^2)^2}\,(-1)^{m+n};$$

we finally obtain

$$\Delta T = \frac{q_0}{2}\left[\sum_{n=1}^{\infty} a^2{}_n\left(\frac{n^2\pi^2}{12} - \frac{1}{4}\right) - 4\sum_n\sum_m a_n a_m \frac{nm(m^2 + n^2)}{(m^2 - n^2)^2}\right], \tag{d}$$

where the double series in the parenthesis contains only terms in which the sum $(m + n)$ is even and m is not equal to n. Substituting (b) and (d) in

Eq. (64), we obtain for the maximum compressive force at the middle the following expression:

$$\frac{q_0 l}{4} = \frac{\dfrac{\pi^4 EI}{8l^2}\displaystyle\sum_{n=1}^{\infty} n^4 a_n^2 + \dfrac{\beta l^2}{8}\displaystyle\sum_{n=1}^{\infty} a_n^2}{\displaystyle\sum_{n=1}^{\infty} a_n^2\left(\dfrac{n^2\pi^2}{12} - \dfrac{1}{4}\right) - 4\displaystyle\sum_n\sum_m a_n a_m \dfrac{nm(m^2+n^2)}{(m^2-n^2)^2}}. \qquad (e)$$

Now, the problem is to find such relations between the coefficients $a_1, a_2, a_3, \ldots$ as to make expression (e) a minimum. Proceeding as in the previous article and setting equal to zero the derivatives of this expression with respect to $a_1, a_2, \ldots$, we finally arrive at a system of homogeneous linear equations in $a_1, a_2, \ldots$ of the following type:

$$\left[(n^4 + \gamma)\pi^2 - 2\alpha\left(\frac{n^2\pi^2}{3} - 1\right)\right]a_n + 16\alpha\sum_m a_m\frac{nm(m^2+n^2)}{(m^2-n^2)^2} = 0, \qquad (f)$$

in which, for simplification, the following notations are used:

$$\alpha = \frac{q_0 l}{4} \div \frac{\pi^2 EI}{l^2}, \qquad \gamma = \frac{\beta l^4}{\pi^4 EI}. \qquad (g)$$

The summation in the second term of Eq. (f) is extended over all values of m different from n such that $(m + n)$ is an even number. Thus, Eq. (f) can be subdivided into two groups, one containing the coefficients a_m with all values of m taken odd and the second with all values of m taken even.

The equations of the first group are:

$$\left[(1 + \gamma)\pi^2 - 2\alpha\left(\frac{\pi^2}{3} - 1\right)\right]a_1 + \alpha\left(\frac{15}{2}a_3 + \frac{65}{18}a_5 + \frac{175}{72}a_7 + \cdots\right) = 0;$$

$$\frac{15}{2}\alpha a_1 + [(3^4 + \gamma)\pi^2 - 2\alpha(3\pi^2 - 1)]a_3 + \alpha\left(\frac{255}{8}a_5 + \frac{609}{50}a_7 + \cdots\right) = 0;$$

$$\frac{65}{18}\alpha a_1 + \frac{255}{8}\alpha a_3 + \left[(5^4 + \gamma)\pi^2 - 2\alpha\left(\frac{25}{3}\pi^2 - 1\right)\right]a_5 + \alpha\left(\frac{1{,}295}{18}a_7 + \cdots\right)$$
$$= 0;$$

$$\frac{175}{72}\alpha a_1 + \frac{609}{50}\alpha a_3 + \frac{1{,}295}{18}\alpha a_5 + \left[(7^4 + \gamma)\pi^2 - 2\alpha\left(\frac{49}{3}\pi^2 - 1\right)\right]a_7 + \cdots$$
$$= 0;$$
$$\cdots \cdots \cdots \cdots \cdots \cdots \cdots \cdots \cdots \cdots \cdots (h)$$

The equations of the second group are:

$$\left[(2^4 + \gamma)\pi^2 - 2\alpha\left(\frac{4}{3}\pi^2 - 1\right)\right]a_2 + \alpha\left(\frac{160}{9}a_4 + \frac{15}{2}a_6 + \cdots\right) = 0;$$

$$\frac{160}{9}\alpha a_2 + \left[(4^4 + \gamma)\pi^2 - 2\alpha\left(\frac{16}{3}\pi^2 - 1\right)\right]a_4 + \alpha\left(\frac{1{,}248}{25}a_6 + \cdots\right) = 0; \quad (i)$$

$$\frac{15}{2}\alpha a_2 + \frac{1{,}248}{25}\alpha a_4 + \left[(6^4 + \gamma)\pi^2 - 2\alpha\left(\frac{36}{3}\pi^2 - 1\right)\right]a_6 + \cdots = 0;$$

Buckling of the chord becomes possible when one of the above two systems of equations gives for coefficients a_m a solution different from zero, *i.e.*, when the determinant of system (h) or of system (i) becomes equal to zero. The system (h) corresponds to a symmetrical shape of the buckled bar. The system (i) corresponds to an unsymmetrical shape of the buckled bar.

Let us begin with the case where the rigidity of the elastic medium is very small. In this case the deflection curve of the buckled bar has only one half-wave (see Art. 20) and is symmetrical with respect to the middle. Equations (h) should be used. The first approximation is obtained by taking only the first term in the series (a) and putting $a_3 = a_5 = \cdots = 0$. Then, the first equation of (h) will give for a_1 a solution different from zero only if

$$(1 + \gamma)\pi^2 - 2\alpha\left(\frac{\pi^2}{3} - 1\right) = 0,$$

from which

$$\alpha = \frac{\pi^2(1 + \gamma)}{2(\frac{1}{3}\pi^2 - 1)}.$$

Using notations (g), we finally obtain

$$\left(\frac{q_0 l}{4}\right)_{cr} = \frac{\pi^2 EI}{l^2}\frac{\pi^2(1 + \gamma)}{2(\frac{1}{3}\pi^2 - 1)}. \tag{j}$$

If there is no lateral elastic resistance and if the bar is compressed by axial load distributed as shown in Fig. 78c, the quantity γ in Eq. (j) becomes zero [see notations (g)] and we obtain

$$\left(\frac{q_0 l}{4}\right)_{cr} = 2.15\frac{\pi^2 EI}{l^2}. \tag{k}$$

Thus the critical load is more than twice as large as in the case where the bar is compressed by the loads applied at the ends.

To get a better approximation for the critical compressive force, we take the two terms in expression (a), with coefficients a_1 and a_3. The corresponding two equations, from system (h), are

$$\left[(1 + \gamma)\pi^2 - 2\alpha\left(\frac{\pi^2}{3} - 1\right)\right]a_1 + \frac{15}{2}\alpha a_3 = 0;$$

$$\frac{15}{2}\alpha a_1 + [(3^4 + \gamma)\pi^2 - 2\alpha(3\pi^2 - 1)]a_3 = 0.$$

Taking γ equal to zero and equating to zero the determinant of the above two equations, we obtain

$$\left[\pi^2 - 2\alpha\left(\frac{\pi^2}{3} - 1\right)\right]\left[81\pi^2 - 2\alpha(3\pi^2 - 1)\right] - \left(\frac{15}{2}\right)^2\alpha^2 = 0.$$

Solving this equation for α, we obtain

$$\alpha = 2.06; \qquad \left(\frac{q_0 l}{4}\right)_{cr} = 2.06\frac{\pi^2 EI}{l^2}. \tag{l}$$

By using three terms of the series (a) with the coefficients a_1, a_3 and a_5 and the three equations of system (h), a third approximation can be calculated. Such calculations show that the error of the second approximation, given by Eq. (l), is less than 1 per cent so that further approximations are of no practical importance and we can put

$$\left(\frac{q_0 l}{4}\right)_{cr} = 2.06\frac{\pi^2 EI}{l^2} = \frac{\pi^2 EI}{(0.696l)^2}.$$

Thus the reduced length in this case is

$$L = 0.696l.$$

In a similar manner the critical load may be calculated for a chord with small lateral elastic reactions ($\gamma < 3$). Where a greater restraint is supplied by the vertical members of the truss, the buckled form of the chord may have two half-waves and we obtain an inflection point at the middle of the bar. To calculate the critical load in such a case, the system (i) should be used. With a further increase of γ, the buckled bar has three half-waves, and we must again turn to the system of equations (h) in calculating the critical value of the compressive load. In all these cases the critical load can be represented by the equation

$$\left(\frac{q_0 l}{4}\right)_{cr} = \frac{\pi^2 EI}{L^2}, \tag{86}$$

in which the reduced length L depends on the rigidity of the elastic foundation. Several values of the ratio L/l are given in the following table:

TABLE 9.—TABLE FOR CALCULATING THE REDUCED LENGTH L

$\beta l^4/16EI$	0	5	10	15	22.8	56.5	100	162.8	200	300	500	1,000
L/l	0.696	0.524	0.443	0.396	0.363	0.324	0.290	0.259	0.246	0.225	0.204	0.174

It is seen from the table that, when the rigidity of the elastic foundation increases, the ratio L/l approaches the values obtained before for a uniformly compressed bar (see table on p. 111).

The method developed above for the case of a bar of uniform cross section supported by an elastic medium of a uniform rigidity along the length of the bar can be extended to include cases of chords of variable cross section and cases where the rigidities of the elastic supports vary along the length.[1]

25. Buckling of Bars of Variable Cross Section.—An examination of the bending-moment diagram for a buckled bar indicates that a bar of uniform cross section is not the most economical

[1] Several applications of the energy method in design of through bridges are given in the paper by S. Kasarnowsky and D. Zetterholm, *Der Bauingenieur,* vol. 8, p. 760, 1927. See also papers by A. Hrennikoff and by K. Kriso in *Publications of the International Association for Bridge and Structural Engineering,* vol. 3, 1935.

form to carry compressive loads. It is evident, for instance, in the case of a bar with hinged ends, compressed by two axial forces, that the stability can be increased by removing a portion of the material from the ends and increasing the cross section over the middle portion. Thus we arrive at the problem of the stability of a compressed bar of variable cross section. In metallic structures such bars are very often used. The cross section usu-ally changes by steps, since the increase in section is accomplished by riveting or welding additional plates or angles along certain por-tions of the column. A simple case of such a column was discussed in Art. 22. Another example is shown in Fig. 79a. To determine the criti-cal value of the load P in this case, it

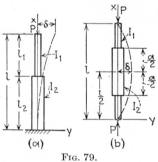

Fig. 79.

is necessary to write the differential equation of the deflection curve separately for each portion of the column. If I_1 and I_2 are the moments of inertia of the cross sections for the thinner and thicker portions of the column, respectively, these equations are:

$$\left.\begin{array}{l} EI_1 \dfrac{d^2y_1}{dx^2} = P(\delta - y_1); \\[2mm] EI_2 \dfrac{d^2y_2}{dx^2} = P(\delta - y_2). \end{array}\right\} \tag{a}$$

Using the notations,

$$\frac{P}{EI_1} = k^2{}_1, \qquad \frac{P}{EI_2} = k^2{}_2,$$

and taking into account the conditions at the built-in end of the column, the solutions of Eqs. (a) are:

$$y_1 = \delta + C \cos k_1 x + D \sin k_1 x;$$
$$y_2 = \delta(1 - \cos k_2 x).$$

The constants of integration C and D are obtained from the conditions that at the top of the column the deflection is δ and that at $x = l_2$ the deflection is the same for both portions. Hence,

$$\delta + C \cos k_1 l + D \sin k_1 l = \delta;$$
$$\delta + C \cos k_1 l_2 + D \sin k_1 l_2 = \delta(1 - \cos k_2 l_2);$$

from which

$$C = -D \tan k_1 l; \qquad D = \frac{\delta \cos k_2 l_2 \cos k_1 l^{\natural}}{\sin k_1 l_1}.$$

Since the two portions of the deflection curve have the same tangent at $x = l_2$, we obtain the equation

$$\delta k_2 \sin k_2 l_2 = -C k_1 \sin k_1 l_2 + D k_1 \cos k_1 l_2.$$

Substituting for C and D the above values, we finally obtain the transcendental equation

$$\tan k_1 l_1 \tan k_2 l_2 = \frac{k_1}{k_2} \qquad (b)$$

for calculating the critical load. Knowing the ratios I_1/I_2 and l_1/l_2, the solution of this equation can be found in each particular case by a trial-and-error method.

By the substitution of $a/2$ for l_2 and $l/2$ for l, the results obtained from Eq. (b) can be applied also for a column with hinged ends and symmetrical with respect to the middle cross section (Fig. 79b). The critical value of the load in this case can be represented by the formula

$$P_{cr} = \frac{mEI_2}{l^2}, \qquad (87)$$

in which m is a numerical factor depending on the ratios a/l and I_1/I_2. Several values of this factor, calculated from Eq. (b), are given below in Table 10.

TABLE 10.—VALUES OF THE FACTOR m IN EQ. (87)

I_1/I_2 ＼ a/l	0.2	0.4	0.6	0.8
0.01	0.15	0.27	0.60	2.26
0.1	1.47	2.40	4.50	8.59
0.2	2.80	4.22	6.69	9.33
0.4	5.09	6.68	8.51	9.67
0.6	6.98	8.19	9.24	9.78
0.8	8.55	9.18	9.63	9.84

The same method can be used also if the number of steps in which the cross section of the bar changes is greater than that considered above. Naturally, with an increase in the number of steps, the derivation of the equation for calculating the critical load and the solution of this equation become more complicated,[1] so that it seems advisable to have recourse to one of the approximate methods.

Considering again the case represented in Fig. 79a, and using the energy method, we can take as a first approximation for the deflection curve

$$y = \delta\left(1 - \cos\frac{\pi x}{2l}\right). \tag{c}$$

Proceeding as before, we find the following expressions for the strain energy of bending and for the work done by the compressive forces P during buckling:

$$\Delta V = \int_0^{l_2}\frac{M^2\,dx}{2EI_2} + \int_{l_2}^{l}\frac{M^2\,dx}{2EI_1} = \frac{P^2\delta^2}{2EI_2}\left(\int_0^{l_2}\cos^2\frac{\pi x}{2l}\,dx + \right.$$
$$\left.\frac{I_2}{I_1}\int_{l_2}^{l}\cos^2\frac{\pi x}{2l}\,dx\right) = \frac{P^2\delta^2}{2EI_2}\left[\frac{l_2}{2} + \frac{I_2}{I_1}\frac{l_1}{2} + \frac{l}{2\pi}\left(1 - \frac{I_2}{I_1}\right)\sin\frac{\pi l_2}{l}\right]; \tag{d}$$

$$\Delta T = \frac{P}{2}\int_0^{l}\left(\frac{dy}{dx}\right)^2 dx = \frac{\pi^2 P\delta^2}{16l}. \tag{e}$$

Substituting (d) and (e) in Eq. (64) gives

$$P_{cr} = \frac{\pi^2 EI_2}{4l^2}\frac{1}{\dfrac{l_2}{l} + \dfrac{l_1}{l}\dfrac{I_2}{I_1} - \dfrac{1}{\pi}\left(\dfrac{I_2}{I_1} - 1\right)\sin\dfrac{\pi l_2}{l}}. \tag{88}$$

For a bar with hinged ends (Fig. 79b), by substituting $a/2$ for l_2 and $l/2$ for l, Eq. (88) becomes

$$P_{cr} = \frac{\pi^2 EI_2}{l^2}\frac{1}{\dfrac{a}{l} + \dfrac{l-a}{l}\dfrac{I_2}{I_1} - \dfrac{1}{\pi}\left(\dfrac{I_2}{I_1} - 1\right)\sin\dfrac{\pi a}{l}}. \tag{89}$$

Comparison of the results obtained from Eq. (89) with values of m from Table 10 (p. 130) shows that this approximate solution gives very satisfactory results if the ratio I_2/I_1 is not very large. Taking, for instance, $I_1/I_2 = 0.4$ and $a/l = 0.2$ and 0.6, we obtain as values of m, from Eq. (89), 5.14 and 8.61, respectively, instead of the numbers 5.09 and 8.51, as given in Table 10, which is sufficiently accurate for all practical purposes.[2]

In Art. 16 a graphical method of obtaining critical loads was described. This method will now be illustrated (Fig. 80) using a column whose critical load has just been obtained, i.e., a column with $I_1/I_2 = 0.4$ and $a/l = 0.6$.

---

[1] Several examples of this type of problem have been discussed by A. Franke, *Z. Math. Physik*, vol. 49, 1901. See also writer's paper in *Bull. Polytech. Inst., Kiev*, 1908.

[2] Solution of several examples of this kind can be found in the book by E. Elwitz, "Die Lehre von der Knickfestigkeit." vol. 1, p. 222, Düsseldorf, 1918.

Since it is symmetrical with respect to the center G, only half of the construction is given.

A portion of a sine curve $ABCDEF$ was selected as the trial deflection curve. The bending-moment diagram for any compressive force P is the area $AB \ldots FGA$ with ordinates multiplied by P. The load for the fictitious beam, according to the area-moment method of finding deflections, is the bending-moment diagram divided by EI. Therefore, the area $ACHJGA$ with ordinates multiplied by P/EI_1 is this load when the bending-moment ordinates on the middle portion of the column have been reduced by the ratio I_1/I_2.

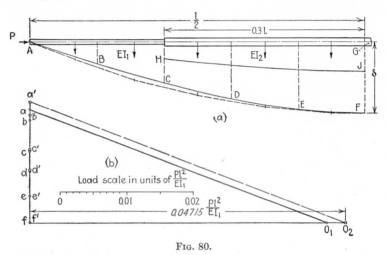

Fig. 80.

This load is divided into a number of sections as shown by the dotted lines. Each section is replaced by an equal load acting at its centroid as indicated by the arrows. These loads are plotted on the load diagram $abcdef$ (Fig. 80b).

O_1 is the position of the pole of the force polygon for which the corresponding funicular polygon passes through A and horizontally through F. The curve tangent to this latter polygon is the deflection curve for the assumed bending-moment diagram. Since the two curves do not check very closely, the new curve is used for a second trial. The new load diagram is $a'b'c'd'e'f'$ and the new pole is found to be O_2. Its corresponding funicular polygon is found practically to coincide with the one previously drawn, showing that the second trial curve was very close to the actual curve of buckling.

To find the value of P necessary to keep the column in this deflected position, the deflections at the center are equated. The assumed deflection was δ; the deflection obtained by construction is the product of the pole distance of the ray polygon, $O_2f = 0.04715\dfrac{Pl^2}{EI_1}$, and the ordinate in the equilibrium polygon, δ. Then

$$0.04715\frac{Pl^2}{EI_1}\delta = \delta$$

and

$$P_{cr} = 21.2\frac{EI_1}{l^2} = 8.48\frac{EI_2}{l^2}.$$

Thus, the value of m in Eq. (89) is found to be 8.48 instead of 8.51 as given in Table 10.

In this problem a sine curve was used for the first trial curve although it can easily be seen that, since it is the true curve of buckling for a uniform bar (see Art. 12), it will not have sufficient curvature along the portion AC of the curve. Had the sine curves been deliberately altered to give more curvature along this portion, a satisfactory value for P_{cr} would have been obtained with only one approximation. For example, a parabola was used as a trial curve from which the first pole distance was found to be

$$O_1f = 0.0472\frac{Pl^2}{EI_1}.$$

From this the critical load is

$$P_{cr} = 8.48\frac{EI_2}{l^2}.$$

Thus the accuracy of this first approximation is equal to that of the second for the solution just outlined. The fact that the two curves checked very closely (when starting with a parabola) indicated that a second trial was unnecessary.

In structures, such as airplanes, where the question of weight is of primary importance, struts of continuously changing cross section are sometimes used. The differential equation of the deflection curve for such cases has been derived by Euler, who applied it in the discussion of buckling of columns of such forms as the truncated cone or pyramid.[1] The problem of the stability of bars limited by a surface of revolution of the second degree has been discussed by Lagrange.[2]

A case of great practical importance, in which the moment of inertia of the cross section varies along the axis of the bar according to an exponential law, has been discussed in a very complete

[1] A German translation of this work can be found in Ostwald's "Klassiker der exakten Wissenschaften," no. 175, Leipzig, 1910.

[2] Lagrange, Sur la figure des colonnes, "Miscellanea Taurinensia," vol. 5, which embraces the years 1770–1773. Reprinted in "Oeuvres de Lagrange," vol. 2, pp. 125–170, Gautier-Villars, Paris, 1868. This memoir is discussed in "History of Elasticity" by J. Todhunter and K. Pearson, vol. I, pp. 61–67. A variety of problems of this kind has been discussed in recent times by A. N. Dinnik, *Phil. Mag.*, vol. 10, p. 785, 1930.

manner by A. N. Dinnik.[1] Let us consider a bar, with the
lower end built in and the upper end free, and assume that the
moment of inertia of the cross section varies as a certain power

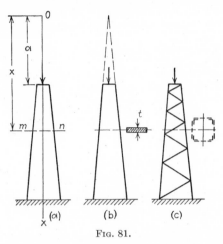

Fig. 81.

of the distance from the fixed point O (Fig. 81a) so that the
moment of inertia of any cross section mn is

$$I_x = I_1\left(\frac{x}{a}\right)^n, \tag{f}$$

where I_1 is the moment of inertia at the top of the bar.

By taking various values for n, we obtain various shapes of
the column. Assuming that $n = 1$ in Eq. (f), we obtain the
case of a column in the form of a plate of constant thickness t
(Fig. 81b) and of varying width.

The assumption $n = 2$ represents, with sufficient accuracy,
the case of a built-up column consisting of four angles connected
by diagonals (Fig. 81c). In this case the cross-sectional area
of the column remains constant and the moment of inertia is

---

[1] A. N. Dinnik, "Iswestia Gornogo Instituta," Ekaterinoslàv, 1914, and
"Westnik Ingenerow," Moscow, 1916. The principal results of these
papers have been translated in English. See *A.S.M.E.*, Applied Mechanics
Division, 1928 and 1932. Independently the same problem was discussed
by A. Ono, "Memoirs of the College of Engineering," Fukuoka, Japan,
vol. 1, 1919. See also L. Bairstow and E. W. Stedman, *Engineering*,
London, vol. 98, p. 403, 1914. Arthur Morley, *Engineering*, London, vol.
97, p. 566, 1914, and vol. 104, p. 295, 1917.

approximately proportional to the square of the distance of the centroids of the angles from the axes of symmetry of the cross section.

By taking $n = 4$ we obtain such cases as a solid truncated cone or a pyramid.

In discussing the deflection curve of the buckled bar, we shall take the coordinate axes as shown in Fig. 82. Then the differential equation of the curve will be

$$EI_1\left(\frac{x}{a}\right)^n \frac{d^2y}{dx^2} = -Py. \qquad (g)$$

This equation, in general, can be solved by means of Bessel's functions.[1] In the particular case of $n = 2$, however, the solution can be obtained in a very simple manner. Denoting by I_1 and I_2 the moments

Fig. 82.

of inertia of the top and bottom cross sections, respectively, and putting

$$I_1 = Aa^2, \qquad I_2 = A(l + a)^2,$$

and

$$\frac{I_1}{I_2} = \left(\frac{a}{l+a}\right)^2 = \alpha^4,$$

where A and α are certain constants depending on the proportions of the column, Eq. (g) becomes

$$AEx^2 \frac{d^2y}{dx^2} = -Py, \qquad (h)$$

which can be reduced to an equation with constant coefficients. Assuming that $P/AE > \frac{1}{4}$ and using the notation

$$\beta = +\sqrt{\frac{P}{AE} - \frac{1}{4}}, \qquad (i)$$

the general solution of this equation can be put in the following form:

$$y = \sqrt{x}\left[C_1 \sin\left(\beta \log_e \frac{x}{a}\right) + C_2 \cos\left(\beta \log_e \frac{x}{a}\right)\right]. \qquad (j)$$

From the condition at the upper end $(y)_{x=a} = 0$, it can be concluded that the constant C_2 must equal zero. At the lower end

[1] See Forsyth, "Treatise on Differential Equations," 4th ed., p. 196.

the tangent to the deflection curve is vertical. Hence

$$\left(\frac{dy}{dx}\right)_{x=a+l} = 0.$$

Substituting expression (j) for y and using the previous notation $\dfrac{a}{a+l} = \alpha^2$, we finally obtain the following transcendental equation for the calculation of the critical value of the compressive load:

$$\tan (2\beta \log_e \alpha) - 2\beta = 0. \qquad (k)$$

Knowing α from the proportions of the column, the smallest root of Eq. (k) can be obtained in each particular case by a trial-and-error method; then, from Eq. (i), the value of the critical load is obtained. This value can be represented in general by the formula

$$P_{cr} = \frac{mEI_2}{l^2}. \qquad (90)$$

Several values of the factor m are given below in Table **11**.

TABLE 11.—VALUES OF THE FACTOR m IN EQ. (90) FOR $n = 2$

I_1/I_2	0	0.1	0.2	0.3	0.4	0.5	0.6	0.7	0.8	0.9	1.0
m	0.250	1.350	1.593	1.763	1.904	2.023	2.128	2.223	2.311	2.392	2.467

When the ratio I_1/I_2 approaches unity, the factor m approaches the value $\pi^2/4$.

In the case of a solid conical bar, we must put $n = 4$ in Eq. (g). Calculations show that we can again use Eq. (90), but the values of the factor m in this case should be taken from Table **12**.

TABLE 12.—VALUES OF THE FACTOR m IN EQ. (90) FOR $n = 4$

I_1/I_2	0.1	0.2	0.3	0.4	0.5	0.6	0.7	0.8	0.9	1.0
m	1.202	1.505	1.710	1.870	2.002	2.116	2.217	2.308	2.391	2.467

By substituting $l/2$ for l in Eq. (90) we obtain the critical load for a bar with hinged ends symmetrical with respect to the middle cross section (Fig. 83a).

A more general case is obtained by combining the solution of Eq. (*g*) with that of the differential equation for a prismatical bar. In this way we can obtain the critical load for a bar with hinged ends, as shown in Fig. 83*b*, the middle portion of which is prismatical. The end portions may be of various shapes, corresponding to various values of the exponent *n* in Eq. (*f*). The critical load again can be represented by Eq. (90). Values of the factor *m* are given for this case in Table 13.[1]

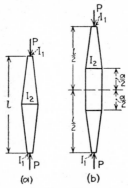

FIG. 83.

By taking various values for the ratios I_1/I_2 and a/l and various values of the number *n*, a variety of cases of practical importance can be solved by using this table.

TABLE 13.—VALUES OF THE FACTOR *m* IN EQ. (90) FOR THE BAR IN FIG. 83*b*

I_1/I_2	n	$a/l =$				
		0	0.2	0.4	0.6	0.8
0.1	1	6.48	7.58	8.63	9.46	9.82
	2	5.40	6.67	8.08	9.25	9.79
	3	5.01	6.32	7.84	9.14	9.77
	4	4.81	6.11	7.68	9.08	9.77
0.2	1	7.01	7.99	8.91	9.63	9.82
	2	6.37	7.49	8.61	9.44	9.81
	3	6.14	7.31	8.49	9.39	9.81
	4	6.02	7.20	8.42	9.38	9.80
0.4	1	7.87	8.59	9.19	9.70	9.84
	2	7.61	8.42	9.15	9.63	9.84
	3	7.52	8.38	9.12	9.62	9.84
	4	7.48	8.33	9.10	9.62	9.84
0.6	1	8.61	9.12	9.55	9.76	9.85
	2	8.51	9.04	9.48	9.74	9.85
	3	8.50	9.02	9.46	9.74	9.85
	4	8.47	9.01	9.45	9.74	9.85
0.8	1	9.27	9.54	9.69	9.83	9.86
	2	9.24	9.50	9.69	9.82	9.86
	3	9.23	9.50	9.69	9.81	9.86
	4	9.23	9.49	9.69	9.81	9.86

[1] This table has been calculated by A. N. Dinnik, *loc. cit.*, p. 134.

It is sometimes of practical interest to find the shape of a solid column such that its weight, for a given value of the critical load, will be a minimum.   Lagrange was the first to undertake the solution of this problem.[1] He stated it in the following form: to find the curve which, by its revolution about an axis in its plane, determines the column of greatest efficiency.   His conclusion was that the most efficient column is a column of a constant circular cross section.   A further investigation of the same problem was made by Clausen.[2] He leaves the form of the cross sections undetermined, and assumes only that they are similar and similarly placed.   The result of his investigation was that the most efficient column has a volume $\sqrt{3}/2$ times the volume of the cylindrical column of the same strength.   A. Ono[3] also arrived at approximately the same result by using various values of the exponent n in Eq. (g).

If a column of variable cross section is submitted to the action of a distributed axial load, the differential equation of the deflection curve of the

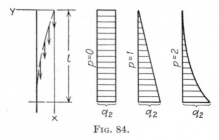

Fig. 84.

buckled column can always be integrated by using Bessel's functions provided the flexural rigidity and the intensity of the distributed load can be represented by the equations

$$EI = EI_2 \left(\frac{x}{l}\right)^n; \Big\}$$
$$q = q_2 \left(\frac{x}{l}\right)^p; \Big\} \qquad (l)$$

where I_2 and q_2 are the moment of inertia and the intensity of the load at the lower built-in end of the column (see Fig. 84).   The critical value of the compressive force will always be given by the equation

[1] *Loc. cit.*, p. 133.

[2] *Bull. phys.-math. acad.*, St. Petersburg, vol. 9, pp. 368–379, 1851.   See also E. L. Nicolai, *Bull. Polytech. Inst., St. Petersburg*, vol. 8, p. 255, 1907, and H. Blasius, *Z. Math. Physik*, vol. 62, pp. 182–197, 1914.

[3] *Loc. cit.*, p. 134.

$$P_{cr} = \int_0^l q_2 \left(\frac{x}{l}\right)^p dx = \frac{mEI}{l^2}. \tag{91}$$

Several values of the factor m for various values of n and p in Eqs. (l) are given in Table 14.[1]

TABLE 14.—VALUES OF THE FACTOR m IN EQ. (91)

n \ p	0	1	2	3	4	5
0	7.84	16.1	27.3	41.3		
1	5.78	13.0	23.1	36.1	52.1	
2	3.67	9.87	18.9	30.9	45.8	63.6
3	....	6.59	14.7	25.7	39.5	

By substituting $l/2$ for l in Eq. (91) we obtain the critical compressive force for a bar with hinged ends, symmetrical and symmetrically loaded, with respect to the middle cross section.

26. The Effect of Shearing Force on the Critical Load.—In the foregoing derivations of formulas for critical loads the usual differential equation of the deflection curve, in which the curvature is taken proportional to the bending moment, was always used. The effect of shearing force on the value of the critical load will now be discussed for the simple case shown in Fig. 85. Taking the positive direction of shearing force as shown in the figure, we find for the magnitude of this force

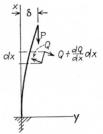

$$Q = P\frac{dy}{dx}. \tag{a}$$

FIG. 85.

The change in slope of the deflection curve produced by this force is nQ/AG, where A is the cross-sectional area, G the modulus in shear and n a numerical factor depending on the shape of the cross section. For a rectangular cross section this factor is $n = 1.2$, for a circular cross section $n = 1.11$. The rate of change of slope produced by the shearing force Q represents the additional curvature due to shear and is equal to

$$\frac{n}{AG}\frac{dQ}{dx} = \frac{nP}{AG}\frac{d^2y}{dx^2}.$$

The total curvature of the deflection curve is obtained by adding to the curvature produced by the bending moment the curvature

[1] This table has been calculated by A. N. Dinnik, *loc. cit.*, p. 134.

produced by the shearing force. Then, for the case in Fig. 85, the differential equation of the deflection curve becomes

$$\frac{d^2y}{dx^2} = \frac{P(\delta - y)}{EI} + \frac{nP}{AG}\frac{d^2y}{dx^2}$$

or

$$\frac{d^2y}{dx^2} = \frac{P}{EI\left(1 - \dfrac{nP}{AG}\right)}(\delta - y). \tag{b}$$

This equation differs from Eq. (a) of Art. 12 (see p. 65) only by the factor $\left(1 - \dfrac{nP}{AG}\right)$ in the denominator on the right side. Proceeding as in Art. 12, we obtain for the critical value of the load P the equation

$$\frac{P}{EI\left(1 - \dfrac{nP}{AG}\right)} = \frac{\pi^2}{4l^2},$$

from which

$$P_{cr} = \frac{P_e}{1 + \dfrac{nP_e}{AG}}. \tag{92}$$

In this expression, $P_e = \pi^2 EI/4l^2$ represents the critical load obtained for this case by Euler. Thus, owing to the action of shearing forces, the critical load is diminished in the ratio[1]

$$\frac{1}{1 + \dfrac{nP_e}{AG}}. \tag{c}$$

It may be seen that in the case of solid columns this ratio differs but very little from unity so that the effect of shearing force can be neglected. But in the case of built-up columns this effect may become of practical importance and should be considered (see Art. 27).

In considering the effect of shearing forces on the critical load, the energy method can also be used. Take, as an example, a bar with hinged ends (Fig. 55). The general expression for the deflection curve is

$$y = a_1 \sin\frac{\pi x}{l} + a_2 \sin\frac{2\pi x}{l} + a_3 \sin\frac{3\pi x}{l} + \cdots.$$

[1] This result was obtained first by F. Engesser, *Zentr. Bauverwaltung*, 1891. See also F. Nussbaum, *Z. Math. Physik*, vol. 55, p. 134, 1907.

Taking into account the strain energy of shear, we find

$$\Delta V = \int_0^l \frac{M^2\,dx}{2EI} + \int_0^l \frac{nQ^2}{2AG}\,dx = \frac{P^2}{2EI}\int_0^l y^2\,dx + \frac{nP^2}{2AG}\int_0^l \left(\frac{dy}{dx}\right)^2\,dx =$$

$$\frac{P^2 l}{4EI}\sum_{m=1}^{m=\infty} a^2{}_m + \frac{n\pi^2 P^2}{4AGl}\sum_{m=1}^{m=\infty} m^2 a^2{}_m. \quad (d)$$

The work done by the forces P during buckling is

$$\Delta T = \frac{\pi^2 P}{4l}\sum_{m=1}^{m=\infty} m^2 a^2{}_m. \quad (e)$$

Substituting in Eq. (64) (see p. 78), we obtain

$$P = \frac{\pi^2 EI}{l^2}\frac{\Sigma m^2 a^2{}_m}{\sum\left(1 + \dfrac{n\pi^2 EI m^2}{AGl^2}\right)a^2{}_m}. \quad (f)$$

The smallest value of P is obtained by taking only the first term in the series of expressions (f). Then

$$P_{cr} = \frac{\pi^2 EI}{l^2}\frac{1}{1 + \dfrac{nP_e}{AG}}, \quad (92')$$

in which

$$P_e = \frac{\pi^2 EI}{l^2}.$$

Thus, owing to shear, the critical load is diminished in the ratio (c). The load P_e in this formula must be taken for a bar with hinged ends.

By using the differential equation of the deflection curve, analogous to Eq. (b), the effect of shear in other cases of buckling of compressed bars can be investigated.

27. Buckling of Latticed Struts.—The critical loads for latticed struts are always less than those for solid columns having the same cross-sectional area and the same slenderness ratio l/r, and depend greatly on the spacing details such as lattice bars, spacing plates and battens. This decrease in the critical stress is due principally to the fact that in the case of latticed struts the shearing force has a much greater effect on deflections than in the case of solid bars. If a latticed strut has many panels, Eqs. (92) and (92'), derived for a solid bar, can be adapted to the calculation of the critical load for a latticed strut.

From the previous article we know that the quantity n/AG is the factor by which we must multiply the shearing force Q to obtain the additional slope of the deflection curve due to the action of the shearing force. In the case of latticed bars, the factor by which the shearing force must be multiplied in calculating the additional slope will be denoted by $1/P_d$. This quantity, in each particular case, can be determined from a consideration of the lateral displacements produced by the shearing force.

Consider first the latticed bar shown in Fig. 86. The displacement due to shear is that due to the lengthening and shortening of the diagonals and battens in each panel (Figs. 86b and

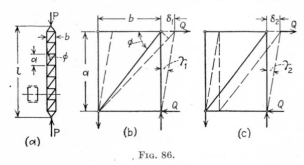

Fig. 86.

86c). The deformations of these elements are neglected when the deflection produced by bending moment alone is considered. Assuming hinges at the joints, the elongation of the diagonal produced by the shearing force Q is (Fig. 86b)

$$\frac{Qa}{A_dE \sin \phi \cos \phi}, \qquad (a)$$

in which ϕ is the angle between the batten and the diagonal, $Q/\cos \phi$ is the tensile force in the diagonal, $a/\sin \phi$ is the length of the diagonal, and A_d is the cross-sectional area of two diagonals, one on each side of the column (Fig. 86a). The corresponding lateral displacement is

$$\delta_1 = \frac{Qa}{A_dE \sin \phi \cos^2 \phi}. \qquad (b)$$

Considering the shortening of the battens (Fig. 86c), the corresponding lateral displacement is

$$\delta_2 = \frac{Qb}{A_bE}, \qquad (c)$$

where b is the length of battens between hinges and A_b is the cross-sectional area of two battens, one on each side of the column.

Adding (b) and (c), the angular displacement produced by the shearing force Q is

$$\gamma = \frac{\delta_1 + \delta_2}{a} = \frac{Q}{A_d E \sin \phi \cos^2 \phi} + \frac{Qb}{aA_b E}. \qquad (d)$$

Defining P_d for a latticed strut in the same manner as for solid bars, *i.e.*, assuming $\gamma = Q/P_d$, we find, from (d),

$$\frac{1}{P_d} = \frac{1}{A_d E \sin \phi \cos^2 \phi} + \frac{b}{aA_b E}. \qquad (e)$$

Substituting this value for n/AG in Eq. (92′), the critical load for a strut with hinged ends (Fig. 86a) is found to be[1]

$$P_{cr} = \frac{\pi^2 EI}{l^2} \frac{1}{1 + \dfrac{\pi^2 EI}{l^2}\left(\dfrac{1}{A_d E \sin \phi \cos^2 \phi} + \dfrac{b}{aA_b E}\right)}. \qquad (93)$$

In this expression I is the moment of inertia of the cross section of the strut, *i.e.*, $I = 2I_c + \dfrac{A_c b^2}{2}$, where A_c is the cross-sectional area of each of the two vertical channels (Fig. 86a) constituting the latticed strut and I_c is the moment of inertia of the cross-sectional area of each channel with respect to its own gravity axis parallel to the axis of bending. It may be seen that, if the cross-sectional areas A_b and A_d are very small in comparison with A_c, the factor in Eq. (93), representing the effect of shearing force, may become considerably smaller than unity. Thus the latticed strut in such cases is considerably weaker than a solid strut with the same value of EI.

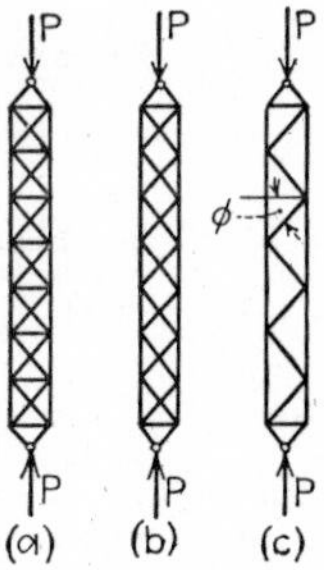

FIG. 87.

An equation similar to Eq. (93) can be obtained also when there are two diagonals in each panel (Fig. 87a). Under the action of shearing force, one diagonal is working in tension and the other in compression. The battens do not take part in the transmission of shearing force and the system is equivalent to that shown in Fig. 87b. The critical load is obtained in this

---

[1] Equation (93) was derived first by F. Engesser, *Zentr. Bauverwaltung,* 1891, p. 483. For a further discussion of the same problem, in connection with the collapse of the Quebec Bridge, see the following papers: F. Engesser, *loc. cit.,* 1907, p. 609, and *Z. Ver. deut. Ing.,* 1908, p. 359; L. Prandtl, *Z. Ver. deut. Ing.,* 1907; and writer's paper in *Bull. Polytech. Inst., Kiev,* 1908.

case by omitting in formula (93) the term containing A_b and doubling the cross-sectional area A_d. Then,

$$P_{cr} = \frac{\pi^2 EI}{l^2} \frac{1}{1 + \frac{\pi^2 EI}{l^2} \frac{1}{A_d E \sin \phi \cos^2 \phi}}, \qquad (94)$$

in which A_d denotes the cross-sectional area of four diagonals, two on each side of the column in the same panel. Equation (94) can be used also in the case of a single system of diagonals

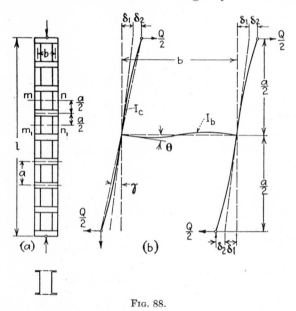

Fig. 88.

(Fig. 87c), A_d being, in such case, the sum of cross-sectional areas of the two diagonals.

In the case of a strut made with battens alone, as in Fig. 88, to obtain the lateral displacement produced by the shearing force Q, it is necessary to consider the deformation of an element of the strut cut out by the sections mn and m_1n_1. Assuming that the deflection curves of the channels have points of inflection at these sections, the bending of the element will be as shown in Fig. 88b. The deflection consists of two parts: (1) the displacement δ_1 due to bending of the batten, and (2) the displacement δ_2 due to bending of the channels. There are couples $Qa/2$ acting at the ends of the batten and the angle of rotation of each end of the batten is

$$\theta = \frac{Qab}{12EI_b},$$

where b is the length of the batten and EI_b is its flexural rigidity. The lateral displacement δ_1 produced by this bending of the batten is

$$\delta_1 = \frac{\theta a}{2} = \frac{Qa^2b}{24EI_b}. \tag{f}$$

The displacement δ_2 can be found, from the usual expression for the deflection of a cantilever beam, to be

$$\delta_2 = \frac{Q}{2}\left(\frac{a}{2}\right)^3 \frac{1}{3EI_c} = \frac{Qa^3}{48EI_c}, \tag{g}$$

in which I_c is moment of inertia of the cross section of a vertical channel. Thus, the total angular displacement produced by the shearing force Q is

$$\gamma = \frac{\delta_1 + \delta_2}{\frac{1}{2}a} = \frac{Qab}{12EI_b} + \frac{Qa^2}{24EI_c}. \tag{h}$$

Then, assuming as before $\gamma = Q/P_d$, we obtain

$$\frac{1}{P_d} = \frac{ab}{12EI_b} + \frac{a^2}{24EI_c}.$$

Substituting $1/P_d$ for n/AG in Eq. (92'), we obtain

$$P_{cr} = \frac{\pi^2 EI}{l^2} \frac{1}{1 + \dfrac{\pi^2 EI}{l^2}\left(\dfrac{ab}{12EI_b} + \dfrac{a^2}{24EI_c}\right)}, \tag{95}$$

in which the factor $\pi^2 EI/l^2$ represents the critical load calculated as for a solid column, i.e., with $I = 2I_c + \dfrac{A_c b^2}{2}$. It may be seen that, when the flexural rigidity of the battens is small, the actual critical load is much lower than that given by Euler's formula.

In calculating angle γ, the shear in the batten is sometimes taken into consideration. From Fig. 88b it may be seen that the shearing force in the batten is

$$\frac{Qa}{b},$$

and the corresponding shearing strain is

$$\frac{nQa}{bA_bG},$$ (i)

where A_b is the cross-sectional area of the two battens and n a numerical factor equal to 1.2 in the case of a rectangular cross section. Adding (i) to expression (h) for angle γ, we obtain, instead of Eq. (95),

$$P_{cr} = \frac{\pi^2 EI}{l^2} \frac{1}{1 + \frac{\pi^2 EI}{l^2}\left(\frac{ab}{12EI_b} + \frac{a^2}{24EI_c} + \frac{na}{bA_bG}\right)}.$$ (96)

If the vertical members (channels) of the built-up column represented in Fig. 88 are very flexible or if the distances between the battens are large, collapse of the column may occur as a result of local buckling of the channels between two consecutive

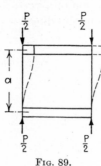

battens. To take this possibility of buckling into account, let us consider an element of the strut which is buckled as shown in Fig. 89. Assuming that the rigidity of the battens is very large, the critical value of the compressive force at which the assumed buckling will occur is

$$P^{\cdot} = \frac{2\pi^2 EI_c}{a^2}.$$ (j)

Fig. 89.

This quantity should now be considered in calculating the deflection δ_2, and Eq. (g) should be taken in the following form:

$$\delta_2 = \frac{Qa^3}{48EI_c} \frac{1}{1 - \alpha},$$ (k)

in which

$$\alpha = P_{cr} : \frac{2\pi^2 EI_c}{a^2}.$$ (l)

The last factor in expression (k) represents the effect of the longitudinal force in a channel on the magnitude of the deflection δ_2 [see Eq. (46), p. 29]. Using expression (k) for δ_2, the critical load P_{cr} for the strut in Fig. 88 becomes

$$P_{cr} = \frac{\pi^2 EI}{l^2} \frac{1}{1 + \frac{\pi^2 EI}{l^2}\left[\frac{ab}{12EI_b} + \frac{a^2}{24EI_c} \frac{1}{(1-\alpha)} + \frac{na}{bA_bG}\right]}.$$ (97)

Since α contains P_{cr} [see Eq. (l)], this equation can be solved only by a trial-and-error method. It may be seen also that the critical load is always less than the value given by Eq. (j). Experiments have been made[1] which show satisfactory agreement with Eq. (97) in all cases in which the number of panels (Fig. 88a) is large, for instance, not less than six.

28. Stability of a System of Elastic Bars.—Several problems dealing with buckling of latticed bars have been discussed in the previous article on the basis of certain assumptions that simplify the problems. To get a more satisfactory solution of these problems, an application of the general theory of stability of a system of elastic bars is necessary.[2] Let us begin with a consideration of trusses which have hinged joints and consider as a first problem the simple case of a system consisting of only two bars (Fig. 90), such that under the action of a vertical load P the vertical bar of the system is compressed and there is no force in the inclined bar.

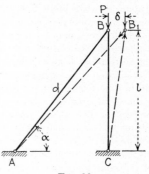

Fig. 90.

Assuming that the vertical bar is absolutely rigid and taking into account only the elasticity of the inclined bar, the critical value of the compressive force P can be easily obtained by using the energy method (see p. 77). However, we can get the solution in another way by assuming that under the action of the vertical load the system may have a form of equilibrium as indicated by the dashed lines and by determining the magnitude of the load necessary to keep the system in equilibrium in such a displaced position. If δ is a small displacement of joint B, the tensile force, produced in the inclined bar, is $A_d E\delta \cos \alpha/d$, where d is the length of the inclined bar, α its angle of inclination and A_d its cross-sectional area. The equation of equilibrium of point B_1 (Fig. 90) in

[1] See writer's paper in *Ann. ponts chaussées*, series 9, vol. 3, p. 551, 1913.

[2] Such a theory has been developed by R. v. Mises, *Z. angew. Math. Mech.*, vol. 3, p. 407, 1923. It was applied to various cases of latticed bars by R. v. Mises and J. Ratzersdorfer, *Z. angew. Math. Mech.*, vol. 5, p. 218, 1925, and vol. 6, p. 181, 1926. Several particular cases have been previously discussed by engineers interested in the theory of structures: H. Müller-Breslau, "Die Neueren Methoden der Festigkeitslehre und der Statik der Baukonstruktionen," 4th ed., p. 398, Leipzig, 1913, and 5th ed., p. 380, Leipzig, 1924; L. Mann, *Z. Bauwesen*, Vol. 59, p. 539, 1909; K. Ljungberg, "*Der Eisenbau*," p. 100, 1922; M. Grüning, "Die Statik des ebenen Tragwerkes," Berlin, 1925; Wilhelm Wenzel, "Über die Stabilität des Gleichgewichtes ebener elastischer Stabwerke," Dissertation, University of Berlin, 1929.

the horizontal direction is

$$A_dE \frac{\delta \cos^2 \alpha}{d} = P\frac{\delta}{l},$$

from which,

$$P_{cr} = A_dE \sin \alpha \cos^2 \alpha. \tag{a}$$

To get a more accurate solution of the problem, the elasticity of the vertical bar should be considered. Under the action of the load P this bar will be compressed. Since there is no force in the inclined bar,[1] any compression of the vertical bar produces some lateral displacement of the system, so that joint B begins to move laterally from the beginning of loading and there does not exist a definite value of the load P (critical value), at which lateral displacement suddenly begins to be possible. To eliminate the necessity of considering the above lateral displacement, let us assume the vertical bar to be compressed by the load P first; only after this deformation is the inclined bar attached to joint B. Thus we finally have the bar BC in a vertical position with the compressive force P acting on it and the inclined bar free from stresses. In calculating the critical value of P, we proceed as before and assume a small lateral displacement of joint B. Owing to this displacement, a force in the inclined bar and a change in compressive force in the vertical bar will be produced. Hence, any lateral displacement δ of joint B will be accompanied by a vertical displacement δ_1 of the same joint, due to change in compression of the vertical bar. If X denotes the tensile force produced in the inclined bar, the corresponding increase in the compressive force in the vertical bar is $X \sin \alpha$ and its shortening is

$$\delta_1 = \frac{Xl \sin \alpha}{A_vE},$$

in which A_v is the cross-sectional area of the vertical bar. The total elongation of the inclined bar is equal to $\delta \cos \alpha - \delta_1 \sin \alpha$. Then the force X is found from the equation

$$\frac{Xd}{A_dE} = \delta \cos \alpha - \frac{Xl \sin^2 \alpha}{A_vE},$$

from which

$$X = \frac{A_dE\delta \cos \alpha}{d\left(1 + \dfrac{A_d}{A_v} \sin^3 \alpha\right)}.$$

Writing the equation of equilibrium of joint B as

$$X \cos \alpha = \frac{P\delta}{l},$$

and substituting the above expression for X, we obtain

$$P_{cr} = \frac{A_dE \sin \alpha \cos^2 \alpha}{1 + \dfrac{A_d}{A_v} \sin^3 \alpha}. \tag{b}$$

---

[1] This is true if we take the initial undeformed configuration of the system, as is usually done in calculating forces in bars.

Comparing this with expression (a), obtained before, it is seen that the effect of compression of the vertical bar is given by the second term in the denominator of formula (b).

The critical load calculated from Eq. (b) will be of practical interest only in case it is smaller than the critical load for the vertical member of the system considered as a bar with hinged ends, since otherwise the system will fail, owing to buckling of the vertical bar and not as a result of the lateral displacement shown in Fig. 90. Thus we may write the equation

$$\frac{A_d E \sin \alpha \cos^2 \alpha}{1 + \dfrac{A_d}{A_v} \sin^3 \alpha} \gtrless \frac{\pi^2 E A_v r^2_v}{l^2},$$

in which l/r_v is the slenderness ratio of the vertical bar. The above equation can be written in the following form:

$$A_d \sin \alpha \cos^2 \alpha \gtrless \frac{\pi^2 A_v r^2_v}{l^2} + \frac{A_d r^2_v \pi^2 \sin^3 \alpha}{l^2}.$$

Remembering that $(r_v/l)^2$ is usually a very small quantity, it can be concluded that the kind of instability represented in Fig. 90 can occur only if A_d is very small in comparison with A_v or if the angle α is very small.[1]   In both cases the second term in the denominator of formula (b) is very small and can be neglected; thus formula (a) is sufficiently accurate for practical purposes.

In the foregoing discussion it was assumed that the vertical bar had been first compressed by the load P and that only after this was the inclined bar attached. If the system is assembled in the unstressed condition, then, as was mentioned before, the application of any vertical load P will produce some lateral displacement. This condition will be analogous to that of a bar compressed by forces applied with a small eccentricity. From the very beginning of compression such a bar starts to bend, but this bending is very small and begins to increase rapidly only as the load approaches the critical value calculated for a straight bar. The same action occurs in the above system and the lateral displacement begins to increase rapidly only as the load P approaches the value given by formula (b).

Let us consider now a general case of a truss with hinged joints and, for simplification, let us assume that all joints are in the same plane. If the initial length of a member between any two joints i and k is denoted by l_{ik} and the length of the same member after loading the truss by a_{ik}, the force in the member produced by the loading is $A_{ik}E(a_{ik} - l_{ik})/l_{ik}$, where A_{ik} is the cross-sectional area of the member. Equations of equilibrium for any joint k can be written in the usual form:

$$\left. \begin{aligned} \sum_i \frac{A_{ik}E(a_{ik} - l_{ik}) \cos \alpha_{ik}}{l_{ik}} - X_k = 0; \\ \sum_i \frac{A_{ik}E(a_{ik} - l_{ik}) \sin \alpha_{ik}}{l_{ik}} - Y_k = 0; \end{aligned} \right\} \qquad (c)$$

[1] The modulus of elasticity for the two bars has been taken the same.

α_{ik} denotes the angle between the member ik and the x-axis after the deformation of the truss; X_k and Y_k are the components of any external load applied at joint k, and the summation is extended over all members meeting at joint k. In calculating the critical value of the load, we proceed as before: assume an infinitely small displacement of the system from the position of equilibrium and find the value of the load necessary to keep the system in equilibrium in this displaced position. This value will be the critical load. Let δx_k and δy_k denote the components of the small displacement of a joint k and δx_i and δy_i the same for a joint i; then from

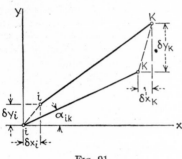

Fig. 91.

a simple geometrical consideration (Fig. 91) it may be seen that the small change δa_{ik} in the length of a member ik and the small change $\delta \alpha_{ik}$ in the angle α_{ik} corresponding to the above small displacements are:

$$\left.\begin{array}{l} \delta a_{ik} = (\delta x_k - \delta x_i)\cos\alpha_{ik} + (\delta y_k - \delta y_i)\sin\alpha_{ik}; \\ \delta\alpha_{ik} = \dfrac{1}{a_{ik}}[-(\delta x_k - \delta x_i)\sin\alpha_{ik} + (\delta y_k - \delta y_i)\cos\alpha_{ik}]. \end{array}\right\} \quad (d)$$

Substituting $a_{ik} + \delta a_{ik}$ for a_{ik} and $\alpha_{ik} + \delta\alpha_{ik}$ for α_{ik} in Eqs. (c), the equations of equilibrium for the new configuration of the system are obtained. Remembering that the displacements δx and δy are infinitely small, and using Eqs. (c), the above equations become

$$\left.\begin{array}{l} \displaystyle\sum_i \frac{A_{ik}E}{l_{ik}}\cos\alpha_{ik}\delta a_{ik} - \sum_i \frac{A_{ik}E(a_{ik} - l_{ik})}{l_{ik}}\sin\alpha_{ik}\delta\alpha_{ik} = 0; \\ \displaystyle\sum_i \frac{A_{ik}E}{l_{ik}}\sin\alpha_{ik}\delta a_{ik} + \sum_i \frac{A_{ik}E(a_{ik} - l_{ik})}{l_{ik}}\cos\alpha_{ik}\delta\alpha_{ik} = 0. \end{array}\right\} \quad (e)$$

Writing such equations for all joints[1] and substituting for δa_{ik} and $\delta\alpha_{ik}$ their values from Eqs. (d), we obtain as many homogeneous linear equations for determining δx and δy as the number of independent displacements δx and δy. The assumed displaced form of equilibrium becomes possible when these equations may yield, for the displacements δx and δy, solutions different from zero. Thus we arrive at the conclusion that the critical value of the load is obtained by equating to zero the determinant of Eqs. (e).

Let us apply this method in the case discussed above (Fig. 92). Since hinges 1 and 3 are fixed, there are only two independent displacements δx_2 and δy_2. The changes of the lengths a_{12} and a_{32}, and of the angles α_{12} and α_{32}, from Eqs. (d) are

[1] In the case of a joint at a fixed support, δx and δy are zero. In the case of a joint on rollers, only one of the displacements δx and δy is independent.

$$\delta a_{12} = \delta x_2 \cos \alpha_{12} + \delta y_2 \sin \alpha_{12}; \qquad \delta a_{32} = \delta y_2;$$

$$\delta \alpha_{12} = \frac{1}{a_{12}}(-\delta x_2 \sin \alpha_{12} + \delta y_2 \cos \alpha_{12}); \qquad \delta \alpha_{32} = -\frac{\delta x_2}{a_{32}}.$$

Substituting in Eqs. (e), we obtain

$$\delta x_2 \left(-\frac{P}{a_{32}} + \frac{A_{12}E}{a_{12}} \cos^2 \alpha_{12} \right) + \delta y_2 \frac{A_{12}E \sin \alpha_{12} \cos \alpha_{12}}{a_{12}} = 0;$$

$$\delta x_2 \frac{A_{12}E \sin \alpha_{12} \cos \alpha_{12}}{a_{12}} + \delta y_2 \left(\frac{A_{12}E \sin^2 \alpha_{12}}{a_{12}} + \frac{A_{32}E}{a_{32}} \right) = 0.$$

Equating to zero the determinant of these equations, the critical value of the load P is obtained, which agrees with the value (b) given before.

Applying the same method to the case shown in Fig. 93, and denoting by l and A the length and the cross-sectional area of the horizontal bars and by l_1 and A_1 the corresponding values for the inclined bars, the critical value of the load P is[1]

$$P_{cr} = \frac{AE}{\cot^2 \alpha \left(3 + \frac{2l_1 A}{lA_1 \cos^2 \alpha} \right)}. \qquad (f)$$

In the case of very rigid inclined bars it becomes

$$P_{cr} = \frac{AE}{3 \cot^2 \alpha}. \qquad (g)$$

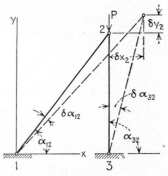

FIG. 92.

This latter result can be obtained from a simple consideration of the displaced form of equilibrium shown in Fig. 93 by dotted lines. If X is the decrease in the compressive force in the upper horizontal bar due to the assumed displacement of the system, the increase in the compressive force

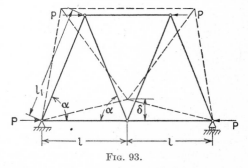

FIG. 93.

of the lower horizontal bars is $\frac{1}{2}X$ and the additional shortening of these bars is $Xl/(2EA)$. Taking into account this shortening and also the

[1] See R. v. Mises and J. Ratzersdorfer, *Z. Math. Physik*, vol. 5, p. 227, 1925.

deflection δ of the middle joint of the lower chord, the elongation of the upper horizontal bar is equal to $2\left(\dfrac{\delta l_1 \sin \alpha}{l} - \dfrac{Xl}{4AE}\right)$ and the force X may be found from the equation

$$\frac{\delta l_1 \sin \alpha}{l} - \frac{Xl}{4AE} = \frac{Xl}{2AE},$$

which gives

$$X = \frac{4AE\delta l_1 \sin \alpha}{3l^2}.$$

Substituting this in the equation of equilibrium for the displaced system

$$P\delta = Xl_1 \sin \alpha,$$

which is obtained by passing a section through the truss and by taking moments about the displaced position of the middle joint of the lower chord, the above value (g) for the critical load is obtained.

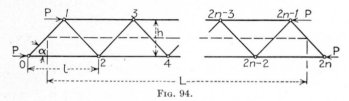

Fig. 94.

In the case of a truss with many panels (Fig. 94), assuming that the diagonals are very rigid, we obtain for the critical value of the compressive force[1]

$$(2P)_{cr} = m\frac{\pi^2 EI}{L^2}, \tag{98}$$

where

$$m = \frac{(4n-2)^2}{\pi^2} \tan^2 \frac{\pi}{4n-2}; \qquad n = \text{number of panels};$$

$$L = \left(n - \frac{1}{2}\right)l; \qquad I = \frac{Ah^2}{2} = \frac{A}{2}\left(\frac{l \tan \alpha}{2}\right)^2;$$

$$A = \text{cross-sectional area of a chord member}.$$

It is seen that, when n increases, the factor m approaches unity and the critical value of the axial compressive load $2P$ approaches Euler's value for a solid bar of length L and with $I = Ah^2/2$ (Fig. 94).

In another extreme case, where the chords are very rigid in comparison with the diagonals and where n is large, the result of rigorous calculations coincides completely with formula (94) (see p. 144), obtained before by an approximate method. The same result is obtained also when the diagonals and the chords have rigidities of the same order of magnitude.[2]

[1] See R. v. Mises and J. Ratzersdorfer, *loc. cit.*, p. 147.
[2] *Ibid.*

The above results are obtained by assuming ideal hinges at all joints. If we assume that the chords are continuous bars and that only the diagonals are attached by hinges, rigorous calculations show[1] that the additional rigidity can be approximately calculated as was shown in deriving Eq. (95) (see p. 145). Hence approximate Eqs. (94) and (95) can always be used in practical calculations providing the number of panels is not small, say not less than five.

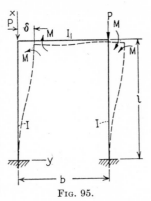

In discussing frame structures, we begin with a single frame shown in Fig. 95. Let I and l be the cross-sectional moment of inertia and the length of verticals and I_1 and b the corresponding quantities for the horizontal bar. Assuming that under the action of the vertical loads P the frame buckles sideways

Fig. 95.

as shown in the figure, and denoting by M the moments at the rigid joints the differential equation for the deflection curve of a vertical is

$$EI\frac{d^2y}{dx^2} = P(\delta - y) - M, \qquad (h)$$

the solution of which is

$$y = A \cos kx + B \sin kx + \delta - \frac{M}{P},$$

where

$$k^2 = \frac{P}{EI}.$$

Determining the constants A and B from the conditions at the built-in end, we obtain

$$y = \left(\delta - \frac{M}{P}\right)(1 - \cos kx). \qquad (i)$$

The conditions at the upper end of the vertical are:

$$(y)_{x=l} = \delta; \qquad \left(\frac{dy}{dx}\right)_{x=l} = \frac{Mb}{6EI_1}. \qquad (j)$$

Substituting Eq. (*i*) for y, we obtain

$$\left.\begin{aligned}
\delta \cos kl + \frac{M}{P}(1 - \cos kl) &= 0; \\
\delta k \sin kl - \frac{M}{P}\left(k \sin kl + \frac{bP}{6EI_1}\right) &= 0.
\end{aligned}\right\} \qquad (k)$$

Equating the determinant of these equations to zero, the following equation for calculating the critical value of the load P is obtained:

[1] See Wilhelm Wenzel, *loc. cit.*, p. 147.

$$\frac{kl}{\tan kl} = -\frac{6lI_1}{bI}. \tag{l}$$

If $I_1 = \infty$,

$$kl = \pi; \qquad P_{cr} = \frac{\pi^2 EI}{l^2}. \tag{m}$$

This condition exists when the horizontal bar is absolutely rigid. In another extreme case, where $I_1 = 0$, we obtain from Eq. (l)

$$kl = \frac{\pi}{2}; \qquad P_{cr} = \frac{\pi^2 EI}{4l^2}. \tag{n}$$

For all intermediate cases the value of P_{cr} is obtained by solving Eq. (l). This can be done in each particular case without any difficulty by using Table 3 (see p. 92).

In the above discussion the changes in lengths of the verticals at buckling have been neglected. From Fig. 95 it is seen that, owing to the action of the moments M, tension in the left vertical and compression in the right vertical equal to $2M/b$ will be produced. The corresponding change in length is $2Ml/(AEb)$ and the resulting rotation of the horizontal bar is $4Ml/(AEb^2)$. Hence the second condition of (j) becomes

$$\left(\frac{dy}{dx}\right)_{x=l} = \frac{Mb}{6EI_1} + \frac{4Ml}{AEb^2}.$$

Making the corresponding changes in Eqs. (k), we finally obtain for determining the critical value of the load P

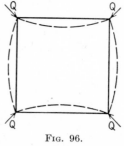

Fig. 96.

$$\frac{kl}{\tan kl} = -\frac{6lI_1}{bI}\frac{1}{1 + \dfrac{24lI_1}{Ab^3}}. \tag{o}$$

The last factor on the right side of this equation represents the effect of the axial deformation of the verticals on the magnitude of the critical load. Since I_1 is usually very small in comparison with Ab^2, this effect is small and usually can be neglected.

In the case where the frame (Fig. 95) is not symmetrical or is not symmetrically loaded, the problem of determining the critical value of the load becomes more complicated since it is necessary to consider displacements and rotations of both upper joints.[1]

In the case of a square frame with all members equal and equally compressed (Fig. 96), buckling will occur as shown in the figure and each bar is in the condition of a bar with hinged ends, so that the critical compressive force is given by formula (60). For any regular polygon with n equal and

[1] Several examples of this kind are discussed by R. v. Mises and J. Ratzersdorfer, loc. cit., p. 147.

with equally compressed sides (Fig. 97), the critical force in the bars is given by the following equations:[1]

$$\text{For } n > 3 \quad P_{cr} = \left(\frac{4\pi}{n}\right)^2 \frac{EI}{l^2};$$
$$\text{For } n = 3 \quad P_{cr} = (1.23\pi)^2 \frac{EI}{l^2}.$$

(99)

For more complicated framed structures, a general theory of stability has been developed.[2] Using a method analogous to that applied above for trusses with hinged joints, the critical values of the loads are found by equating to zero the determinant of the system of homogeneous linear equations representing the conditions of equilibrium of the joints of the system in a slightly deflected condition.

Applying this method to the case of batten-plate columns (Fig. 88) and using the same notations as in Art. 27, the following expression for the critical load in the case of very rigid battens is obtained:

$$P_{cr} = \frac{2z^2 EI_c}{a^2}.$$

(100)

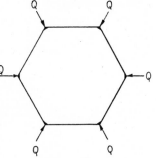

The numerical factor z is obtained from the transcendental equation

$$\frac{4I_c}{A_c b^2} = \frac{1 - \cos \dfrac{\pi}{n}}{\cos \dfrac{\pi}{n} - \cos z} \frac{\sin z}{z}, \quad (p)$$

where $n = l/a$ denotes the number of panels in the batten-plate column, A_c is cross-sectional area of one channel, b is the length

Fig. 97.

of a batten, equal to the distance between the center lines of the channels, and I_c is moment of inertia of the cross-sectional area of one channel. Calculations show that the approximate equation (96) given before (see p. 146) is in satisfactory agreement with the more rigorous solution (100).

Take, as a numerical example,

$$\frac{A_c b^2}{4I_c} = 180; \quad n = 10;$$
$$I = 2I_c + \frac{A_c b^2}{2} = 362 I_c.[3]$$

Substituting these data into Eq. (p), we obtain

$$z = 2.583,$$

[1] *Ibid.*

[2] *Ibid.*, p. 147.

[3] These numerical data are taken from the dimensions of the specimens used by the writer in his experiments with models of batten-plate columns, *loc. cit.*, p. 147.

and the critical load, from Eq. (100), becomes

$$P_{cr} = 0.369 \frac{\pi^2 EI}{l^2}.$$

The approximate Eq. (96) (p. 146) gives, for $I_b = \infty$ and $A_b = \infty$

$$P_{cr} = \frac{\pi^2 EI}{l^2} \frac{1}{1 + \dfrac{\pi^2 I a^2}{24 I_c l^2}} = 0.403 \frac{\pi^2 EI}{l^2}.$$

Thus in this extreme case, where the critical load for the batten-plate column is only about 40 per cent of that calculated for the corresponding solid column, the error of the approximate equation is about 9 per cent. For cases where the critical load for a batten-plate column does not differ much from that calculated for the solid column, Eq. (96) represents a better approximation and can be used with sufficient accuracy in practical design and also in cases where the flexural rigidity of the batten plates is not large.

29. Buckling of Bars Compressed beyond Proportional Limit.

In our previous discussions of stability problems the assumption

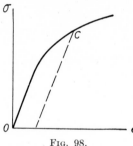

FIG. 98.

was made that stresses remain within the elastic region and that the material follows Hooke's law. Let us assume now that the material, although perfectly elastic, does not follow Hooke's law and that the compression-test diagram is similar to that shown in Fig. 98. If a bar of such material is compressed up to point C and then some small change of load is produced, the relation between the change in stress and the change in strain depends on the magnitude of the initial stress and is given by the slope of the compression-test curve at point C. The magnitude of the ratio $d\sigma/d\epsilon$ can be considered as a variable modulus of elasticity of the material which is a function of σ and will be denoted by E_σ.

Let us consider now an axially compressed prismatical bar with hinged ends (Fig. 44), the elastic properties of which may be shown by the curve in Fig. 98. In discussing the elastic stability of such a bar, we assume an infinitesimal deflection of the bar and calculate the force that is necessary to keep the bar in this slightly deflected shape. Since the assumed deflection is very small, the corresponding bending stresses are very small in comparison with the initial compressive stress and the relation between bending stress and bending strain is determined by the modulus E_σ. Then, assuming that cross sections of the bar remain plane during bending, the differential equation of the deflection curve will be the same as in the case of materials following Hooke's law, except that E_σ will replace E. Proceeding as in Art. 12, we find, by integration of the equation, the critical load:

$$P_{cr} = \frac{\pi^2 E_\sigma I}{l^2}, \tag{101}$$

and the corresponding critical stress:

$$\sigma_{cr} = \pi^2 E_\sigma \frac{r^2}{l^2}. \tag{102}$$

The difference between these formulas and the formulas that were obtained before for materials following Hooke's law consists in replacing the constant modulus E by a modulus E_σ which varies with the magnitude of the direct compressive stress σ. If a compression-test diagram for the material is given (Fig. 98), the value of E_σ for any value of σ can be determined. Taking a series of values for σ_{cr} and E_σ and substituting them into Eq. (102), we find from this equation the corresponding values of l/r. In this way the relation between the critical stress and the slenderness ratio is established and can be represented by a curve analogous to the curve in Fig. 46 obtained for materials following Hooke's law.

This method of solving stability problems in the case of materials that do not follow Hooke's law was proposed by F. Engesser,[1] who also suggested its use in the case of such material as structural steel when stressed beyond the proportional limit. In this case, however, the problem is more complicated since a part of the deformation is inelastic; if, after loading the material up to the point C (Fig. 98), we begin to diminish the load, the stress-strain relation will no longer be represented by the curve OC but will follow a linear law as indicated by the dashed line. Thus, conditions are the same as in the case of a material having two different moduli, namely, a modulus E_σ for an increase of load and the usual modulus E when the load decreases.[2]

[1] ENGESSER, F., *Z. Arch. Ing., Wesen*, 1889, p. 455. See also Considère, *Congrès international des procédés de construction*, Paris, vol. 3, p. 371, 1889, and E. Elwitz, *Forschungsarbeiten*, no. 236, 1921.

[2] The necessity of taking into consideration this fact of two different moduli has been indicated by F. S. Jasinsky, *Schweiz. Bauzeitung*, Vol. 25,

When a compressed bar bends slightly sideways, there will be some increase of the compressive stresses on the concave side and a decrease on the convex side. Assuming that plane cross sections of the bar remain plane during bending, the small bending stresses will be distributed along the depth of the cross section as shown in Fig. 99. If ρ denotes the radius of curvature

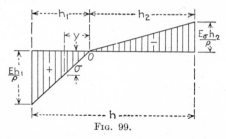

Fig. 99.

of the deflection curve, the maximum tensile and compressive stresses are Eh_1/ρ and $E_\sigma h_2/\rho$, respectively, and the position of the neutral axis 0 is found from the condition that the resultants of the tensile and compressive forces must be equal. In the case of a rectangular cross section of depth h this condition requires

$$Eh^2{}_1 = E_\sigma h^2{}_2. \tag{a}$$

Noting also that

$$h_1 + h_2 = h,$$

we obtain

$$h_1 = \frac{h\sqrt{E_\sigma}}{\sqrt{E} + \sqrt{E_\sigma}}; \qquad h_2 = \frac{h\sqrt{E}}{\sqrt{E} + \sqrt{E_\sigma}}. \tag{b}$$

If b is the width of the rectangular cross section, the bending moment represented by the stresses shown in Fig. 99 is

$$M = \frac{Eh_1}{\rho} \frac{bh_1}{2} \frac{2}{3} h = \frac{bh^3}{12\rho} \frac{4EE_\sigma}{(\sqrt{E} + \sqrt{E_\sigma})^2}. \tag{c}$$

This equation can be made to coincide with the usual equation for the deflection curve by introducing the quantity

p. 172, 1895. It was considered by F. Engesser in his subsequent publications, see *Schweiz. Bauzeitung*, vol. 26, p. 24, 1895, and *Z. Ver. deut. Ing.*, vol. 42, p. 927, 1898. Further discussion of buckling of bars beyond proportional limit can be found in papers by Th. v. Kármán, *loc. cit.*, p. 45, and R. V. Southwell, *Phil. Trans. Roy. Soc.*, London, series A, vol. 213, p. 187, 1913.

$$E_r = \frac{4EE_\sigma}{(\sqrt{E} + \sqrt{E_\sigma})^2}, \qquad (d)$$

which is called the *reduced modulus of elasticity*. Then

$$M = \frac{E_r I}{\rho}. \qquad (103)$$

Integrating this equation, we obtain for a bar with hinged ends

$$P_{cr} = \frac{\pi^2 E_r I}{l^2}. \qquad (104)$$

The corresponding critical stress is:

$$\sigma_{cr} = \pi^2 E_r \frac{r^2}{l^2}. \qquad (105)$$

Hence, Euler's formula, derived before for materials following Hooke's law, can be used also beyond the proportional limit simply by substituting the reduced modulus E_r for the usual modulus E. It will be noted that the value of E_r from Eq. (d) reduces to the usual modulus E so long as E_σ is constant and equal to E.

For a material with a pronounced yield point, as in the case of structural steel, the moduli E_σ and E_r diminish rapidly as the yield-point stress is approached, and the slenderness ratio l/r, as determined from Eq. (105), also diminishes rapidly. Hence for such materials the yield-point stress is practically always the critical stress at which buckling occurs. To obtain a compressive load on a bar larger than the load producing the yield-point stress, it is necessary to prevent the bar from lateral buckling at the yield point by applying some lateral constraint. Then, after yielding, the material recovers, owing to strain hardening; E_σ and E_r begin to increase and the bar becomes capable of sustaining a compressive stress larger than the yield-point stress.

It should be noted also that the value of the yield-point stress for such a material as structural steel cannot be defined with a high accuracy. It depends on the shape of the cross section, on the smoothness of the surface of the test bar, on the rate of application of the load, etc. At the yield-point stress the material is in a condition of instability and any disturbance may suddenly cause yielding. After yielding starts it proceeds at a somewhat lower stress than that required to start it and we distinguish between the upper and lower yield points. When approaching the yield point, time effect on the stress-strain diagram also becomes pronounced. All these circumstances make calculations of critical stresses in the region of the yield-point stress very uncertain and all discussions regarding various refinements of the formula for critical stress in the above region are more of academic than of practical interest.[1]

The method of calculating the reduced modulus, explained above for the case of a rectangular cross section, can be used also in the general case. We begin with the determination of the position of the neutral axis 0 (Fig. 99). Denoting by y distances from the neutral axis and considering y as positive when it is to the left of 0, the tensile stress at any point, due to bending, is Ey/ρ and the compressive stress is $E_\sigma y/\rho$. From the condition that the internal forces represent a couple, and denoting by dA an element of the cross-sectional area, we obtain

$$\int^{h_1} Ey \, dA + \int^{-h_2} E_\sigma y \, dA = 0,$$

or

$$\frac{E}{E_\sigma} \int^{h_1} y \, dA + \int^{-h_2} y \, dA = 0. \qquad (e)$$

From this we see that, if the width of the cross section on the tension side is increased in the ratio E/E_σ, the neutral axis will pass through the centroid of such a distorted cross section. Thus the position of the point 0 (Fig. 99) can always be determined.

The expression for bending moment is

$$M = \frac{E}{\rho} \int^{h_1} y^2 \, dA + \frac{E_\sigma}{\rho} \int^{-h_2} y^2 \, dA = \frac{E}{\rho}\left(I_1 + \frac{E_\sigma}{E}I_2\right), \qquad (f)$$

in which I_1 and I_2 are the moments of inertia with respect to the neutral axis of the two portions of the cross section. Comparing Eqs. (f) and (103), we conclude that in the general case the reduced modulus can be represented by the following formula:

---

[1] Some discussion of Engesser's formula is given by M. Broszko, *Compt.-rend. acad. sci.*, Paris, vol. 186, p. 1041, 1928, and International Association for Bridge and Structural Engineering, Publications, vol. 1, p. 1, 1932, Zürich. See also W. Rein, "Versuche zur Ermittlung der Knickspannungen für verschiedene Baustähle," J. Springer, Berlin, 1930.

$$E_r = \frac{1}{I}(EI_1 + E_\sigma I_2).$$ (106)

It is seen that the magnitude of the reduced modulus depends not only on the value of the axial compressive stress σ but also on the shape of the cross section. Calculations based on Eq. (106) show that in the case of structural steel the effect of the shape of the cross section is not of great importance[1] and can usually be disregarded.

Having a compression-test diagram for a material, and using Eq. (106), the value of E_r for any value of σ can be determined.

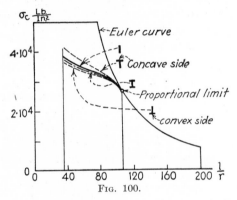

FIG. 100.

Substituting a series of values of σ_{cr} and E_r into Eq. (105) and calculating from it the corresponding values of l/r, a curve representing σ_{cr} as a function of the slenderness ratio can be constructed. In Fig. 100 such curves are shown for several shapes of the cross section.[2] Up to the proportional limit the critical stress is independent of the shape of the cross section, and we have a single curve calculated from the Euler formula. Beyond that limit the curves are different for different cross sections. It is interesting to note that the value of σ_{cr} depends not only on the shape of the cross section but also on the direction of buckling. Two curves, for instance, are given in the figure for a T cross section. Naturally, if a bar is free to buckle in either of the two above directions, only the curve giving the lower values for σ_{cr} shall be considered.

[1] See W. Gehler, *Reports 2d Intern. Cong. Appl. Mech.*, Zürich, p. 364, 1926, and M. Roš, *Reports 2d Intern. Cong. Appl. Mech.*, p. 368, 1926.

[2] The compressive-test diagram for this material is shown in Fig. 33.

Up to this point we have been discussing the fundamental case in which the ends of a uniformly compressed bar are hinged. The same reasoning can be applied in the other cases discussed in Arts. 12 and 17. Since the compressive stress in these cases is constant along the length of the bar, the differential equation of the deflection curve of the buckled bar, when compressed beyond the proportional limit, is of the same form as that used within the elastic region, except that the constant modulus E is replaced by the reduced modulus E_r. The end conditions also remain unchanged. Hence the formulas for critical loads beyond the proportional limit will be obtained from the formulas previously derived for elastic conditions by replacing E by E_r. The values found before for reduced lengths remain unchanged and the curve for critical stresses given in Fig. 100 for the fundamental case can be used in all the above cases provided the actual length is replaced by the reduced length.

In the case of bars with elastically built-in ends, the problem is more complicated and the reduced length beyond the proportional limit depends not only on the degree of fixity at the ends but also on the magnitude of l/r. Take, as an example, the case of a rectangular frame shown in Fig. 58. The critical value of the compressive forces P within the elastic limit [see Eq. (68), p. 91] is obtained from the equation

$$\tan \frac{kl}{2} + \frac{kl}{2}\left(\frac{b}{l}\frac{EI}{EI_1}\right) = 0, \qquad (g)$$

in which

$$k = \sqrt{\frac{P}{EI}}.$$

Beyond the proportional limit the flexural rigidity of the vertical compressed bars becomes E_rI while the flexural rigidity of the horizontal bars remains unchanged. Hence the factor in parentheses in Eq. (g) changes with the value of σ_{cr}, and the root of this equation, which defines the reduced length, changes also. Take, for instance, a square frame with $I = I_1$. Within the elastic limit Eq. (g) for this case is

$$\tan \frac{kl}{2} + \frac{kl}{2} = 0,$$

and gives

$$\frac{kl}{2} = 2.029.$$

Then,

$$P_{cr} = \frac{\pi^2 EI}{(0.774l)^2},$$

so that the reduced length is $L = 0.774l$.

Beyond the proportional limit, Eq. (g) for the above square frame becomes

$$\tan \frac{kl}{2} + \frac{kl}{2} \frac{E_r}{E} = 0, \tag{h}$$

where

$$k = \sqrt{\frac{P}{E_r I}} = \frac{1}{r} \sqrt{\frac{\sigma}{E_r}}.$$

Since E_r is smaller than E, the root of this equation determining the critical load is larger and the corresponding reduced length is smaller than that obtained above for elastic conditions. Taking a series of values for σ_{cr} and the corresponding values of E_r, we can calculate from Eq. (h) the corresponding values of l/r and can represent by a curve the relation between the value of σ_{cr} and the slenderness ratio l/r. In this way it can be shown that the reduced length in this case varies from $L = 0.774l$ when $E_r = E$ to $L = 0.5l$ when $E_r = 0$. This should be expected since, with the increase of σ_{cr}, E_r and the flexural rigidity of the vertical bars decrease, while the flexural rigidity of horizontal bars remains unchanged. Thus the fixity at the ends is relatively increasing; when σ_{cr} approaches the yield-point stress, the end conditions approach those of a bar with rigidly built-in ends, for which case $L = 0.5l$.

We have a similar condition in the case of continuous compressed bars on elastic supports and bars on elastic foundations. Beyond the proportional limit the relative rigidity of the supports and foundation is larger than within the elastic limit and the reduced length is smaller than that calculated before (see Arts. 19, 20, 21) on the basis of Hooke's law.

In the case of prismatical bars compressed by forces distributed along the length, the compressive stress is not constant along the length of the bar; in the case of buckling beyond the proportional limit, the reduced modulus E_r also is not constant for the entire length, so that, as a result of compression beyond the proportional limit, a bar with a variable flexural rigidity is obtained. Take the case in Fig. 75. If by the uniformly distributed compressive load a stress beyond the proportional limit is produced at the lower end of the bar, the stress in the upper portion of the bar continues to be within the elastic limit. For calculating the critical load in this case, it will be necessary to consider the lower portion of the bar as a portion with a variable flexural rigidity $E_r I$ while the upper portion has a constant flexural rigidity EI. Thus, the problem of calculating critical load beyond proportional limit becomes in this case very complicated. If, for an approximate calculation of the critical load, we use the same formula as was obtained for elastic conditions (see p. 113) and substitute for E the reduced modulus E_r, calculated for the lower end of the bar, this will be equivalent to the assumption that beyond proportional limit the bar continues to possess a constant flexural rigidity and that this rigidity is the same as that at the lower end of the bar which is subjected to the highest compressive stress. Quite naturally, such an assumption results in too low a value for the critical load, and in using it we shall always be on the safe side.

A similar problem is also found in the case of bars of variable cross section. If the compressive stress varies along the length of the bar, an accurate calculation of the critical load beyond the proportional limit requires the introduction of a reduced modulus E_r for the inelastically compressed portions of the bar. If E_r is constant along these portions, as in the cases shown in Fig. 75, the accurate calculation of the critical load can be accomplished without much difficulty. But the problem becomes more complicated if E_r is variable. We shall always be on the safe side if in such cases we use formulas derived for elastic conditions and substitute in them for E the reduced modulus E_r calculated for the cross section with the maximum compressive stress.

In the case of built-up columns the critical load beyond the proportional limit can also be calculated by introducing E_r instead of E. Take the case shown in Fig. 88. Under the action of an axial load the chords of the column will be uniformly compressed while the battens are unstressed. Hence in calculating the critical load beyond the proportional limit we can use formula (96). It will be necessary to substitute E_r for E only in those terms relating to the chords and to keep E and G in those terms relating to the battens. Thus, if compression of the column exceeds the proportional limit, the battens become relatively more rigid and the properties of the built-up column approach those of a solid column.

30. Lateral Buckling of Compressed Helical Springs.—The problem of lateral buckling of compressed helical springs is of some practical interest and can be investigated by the same methods as the buckling of prismatical bars;[1] it is necessary to take into account only the change in length of the spring due to compression since this change is not negligible as in the case of compressed bars.[2] The effect of shearing force on the magnitude of the critical load is also of importance in this case and we use Eq. (92) for our calculation. We assume the close coiled spring and the following notations:

l_0 is the initial length of the spring,

h_0 is the pitch of the helix,

n is the number of coils, so that $nh_0 = l_0$,

r is the radius of the helix,

l is the length of the spring after compression,

I is the moment of inertia of the cross section of the wire with respect to its diameter,

α_0, β_0 and γ_0 are the compressive, flexural and shearing rigidities of the helical spring. They take the place of the quantities AE, EI and AG/n for the case of a solid bar.

α, β and γ are the same quantities after compression of the spring. It will be shown that these quantities are inversely proportional to the number of coils per unit length of the spring, hence,

$$\alpha = \alpha_0 \frac{l}{l_0}; \qquad \beta = \beta_0 \frac{l}{l_0}; \qquad \gamma = \gamma_0 \frac{l}{l_0}. \tag{a}$$

Using Eq. (92) for a spring with hinged ends, we obtain

$$P_{cr} = \frac{\pi^2 \beta}{l^2} \frac{1}{1 + \frac{\pi^2 \beta}{l^2 \gamma}},$$

or, substituting from (a),

$$P_{cr} = \frac{\pi^2 \beta_0}{l l_0} \frac{1}{1 + \frac{\pi^2 \beta_0}{l^2 \gamma_0}}. \tag{b}$$

[1] The first investigation in this field was made by E. Hurlbrink, *Z. Ver. deut. Ing.*, vol. 54, p. 138, 1910. The problem was further discussed by R. Grammel, *Z. angew. Math. Mech.*, vol. 4, p. 384, 1924, and by C. B. Biezeno and J. J. Koch, *Z. angew. Math. Mech.*, vol. 5, p. 279, 1925.

[2] In the case of structural materials, such as steel or wood, the critical stress is small in comparison with the modulus E and the change in length of the bar can always be neglected, but in the case of such material as rubber this is no longer permissible and the length after compression, instead of the initial length, should be used in formulas for calculating critical load.

From a consideration of the compression of the spring, we have

$$\frac{l_0 - l}{l_0} = \frac{P_{cr}}{\alpha_0}.$$

Determining P_{cr} from this equation and substituting in Eq. (b), we obtain

$$\frac{\alpha_0(l_0 - l)}{l_0} = \frac{\pi^2 \beta_0}{l l_0} \frac{1}{1 + \frac{\pi^2 \beta_0}{l^2 \gamma_0}}. \tag{c}$$

From this equation the axial compression of the spring at buckling can be calculated. Introducing the notation $l/l_0 = z$, Eq. (c) becomes

$$z^3 - z^2 + \frac{\pi^2}{l^2_0}\left(\frac{\beta_0}{\gamma_0} + \frac{\beta_0}{\alpha_0}\right)z - \frac{\pi^2 \beta_0}{l^2_0 \gamma_0} = 0. \tag{d}$$

The constants α_0, β_0 and γ_0 appearing in this equation can be calculated from the known dimensions of the spring as follows: the deflection of a close coiled helical spring if compressed axially by the load P is

$$\delta = \frac{\pi n r^3}{GI}P;$$

hence,

$$\alpha_0 = \frac{GIl_0}{\pi n r^3}. \tag{e}$$

In calculating the flexural rigidity of the spring, let us consider the case of pure bending of the spring (Fig. 101). For an element $rd\alpha$, shown in

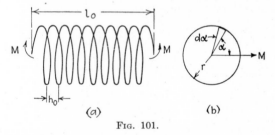

(a) (b)

Fig. 101.

Fig. 101b, the bending and the twisting moments are $M \cos \alpha$ and $M \sin \alpha$, respectively. The strain energy for one coil then is

$$\int_0^{2\pi} \left(\frac{M^2 \cos^2 \alpha}{2EI} + \frac{M^2 \sin^2 \alpha}{4GI}\right)rd\alpha = \frac{\pi r M^2}{2I}\left(\frac{1}{E} + \frac{1}{2G}\right).$$

The curvature $1/\rho$ of the deflected axis of the spring is now obtained by equating the above strain energy to the work done on one coil by the bending moment M. Then

$$\frac{Mh_0}{2\rho} = \frac{\pi r M^2}{2I}\left(\frac{1}{E} + \frac{1}{2G}\right)$$

and

$$\frac{1}{\rho} = \frac{\pi r M}{h_0 I} \frac{E + 2G}{2EG}.$$

Hence

$$\beta_0 = \frac{2EGIh_0}{\pi r(E + 2G)}. \qquad (f)$$

The rigidity in shear is obtained from a consideration of the relative displacement e of the ends A and B of one coil due to the shearing force Q (Fig. 102). From this consideration we obtain

$$e = \frac{\pi r^3 Q}{EI}.$$

Dividing this by h_0, we find

$$\gamma_0 = \frac{EIh_0}{\pi r^3}. \qquad (g)$$

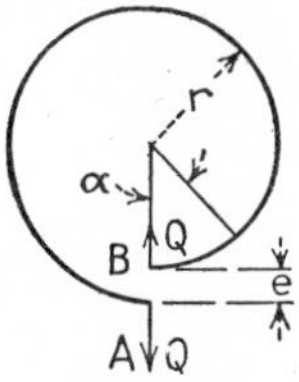

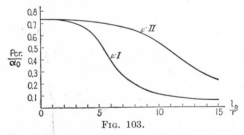

FIG. 102.

Substituting expressions (e), (f) and (g) in Eq. (d) and using the notation

$$m = \frac{\pi^2 r^2}{l^2_0(2 + \nu)}, \qquad (h)$$

in which ν is Poisson's ratio, we finally obtain for z the equation

$$z^3 - z^2 + (3 + 2\nu)mz - m = 0. \qquad (i)$$

This equation has one real positive root, which determines the value $z = l/l_0$ at which buckling of the spring occurs. Knowing z, the corresponding value of P_{cr} is found from the equation

$$\frac{P_{cr}}{\alpha_0} = \frac{l_0 - l}{l_0} = (1 - z).$$

Curve[1] I in Fig. 103 gives the values of P_{cr}/α_0 as a function of l_0/r calculated from Eq. (i). Curve II of the same figure gives the values of P_{cr}/α_0 for the case of a helical spring with built-in ends.

FIG. 103.

The results of the above calculations are in good agreement with experiments made by C. B. Biezeno and J. J. Koch, providing the number of coils is not small and the coils do not touch before buckling occurs.

31. Stability of a Shaft Subjected to Twisting Couple and Thrust.— Assume that a prismatical bar AB with hinged ends is submitted to the

[1] The curve is taken from C. B. Biezeno and J. J. Koch's article, *loc. cit.*, p. 165.

simultaneous action of a compressive force P and a twisting couple M_t (Fig. 104).   To determine the values of P and M_t at which lateral buckling of the bar occurs, we proceed as before; assume that under the action of external forces the bar buckles sideways and determine the values of M_t

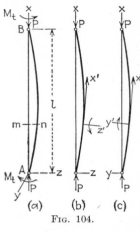

(a)   (b)   (c)

Fig. 104.

and P which are necessary to keep the axis of the bar in a slightly bent condition.   The values determined in this way are the critical values of the twisting couple and compressive force.

The deflection curve in this case will not be a plane curve and we must consider the two projections of the curve as shown in Figs. 104b and 104c.   We assume also that the principal moments of inertia of the cross section of the bar are equal so that any two central perpendicular axes in the plane of the cross section can be taken as the principal axes.   Considering any cross section mn of the bar, and taking the principal axes parallel to y and z, the direction of these axes after buckling will be y' and z'.   In deriving the differential equations of the deflection curve, we consider the upper portion of the bar and calculate the moments of the forces applied to this part of the bar with respect to the y' and z' axes.   Taking the moments positive as indicated in the figures, we find that the moments, with respect to the y' and z' axes, of the compressive force P are Pz and $-Py$, respectively. The moments with respect to the same axes of the twisting couple M_t, represented as a vector in the direction of the x-axis, are $-M_t\,dy/dx$ and $-M_t\,dz/dx$.   The differential equations of the deflection curve in each plane now become

$$\left.\begin{aligned} EI\frac{d^2z}{dx^2} &= -Pz + M_t\frac{dy}{dx}; \\[2mm] EI\frac{d^2y}{dx^2} &= -Py - M_t\frac{dz}{dx}. \end{aligned}\right\} \tag{a}$$

The general solutions of these equations are

$$y = A\sin\,(m_1x + \alpha_1) + B\sin\,(m_2x + \alpha_2); \tag{b}$$

$$z = A\cos\,(m_1x + \alpha_1) + B\cos\,(m_2x + \alpha_2);$$

in which A, B, α_1 and α_2 are constants of integration and m_1 and m_2 are the two roots of the quadratic equation

$$EIm^2 + M_tm - P = 0. \tag{c}$$

Substituting (b) into Eqs. (a), it can be shown that these equations are satisfied.

For determining the constants A, B, α_1 and α_2 we have the following conditions at the ends:

$$(y)_{x=0} = 0; \quad (y)_{x=l} = 0; \quad (z)_{x=0} = 0; \quad (z)_{x=l} = 0. \quad (d)$$

Substituting expressions (b) for y and z, we obtain:

$$A \sin \alpha_1 + B \sin \alpha_2 = 0; \quad A \cos \alpha_1 + B \cos \alpha_2 = 0;$$
$$A \sin (m_1 l + \alpha_1) + B \sin (m_2 l + \alpha_2) = 0;$$
$$A \cos (m_1 l + \alpha_1) + B \cos (m_2 l + \alpha_2) = 0.$$

On substituting for $B \sin \alpha_2$ and $B \cos \alpha_2$ from the first two equations in the second two, we find that

$$A[\sin (m_1 l + \alpha_1) - \sin (m_2 l + \alpha_1)] = 0;$$
$$A[\cos (m_1 l + \alpha_1) - \cos (m_2 l + \alpha_1)] = 0,$$

from which it follows that $m_1 l$ and $m_2 l$ differ by a multiple of 2π. The smallest values for M_t and P at which buckling will occur are obtained from the condition

$$m_1 l - m_2 l = \pm 2\pi,$$

or, by using Eq. (c),

$$\frac{M^2_t}{4(EI)^2} + \frac{P}{EI} = \frac{\pi^2}{l^2}. \quad (107)$$

When M_t is zero, this equation gives the known Euler formula. When P is equal to zero, we obtain the value of the torque, which, acting alone, will produce buckling of the shaft.[1] If the shaft is in tension, the sign of P in Eq. (107) must be changed. Thus the stability of the shaft against buckling produced by a torque is increased if a tensile force is applied.

[1] Formula (107) has been obtained by A. G. Greenhill, *Proc. Inst. Mech Eng.*, London, 1883. Further discussion of the problem is given in the papers by E. L. Nicolai, Dissertation, St. Petersburg, 1916 (Russian) and *Z. angew. Math. Mech.*, vol. 6, p. 30, 1926. The case of a shaft with the two different flexural rigidities has been discussed by R. Grammel, *Z. angew. Math. Mech.*, vol. 3, p. 262, 1923.

CHAPTER III

EXPERIMENTS AND DESIGN FORMULAS

32. Experiments with Solid Columns.—The first experiments with lateral buckling of centrally compressed prismatical bars were made by Musschenbroek.[1] He discovered that the resistance of such bars is in the inverse ratio of the squares of their lengths, a result theoretically deduced thirty years later by Euler. At first, engineers did not accept the results of Musschenbroek's experiments and of Euler's theory; such an authority, for instance, as Coulomb[2] continued to assume that the strengths of columns were directly proportional to their cross-sectional area and independent of their lengths. These views were supported by experiments made on wooden and cast-iron columns of comparatively short length, which usually showed that columns fail under loads much less than Euler's critical load and that failure is due principally to the crushing of the material and not to lateral buckling. E. Lamarle[3] was the first to give a satisfactory explanation of the discrepancy between the theory and experiments; he showed that Euler's theory is in agreement with experiments provided the fundamental assumptions of the theory regarding perfect elasticity of the material and ideal conditions at the ends are fulfilled.

With the increase in the use of steel in engineering structures, experiments with steel columns became necessary in the second half of the last century. Such experiments were made by I. Bauschinger[4] in Germany, A. Considère[5] in France and

[1] MUSSCHENBROEK, P. VAN, "Introductio ad cohaerentiam corporum firmorum," Lugduni, 1729. See also a French translation by P. Massuet, "Essai de physique," Leyden, 1739.

[2] See Coulomb's memoir in the "Mémoires . . . par divers savans," Paris, 1776.

[3] LAMARLE, E., "Annales des travaux publics de Belgique," vol. 3, pp. 1–64, and vol. 4, pp. 1–36, Brussels, 1845 and 1846.

[4] BAUSCHINGER, I., *Mitt. mech.-tech. Lab. tech. Hochschule, München*, no. 15, 1889.

[5] CONSIDÈRE, A., *Congrès international des procédés de construction*, Paris, vol. 3, p. 371, 1889.

L. Tetmajer[1] in Switzerland and Austria. In these experiments much greater care was taken in order to realize the fulfillment of the end conditions assumed in theory. Pointed ends were introduced and care was taken to secure central application of the compressive load.[2] These experiments definitely proved the validity of Euler's formula and showed that experimental values of σ_{cr} fall on Euler's curve provided the slenderness ratio of the

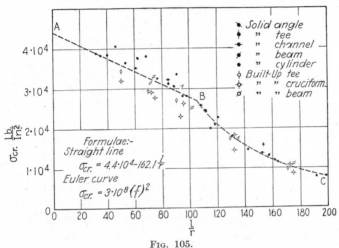

Fig. 105.

column is such that buckling occurs at a compressive stress below the proportional limit of the material. Figure 105 represents some of Tetmajer's results obtained with mild structural steel specimens of various shapes of cross section. It is seen that for $l/r > 105$ the results obtained follow Euler's curve satisfactorily. The limiting value of l/r, above which Euler's formula can be satisfactorily applied, depends, naturally, on the proportional limit of the material; in the case of nickel steel, such as is used in bridge engineering, Euler's formula gives satisfactory results[3] beginning at $l/r = 80$.

[1] TETMAJER, L., "Die Gesetze der Knickung- und der zusammengesetzten Druckfestigkeit der technisch wichtigsten Baustoffe," 3d. ed., Leipzig and Vienna, 1903.

[2] A. Considère was the first to introduce an adjustable arrangement at the ends such that the point of application of the load could be shifted slightly with the column under the load.

[3] See J. A. L. Waddell, *Eng. News*, vol. 59, p. 60, 1908. The columns tested had pin-connected ends. Chemical content was 3.5 Ni, 0.38 C, 0.75 Mn.

Further progress in the experimental study of buckling problems was accomplished by Th. von Kármán.[1] In his experiments rectangular steel bars with a proportional limit of 35,000 lb. per square inch and a yield point of 46,000 lb. per square inch were tested. The construction of the knife edges used to assure freedom of rotation of the ends is shown in Fig. 106. By adjusting the wedges it was possible to get a very accurate alignment of the load. With these precautions, the experimental results checked Euler's formula with an accuracy of $1\frac{1}{2}$ per cent. Kármán extended his experiments also in the region of plastic deformation. By using the compression-test diagram for his material and by calculating the reduced modulus, as was explained in Art. 29, he showed that Euler's formula can be applied also in the case of shorter bars in which the critical stress exceeds the proportional limit of the material. The upper curve in Fig. 107 gives values of σ_{cr} as a function of the slenderness ratio calculated from Euler's formula by using the reduced modulus. The lower curve in the same figure gives the critical stress when the load is applied with an eccentricity equal to $0.005h$ (see Fig. 39, p. 58), where h is the depth of the cross section. It is seen that most of the experimental results, shown by the small circles, are within the region between the two curves. For $l/r > 90$, the experimental results follow Euler's curve very closely. Between the proportional limit and the yield point the experimental results are in good agreement with the results obtained theoretically by using the reduced modulus. For $l/r < 40$, the critical stress is above the yield point of the material and the curve of σ_{cr} turns sharply upward. Such values for critical stresses can be obtained experimentally only if special precautions are taken against buckling at the yield-point

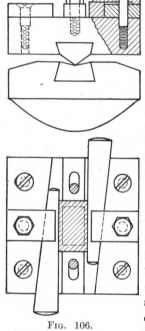

Fig. 106.

---

[1] Kármán, Th. v., *Forschungsarbeiten*, no. 81, 1910, Berlin, *loc. cit.*, p. 45.

stress; thus they have no practical significance in the design of columns.

In experimenting with the buckling of columns, it is usual practice to represent the deflections of a column as a function of the centrally applied load. In an ideal case there will be no deflection up to the critical value of the load and above this point the load-deflection curve is as shown in Fig. 49. Owing to various kinds of imperfections, such as some unavoidable initial curvature of the column, eccentricity in application of the load and non-homogeneity of the material, the column begins to deflect with the beginning of loading and usually fails before Euler's

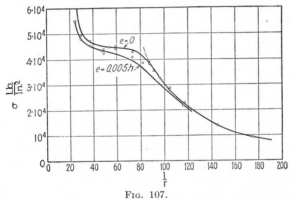

Fig. 107.

load is reached. The shapes of the load-deflection curves depend on the accuracy with which the theoretical assumptions are fulfilled. Several curves of this kind, as obtained by various experimenters working within the elastic range, are shown in Fig. 108. It is seen that, with the improvement of experimental technique so that the end conditions approach more closely the theoretical assumptions, the load-deflection curves approach more and more closely the horizontal line corresponding to Euler's load.

The most accurate experiments, up to the present time, were made in the Berlin-Dahlem material-testing laboratory by using a very elaborate construction for the end supports of the columns.[1] In Fig. 109 some experimental results obtained in this laboratory are shown. The material tested was a structural

[1] See paper by K. Memmler, *Reports 2d Intern. Cong. Appl. Mech.*, Zürich, p. **357**, 1926.

steel with a pronounced yield point at about 45,000 lb. per square inch. It is seen that for $l/r > 80$ the results follow

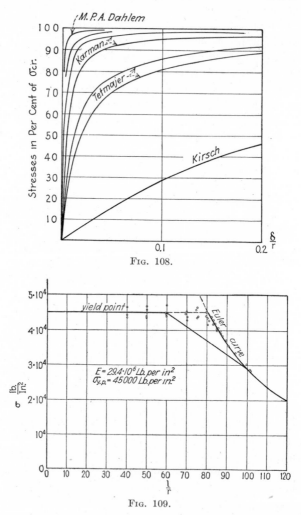

Fig. 108.

Fig. 109.

Euler's curve very satisfactorily. For shorter bars the yield-point stress should be considered as the critical stress.[1] Hence,

[1] More details about these experiments can be found in the book by W. Rein, "Versuche zur Ermittlung der Knickspannungen für verschiedene Baustähle," J. Springer, Berlin, 1930.

the application of materials having a high yield-point stress, such as silicon steel, may become economical in such cases. It may be seen also that all factors which cause an increase in yield-point stress will contribute to the increase of the critical load. Considère,[1] on the basis of his experiments, remarks that annealing of structural steel bars reduces their resistance to buckling in a higher proportion than their tensile strength. He also states that thick bars, by annealing, lose less in their resistance to buckling than thin ones and that the best steels for columns are those which have been rolled at the lowest temperature.

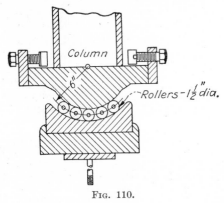

Fig. 110.

The significance of the yield-point stress in column tests was indicated also by the experiments of the A.S.C.E. Special Committee on Steel Column Research.[2] In this investigation special roller-bearing blocks were used to obtain the pivoted-end conditions (Fig. 110). This arrangement proved a very useful one in the case of large columns requiring the application of considerable axial load, which cannot be easily transmitted through knife edges. Figure 111 represents some of the results obtained by the committee in testing columns having H-sections. The tests were made with eccentrically applied loads. In one series of tests eccentricities were taken in the plane of the web, and in the other series they were taken in the plane perpendicular to the web. The ratio e/s of the eccentricity to the core radius was taken equal to unity in both cases. The

[1] *Loc. cit.*, p. 170.

[2] See *Trans. Am. Soc. Civil Eng.*, vol. 89, p. 1485, 1926, and vol. 95, p. 1152, 1931.

average compressive stresses $\sigma_c = P/A$, producing failure, are plotted in the figure against the slenderness ratio l/r.   The small black circles give the ultimate strength when the columns are bent in the plane of the web and the light circles give the ultimate strength if bending is perpendicular to the web.

For comparison, there is also plotted in the figure a curve that gives the average compressive stress at which yielding begins in the outermost fiber.   The ordinates of this curve are calculated

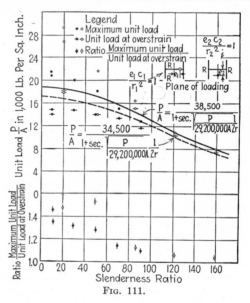

Fig. 111.

from Eq. (50′) (see p. 40) by taking an average value for the yield-point stress, $\sigma_{\text{Y.P.}} = 38,500$ lb. per square inch, as obtained from tension tests of specimens taken from various portions of the columns.   It is seen that for $l/r > 60$ the ultimate values of the average compressive stress are very close to the values producing the beginning of yielding in the outermost fibers.   For shorter columns, bent in the plane of the web, the ultimate strength is somewhat higher than the load at which yielding begins, but the difference is not larger than 10 per cent of the ultimate load.   When a short column is bent in the plane perpendicular to the web, the ultimate loads are considerably higher than the loads producing the beginning of yielding.   This result should be expected if bending beyond the yield point is considered, as has been explained in Art. 11. Similar results have been obtained also by M. Roš.[1]

When a load-deflection curve similar to those shown in Fig. 108 is obtained experimentally, the magnitude of the critical load is usually obtained by drawing the horizontal asymptote to the curve. A very useful method of determining the critical load from the test data within the elastic region has been suggested recently by R. V. Southwell.[2] Assuming that the deflection of a column, under a load that is below the critical value, is due to initial curvature, and using for the deflections the general expression (49) in the form of a trigonometric series, it may be seen that, when the load approaches the critical value, the first term in the series (49) becomes pre-

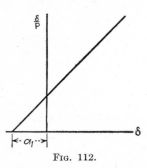

Fig. 112.

dominant, and it may be assumed that the deflection δ at the middle of the column, measured at various stages of the loading, will be given with sufficient accuracy by the equation

$$\delta = \frac{a_1}{\dfrac{P_{cr}}{P} - 1}, \qquad (a)$$

in which a_1 is the initial deflection corresponding to the first term in series (49). From this equation we obtain

$$\frac{\delta}{P}P_{cr} - \delta = a_1, \qquad (b)$$

which shows that, if we plot the ratio δ/P against the measured deflection δ, the points will fall on a straight line (Fig. 112). This line will cut the horizontal axis ($\delta/P = 0$) at the distance a_1 from the origin, and the inverse slope of the line gives the critical load.

If, instead of assuming an initial curvature, we assume that bending of the column is due to eccentric application of the load P, it will be found that the deflection at the middle is represented

[1] *Loc. cit.*, p. 54.

[2] Southwell, R. V., *Proc. Roy. Soc., London*, series A, vol. 135, p. 601, 1932.

with sufficient accuracy by the equation

$$\delta = \frac{4e}{\pi} \frac{1}{\dfrac{P_{cr}}{P} - 1}, \qquad (c)$$

analogous to Eq. (*a*) above [see Eq. (*j*), p. 30]. Considering a general case of the combined effect of an initial curvature and some eccentricity in application of the load, the deflection at the middle of the column is

$$\delta = \left(a_1 + \frac{4e}{\pi}\right)\frac{1}{\dfrac{P_{cr}}{P} - 1} \qquad (d)$$

and an equation, analogous to Eq. (*b*), again holds. Thus for any combination of initial curvature and eccentricity in application of the load, the critical load can be obtained as the inverse slope of a straight line such as shown in Fig. 112.

It is seen from Eq. (*d*) that, by taking $e = -\dfrac{\pi}{4}a_1$, we can eliminate the deflections at the middle of the column produced by a load below the critical value. This explains why, by using an adjustable support for the ends of the column, a very accurate value for P_{cr} can be obtained. In such experiments the magnitude of the eccentricities is determined by adjusting the point of application of the load in such a way as to compensate for the initial curvature.

It should be noted that an approximate value for the deflection due to eccentricity has been used in the derivation of Eq. (*d*). If the exact value of that deflection is used [see Eq. (27), p. 13], it can be shown that at the beginning of loading the column may deflect in one direction and later on suddenly buckle in the opposite direction.[1]

In the case of shorter bars for which the critical load is above the proportional limit of the material, the load-deflection curves have the form indicated in Fig. 39. It is seen that at a very

---

[1] This phenomena of a reversal in the direction of deflection has been investigated by H. Zimmermann, *Sitzungsb. Acad. Wiss.*, Berlin, vol. 25, p. 262, 1923. See also his book, "Lehre vom Knicken auf neuer Grundlage," Berlin, 1930. Experiments are in satisfactory agreement with this theory, see K. Memmler, *loc. cit.*, p. 173.

small deflection the load reaches its maximum and then the column buckles suddenly since the load necessary to maintain any further deflection falls off rapidly as the deflection is increased. The maximum load reached in the experiment is usually taken as the critical load. It may be seen that this maximum approaches the critical value calculated from Euler's equation by using the reduced modulus, when the eccentricity in the application of the load approaches zero. The shape of the deflection curve of the buckled bar in this case is no longer sinusoidal, the permanent deformation being concentrated principally at the middle, where the bending moment is a maximum (see p. 50).

From the discussion in this article it can be seen that, owing to various kinds of imperfections, actual columns will behave under load quite differently from ideal columns. To take this into account in determining working stresses, three rather distinct approaches can be made to the problem of designing columns in structures: (1) The ideal column formulas may be taken as a basis of column design and a suitable factor of safety applied to compensate for the effect of various imperfections. (2) A factor of safety may be applied to an empirical formula, certain constants of which have been adjusted to make the formula fit the results of tests. (3) The column may be assumed from the very beginning to have certain amounts of imperfection and the safe load can be determined as a certain portion of the load at which yielding of the material begins. Each of these methods of designing columns will be discussed in the following articles.

33. Critical Stress Diagram as a Basis of Column Design.— The experiments discussed in the previous article indicate that, in the case of a straight column with a centrally applied compressive force, the critical value of the compressive stress can be calculated with sufficient accuracy if the compression-test diagram for the material of the column is known. Euler's formula must be used for such calculations within the elastic range, while beyond the proportional limit the modified Euler's formula (see p. 159) must be applied, using the reduced modulus E_r instead of E. As a result of such calculations a diagram representing σ_{cr} as a function of the slenderness ratio can be obtained. In Fig. 113 are shown two diagrams of this kind, calculated for the two different kinds of structural steel: steel

No. 54 with $\sigma_{Y.P.} \approx 50,000$ lb. per square inch and steel No. 37 with $\sigma_{Y.P.} \approx 34,000$ lb. per square inch. There are given[1] also the necessary portions of the compression-test diagrams and the curves representing the reduced moduli as functions of the direct compressive stress. Up to the proportional limit Euler's curve is used in each case and above that limit curves based on the reduced moduli are used. At $l/r \approx 50$ the critical stress diagram turns up and σ_{cr} begins to increase with the diminishing of the slenderness ratio. This increase of σ_{cr} above the yield-point stress should not be considered in a practical design since it can be obtained only if special precautions are taken to prevent the column from buckling at the yield-point stress.

For practical application, each of the above diagrams can be replaced, in the inelastic region, with sufficient accuracy by two straight lines: a horizontal line for the portion above yield-point stress, and an inclined line for the portion between the yield point and the proportional limit. In this way a complete critical stress diagram is obtained provided the yield point and the proportional limit of the material are determined from experiments. Such approximate diagrams are shown in Fig. 113 by dotted lines.[2]

When the diagram of critical stress is known, the allowable stress is obtained for any value of the slenderness ratio by dividing σ_{cr} with the proper factor of safety. The selection of a proper factor of safety represents great difficulty in designing columns. The principal cause of this difficulty lies in the fact that the behavior of columns under compression is different from that assumed in Euler's theory and is determined principally by the magnitudes of the various kinds of imperfection, such as initial curvature of the column, eccentricity in application of the load and non-homogeneity of the material. The same kinds of imperfection are encountered also in other structures, such as beams subjected to the action of lateral loading; but there the effect of imperfections is negligible, while in the case of columns

[1] These curves are taken from the paper by W. Gehler, *Reports 2d Intern. Cong. Appl. Mech.*, Zürich, p. 364, 1926.

[2] This kind of diagram is used in the specifications of the *German State Railways*. See "Vorschriften für Eisenbauwerke," Berlin, 1926. For ordinary structural steel No. 37, with proportional limit equal to 30,000 lb. per square inch and yield-point stress of 34,000 lb. per square inch, they use a horizontal line for $l/r < 60$ and an inclined line for $60 < l/r < 100$.

imperfections have a very great effect on the deformation. There is very little known about the magnitudes of imperfections that are encountered in actual construction and this fact is usually compensated for by choosing a larger factor of safety.

The simplest method of choosing the factor of safety is to assume that the effect of various imperfections on the deformation of columns and on the maximum fiber stress produced is independent of the slenderness ratio. Then the factor of safety

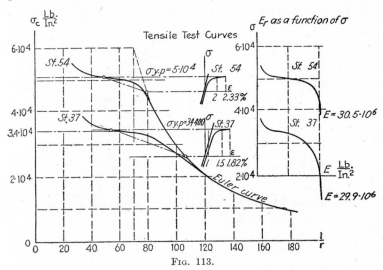

Fig. 113.

must be constant. A factor of 2.5 has been recently suggested[1] for structural steel in those cases in which the allowable tensile stress is taken equal to 20,000 lb. per square inch.[2] For such material as is represented by the lower curve in Fig. 113, the allowable stress for $l/r < 60$ will then be 13,700 lb. per square inch and for $l/r = 100$ it will be equal to 12,000 lb. per square inch if the proportional limit of the material is taken equal to 30,000 lb. per square inch.

If it is assumed that as the slenderness ratio increases such imperfections as an initial curvature of the column are likely to

---

[1] See F. Bleich, "Stahlhochbauten," vol. 1, p. 144, J. Springer, Berlin, 1932.

[2] Such stress is assumed in German specifications for structural steel No. 37 if the most unfavorable combination of dead load, live load and wind pressure is considered.

increase, it appears logical to introduce a variable factor of safety which increases with the slenderness ratio. In German specifications, for instance, the factor of safety increases from 1.7 for $l/r = 0$ to 3.5 for $l/r = 100$. It varies in such a way that the allowable stress in the inelastic range follows a parabolic law. For $l/r > 100$, the factor of safety remains constant at 3.5, and the allowable stresses are calculated from Euler's curve. In Fig. 114 curves are given which represent the allowable stress and the factor of safety as functions of the slenderness ratio for

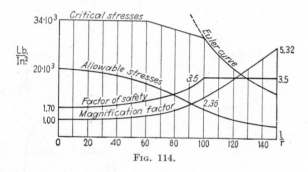

Fig. 114.

structural steel with a yield-point stress of 34,000 lb. per square inch as assumed in German specifications.

To simplify the calculations, we can always work with a constant allowable stress, such as that for simple tension, and compensate for column action by multiplying the force acting in the member by a *magnification factor*, which is equal to the ratio of the allowable stress in tension to the allowable stress in the column for the corresponding value of l/r. The curve representing this factor as a function of the slenderness ratio is also given in Fig. 114. Having such a curve, the selection of the proper cross section of a column may be made very readily by the trial-and-error method.

In the above discussion we assumed the fundamental case of buckling where the ends of the column are hinged. Working stresses established for this case can also be used in other cases provided we take, instead of the actual length of a column, a reduced length, the magnitude of which depends on the conditions at the ends of the column, on the manner of distribution of the compressive loads along the length of the column, and, in the case of variable cross sections, on the shape of the column.

A variety of cases has been discussed in the second chapter of this book and the numerical data necessary for the calculation of the reduced length in the elastic range of the material have been given. In discussing buckling of columns beyond the proportional limit (see Art. 29), it was shown that, by using in the inelastic range the same reduced length as in the elastic range, the design will always be on the safe side provided that, in calculating the reduced length, the cross section with the maximum compressive stress is taken as a basis.

This discussion has assumed also that we have solid columns. The results obtained, however, can also be used if the column consists of several rolled portions tightly riveted together. (There will be no substantial reduction in the strength of such columns as compared with solid columns in the case of the usual spacing of rivets.[1]) The presence of rivets does not reduce appreciably the flexural rigidity of the column and it is usual practice in calculating the slenderness ratio l/r to disregard the rivet holes and use the gross cross-sectional area.[2] The same area is also used in calculating the allowable load for the column.[3]

34. Empirical Formulas for Column Design.—Instead of the critical stress diagrams discussed in the previous article, empirical formulas are sometimes used in column design.

One of the oldest formulas of this kind was originated by Tredgold.[4] It was adapted by Gordon to represent the results of Hodgkinson's experiments and was given in final form by Rankine. The allowable average compressive stress, as given by the *Rankine formula*, is

$$(\sigma_c)_w = \frac{a}{1 + b\left(\dfrac{l}{r}\right)^2}, \tag{a}$$

[1] The question of distances between the rivets will be discussed in Art. 37.

[2] The question of the effect of rivet holes on the magnitude of the buckling load has been investigated by A. Föppl, *Mitt. Mech.-Tech. Lab. Tech. Hochschule, München*, no. 25, 1897. See also writer's paper in *Bull. Polytech. Inst., Kiev*, 1908.

[3] See, for instance, American Institute of Steel Construction specifications and German specifications for designing compressed members, *loc. cit.*, p. 180.

[4] Regarding the history of the formula, see E. H. Salmon, "Columns," London, 1921. See also Todhunter and Pearson, "History of the Theory of Elasticity," vol. 1, p. 105, Cambridge, 1886.

in which a is a stress and b is a numerical factor, both of which are constant for a given material. Tetmajer showed[1] that, to bring this equation into agreement with experiments, the factor b cannot be constant and must diminish as l/r increases. This fact is usually disregarded and Eq. (a) is still often used in column design. By a proper selection of constants, it can be made to agree satisfactorily with the results of experiments within certain limits. For instance, the American Institute of Steel Construction, in its specifications of 1928, takes for the safe stress on the gross section of a column

$$(\sigma_c)_w = \frac{18{,}000}{1 + \dfrac{l^2}{18{,}000r^2}} \qquad (b)$$

for $l/r > 60$.

The *straight-line formula* gives the critical value of the average compressive stress in the following form:

$$\sigma_{cr} = a - b\frac{l}{r}, \qquad (c)$$

in which the constants a and b depend upon the mechanical properties of the material. For structural steel columns with hinged ends, from experiments by Tetmajer and Bauschinger, Eq. (c) becomes[2]

$$\sigma_{cr} = 48{,}000 - 210\frac{l}{r}. \qquad (d)$$

This formula was recommended by Tetmajer for $l/r \leq 110$. For larger slenderness ratios the use of Euler's formula has been proposed.

The straight-line formulas used in this country generally give the safe working stress rather than the critical stress. One of the common ones is the American Railway Engineering Association formula which is incorporated also in the building

---

[1] *Loc. cit.*, p. 171.

[2] See F. S. Jasinsky, "Scientific Papers," vol. 1, St. Petersburg, 1902, and *Ann. ponts chaussées*, 7 série, vol. 8, p. 256, 1894. See also an extensive analysis of experimental results made by J. M. Moncrieff, *Proc. Am. Soc. Civil Eng.*, vol. 45, 1900, and his book "The Practical Column under Central or Eccentric Loading," New York, 1901.

codes of the cities of Chicago and New York. It gives for the working stress[1]

$$(\sigma_c)_w = 16,000 - 70\frac{l}{r}, \qquad (e)$$

to be used for $30 < l/r < 120$ for main members and as high as $l/r = 150$ for secondary members. For values of $l/r < 30$, $(\sigma_c)_w = 14,000$ lb. per square inch is used.

The *parabolic formula* proposed by J. B. Johnson[2] is also sometimes used.[3] It gives for the critical value of the average compressive stress

$$\sigma_{cr} = a - b\left(\frac{l}{r}\right)^2, \qquad (f)$$

in which the constants a and b depend upon the mechanical properties of the material; they are usually chosen to make the parabola, represented by Eq. (f), tangent to Euler's curve and to make σ_{cr} equal the yield-point stress for short columns. For structural steel, Eq. (f) is sometimes taken in the form

$$\sigma_{cr} = 40,000 - 1.33\left(\frac{l}{r}\right)^2. \qquad (g)$$

This gives a parabola tangent to Euler's curve at $l/r = 122.5$ and makes $\sigma_{cr} = 40,000$ lb. per square inch for short columns. A suitable factor of safety varying from $2\frac{1}{2}$ to 3 should be used with this formula to obtain working stresses.

A variety of formulas, giving the critical stress as a function of the slenderness ratio, have been derived by using the modified Euler formula (see p. 159) and by taking the reduced modulus as a certain function of the critical compressive stress. We shall mention here a formula by Strand,[4] which can be adapted to

---

[1] It is obtained from formula (d) by introducing factor of safety 3.

[2] See C. E. Fuller and W. A. Johnston, "Applied Mechanics," vol. 2, p. 359, 1919. See also the paper by A. Ostenfeld, *Z. Ver. deut. Ing.*, vol. 42, p. 1462, 1898.

[3] Such a formula is specified for the design of struts by the U. S. Department of Commerce in its "Airworthiness Requirements of Air Commerce Regulations for Aircraft."

[4] STRAND, TORBJÖRN, *Zentr. Bauverwaltung*, 1914, p. 88. See also R. Mayer, "Die Knickfestigkeit," p. 74, J. Springer, Berlin, 1921.

represent with sufficient accuracy the experimental results obtained by Tetmajer with steel, cast-iron and wooden columns, and also a formula by P. M. Frandsen.[1]

35. Assumed Inaccuracies as a Basis of Column Design.—In

our discussion of the application of Euler's formula in column design (Art. 33), it was indicated that the principal difficulty encountered lies in the selection of a proper factor of safety, which should compensate for the various imperfections in a column. Under such circumstances, instead of considering an ideal case, it seems logical to assume, from the very beginning, certain inaccuracies in a column and then to derive a formula that contains not only the dimensions of the column and the quantities defining the mechanical properties of the material but also the values of the assumed inaccuracies. Having these inaccuracies explicitly appearing in a design formula, the selection of a proper factor of safety can be put on a more reliable basis.

The principal imperfections that make the behavior of actual columns so different from what is assumed in Euler's theory are: (1) an unavoidable eccentricity in the application of the compressive load, (2) initial curvature of the column and (3) non-homogeneity of the material. In the discussion of load-deflection curves obtained from experiments with columns, it was shown (see p. 178) that the effect of any eccentricity in load application on the deflection can be compensated for by assuming a properly chosen initial curvature of the column. Lack of homogeneity of the material can also be compensated for in an analogous manner. Assume for simplicity that a column consists of two parallel bars of different moduli joined together. To have uniform compression without lateral bending in such a column, the load must be applied, not at the centroid of the cross section, but at some other point, the position of which depends not only on the shape of the cross section but also on the ratio of the two moduli. Hence, the effect of the non-homogeneity of the material in this case is equivalent to the effect of a certain eccentricity and can also be compensated for by a properly chosen initial curvature of the column. In the same way we can make

[1] FRANDSEN, P. M., *Pub. Intern. Assoc. Bridge and Structural Eng.*, Zürich, vol. 1, p. 195, 1932. See also the paper by W. R. Osgood, *Bureau of Standards, Research Paper*, 492, 1932.

allowance for the variation in cross-sectional areas of rolled sections of which a column is built up.

Many investigators have tried to establish the amount of imperfection in actual columns by analyzing available experimental data on deflections of compressed columns. These calculations usually assume a constant eccentricity at both ends of the column and a certain value for the yield-point stress; then, from the magnitude of the load producing failure, the value of the eccentricity can be calculated. Analyzing Tetmajer's experiments in this way, Marston,[1] and later Jensen,[2] found as average values of the ratio of the eccentricity to the core radius the values $e/s = 0.06$ and $e/s = 0.07$.[3] The same values have been obtained also from the analysis of Lilly's experiments.[4]

There is no reason to assume that the eccentricity should be proportional to the core radius, and it seems more logical to assume that it depends on the length of the column.[5] On the basis of a comparative study of experimental data, Salmon recommends, for instance,

$$e = 0.001l. \qquad (a)$$

The question of initial curvature also was studied by various experimenters. The results of these investigations were collected by Salmon and are presented in Fig. 115, in which the initial deflection a (the maximum distance of any point on the center line from the straight line joining the centroids of the end cross sections) is plotted against the length of the column. It is seen that practically all the points are below the straight line

$$a = \tfrac{1}{750}l, \qquad (b)$$

which is proposed for calculating the probable initial deflection in actual columns.

[1] MARSTON, A., *Trans. Am. Soc. Civil Eng.*, vol. 39, p. 108, 1897.

[2] JENSEN, C., *Engineering*, London, vol. 85, p. 433, 1908.

[3] Considerable data regarding inaccuracies in columns have been collected by E. H. Salmon, "Columns," London, 1921. See also his discussion in *Trans. Am. Soc. Civil Eng.*, vol. 95, p. 1258, 1931.

[4] LILLY, W. E., *Trans. Am. Soc. Civil Eng.*, vol. 76, p. 258, New York.

[5] Several empirical formulas expressing the ratio e/s as a function of slenderness ratio are given in Salmon, *loc. cit.*

In addition to the imperfections (*a*) and (*b*), the effect of non-homogeneity of the material and of unavoidable variation in the cross-sectional area of the flanges should be considered.

All these imperfections can be replaced by an equivalent initial deflection of the column. To get this deflection from experiments, the load-deflection curves should be studied. From the discussion of the compression of initially curved bars (Art. 8) we know that for small loads an irregular behavior in the lateral deflection of the column should be expected. This fact was stated also by various experimenters. When the load

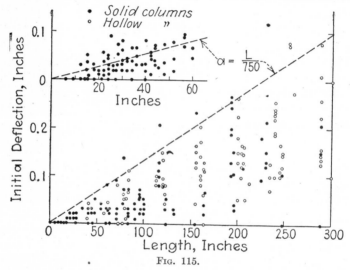

Fig. 115.

approaches its critical value, the first term in the series representing the deflection curve [see Eq. (49), p. 32] becomes predominant and we can get the equivalent initial deflection by plotting straight lines analogous to that shown in Fig. 112 (see p. 177). There is but little experimental data of this kind, and, in choosing the value of an equivalent initial deflection, it is necessary to rely for the present on older experimental data previously discussed. Assuming that all inaccuracies increase in the same proportion to the length of the column, and considering such eccentricities as given by Eq. (*a*) and such initial deflection as given by Eq. (*b*), we can finally take as an initial deflection

$$a = \tfrac{1}{400}l, \qquad\qquad (c)$$

which will be sufficient to compensate for all probable imperfections in a column.[1]

Accepting this, the design of a column is reduced to the problem of compression of an initially curved bar. If the initial deflection of the bar is given, the value of the average stress $(\sigma_c)_{Y.P.}$, at which the yield-point stress is reached at the outermost fiber, can be obtained with sufficient accuracy by

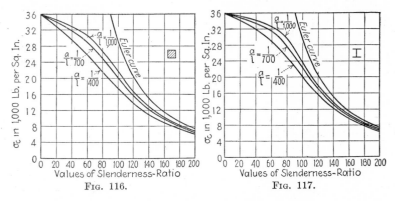

FIG. 116. FIG. 117.

interpolation from the curves in Fig. 42. From these curves it is possible to derive also a single curve for any given ratio between initial deflection a and the length of the column l.[2] Since the ratio of the core radius s to the radius of gyration depends on the shape of the cross section, the above curve will also depend on the shape of the cross section. In Figs. 116 and 117 two series of such curves[3] are shown calculated for a solid rectangular cross section and for a theoretical cross section in which all the material is assumed concentrated in the flanges.

[1] H. Kayser, in the paper in *Bautechnik*, Berlin, vol. 8, 1930, by working backward from test results to find the amount of initial deflection that must have been present, found values of a ranging from $a = \frac{1}{400}l$ to $a = \frac{1}{1000}l$. He recommended the use of $a = \frac{1}{400}l$.

[2] In such case the initial deflection a increases with the slenderness ratio and as a result of this $(\sigma_c)_{Y.P.}$ decreases more rapidly than that given by curves in Fig. 41.

[3] These curves are taken from the paper by D. H. Young, *Proc. Am. Soc. Civil Eng.*, December, 1934. Analogous curves, calculated on the assumption that the imperfections of the column are compensated for by a certain eccentricity, proportional to the length of the column, are given in the author's paper, *Trans. Am. Soc. Mech. Eng.*, Applied Mechanics Division, vol. 1, p. 173, 1933.

It is assumed that the structural steel has a yield-point stress of 36,000 lb. per square inch and that the imperfections in the column are equivalent to an initial deflection a at the middle such that $a/l = \frac{1}{400}, \frac{1}{700}$ and $1/1,000$. These curves show how $(\sigma_c)_{\text{Y.P.}}$ varies when the inaccuracies in a column increase.

Having such curves, the value of the average compressive stress $(\sigma_c)_{\text{Y.P.}}$ at which yielding in the outermost fiber begins can be obtained for any slenderness ratio l/r. In discussing the bending

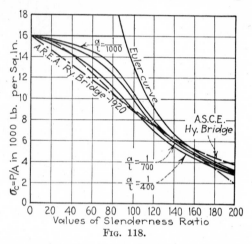

Fig. 118.

of initially curved columns beyond the yield point (see p. 62), it was shown that the loads producing the beginning of yielding do not differ much from the loads producing complete failure and that they approach these loads as the slenderness ratio increases. By taking $(\sigma_c)_{\text{Y.P.}}$ as a basis for calculating the allowable compressive stress $(\sigma_c)_w$, and using a constant factor of safety, we shall be on the safe side in all practical cases.[1] The margin of safety with respect to complete failure will be somewhat larger for smaller values of the slenderness ratio. Taking, for instance, the factor of safety 2.25[2] and using the curves shown in Fig. 117, we obtain for the allowable average stress $(\sigma_c)_w$ the values shown in Fig. 118.

[1] See footnote on p. 60.

[2] This value has been selected to make the results comparable with the usual standard formulas which are based on a working stress of 16,000 lb. per square inch. Thus the factor of safety for columns is taken the same as for tensile members since the weakening effect of various imperfections is compensated for by the assumed initial deflection.

For comparison there are given also curves obtained from standard American formulas of the Rankine and straight-line types. It may be seen that the proposed curve, corresponding to $a/l = \frac{1}{400}$, is in satisfactory agreement with accepted practice. Since this curve is based on a theoretically derived formula for average stress at which yielding begins, it can be easily adapted to any value of the yield-point stress and any value of the initial equivalent deflection.

In the previous discussion it was assumed that the imperfections in a column are proportional to the length of the column

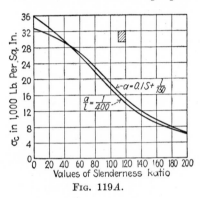

Fig. 119*A*.

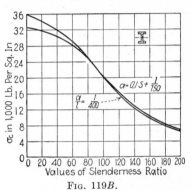

Fig. 119*B*.

and become very small for a column with a small slenderness ratio. Several authors have proposed dividing all imperfections into two kinds, one of which is independent of the length of the column and can be compensated for by an initial deflection proportional to the core radius s, and another which can be compensated for by an initial deflection proportional to the length of the column.[1] By using the curves shown in Fig. 42, a curve for $(\sigma_c)_{\text{Y.P.}}$ for any values of the above two types of imperfection can be readily obtained. In Fig. 119 are shown two curves of this kind calculated on the assumption that the initial deflection compensating for all imperfections is given by the formula

$$a = 0.1s + \tfrac{1}{750}l.$$

[1] Such a proposition was made first by F. S. Jasinsky, *loc. cit.*, p. 184. See also paper by H. S. Prichard, *Proc. Eng. Soc. Western Penn.*, Pittsburgh, Pa., vol. 23, p. 325, 1908, and O. H. Basquin, *Jour. Western Soc. Eng.*, Chicago, vol. 18, p. 457, 1913.

One of these curves assumes a solid rectangular cross section and the other a theoretical cross section in which all the material is concentrated in the flanges. For comparison, the previous two curves (Figs. 116 and 117), calculated for $a = \frac{1}{400}l$, are also shown in the figure.

36. Various End Conditions.—In the discussion of the preceding article it was always assumed that the ends of the compressed column were free to rotate. There are cases where actual conditions approach this assumption, but the ends of columns, as encountered in practice, usually are restrained to some degree and cannot rotate freely. The critical value of the load in such cases depends on the magnitude of the coefficients of restraint and becomes a maximum when the ends are absolutely fixed. Let us begin with a discussion of this extreme case. If the ends of the column are not free to rotate during compression, any eccentricities in the application of the compressive forces do not result in bending of the column and a straight column will undergo only a uniform compression. Hence, in the discussion of imperfections in columns with built-in ends, only initial curvature need be considered. The bending stresses due to this factor naturally will depend on the shape of the initial curvature of the column.

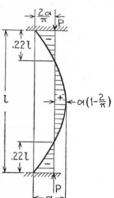

Fig. 120.

Assuming, for example, an initial curvature as given by the sine curve $y = a \sin (\pi x/l)$ (Fig. 120), we conclude that for small loads P, where the deflections due to bending can be neglected in comparison with the initial deflections, there must be at the ends an eccentricity equal to $2a/\pi$, since only under this condition will the total bending-moment area, shaded in the figure, give zero rotation of one end of the column with respect to the other.

With the increase of the compressive load, the additional deflection due to bending should be considered. By using Eqs. (j) and (k) of Art. 8, we find that the bending moments M_1 at the ends and the bending moment M_2 at the middle are

$$M_1 = -\frac{aP}{(1 - \alpha)} \frac{\pi\alpha}{2u \tan u}; \qquad M_2 = \frac{aP}{1 - \alpha}\left(1 - \frac{\pi\alpha}{2u \sin u}\right); \quad (a)$$

in which,

$$\alpha = \frac{Pl^2}{\pi^2 EI}; \qquad u = \frac{l}{2}\sqrt{\frac{P}{EI}}. \qquad (b)$$

For small values of the load P we can assume $u \approx \sin u \approx \tan u$ and neglect α in comparison with unity. Then

$$M_1 = -\frac{2aP}{\pi}; \qquad M_2 = aP\left(1 - \frac{2}{\pi}\right), \qquad (c)$$

which requires an eccentricity of $2a/\pi$ in the application of the load, as mentioned above. It is seen that the moments at the ends are larger than the moment at the middle, and the ratio of these moments is:[1]

$$\frac{M_1}{M_2} = -\frac{2}{\pi} : \left(1 - \frac{2}{\pi}\right) \approx -1.75.$$

In the case of short columns the ultimate load is usually small in comparison with the Euler load and the above discussion regarding the moments M_1 and M_2 can be applied.

With the increase of the load P the bending moments M_1 and M_2 increase also, and at the same time their ratio diminishes. Take, for instance, $P = \pi^2 EI/l^2$, *i.e.*, a compressive load equal to one-quarter of the critical load for a column with built-in ends. Then, from Eqs. (a), we find

$$M_1 = -\frac{\pi aP}{4}; \qquad M_2 = \frac{aP}{2};$$

and

$$M_1 : M_2 = -\frac{\pi}{2} \approx -1.57.$$

In the case of slender columns, the ultimate load, for a small initial curvature, approaches the value $4\pi^2 EI/l^2$ and the quantity u in Eqs. (a) approaches the value π. The moments M_1 and M_2 at such values of u increase indefinitely and their ratio approaches unity. The conditions of bending of the column approach those in which the initial curvature of the column is given by the equation

---

[1] It should be noted that this ratio depends to a certain extent on the shape of the initial curvature. Assuming, for instance, that the initial curve is a parabola symmetrical about the middle of the bar, and considering such shaded area as shown in Fig. 120, we will find for this case $M_1/M_2 = -2$.

$$y = \frac{a}{2}\left(1 - \cos \frac{2\pi x}{l}\right).$$

In this case (see Fig. 121) the moments at the ends and at the middle are always numerically equal and the maximum stress is the same as for a compressed column with hinged ends having a length equal to $l/2$ and an initial deflection represented by a sine curve with the deflection $a/2$ at the middle. The expression for the maximum bending moment in this case is [see Eq. (48), p. 32]

FIG. 121.

$$M = \frac{aP}{2\left(1 - \frac{\alpha}{4}\right)}.$$

The ratio of the absolute value of the moment M_1, from Eqs. (a), to the moment M is

$$M_1 : M = \frac{2\sqrt{\alpha}\left(1 - \frac{\alpha}{4}\right)}{(1 - \alpha)\tan\left(\pi\sqrt{\alpha}/2\right)}.$$

For small values of α this ratio approaches the value $4/\pi$. With the increase of the load P, α increases and the ratio diminishes. For $\alpha = 1$ the ratio is equal to $3\pi/8$. When α approaches the value 4, corresponding to Euler's load for a column with built-in ends, the ratio of the moments approaches the value $8/3\pi$.

From this discussion it can be concluded that, if the column represented in Fig. 120 is a slender column which fails principally because of bending stresses, we will be on the safe side in taking the reduced length of the column equal to half of the actual length and using the curves calculated for columns with hinged ends (Fig. 118). In the case of short columns the maximum bending stress may be somewhat larger than that obtained by using the above procedure, but in such columns the bending stresses at failure are usually small in comparison with the direct stress; hence, it seems satisfactory to use also in this case the reduced length $l/2$ and the curves in Fig. 118. Such procedure is further justified if we note that, in discussing columns with hinged ends, the magnitude of the initial curvature was chosen so as to compensate, not only for the crookedness of the column, but also for eccentricity in application of the load, and that in the case of built-in ends this eccentricity is absent. Thus, discussing the design of columns with built-in ends on the basis of assumed inaccuracies, we arrive at the same conclusion regarding reduced length as we did when the diagram of critical stresses was used for determining working stresses.

Up to this point we have considered only two extreme cases, columns with hinged ends and columns with built-in ends. Compressed members in structures are usually in somewhat intermediate conditions, the restraint at the ends being dependent on the rigidity of adjacent members of the structure. The degree of fixity of the ends can be obtained only on the basis of investigation of the stability of the entire structure. Several examples of such investigations have been discussed in Chap. 2 of this book, and it was shown that in each particular case the critical load for a compressed member of a structure can be calculated as for a column with hinged ends having a certain reduced length. Having this reduced length, the design of the compressed member can be made by using the curves of Fig. 118.

Only in the case of the simplest structures can the stability conditions be established without much difficulty. Generally, in designing compression members of a structure, the reduced length of these members is taken on the basis of some approximate considerations. So, for instance, in discussing the stability of the compressed top chord of a truss, it may be seen that the wind bracing and the members in the plane of the truss do not represent much resistance to lateral buckling of the chord members in alternate directions in successive panels and it is common practice to consider these members in lateral buckling as pinended columns, so that the actual length between the theoretical hinges should be used in this case. The same conclusion can be made also regarding the lateral buckling of compressed diagonals and verticals of a truss.

In considering the buckling of compressed members in the plane of a truss, it should be noted that, owing to rigidity of the joints, certain bending moments will be produced at the ends of these members. The magnitude of these moments can be calculated by the methods used in analyzing secondary stresses in trusses. In this analysis the effect of axial forces on the bending of truss members is usually neglected[1] so that the moments are proportional to the loads. Under such a condition each compression member may be considered as an eccentrically loaded column with known eccentricities at the ends, and the allowable average compressive stress can be obtained by interpolation from the curves given in Figs. 21 to 24 (see p. 42). The presence of initial curvature in a compressed member will add to the bending stresses and should be allowed for by superposing at each end an equivalent eccentricity e on the actual eccentricities mentioned above and calculated from the secondary stress analysis. These modified values of the eccentricities will then be used in calculating working stresses from the curves in Figs. 21 to 24. In a similar manner, the deflection of a compressed member due to its own weight can be compensated for by introducing certain additional eccentricity.

37. The Design of Built-up Columns.—In discussing buckling of latticed columns in Art. 27, Eq. (93), for calculating critical loads for latticed columns, and Eq. (96), for batten-plate columns, were established. In using these equations the actual built-up column is replaced by an equivalent column of a reduced length, which is to be determined, in the case of a latticed column as shown in Fig. 86a, from the equation

$$L = l\sqrt{1 + \frac{\pi^2 EI}{l^2}\left(\frac{1}{A_d E \sin \phi \cos^2 \phi} + \frac{b}{A_b E a}\right)}, \quad (108)$$

and, in the case of a batten-plate column as shown in Fig. 88, from the equation

$$L = l\sqrt{1 + \frac{\pi^2 EI}{l^2}\left(\frac{ab}{12 EI_b} + \frac{a^2}{24 EI_c} + \frac{na}{b A_b G}\right)}. \quad (109)$$

These formulas, derived for the case of buckling in the elastic range, can also be used beyond the elastic limit by replacing the modulus of elasticity E with the reduced modulus E_r (see Art. 29) in the expressions for the flexural rigidity EI of the column and flexural

---

[1] This can be justified if we note that the slenderness ratio of the chord members is usually small so that the acting compressive forces are small in comparison with Euler's loads. The slenderness ratio of diagonals and verticals may be larger but they are very often bent in an *s*-shape. Under such conditions the effect of the axial forces on deflections, as can be concluded from the general discussion of Art. 7, is small.

rigidity EI_c of one chord. In calculating the reduced modulus, we can use, with sufficient accuracy, the actual slenderness ratio l/r of the column and take the ratio E_r/E, for any value of l/r, equal to the ratio of the ordinate of the curve for σ_{cr}, such as shown in Fig. 113, to the corresponding ordinate of Euler's curve.

When the reduced length of a built-up column is determined, the allowable stress for the corresponding value of L/r is found from the curve shown in Fig. 118 by using a proper factor of safety. The use of this curve for built-up columns amounts to assuming that the imperfections are a function of the reduced length L rather than the true length. This means that a slightly higher factor of safety will be used in the case of built-up columns, which seems completely satisfactory.

A considerable number of experiments have been made with built-up columns,[1] but only in a few cases were the experiments made with the intention of verifying any theory. Therefore, only those few contain the information necessary for such verification. Of particular importance are experiments made by Petermann[2] and by J. Kayser,[3] dealing with batten-plate columns. The flexibility of such columns in the plane parallel to the batten plates depends very much on the dimensions of the battens and the distance between them. Experimental values of critical loads are in satisfactory agreement with those calculated by using Eq. (109).

In the design of built-up columns the proper dimensioning of the lattice bars and batten plates is of great practical importance. In these calculations we shall proceed as before and shall take as a basis for determining stresses in these details some imperfections in the column, such as an initial curvature or some eccentricity in load application. When this is taken, it will be possible to evaluate the maximum shearing force that arises for any value of the compressive load P. This maximum shearing force will then be calculated for the value of the load P at which

---

[1] A discussion of some of these experiments is given in the report of the Steel Column Research Committee, *loc. cit.*, p. 175. See also R. Mayer, "Die Knickfestigkeit," p. 387, Berlin, 1921, and D. Rühl, "Berechnung gegliederter Knickstäbe," Berlin, 1932.

[2] *Bauingenieur*, vol. 4, p. 1009, Berlin, 1926, and *Bauingenieur*, vol. 9, p. 509, 1931.

[3] *Bauingenieur*, vol. 8, p. 200, 1930.

yielding in the extreme fibers of the column begins. It is logical to design the lattice bars and batten plates on the basis of this maximum shearing force so that they and the extreme fibers of the column will begin to yield simultaneously.

The imperfections in a column should be taken so as to assume the most unfavorable condition in so far as shearing forces are concerned. Possible types of imperfection, consisting of an initial curvature or an initial eccentricity in the application of the load, are shown in Fig. 122. The value of the initial

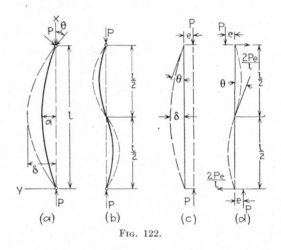

Fig. 122.

deflection a or initial eccentricity e will be taken, as before, proportional to the length, which will be, in this case, the reduced length of the column, calculated from Eq. (108) or (109). Considering the case in which the initial curvature is represented by one half-wave of a sine curve (Fig. 122a), the maximum shearing force takes place at the ends of the column. For the small deflections, which we have in practice, we take $Q_{max.} = P\theta$. In the case of an S-shaped initial curvature (Fig. 122b), each half of the column can be considered as a column of the previous kind but of length $l/2$ and deflection $\delta/2$. The initial shearing force at the ends will be the same as in the previous case but the value of the shearing force at failure will be smaller than in the previous case since, at failure, regardless of its initial shape, the column will buckle in one half-wave at the critical load for the length l, which is smaller than the critical load for the length $l/2$.

The case of two equal eccentricities in the same direction (Fig. 122c) is also more favorable than the case in Fig. 122a. Assuming that eccentricity e is such that both columns fail at the same load P, the bending moments at the middle will be equal at failure for both cases; hence the corresponding values of δ, θ and Q_{max} will be smaller for case (c) than for case (a). In the case of equal eccentricities in opposite directions (Fig. 122d), there will be horizontal reactions at the ends equal to $2Pe/l$; the maximum shearing force takes place at the middle and is equal to $\dfrac{2Pe}{l} + P\theta$. It is possible that under certain conditions this case will be more unfavorable than case (a). Thus, finally, cases (a) and (d) should be considered in detail.[1]

Beginning with case (a) and using Eq. (48) for the deflection curve, we find that the angle θ at the ends is

$$\theta = \left(\frac{dy}{dx}\right)_{x=0} = \frac{\pi a}{l(1 - \alpha)}, \tag{a}$$

where $\alpha = Pl^2/\pi^2 EI$; and we obtain for the maximum shearing force

$$Q_{max.} = P\frac{\pi a}{l(1 - \alpha)}.$$

Dividing both sides of this equation by the cross-sectional area A and using the notation $(\sigma_c)_{Y.P.}$ for the average compressive stress when yielding in the most extreme fiber of the column begins, the value of the maximum shearing force per unit of cross-sectional area at which yielding begins is

$$\frac{Q_{max.}}{A} = (\sigma_c)_{Y.P.} \frac{\pi a}{l(1 - \alpha)}. \tag{110}$$

For any slenderness ratio l/r and a given initial deflection a, we find $(\sigma_c)_{Y.P.}$ from the curves in Fig. 118. Then $Q_{max.}$ is calculated from Eq. (110). This calculation can be simplified if we solve Eq. (52) (see p. 44) for a and substitute its value in Eq. (110). We obtain, then,

[1] This question is discussed in more detail in the paper by D. H. Young, *Proc. Am. Soc. Civil Eng.*, December, 1934, and another paper by the same author in *Pub. Intern. Assoc. Bridge and Structural Eng.*, Zürich, vol. 2, p. 480, 1934.

$$\frac{Q_{max.}}{A} = \frac{\pi s}{l}[\sigma_{Y.P.} - (\sigma_c)_{Y.P.}]. \tag{111}$$

Knowing $\sigma_{Y.P.}$ and using the curves in Fig. 118 for determining $(\sigma_c)_{Y.P.}$, we can, for any value of the initial deflection a, represent $Q_{max.}/A$ as a function of the slenderness ratio l/r. In Fig. 123 two curves of this kind are shown calculated for $a/l = \frac{1}{400}$ and $a/l = \frac{1}{700}$. It is assumed that all the material of the column is concentrated in the flanges; hence we have $s = r$.

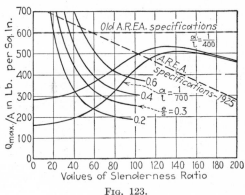

Fig. 123.

In case (d), the angle of rotation θ of the middle cross section of the column is found by considering each half of the column as a compressed beam of span $l/2$ simply supported at the ends and bent by a couple Pe. Then, from Eq. 19 (see p. 12),

$$\theta = \frac{e}{l}\left(\frac{kl}{\sin\frac{kl}{2}} - 2\right),$$

where

$$k = \sqrt{\frac{P}{EI}}.$$

The maximum shearing force, then, is

$$Q_{max.} = \frac{2Pe}{l} + P\theta = \frac{Pe}{l}\frac{kl}{\sin\frac{kl}{2}}. \tag{b}$$

In the case of short columns, failure occurs at a load that is small in comparison with Euler's load; then $kl/2$ is small and we can assume $\sin \dfrac{kl}{2} \approx \dfrac{kl}{2}$. Equation (b) gives in this case

$$Q_{\text{max.}} = \frac{2Pe}{l}.$$

That is, the maximum shearing force is equal to the lateral reaction at either end (Fig. 122d). In the case of slender columns, in which the load P may reach Euler's load before the maximum fiber stress reaches the yield-point stress, $kl/2$ approaches the value $\pi/2$ and we see from Eq. (b) that the maximum shearing force may become 57 per cent higher than the value of the lateral reactions $2Pe/l$.

Dividing Eq. (b) by the cross-sectional area, we obtain the maximum shearing force per unit area for the beginning of yielding in the extreme fiber:

$$\frac{Q_{\text{max.}}}{A} = (\sigma_c)_{\text{Y.P.}} \frac{e}{l} \frac{kl}{\sin \dfrac{kl}{2}}. \tag{112}$$

For any value of e/l and slenderness ratio l/r the value of $(\sigma_c)_{\text{Y.P.}}$ can be obtained from the curves in Fig. 24. Then, by using Eq. (112), the value $Q_{\text{max.}}/A$ can be calculated for various values of e/l and l/r. Such calculations show that in general the assumption of an initial curvature results in a larger value for $Q_{\text{max.}}$ and should be taken as a basis for the design of the details of built-up columns if the imperfections given by a or e are proportional to the length l. If the eccentricities in case (d) are given some constant value instead of being assumed proportional to l, much higher shearing force will be obtained from Eq. (112) for small values of the slenderness ratio l/r. Curves are shown in Fig. 123, in which constant values of $e/s = 0.2, 0.3, 0.4, 0.6$ have been used.

For comparison, there are shown in Fig. 123 also two straight lines representing the old and the new American Railway Engineering Association specifications regarding allowance for shearing forces in columns. For the amount of imperfections assumed in our previous discussion, the old specifications are always on the safe side. The new specification underestimates shearing force for slender columns[1] and at the same time seems to give too large requirements for shorter columns.   It must be kept in mind, however, that the curves shown in Fig. 123 take account of shearing force due to initial imperfections only. When a compressed member in a truss is subjected to secondary end moments as discussed on p. 195, the shearing force may become very large, and it seems logical to design the details of such members to resist the shearing forces that actually arise because of end moments.[2]

Having curves such as shown in Fig. 123, the procedure of the design of a built-up column will be as follows: Assume certain cross-sectional dimensions of the column and also some dimen-

FIG. 124.

sions for details.   Then the reduced length of the column will be calculated from Eq. (108) or (109) and the allowable average compressive stress will be obtained from the curve in Fig. 118.   By using this trial-and-error method the necessary cross-sectional dimensions will be established.   The necessary strength of the lattice bars or batten plates and the necessary number of rivets at the joints should now be checked by using the curve in Fig. 123.   The same curve can be used also for checking the distance between the rivets in riveted columns.

It is assumed in this discussion that buckling of the column occurs in the plane parallel to the batten plates or lattice bars. Sometimes the possibility of distortion of the cross section of a built-up column should be considered.   For instance, in the case of a column consisting of four longitudinal bars connected by lattice bars (Fig. 124), a distortion may occur such as shown in the figure by dotted lines.   To eliminate the possibility of such distortion, certain bracing in the cross-sectional planes of the column or use of diaphragms is necessary.   Between the two planes with cross-sectional bracings or two diaphragms, each longitudinal bar can be considered as a strut with hinged ends elastically supported along the length by lattice bars.   By using the energy method, the required distance between the braced cross sections can be checked.

---

[1] It should be noted, however, that these specifications also limit slenderness ratio to 100 for main compression members.

[2] This problem is discussed in the paper by D. H. Young, *loc. cit.*, p. 199.

In the case of built-up columns consisting of comparatively thin plates, local failure may occur owing to buckling of compressed plates if the unsupported width of these plates surpasses certain limits. The requirements regarding unsupported width of plates and the methods of reinforcing plates by introducing stiffeners will be discussed later in the chapter on the stability of plates.

CHAPTER IV

BUCKLING OF COMPRESSED RINGS AND CURVED BARS

38. Bending of a Thin Curved Bar with a Circular Axis.—Let us consider a curved bar AB (Fig. 125) bent in the plane of its initial curvature and let us assume that one of the principal axes of the cross sections lies in the same plane. Denoting by r_0 the initial radius of curvature of the center line of the bar and by r the radius of curvature after deformation at any point

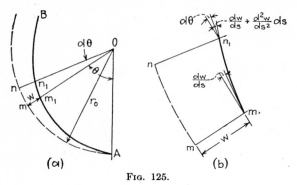

Fig. 125.

of the center line, defined by the angle θ, the relation between the change in curvature and the magnitude of the bending moment M in the case of a thin bar is given by the equation

$$EI\left(\frac{1}{r} - \frac{1}{r_0}\right) = -M, \qquad (a)$$

in which EI is the flexural rigidity of the bar in the plane of its initial curvature. The minus sign on the right side of the equation follows from the sign of the bending moment, which is taken to be positive when it produces a decrease in the initial curvature of the bar.

The change in the curvature of the bar during bending will be found from a consideration of the deformation of a small element mn of the ring included between two radii with the angle $d\theta$ between them. The initial length of the element and its initial curvature are

$$ds = r_0 \, d\theta; \qquad \frac{d\theta}{ds} = \frac{1}{r_0}. \qquad (b)$$

We will consider only small deformations of the ring. The radial displacement of a point m during bending is designated by w and is taken positive when it is directed toward the center. There will also be some displacement of the point m in a tangential direction, but we will disregard this and assume that the curvature of the element mn after deformation is the same as the curvature of the element $m_1 n_1$ included between the same radii mO and nO. This later curvature is given by the equation

$$\frac{1}{r} = \frac{d\theta + \Delta \, d\theta}{ds + \Delta \, ds}, \qquad (c)$$

in which $d\theta + \Delta \, d\theta$ denotes the angle between the normal cross sections m_1 and n_1 of the deformed bar and $ds + \Delta \, ds$ the length of the element $m_1 n_1$. In calculating the small angle $\Delta \, d\theta$, we note that the angle between the tangent to the center line at m_1 and the perpendicular to the radius mO is dw/ds (Fig. 125b). The corresponding angle at the cross section n_1 is

$$\frac{dw}{ds} + \frac{d^2w}{ds^2} \, ds.$$

Hence,

$$\Delta \, d\theta = \frac{d^2w}{ds^2} \, ds. \qquad (d)$$

In comparing the length of the element $m_1 n_1$ with that of the element mn, the small angle dw/ds is neglected and the length $m_1 n_1$ is taken equal to $(r_0 - w)d\theta$. Then

$$\Delta \, ds = -w \, d\theta = -\frac{w \, ds}{r_0}. \qquad (e)$$

Substituting expressions (d) and (e) in Eq. (c) gives

$$\frac{1}{r} = \frac{d\theta + \dfrac{d^2w}{ds^2} \, ds}{ds\left(1 - \dfrac{w}{r_0}\right)},$$

or, neglecting the small quantities of higher order,

$$\frac{1}{r} = \frac{1}{r_0}\left(1 + \frac{w}{r_0}\right) + \frac{d^2w}{ds^2}.$$

Substituting this into Eq. (*a*), we obtain

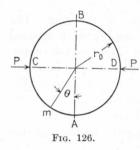

FIG. 126.

$$\frac{d^2w}{ds^2} + \frac{w}{r^2_0} = -\frac{M}{EI} \qquad (f)$$

or

$$\frac{d^2w}{d\theta^2} + w = -\frac{Mr^2_0}{EI}. \qquad (113)$$

This is the differential equation for the deflection curve of a thin bar with a circular center line.[1] For an infinitely large r_0 this equation coincides with that for a straight bar.

As an example of the application of Eq. (113), let us consider the case of compression of a ring by two forces P acting along a diameter (Fig. 126). From the principle of least work, the bending moment at A and B is found[2] equal to $\dfrac{-Pr_0\left(1 - \dfrac{2}{\pi}\right)}{2}$;

then, for any cross section m, bending moment is

$$M = \frac{Pr_0}{2}\left(\frac{2}{\pi} - \cos\theta\right).$$

Using this value in Eq. (113), we obtain

$$\frac{d^2w}{d\theta^2} + w = -\frac{Pr^3_0}{2EI}\left(\frac{2}{\pi} - \cos\theta\right), \qquad (g)$$

from which, by integration,

$$w = A\cos\theta + B\sin\theta - \frac{Pr^3_0}{\pi EI} + \frac{Pr^3_0}{4EI}\theta\sin\theta.$$

---

[1] This equation was established by J. Boussinesq, *Compt. rend.*, vol. 97, p. 843, 1883. See also H. Lamb, *Proc. London Math. Soc.*, vol. 19, p. 365, 1888, and R. Mayer, *Z. Math. Physik*, vol. 61, p. 246, 1913.

[2] See writer's "Strength of Materials," vol. 2, p. 437. We take this expression for the bending moment instead of deriving it here since the latter requires the discussion of the extension of the axis of the ring, which will be given in the next article.

The constants of integration A and B are determined from the conditions of symmetry:

$$\frac{dw}{d\theta} = 0, \quad \text{for} \quad \theta = 0 \quad \text{and for} \quad \theta = \frac{\pi}{2}.$$

Then,

$$w = -\frac{Pr^3{}_0}{\pi EI} + \frac{Pr^3{}_0}{4EI}\theta \sin \theta + \frac{Pr^3{}_0}{4EI} \cos \theta.$$

For $\theta = 0$ and $\theta = \pi/2$, we obtain

$$(w)_{\theta=0} = -\frac{Pr^3{}_0}{EI}\left(\frac{1}{\pi} - \frac{1}{4}\right); \quad (w)_{\theta=\frac{\pi}{2}} = \frac{Pr^3{}_0}{EI}\left(\frac{\pi}{8} - \frac{1}{\pi}\right); \quad (114)$$

and the points C and D approach each other by the amount

$$\delta = \frac{2Pr^3{}_0}{EI}\left(\frac{\pi}{8} - \frac{1}{\pi}\right). \tag{115}$$

An equation analogous to Eq. (113) can be obtained also for the bending of a long circular tube if the load does not change along the axis of the tube. In such case we consider an elemental ring cut out of the tube by two cross sections perpendicular to the axis of the tube and unit length apart. Since the ring is a portion of the long tube, the rectangular cross sections of the ring do not distort during bending, as in the case of an isolated ring, and thus the quantity $\frac{E}{1 - \nu^2}$, where ν is Poisson's ratio, should be used in place of E in Eq. (113). Denoting by h the thickness of the tube, the moment of inertia of the cross-sectional area of the elemental ring is $h^3/12$ and the differential equation for deflection of such a ring becomes

$$\frac{d^2w}{d\theta^2} + w = -\frac{12(1 - \nu^2)Mr^2{}_0}{Eh^3}. \tag{113'}$$

This equation, instead of Eq. (113), should be used in investigating bending of long circular tubes. M in this case denotes the bending moment per unit length of tube.

39. Application of Trigonometric Series in the Study of Bending of a Thin Circular Ring.—In discussing small deflections of a ring in its plane, we resolve the displacement of any point m of the center line into two components, w in a radial direction toward the center of the ring (Fig. 127) and v in a tangential direction. In the most general case the radial displacement w can be represented in the form of the trigonometric series

$$w = a_1 \cos \theta + a_2 \cos 2\theta + \cdots + b_1 \sin \theta +$$
$$b_2 \sin 2\theta + \cdots . \qquad (a)$$

The tangential displacement will be taken in such a form as to make the extension of the center line of the ring zero. In this manner the actual ring is replaced by a certain hypothetical ideal ring with an inextensible center line. The discussion of *inextensional deformations* of rings and shells was originated by Lord Rayleigh.[1] He noticed that, in the case of bending of thin rings, the displacements due to extension of the center line of a ring are very small in comparison with the displacement due to bending and usually can be neglected.

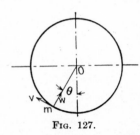

Fig. 127.

The unit elongation of the center line of a ring during bending consists, in general, of two parts: the part due to tangential displacement v, equal to dv/ds, and the part due to radial displacements, equal to $-w/r_0$. Hence we have

$$\epsilon = \frac{1}{r_0}\left(\frac{dv}{d\theta} - w\right).$$

The condition of inextensional deformation of the ring is

$$\frac{dv}{d\theta} - w = 0, \qquad (b)$$

from which, by using Eq. (a), we obtain

$$v = a_1 \sin \theta + \tfrac{1}{2}a_2 \sin 2\theta + \cdots - b_1 \cos \theta -$$
$$\tfrac{1}{2}b_2 \cos 2\theta - \cdots . \qquad (c)$$

Thus the problem of bending of a ring reduces to that of calculating the coefficients $a_1, a_2, \ldots$ and $b_1, b_2, \ldots$ in expressions (a) and (c). For this calculation the same method as in the case of straight beams (see Art. 7) will be used. We derive the expression for strain energy of the ring in bending and

[1] Lord Rayleigh, "Theory of Sound," 2d ed., Chap. X$_A$. See also author's paper on Application of Normal Coordinates, *Bull. Polytech. Inst., Kiev*, 1910.

determine the coefficients of the above series by using the principle of virtual displacements.

The strain energy of bending of a thin ring is obtained by applying the same formula as in the case of a straight bar; then, by using Eq. (113),

$$V = \int_0^{2\pi} \frac{M^2 r_0\, d\theta}{2EI} = \frac{EI}{2r_0^3} \int_0^{2\pi} \left(\frac{d^2 w}{d\theta^2} + w \right)^2 d\theta.$$

Substituting series (a) for w and integrating, we obtain

$$V = \frac{\pi EI}{2r_0^3} \sum_{n=2}^{n=\infty} (n^2 - 1)^2 (a^2_n + b^2_n). \tag{116}$$

This series does not contain terms with coefficients a_1 and b_1 since the corresponding displacements

$$\left. \begin{aligned} w &= a_1 \cos \theta + b_1 \sin \theta; \\ v &= a_1 \sin \theta - b_1 \cos \theta \end{aligned} \right\} \tag{d}$$

represent the displacement of the ring as a rigid body in its plane. It may be seen readily that if a_1 and b_1 are vertical and horizontal components of the latter displacement, expressions (d) represent the radial and tangential displacements for any point m (Fig. 127).

Having expression (116) for the strain energy, we can, in each particular case, easily calculate the coefficients a_1, a_2, . . . , b_1, b_2, ... Take as an example the case represented in Fig. 126. From the condition of symmetry it can be concluded that the coefficients b_1, b_2, . . . in expression (a) vanish. In calculating any coefficient a_n we assume that this coefficient is increased by δa_n. The corresponding deflection of the ring, from Eq. (a), is $\delta a_n \cos n\theta$, and during this displacement the forces P produce the work

$$P\delta a_n \left(\cos \frac{n\pi}{2} + \cos \frac{3n\pi}{2} \right).$$

For n equal to an odd number, this work is equal to zero; for n equal to an even number, we have

$$\cos \frac{n\pi}{2} = \cos \frac{3n\pi}{2} = (-1)^{\frac{n}{2}},$$

and the above expression for the work is equal to

$$(-1)^{\frac{n}{2}}2P\delta a_n. \qquad (e)$$

Applying the principle of virtual work, the equation for determining the coefficient a_n, for n equal to an even number, becomes

$$\frac{\partial V}{\partial a_n}\delta a_n = (-1)^{\frac{n}{2}}2P\delta a_n.$$

Substituting for V its expression (116), we obtain

$$a_n = \frac{(-1)^{\frac{n}{2}}2Pr^3_0}{\pi(n^2-1)^2EI}. \qquad (f)$$

In the same way it can be shown that all coefficients with n equal to an odd number vanish.[1] Thus the series (a) and (c), representing deflections of the center line of the ring, contain only terms with coefficients a_n where $n = 2, 4, 6, \cdots$. For radial displacements we obtain, from (a),

$$w = \frac{2Pr^3_0}{\pi EI}\sum_{n=2,4,6,\cdots}^{\infty}\frac{(-1)^{\frac{n}{2}}\cos n\theta}{(n^2-1)^2}. \qquad (117)$$

The points C and D where the forces P are applied will approach each other by the quantity

$$\delta = (w)_{\theta=\frac{\pi}{2}} + (w)_{\theta=\frac{3\pi}{2}} = \frac{4Pr^3_0}{\pi EI}\sum_{n=2,4,6,\cdots}^{\infty}\frac{1}{(n^2-1)^2}. \qquad (117')$$

It can be shown that this series gives the same result as formula (115) obtained before (see p. 207).

As a second example, let us consider the bending of a circular ring by hydrostatic pressure (Fig. 128). The center of the ring is held at a constant depth d by the force P. Then, assuming that the width of the ring in the direction perpendicular to the plane of the figure is unity, and denoting by γ the weight of the liquid per unit volume, the intensity of hydrostatic pressure at any point m is

$$\gamma(d + r_0 \cos \theta).$$

---

[1] The same conclusion follows from the condition of symmetry with respect to horizontal diameter of the ring.

From statics the force P is equal to $\pi r^2_0 \gamma$. Using again the principle of virtual displacements and noting that hydrostatic pressure produces work only on radial displacements w, the

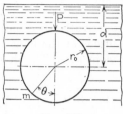

FIG. 128.

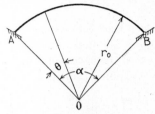

FIG. 129.

equation for calculating coefficients a_n in the series (a) and (c) becomes

$$\frac{\partial V}{\partial a_n} \delta a_n = \delta a_n \left[P \cos n\pi + r_0 \gamma \int_0^{2\pi} (\mathrm{d} + r_0 \cos \theta) \cos n\theta \, d\theta \right] = \delta a_n P(-1)^n, \quad \text{for} \quad n > 1.$$

For $n = 1$, the right side of the equation becomes equal to zero. Substituting for V its expression (116), we obtain

$$a_n = \frac{(-1)^n P r^3_0}{\pi (n^2 - 1)^2 EI}, \quad \text{for} \quad n > 1; \quad a_1 = 0.$$

All the coefficients b_n in series (a) and (c) vanish in virtue of symmetry. Hence we obtain

$$w = \frac{P r^3_0}{\pi EI} \sum_{n = 2, 3, 4, \cdots}^{\infty} \frac{(-1)^n \cos n\theta}{(n^2 - 1)^2};$$

$$v = \frac{P r^3_0}{\pi EI} \sum_{n = 2, 3, 4, \cdots}^{\infty} \frac{(-1)^n \sin n\theta}{n(n^2 - 1)^2}.$$

In this analysis the effect of the compressive force in the ring on bending is entirely neglected, which is legitimate only if this compressive force is small in comparison with the critical value of the same force at which the ring buckles. This question is discussed further in the following article.

If, instead of a complete circular ring, we have a curved bar with a circular center line and hinged ends (Fig. 129), the same method as in the previous discussion can be applied. Designating the central angle of the arch by α, the radial displacement w can be taken in the form of a series

$$w = a_1 \sin \frac{\pi\theta}{\alpha} + a_2 \sin \frac{2\pi\theta}{\alpha} + a_3 \sin \frac{3\pi\theta}{\alpha} + \cdots. \qquad (g)$$

It is seen that this series and its second derivative become equal to zero at the ends, satisfying the conditions at the hinges with respect to displacements and bending moments. The displacement v, from Eq. (b) is

$$v = -\frac{\alpha}{\pi}\left(a_1 \cos \frac{\pi\theta}{\alpha} + \frac{1}{2}a_2 \cos \frac{2\pi\theta}{\alpha} + \frac{1}{3}a_3 \cos \frac{3\pi\theta}{\alpha} + \cdots \right). \qquad (h)$$

This displacement, in general, does not vanish at the ends.

By taking only those terms in series (g) and (h) which have the coefficients $a_2, a_4, \ldots$, we find that

$$(v)_{\theta=0} = (v)_{\theta=\alpha} = -\frac{\alpha}{\pi}\left(\frac{1}{2}a_2 + \frac{1}{4}a_4 + \cdots \right)$$

and we can make the tangential displacement at the ends vanish by superposing on the deformation represented by this series a rotation of the bar as a rigid body about the center O by an angle equal to

$$\frac{\alpha}{\pi r_0}\left(\frac{1}{2}a_2 + \frac{1}{4}a_4 + \cdots \right).$$

Thus, one kind of inextensional deformation of a circular arch with hinged ends is given by the series

$$w = a_2 \sin \frac{2\pi\theta}{\alpha} + a_4 \sin \frac{4\pi\theta}{\alpha} + \cdots ;$$

$$v = \frac{\alpha}{\pi}\left[\frac{1}{2}a_2\left(1 - \cos \frac{2\pi\theta}{\alpha} \right) + \frac{1}{4}a_4\left(1 - \cos \frac{4\pi\theta}{\alpha} \right) + \cdots \right], \qquad (i)$$

in which each term by itself represents an inextensional deflection curve with an inflection point at the center of the bar. We will use such deflection curves later in discussing the stability of compressed curved bars (see Art. 43).

If we take in series (g) only those terms with coefficients $a_1, a_3, \ldots$, we obtain deflection curves which are symmetrical with respect to the center of the bar. It is seen from series (h) that displacements v corresponding to each of the above terms do not vanish at the ends, and we can satisfy the conditions at the hinged ends only by taking a series of such terms with a definite relation between the coefficients a_1, a_3, a_5, ...

From the general requirement for inextensional deformation (Eq. *b*), it follows that the tangential displacements *v* vanish at the ends only if

$$\int_0^\alpha w \, d\theta = 0, \qquad (j)$$

from which it follows that, in the case of deflection curves symmetrical with respect to the center of the buckled bar, the half-waves cannot be equal. The simplest curve of this kind will be obtained by taking three half-waves. Then, from (j), the area of

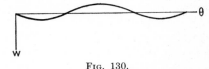

Fig. 130.

the middle half-wave must be larger than that of either of the remaining two; if we represent *w* as a function of θ, the curve shown in Fig. 130 will be obtained. The area of the middle wave in this curve is equal to the sum of areas of the two other waves.

40. Effect of Axial Compression or Tension on Bending of a Circular Ring.—So far we have neglected the effect of compression or tension in the ring on its bending. For example, in the discussion of the problem shown in Fig. 128, the compression of the ring due to hydrostatic pressure was entirely disregarded, although it may become of great importance in the case of thin rings, in which buckling may occur owing to the action of uniform pressure acting alone. To take into account the effect of the longitudinal force on the deformation of the ring, we again consider only inextensional deformations and assume that the internal forces over any cross section of the ring reduce to a constant axial force *S* and a bending moment. Considering, for instance, the ring of unit width under hydrostatic pressure (Fig. 128), we assume first a uniform pressure of intensity γd, which produces in the ring a uniform compressive force $S = \gamma d r_0$. On this uniform compression we superpose bending produced by a non-uniform pressure of a magnitude $\gamma r_0 \cos \theta$ and we assume that this bending is inextensional, so that the axial compressive force *S* remains unchanged and only bending moment is produced.

The effect of the force S on the bending of the ring can be replaced by the action of an equivalent distributed load, acting radially, the intensity of which is found as follows: Consider an element AB (Fig. 131), of a uniformly compressed ring. The

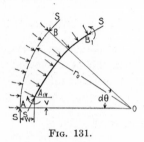

axial compressive forces S keep in equilibrium the uniformly distributed pressure that is acting on the element. Assume now an inextensional deformation of the ring such that the element AB takes the position A_1B_1. There will be some bending moments produced in the cross sections A_1 and B_1, the magnitude of which can be found from Eq. (113) provided the displacements

FIG. 131.

w are known. Owing to the change in curvature, represented by the left side of Eq. (f) (p. 206), cross section B of the ring rotates with respect to cross section A by the angle

$$r_0 \, d\theta\left(\frac{d^2w}{ds^2} + \frac{w}{r^2_0}\right).$$

Because of this rotation the axial forces S are no longer in equilibrium with the uniform pressure and they give an additional force acting in a radial direction away from the center O, the magnitude of which is

$$Sr_0 \, d\theta\left(\frac{d^2w}{ds^2} + \frac{w}{r^2_0}\right).$$

Thus, to the given external loads producing bending of a uniformly compressed ring, a distributed fictitious load of the intensity

$$S\left(\frac{d^2w}{ds^2} + \frac{w}{r^2_0}\right) = \frac{S}{r^2_0}\left(\frac{d^2w}{d\theta^2} + w\right) \qquad (a)$$

must be added in order to take into account the effect of the compressive force S on bending of the ring.

Let us apply this general reasoning to the case represented in Fig. 126 and consider the effect, on the deflections of the ring, of a uniform external pressure producing in the ring a compressive force S. Using for the displacement w the trigonometric series (a) of the previous article, and considering a

virtual displacement $w = \delta a_n \cos n\theta$, the equation for determining
a coefficient a_n, for n equal to an even number, is

$$\frac{\partial V}{\partial a_n}\delta a_n = 2P\delta a_n(-1)^{\frac{n}{2}} - \frac{S}{r_0}\delta a_n \int_0^{2\pi}\left(\frac{d^2w}{d\theta^2} + w\right)\cos n\theta \, d\theta. \quad (b)$$

The second term on the right side of this equation represents the
work done through the virtual displacement of the fictitious load
(*a*). It is taken with negative sign since the load is directed
opposite to positive w.

Substituting series (*a*) of the previous article for w and performing the integration, we obtain

$$a_n = \frac{2Pr^3_0(-1)^{\frac{n}{2}}}{\pi EI(n^2 - 1)^2\left[1 - \dfrac{Sr^2_0}{(n^2 - 1)EI}\right]}, \quad (c)$$

where values of n are even numbers. The coefficients a_n for
which n is an odd number and all the coefficients b_n in the series
for w must be taken equal to zero for the symmetrical loading,
shown in Fig. 126. Thus we obtain

$$w = \frac{2Pr^3_0}{\pi EI}\sum_{n=2,4,\cdots}^{n=\infty}\frac{(-1)^{\frac{n}{2}}\cos n\theta}{(n^2 - 1)^2\left[1 - \dfrac{Sr^2_0}{(n^2 - 1)EI}\right]}. \quad (118)$$

Comparing this result with Eq. (117), which was obtained before
for an uncompressed ring, it may be seen that, owing to compressive force S, each coefficient of the series for w increases in
the ratio

$$\frac{1}{1 - \dfrac{Sr^2_0}{(n^2 - 1)EI}}.$$

We see that the deflection increases indefinitely when the compressive force S approaches the value

$$S = \frac{(n^2 - 1)EI}{r^2_0}. \quad (d)$$

The smallest value of the force at which this happens is obtained
by taking $n = 2$, which gives the *critical value* of the compressive
force as

$$S_{cr} = \frac{3EI}{r^2_0}. \tag{119}$$

When S approaches S_{cr}, the first term in the series (118) becomes predominant and we obtain for the radial displacement, by taking this term alone, the expression

$$w = -\frac{2Pr^3_0}{9\pi EI} \frac{\cos 2\theta}{1 - \dfrac{S}{S_{cr}}}, \tag{120}$$

from which an equation, analogous to Eq. (46) for a compressed straight beam under lateral loading, can be obtained.

In the case of a long circular tube uniformly compressed by external pressure, we consider an elemental ring of unit width and we obtain the critical value of the compressive force S_{cr} in such a ring by using $E/(1 - \nu^2)$ instead of E and by taking $I = h^3/12$; then, from Eq. (119),

$$S_{cr} = \frac{Eh^3}{4(1 - \nu^2)r^2_0}. \tag{121}$$

Observing that the compressive force in the elemental ring of unit width is equal to qr_0, where q is the uniform pressure, we obtain from Eq. (121) the critical value of this pressure:

$$q_{cr} = \frac{E}{4(1 - \nu^2)}\left(\frac{h}{r_0}\right)^3. \tag{122}$$

41. Buckling of Circular Rings and Tubes under Uniform External Pressure.—In the discussion of combined uniform compression and bending of a circular ring by external forces, it was found in the previous article that the deflections increase indefinitely if the uniform pressure approaches a certain critical value, which can be calculated from Eq. (119). The same value of the critical pressure can be obtained in another way by considering an ideal uniformly compressed ring and assuming some slight deflection from the circular form of equilibrium. Then the critical value of the uniform pressure is that

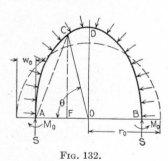

Fig. 132.

value which is necessary to keep the ring in equilibrium in the assumed slightly deformed shape.

In Fig. 132 half of the ring is shown. The dotted line indicates the initial circular shape of the ring and the full line represents the slightly deflected ring on which a uniformly distributed pressure is acting. It is assumed that AB and OD are axes of symmetry for the buckled ring; then, the action of the removed lower portion of the ring on the upper portion can be represented by a longitudinal compressive force S and by a bending moment M_0 acting on each of the cross sections A and B. Let q be the uniform pressure per unit length of the center line of the ring and w_0 the radial displacement at A and B. Then the compressive force at A and B is

$$S = q(r_0 - w_0) = q\overline{AO},$$

and the bending moment at any cross section C of the buckled ring is

$$M = M_0 + q\overline{AO} \cdot \overline{AF} - \frac{q}{2}\overline{AC}^2. \tag{a}$$

Now, considering the triangle ACO,

$$\overline{OC}^2 = \overline{AC}^2 + \overline{AO}^2 - 2\overline{AO} \cdot \overline{AF}$$

or

$$\tfrac{1}{2}\overline{AC}^2 - \overline{AO} \cdot \overline{AF} = \tfrac{1}{2}(\overline{OC}^2 - \overline{AO}^2).$$

Substituting this in the expression (a) for the bending moment, we obtain

$$M = M_0 - \tfrac{1}{2}q(\overline{OC}^2 - \overline{AO}^2). \tag{b}$$

Observing that $\overline{AO} = r_0 - w_0$ and that $\overline{OC} = r_0 - w$, and neglecting squares of the small quantities w and w_0, the bending moment becomes

$$M = M_0 - qr_0(w_0 - w). \tag{c}$$

With this expression for bending moment, the differential equation of the deflection curve (113) is

$$\frac{d^2w}{d\theta^2} + w = -\frac{r^2{}_0}{EI}\left[M_0 - qr_0(w_0 - w)\right]. \tag{d}$$

The critical value of the uniform pressure therefore is now obtained by integrating this equation. Putting the equation in the form

$$\frac{d^2w}{d\theta^2} + w\left(1 + \frac{qr^3_0}{EI}\right) = \frac{-M_0r^2_0 + qr^3_0w_0}{EI},$$

and using the notation

$$k^2 = 1 + \frac{qr^3_0}{EI}, \tag{e}$$

the general solution becomes

$$w = A \sin k\theta + B \cos k\theta + \frac{-M_0r^2_0 + qr^3_0w_0}{EI + qr^3_0}. \tag{f}$$

Let us consider the conditions at the cross sections A and D of the buckled ring. From symmetry we conclude that

$$\left(\frac{dw}{d\theta}\right)_{\theta=0} = 0, \qquad \left(\frac{dw}{d\theta}\right)_{\theta=\frac{\pi}{2}} = 0.$$

From the first of these conditions it follows that $A = 0$ and from the second we obtain

$$\sin \frac{k\pi}{2} = 0. \tag{g}$$

The smallest root of this equation, different from zero, is $k\pi/2 = \pi$ and $k = 2$. Substituting this in (e), we obtain for the value of the critical pressure[1]

$$q_{cr} = \frac{3EI}{r^3_0}. \tag{123}$$

The corresponding compressive force in the ring is seen to be that given by formula (119) obtained before.

The radial deflections of the buckled ring, from (f), are

$$w = \frac{1}{4}\left(\frac{M_0r^2_0}{EI} + w_0\right) \cos 2\theta - \frac{M_0r^2_0}{4EI} + \frac{3}{4}w_0. \tag{h}$$

Then, from the condition of inextensibility [see Eq. (b), p. 208],

$$v = \frac{1}{8}\left(\frac{M_0r^2_0}{EI} + w_0\right) \sin 2\theta + \left(-\frac{M_0r^2_0}{4EI} + \frac{3}{4}w_0\right)\theta. \tag{i}$$

---

[1] This result was obtained by M. Levy, *J. math. pure et appl. (Liouville)*, series 3, vol. 10, p. 5, 1884. See also A. G. Greenhill, *Math. Annalen*, vol. 52, p. 465, 1899.

For $\theta = 0$ and $\theta = \pi/2$ the displacement v must vanish from the condition of symmetry. Hence

$$-\frac{M_0 r^2{}_0}{4EI} + \frac{3}{4}w_0 = 0$$

or

$$M_0 = \frac{3w_0 EI}{r^2{}_0} = q_{cr}w_0 r_0. \tag{j}$$

Substituting this in (h) and (i), we obtain

$$w = w_0 \cos 2\theta; \qquad v = \tfrac{1}{2}w_0 \sin 2\theta. \tag{124}$$

From Eq. (j) it is seen that the moment M_0 can be produced by applying at A and B (see Fig. 132) the compressive force S with an eccentricity w_0. In such case the dotted circle in Fig. 132 can be considered as a funicular curve for the uniform pressure and the area between this curve and the center line of the buckled ring represents the bending-moment diagram for the ring. The same follows also from Eq. (c), by substituting in it, from (j), $M_0 = qw_0 r_0$. For $\theta = \pm\dfrac{\pi}{4}$ and $\theta = \pm\dfrac{3}{4}\pi$ the radial displacement w is zero and the bending moment vanishes.

So far we have discussed only the solution of Eq. (d) corresponding to the smallest root of Eq. (g). By taking $k = 4$, $6, \ldots$, we can obtain a series of possible shapes of a buckled ring with more and more waves in them. Another limitation introduced in the above discussion is the condition of symmetry of the buckled ring with respect to the horizontal and vertical axes. As a result of this we have obtained for k only even numbers. By assuming that only one axis, for instance the horizontal axis AB (Fig. 132), is an axis of symmetry and that at the ends of the vertical axis the bending moments are zero, we obtain solutions with odd numbers for k, namely, $k = 3$, $5, \ldots$. The case $k = 1$ has been discussed before (p. 209); it was shown that it represents a translation of the ring as a rigid body and should not be considered in discussing buckling of the ring. Thus $k = 2$ is the smallest root and the corresponding load [Eq. (123)] is the critical load. The buckling forms of higher order corresponding to larger roots can be obtained only by introducing certain additional constraints. Without such constraints, buckling will always be such as is shown in Fig. 132.

The results obtained for a circular ring can be applied also in investigating the buckling of long[1] circular tubes submitted to the action of uniform external pressure.[2] To get q_{cr} for the tube it is only necessary to substitute $E/(1 - \nu^2)$ for E in formula (123) and $h^3/12$ for I; in this manner we obtain formula (122) (see p. 216).

This formula can be used for calculating the critical value of the pressure q so long as the corresponding compressive stress

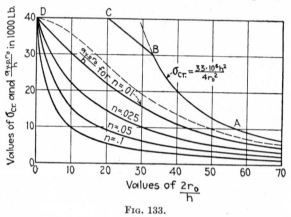

Fig. 133.

does not exceed the proportional limit of the material. The limiting value of the ratio $h/2r_0$, up to which the formula can be used, is obtained by dividing Eq. (121) by the cross-sectional area of the elemental ring. Then

$$\sigma_{cr} = \frac{E}{1 - \nu^2}\left(\frac{h}{2r_0}\right)^2. \tag{125}$$

Taking, for instance, steel with $E = 30 \cdot 10^6$ lb. per square inch and $\nu = 0.3$ and plotting σ_{cr} against $2r_0/h$, we obtain a curve AB (Fig. 133). This curve gives the actual critical stress only if the magnitude of this stress does not exceed the proportional limit. Beyond this limit the curve gives exaggerated values for the critical stress. To get the true values of this stress we must proceed in the same manner as in the case of a column (Art. 29) and use in Eq. (125) the reduced modulus E_r instead

[1] The case of shorter tubes is discussed in Art. 83.

[2] See paper by G. H. Bryan, *Proc. Cambridge Phil. Soc.*, vol. 6, p. 287, 1888.

of E. If the compression-test diagram of the material is given, E_r can be calculated readily for any value of σ_{cr} and then the corresponding value of $h/2r_0$ will be found from the equation

$$\sigma_{cr} = \frac{E_r}{1 - \nu^2}\left(\frac{h}{2r_0}\right)^2. \tag{126}$$

In this manner a curve of critical stresses beyond the proportional limit analogous to that calculated for columns (Fig. 113) can be obtained. For practical purposes this curve can be replaced by two straight lines as was done in the case of columns. In the case of materials with a pronounced yield point, the yield-point stress must be taken as the critical stress for thicker tubes. Taking, for instance, a steel with a yield point $\sigma_{Y.P.} = 40,000$ lb. per square inch and a proportional limit $\sigma_p = 30,000$ lb. per square inch, we find that the smallest value of $2r_0/h$ for which Eq. (125) can be used is about 33 (see Fig. 133). This corresponds to point B on the curve AB. For thicker tubes the horizontal line DC giving $\sigma_{cr} = \sigma_{Y.P.}$ can be used. For intermediate thickness, where $20 < 2r_0/h < 33$, we can use the inclined line BC for determining the critical stress. Thus the line $ABCD$ gives the critical values of compressive stress for all proportions of tubes, and, if a factor of safety is decided upon, there is no difficulty in each particular case in finding the safe thickness of the tube.

Instead of the broken line $ABCD$, it is sometimes useful to have a continuous curve, as the one given by the equation.[1]

$$\sigma_{cr} = \frac{\sigma_{Y.P.}}{1 + \dfrac{\sigma_{Y.P.}(1 - \nu^2)}{E}\dfrac{4r_0^2}{h^2}}. \tag{127}$$

This curve is shown in the figure by the dotted line. Formula (127) is analogous to Rankine's formula for columns (p. 183). For thick tubes it gives a critical stress approaching $\sigma_{Y.P.}$ and for thin tubes it approaches values given by Eq. (126). For the usual proportions of tubes the curve gives much lower stresses than those given by the line $ABCD$. This additional safety introduced by Eq. (127) can be considered as compensating for the effect of any initial ellipticity of the tube which always can be expected in practice.

[1] This curve was proposed by R. V. Southwell, *Phil. Mag.*, vol. 29, p. 67, 1915.

42. The Design of Tubes under Uniform External Pressure on the Basis of Assumed Inaccuracies.—Since the failure of tubes under uniform external pressure depends very much upon the various kinds of imperfections in them, it seems logical to derive a design formula for such tubes in which the quantities depending on imperfections will appear explicitly. The most common imperfection in tubes is an initial ellipticity, the limiting value of which in each type of tube is usually well-known from

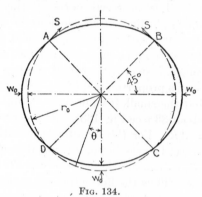

, Fig. 134.

numerous inspection measurements. The deviation of the shape of the tube from a perfect circular form can be defined by the initial radial deflections w'. To simplify our investigation we assume that these deflections are given by the equation[1]

$$w' = w_0 \cos 2\theta, \qquad (a)$$

in which w_0 is the maximum initial radial deviation from a circle and θ is the central angle measured as shown in Fig. 134.

Under the action of external uniform pressure q, there will be an additional flattening of the tube. The corresponding radial displacements will be called w. To determine w, we will use the differential equation

$$\frac{d^2w}{d\theta^2} + w = -\frac{12(1 - \nu^2)}{Eh^3}Mr^2_0. \qquad (113')$$

which is obtained from Eq. (113), for a ring, by substituting $E/(1 - \nu^2)$ for E and $h^3/12$ for I. Following our rule regarding

---

[1] See writer's paper, *Trans. Am. Soc. Mech. Eng.*, Applied Mechanics Division, vol. 1, p. 173, 1933.

signs of bending moments (Art. 38), we conclude that in the portions AB and CD there will be produced by a uniform external pressure a positive bending moment and in the portions AD and BC a negative bending moment. At points A, B, C and D the bending moment is zero, and the actions between the parts of the tube are represented by forces S tangential to the dotted circle representing the ideal shape of the tube. This circle can be considered as a funicular curve for the external pressure (see p. 219). The compressive force along this curve remains constant and equal to S. Thus the bending moment at any cross section is obtained by multiplying S by the total radial displacement $w' + w$ at this cross section. Then

$$M = qr_0(w + w_0 \cos 2\theta). \tag{b}$$

Substituting in Eq. (113'), we obtain

$$\frac{d^2w}{d\theta^2} + w = -\frac{12(1 - \nu^2)}{Eh^3}qr^3{}_0(w + w_0 \cos 2\theta)$$

or

$$\frac{d^2w}{d\theta^2} + w\left[1 + \frac{12(1 - \nu^2)}{Eh^3}qr^3{}_0\right] = -\frac{12(1 - \nu^2)}{Eh^3}qr^3{}_0w_0 \cos 2\theta.$$

The solution of this equation satisfying the conditions of continuity at the points A, B, C and D is

$$w = \frac{w_0q}{q_{cr} - q} \cos 2\theta, \tag{128}$$

in which q_{cr} is the critical value of the uniform pressure given by Eq. (122). It is seen that at points A, B, C and D, w and $d^2w/d\theta^2$ are zero. Hence the bending moments at these points are zero, as was assumed above. The maximum moment occurs at $\theta = 0$ and at $\theta = \pi$ where

$$M_{\text{max.}} = qr_0\left(w_0 + \frac{w_0q}{q_{cr} - q}\right) = qr_0\frac{w_0}{1 - \dfrac{q}{q_{cr}}}. \tag{129}$$

It is seen that for small values of the ratio q/q_{cr} the change in the ellipticity of the tube due to pressure q can be neglected and the maximum bending moment obtained by multiplying the compressive force qr_0 by the initial deflection w_0. When the ratio q/q_{cr} is not small, the change in the initial ellipticity of the tube should be considered and Eq. (129) must be used in calculating $M_{max.}$.

The maximum compressive stress is now obtained by adding to the stress produced by the compressive force qr_0 the maximum compressive stress due to bending moment $M_{max.}$. Thus we find

$$\sigma_{max.} = \frac{qr_0}{h} + \frac{6qr_0}{h^2} \frac{w_0}{1 - \dfrac{q}{q_{cr}}}. \qquad (c)$$

Assuming that this equation can be used with sufficient accuracy up to the yield-point stress of the material, we obtain the following equation:

$$\sigma_{Y.P.} = \frac{q_{Y.P.}r_0}{h} + 6q_{Y.P.} \frac{r_0^2}{h^2} \frac{w_0}{r_0} \frac{1}{1 - \dfrac{q_{Y.P.}}{q_{cr}}}, \qquad (d)$$

from which the value of the uniform pressure $q_{Y.P.}$, at which yielding in the extreme fibers begins, can be calculated. Using the notations $r_0/h = m$ and $w_0/r_0 = n$, the equation for calculating $q_{Y.P.}$ becomes

$$q^2_{Y.P.} - \left[\frac{\sigma_{Y.P.}}{m} + (1 + 6mn)q_{cr}\right]q_{Y.P.} + \frac{\sigma_{Y.P.}}{m}q_{cr} = 0. \qquad (e)$$

It should be noted that the pressure $q_{Y.P.}$ determined in this manner is smaller than the pressure at which the collapsing of the tube occurs, and it becomes equal to the latter only in the case of a perfectly round tube. Hence, by using the value of $q_{Y.P.}$ calculated from Eq. (e) as the ultimate value of pressure, we are always on the safe side.[1] In Fig. 133 several curves are shown giving the values of the average compressive stress $q_{Y.P.}r_0/h$ at which yielding begins, calculated from Eq. (e) by taking $w_0/r_0 = 0.1, 0.05, 0.025, 0.01$, and $\sigma_{Y.P.} = 40,000$ lb. per square inch.

[1] Experiments with long tubes submitted to uniform external pressure were made by R. T. Stewart, *Trans. Am. Soc. Mech. Eng.*, vol. 27, 1906.   See also H. A. Thomas, *Bull. Am. Petroleum Inst.*, vol. 5, p. 79, 1924, and B. V. Bulgakov, *Nauch.-Tehn. Upravl. V.S.N.H.*, Moscow, no. 343, 1930.

These curves can be used for calculating safe pressures on the tubes if the ellipticity of the tubes is known and if a suitable factor of safety is chosen.

43. Buckling of a Uniformly Compressed Circular Arch.—If a curved bar with hinged ends and with its center line in the form of an arc of a circle is submitted to the action of a uniformly distributed pressure q, it will buckle as shown by the dotted line in Fig. 135. The critical value of the pressure q at which this buckling occurs can be found from the differential equation of the

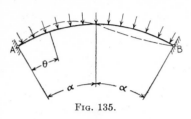

Fig. 135.

deflection curve of the buckled bar. Considering, as before, the initial circular arc as a funicular curve for the uniform pressure, this equation becomes

$$\frac{d^2w}{d\theta^2} + w = -\frac{r^2{}_0 S w}{EI}, \qquad (a)$$

where $S = qr_0$ is the axial compressive force and w the radial displacement toward the center.

Using the previous notation

$$k^2 = 1 + \frac{qr^3{}_0}{EI}, \qquad (b)$$

we obtain

$$\frac{d^2w}{d\theta^2} + k^2w = 0.$$

The general solution of this equation is

$$w = A \sin k\theta + B \cos k\theta.$$

To satisfy the conditions at the left end ($\theta = 0$), we must take $B = 0$. The conditions at the right end ($\theta = 2\alpha$) will be satisfied if we take

$$\sin 2\alpha k = 0. \qquad (c)$$

The smallest root of this equation, satisfying the condition of inextensibility of the center line of the bar [see Eq. (j), Art. 39] is

$$k = \frac{\pi}{\alpha}$$

and we obtain[1] from (b)

$$q_{cr} = \frac{EI}{r^3_0}\left(\frac{\pi^2}{\alpha^2} - 1\right). \tag{130}$$

By taking $\alpha = \pi/2$, Eq. (130) gives the same value of q_{cr} as for a complete ring [Eq. (123)]. This result should be expected since at this value of α the bar represented in Fig. 135 is in exactly the same condition as each half of a buckled ring (Fig. 132) between the two opposite inflection points.

When α approaches the value π, *i.e.*, when the arc approaches the complete ring, the value of q_{cr}, from Eq. (130), approaches zero. This can be explained if we observe that for $\alpha = \pi$ both hinges coincide and that the ring will be free to rotate as a rigid body about this common hinge.

When α is small in comparison with π, unity can be neglected in comparison with π^2/α^2 in the parenthesis of formula (130). Then the critical compressive force $q_{cr}r_0$ becomes equal to the critical load for a prismatical bar with hinged ends and of the length $r_0\alpha$.

In the derivation of formula (130) it was assumed that the buckled arch had an inflection point at the middle (Fig. 135). From the general discussion of inextensional deflection of an arc (Art. 39), we know that it is possible to have also inextensional deflection curves symmetrical with respect to the middle of the bar. The simplest of these curves has two inflection points. By taking such a curve as a basis for calculating critical load, we obtain a critical value larger than that given by Eq. (130).[2] Hence, this latter equation should be used for calculating q_{cr}.

If, instead of a circular arch, we have a flat parabolic arch and a vertical load uniformly distributed along the span AB (Fig. 135), the variation of the compressive force along the length of the arch can be neglected and its critical value can be calculated by taking half the length of the arch and applying Euler's formula as for a bar with hinged ends.[3]

---

[1] This solution was obtained by E. Hurlbrink, *Schiffbau*, vol. 9, p. 517, 1908. See also writer's paper in *Bull. Polytech. Inst., Kiev*, 1910.

[2] Calculations of this kind were made by E. Chwalla, see *Sitzungsb. Akad. Wiss., Wien.*, Abt. IIa, vol. 136, p. 645, 1927.

[3] The results of experiments are in satisfactory agreement with such calculations. See R. Mayer, *Der Eisenbau*, vol. 4, p. 361, 1913, and his book, *loc. cit.*, p. 197. In these papers the case of an arch with three hinges is con-

In the derivation of Eq. (130) it was assumed that the curved bar, before buckling, had its center line in the form of an arc of a circle. This condition is fulfilled only if uniform unit compression $q_{cr}r_0/AE$ of the center line of the bar is produced before fastening the ends to the supports; otherwise some bending under the action of uniform pressure will start at the very beginning of loading. This bending is very small so long as the compression q is small in comparison with q_{cr}, and the conditions are analogous to the bending that occurs in columns because of various kinds of imperfections.

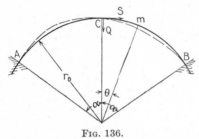

FIG. 136.

Substituting in Eq. (130) $E/(1 - \nu^2)$ instead of E and $h^3/12$ instead of I, we obtain the equation

$$q_{cr} = \frac{Eh^3}{12(1 - \nu^2)r_0}\left(\frac{\pi^2}{\alpha^2} - 1\right), \tag{131}$$

which can be used in calculating the critical load for a cylindrical shell hinged along the edges $\theta = 0$ and $\theta = 2\alpha$ (Fig. 135) and submitted to the action of uniform pressure.

If the ends of a uniformly compressed arch are built in[1] (Fig. 136), the shape of buckling will be as shown by the dotted line. At the middle point C there will act after buckling not only the horizontal compressive force S but also a vertical shearing force Q. Considering again the initial circular arc as

sidered and the effects on the critical load of the compression of the center line of the arch and of the lowering of the middle hinge are discussed. Recently an interesting series of tests on uniformly loaded arches with three hinges were made by E. Gaber, *Bautechn.*, 1934, p. 646. The results of these tests are in agreement with Eq. (130). The discussion of buckling of arches with three hinges under the action of non-symmetrical loading is given by E. Chwalla, *Der Stahlbau*, 1935, no. 16.

[1] It is assumed again that the arch is uniformly compressed before fixing the ends.

the funicular curve for uniform pressure and designating with w the radial displacement toward the center, the bending moment at any cross section, defined by the angle θ, is

$$M = Sw - Qr_0 \sin \theta,$$

and the differential equation (113) becomes

$$\frac{d^2w}{d\theta^2} + w = -\frac{r^2_0}{EI}(Sw - Qr_0 \sin \theta),$$

or, by using notation (b),

$$\frac{d^2w}{d\theta^2} + k^2w = \frac{Qr^3_0 \sin \theta}{EI}.$$

The general solution of this equation is

$$w = A \sin k\theta + B \cos k\theta + \frac{Qr^3_0 \sin \theta}{(k^2 - 1)EI}. \tag{d}$$

The conditions for determining the constants A and B and the force Q are

$$w = \frac{d^2w}{d\theta^2} = 0 \quad \text{for} \quad \theta = 0; \tag{e}$$

$$w = \frac{dw}{d\theta} = 0 \quad \text{for} \quad \theta = \alpha. \tag{f}$$

Conditions (e) are satisfied by taking $B = 0$ in solution (d). From conditions (f) we then obtain

$$\left. \begin{array}{l} A \sin k\alpha + Q\dfrac{r^3_0 \sin \alpha}{(k^2 - 1)EI} = 0; \\[2mm] Ak \cos k\alpha + Q\dfrac{r^3_0 \cos \alpha}{(k^2 - 1)EI} = 0. \end{array} \right\} \tag{g}$$

The equation for calculating the critical value of uniform pressure q is obtained by equating to zero the determinant of Eqs. (g). Then

$$\sin k\alpha \cos \alpha - k \sin \alpha \cos k\alpha = 0$$

or

$$k \tan \alpha \cot k\alpha = 1. \tag{h}$$

The value of k and the critical value of the pressure q depend on the magnitude of the angle α. Several solutions of Eq. (h) for various values of α are given in Table 15.[1]

TABLE 15

α	30°	60°	90°	120°	150°	180°
k	8.621	4.375	3	2.364	2.066	2

Substituting k in Eq. (b), the critical value of the uniform pressure is found to be

$$q_{cr} = \frac{EI}{r^3_0}(k^2 - 1). \tag{132}$$

This value of q_{cr} is always greater than that obtained from Eq. (130).

TABLE 16.—VALUES OF m IN EQ. (134)

α	I_1/I_0					
	0.1	0.2	0.4	0.6	0.8	1
0	4.67	5.41	6.68	7.80	8.85	π^2
30°	4.54	5.20	6.48	7.58	8.62	9.60
60°	4.16	4.82	5.94	6.94	7.89	8.77
90°	3.53	4.08	5.02	5.86	6.66	7.40

The problem of elastic stability of the arch shown in Fig. 135 can also be solved in certain cases for a variable cross section. Assuming, for instance, that the cross-sectional moment of inertia for the left side of the symmetrical arch varies along the length of the arc following the law

$$I = I_0\left[1 - \left(1 - \frac{I_1}{I_0}\right)\frac{\theta}{\alpha}\right], \tag{133}$$

in which I_0 and I_1 are the moments of inertia for $\theta = 0$ and $\theta = \alpha$, respectively, we obtain for the critical compressive force

$$S_{cr} = q_{cr}r_0 = \frac{mEI_0}{\alpha^2 r^2_0}, \tag{134}$$

where m is a numerical factor depending on the angle α and on the ratio I_1/I_0. Several values of this factor[2] are given in Table 16.

[1] This solution is due to E. L. Nicolai, *Bull. Polytech. Inst.*, *St. Petersburg*, vol. 27, 1918. See also his paper in *Z. angew. Math. Mech.*, vol. 3, p. 227, 1923.

[2] This solution was communicated to the writer by Professor A. N. Dinnik, who succeeded in solving the problem for several cases of an arch

The second line in the table ($\alpha = 0$) gives the values of the coefficient m for the case of a straight bar of variable cross section when buckled with an inflection point at the middle. The last column in the table gives m for an arch of constant cross section [see Eq. (130)].

44. Buckling of Curved Bars with Small Curvature.[1]—In the previous discussion only extensionless forms of buckling of curved bars have been considered. In the case of very flat curves, buckling with axial strain may occur at a smaller load than extensionless buckling and must be investigated. As an example of such buckling, let us consider a flat uniformly loaded

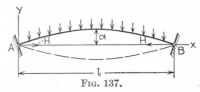

FIG. 137.

arch with hinged ends (Fig. 137), the initial center line of which is given by the equation

$$y = a \sin \frac{\pi x}{l}. \tag{a}$$

If the rise a of the arch is large, the axial deformation of the arch under the action of load can be neglected and the critical load obtained by assuming that during buckling there is an inflection point at the middle of the arch (see Art. 43). If a is very small, the axial deformation of the arch during loading cannot be neglected and the arch can buckle in a symmetrical form as shown in the figure by the dotted line.

In investigating the deformation of the arch, let us assume first that one of the hinges is on rollers; then the center line of the arch after loading can be represented with sufficient accuracy (see p. 26) by the equation

$$y_1 = \left(a - \frac{5}{384}\frac{ql^4}{EI}\right) \sin \frac{\pi x}{l} = a(1 - u) \sin \frac{\pi x}{l}, \tag{b}$$

in which q is the intensity of the uniform load, EI is the flexural

---

of variable cross section. The same problem was discussed also by I. J. Steurman; see his paper in *Bull. Polytech. Inst., Kiev*, 1929, and his booklet "Stability of Arches," Kiev, 1929.

[1] See writer's paper, *J. Appl. Mech., A.S.M.E.*, vol. 2, p. 17, 1935.

rigidity of the bar in the plane of the center line and

$$u = \frac{5}{384} \frac{ql^4}{EI} \frac{1}{a}. \qquad (c)$$

In the case of immovable hinges, a thrust H will be produced by the loading and the final equation of the center line will be (see Art. 8)

$$y_2 = \frac{a(1 - u)}{1 - \alpha} \sin \frac{\pi x}{l}, \qquad (d)$$

in which

$$\alpha = \frac{Hl^2}{\pi^2 EI}. \qquad (e)$$

This equation can be used not only for $u < 1$ but also for $u > 1$, *i.e.*, in cases where the deflection of the curved bar, calculated as for a simple beam, is larger than the initial rise of the arch. The quantity α can also be larger than 1, but it must be smaller than 4, since for $\alpha = 4$ there occurs buckling of the arch with an inflection point at the middle, and our assumption [Eq. (d)] that the arch remains symmetrical with respect to the middle is no longer fulfilled.

Assuming first that $u < 1$, we find, from Eq. (d), that y_2 is positive if $\alpha < 1$ and negative for $\alpha > 1$. This means that. if the thrust is smaller than the Euler load for a bar with hinged ends, the arch has the form shown by the full line in Fig. 137. The same arch can be kept deflected downward, as shown in the figure by the dotted line, if a thrust larger than the Euler load is applied. When $u > 1$, y_2 is positive for $\alpha > 1$ and becomes negative for $\alpha < 1$.

The actual shape of the arch, after loading, can be determined only when the quantity α, *i.e.*, the thrust H, is known. The equation for calculating the thrust H is obtained by putting the change in length of the span due to deflection equal to the compression of the bar due to thrust. Assuming for flat curves that the compressive force along the length of the bar is constant and equal to H, we obtain the equation

$$\frac{Hl}{AE} = \frac{1}{2} \int_0^l \left(\frac{dy}{dx}\right)^2 dx - \frac{1}{2} \int_0^l \left(\frac{dy_2}{dx}\right)^2 dx, \qquad (f)$$

in which A is the cross-sectional area of the bar. Substituting for y and y_2 their expressions (a) and (d) and integrating, we obtain

$$(1 - u)^2 = (1 - m\alpha)(1 - \alpha)^2, \qquad (g)$$

in which

$$m = \frac{4I}{Aa^2}. \qquad (h)$$

For a given arch the quantity m is easily calculated and, if the load q is given, the quantity u can be determined from Eq. (c). Then the corresponding value of α and consequently the thrust H are obtained from Eq. (g). Since this equation is not linear, more than one real root for α can be obtained under

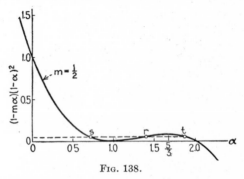

Fig. 138.

certain conditions, which indicates that there are several possible forms of equilibrium and that the stability of these forms must be investigated.

Considering the right side of Eq. (g) as a function of α, we find that for $m < 1$ this function has a minimum equal to 0 for $\alpha = 1$ and a maximum for $\alpha = \dfrac{2 + m}{3m}$. The magnitude of this maximum is

$$\frac{4}{27} \frac{(1 - m)^3}{m^2}. \qquad (i)$$

In Fig. 138 the right side of Eq. (g) is represented graphically for the case where $m = \frac{1}{2}$. For this value of m the maximum occurs at $\alpha = \frac{5}{3}$ and the magnitude of this maximum, from (i), is equal to $\frac{2}{27}$. If the load q is of such magnitude that the left side of Eq. (g) is larger than the above maximum, we obtain only one real solution for α, which indicates that only one form of equilibrium is possible; hence the equilibrium is stable. If the left side of Eq. (g) is smaller than the quantity (i), three solutions for α are obtained as shown by intersection points s, r and t in Fig. 138 and the question of stability of the corresponding forms of equilibrium must be considered. Applying these conclusions in the above numerical example, we find that the equilibrium is always stable if

$$(1 - u)^2 > \tfrac{2}{27},$$

which is equivalent to the conditions

$$\left. \begin{aligned} u &< 1 - \sqrt{\tfrac{2}{27}}; \\ u &> 1 + \sqrt{\tfrac{2}{27}}. \end{aligned} \right\} \tag{j}$$

The first of these conditions corresponds to the form of equilibrium convex upward, as shown in Fig. 137 by the full line, and the second to the form convex downward as indicated in the figure by the dotted line.

For any value of m smaller than 1 the conditions of stability, equivalent to conditions (j), are

$$\left. \begin{aligned} u &< \left(1 - \sqrt{\frac{4}{27} \frac{(1 - m)^3}{m^2}}\right); \\ u &> \left(1 + \sqrt{\frac{4}{27} \frac{(1 - m)^3}{m^2}}\right). \end{aligned} \right\} \tag{k}$$

Hence, conditions which make possible more than one form of equilibrium and for which an investigation of stability is necessary are

$$\left. \begin{aligned} u &> \left(1 - \sqrt{\frac{4}{27} \frac{(1 - m)^3}{m^2}}\right); \\ u &< \left(1 + \sqrt{\frac{4}{27} \frac{(1 - m)^3}{m^2}}\right). \end{aligned} \right\} \tag{l}$$

If $m \geqq 1$, Eq. (g) has only one real root, as can be seen from Fig. 139, in which the right side of Eq. (g) is represented by curves for $m = 2$ and $m = 1$. It is seen that for any positive value of $(1 - u)^2$ we obtain only one value for α, and this value is less than unity. Hence for $m \geqq 1$ there is only one possible form of equilibrium that will be stable. The question of instability will arise only if $m < 1$ and if the load is within the limits indicated by conditions (l).

In the investigation of the stability it is advantageous to represent graphically the rise of the arch as a function of the load

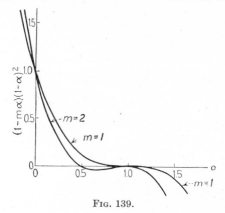

FIG. 139.

or as a function of the quantity u.   By using Eq. (d) this rise is

$$a_1 = \frac{a(1 - u)}{1 - \alpha}.\tag{m}$$

By taking in each particular case a series of values of α, the corresponding values of u can be calculated from Eq. (g) and the rise a_1 from Eq. (m).   In Fig. 140 the values of a_1/a are

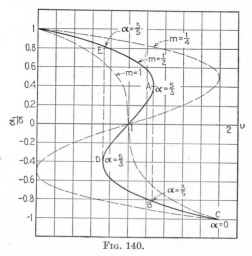

FIG. 140.

plotted against u.   The full line represents the case where $m = \frac{1}{2}$, and the two dotted lines represent the cases where $m = \frac{1}{4}$ and

$m = 1$. Considering the case $m = \frac{1}{2}$, it is seen from the curve that the deflection gradually increases with increasing of the load up to the point A, which corresponds to the maximum (at $\alpha = \frac{5}{3}$) on the curve shown in Fig. 138. Beginning at this point, further deflection continues with the decreasing of u, *i.e.*, with the decreasing of the load q. This fact indicates that at the point A, *i.e.*, for

$$(1 - u)^2 = \tfrac{2}{27},$$

the form of equilibrium of the arch shown in Fig. 137 by the full line becomes unstable and the arch buckles downward as shown by the dotted line. The sag of this new form of equilibrium is given in Fig. 140 by the position of the point B. This new form is stable and any further increase of the load produces a gradual increase in deflection as shown by the portion BC of the curve in Fig. 140. The thrust H during this loading decreases, becoming zero at the point C and negative with further increase of the load. If, starting from the point B, we begin to diminish the load, the deflection of the arch gradually diminishes up to the point D. At this point the load becomes insufficient to keep the arch deflected convex down and it buckles upward to the position given in Fig. 140 by the point E. From this discussion we see that there exists a possibility of having more than one form of equilibrium in the region limited by the verticals $\overline{ED}$ and $\overline{AB}$ which corresponds to the conditions (*j*). In the general case this region is defined by conditions (*l*) and we conclude that the critical load at which the arch will buckle convex down is determined from the equation

$$u = 1 + \sqrt{\frac{4}{27}\frac{(1 - m)^3}{m^2}}. \tag{135}$$

From the curves in Fig. 140 it may be concluded that the region in which more than one form of equilibrium is possible becomes smaller and smaller with the increase of m and that, when m becomes equal to 1, the two limits given by (*l*) coincide; hence, beginning from this value of m, there will always be only one form of equilibrium possible.

In the above discussion it was assumed that a uniformly distributed load is acting on the arch, but the results obtained can be used for all cases in which the deflection of the arch, considered as a beam, can be represented with sufficient accuracy by the first term of the sine series (see Art. 7). Taking, for instance, a concentrated vertical load P applied at the middle of the arch, the critical value of this load is obtained from Eq. (135),[1] it being only necessary to substitute in this equation

$$u = \frac{Pl^3}{48EI}\frac{1}{a}.$$ (n)

In an analogous manner the problem can be solved also if the load P is applied at some point other than the middle. It is only necessary to substitute for $Pl^3/(48EI)$ in Eq. (n) the corresponding deflection at the middle of the beam.

45. Buckling of a Bimetallic Strip.—The results of the previous article can be used in investigating buckling of a bimetallic strip submitted to a variation of temperature. Such strips are used as a part of instruments

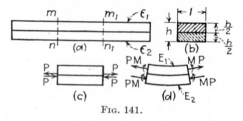

Fig. 141.

(thermostats) serving for regulating temperature. Let us consider a simple case when a bimetallic strip of unit width consists of two metals of equal thickness and having the same modulus of elasticity but two different coefficients of thermal expansion ϵ_1 and ϵ_2 (Fig. 141). If $\epsilon_2 > \epsilon_1$, any increase of temperature from the initial temperature t_0 to a temperature t will produce bending of the strip convex downward. The corresponding curvature can be calculated if we consider the reactive forces P arising at the surface of contact of the two metals (Fig. 141c) because of their difference in expansion. Replacing these forces by forces centrally applied and by couples $M = Ph/4$, as shown in Fig. 141d, we find the curvature for the strip of each metal from the known equation

$$\frac{1}{\rho} = \frac{M}{EI} = \frac{24Ph}{Eh^3}.$$ (a)

---

[1] This particular problem has been discussed by Navier, "Résumé des leçons sur l'application de la mécanique," 2d ed., p. 273, Paris, 1833. See also C. B. Biezeno, *Koninklijke Akad. Wetenschappen Amsterdam, Proceedings*, vol. 32, p. 990, 1929. The case when the center line of the arch is not a flat curve has been considered by A. Nadai, *Tech. Blättern*, Prague, Heft. 3, u. 4, 1915.

Another equation for determining ρ and P is obtained from the condition that the length of the longitudinal fibers of both metals at the surface of contact is the same; hence

$$\epsilon_1(t - t_0) + \frac{2P}{Eh} + \frac{h}{4\rho} = \epsilon_2(t - t_0) - \frac{2P}{Eh} - \frac{h}{4\rho}. \tag{b}$$

Eliminating P from Eqs. (a) and (b), we obtain

$$\frac{1}{\rho} = \frac{3}{2} \frac{(\epsilon_2 - \epsilon_1)(t - t_0)}{h}. \tag{136}$$

Thus the curvature of the bimetallic strip produced by heating is proportional to the rise in temperature and to the difference of the two coefficients of expansion and is inversely proportional to the thickness of the strip. Equation (136) can be used with sufficient accuracy also in the case where the materials have somewhat different moduli of elasticity, as, for instance, in the case of monel metal and nickel steel.[1]

Having the curvature, the deflection at the middle of the strip (supported at both ends), due to an increase in temperature $t - t_0$, is obtained as for a flat arc of a circle and is equal to

$$\delta = \frac{l^2}{8\rho}, \tag{c}$$

in which l is the length of the strip and ρ the radius of curvature determined from (136).

Let us consider now a bimetallic strip which has a slight initial curvature and let us assume that the ends of the strip are hinged as shown in Fig. 137 by the full line. If the metal on the concave side has a larger coefficient of thermal expansion than the metal on the convex side, the strip will deflect down during heating and a certain thrust H will be produced owing to this deflection. At a certain temperature, depending on the proportions of the strip and on the difference of the coefficients of expansion of the two metals, the form of the strip, shown in Fig. 137 by the full line, becomes unstable and the strip buckles suddenly downward as indicated by the dotted line. In a thermostat the source of heating is cut off at the instant of buckling and cooling begins, which results finally in buckling of the strip in the upward direction, thus turning on the source of heat again. This phenomenon is analogous to that of buckling of a flat arch during loading and unloading as discussed in the previous article. To determine the temperature at which buckling occurs we need only use the deflection (c) instead of the deflection produced by loading. Equation (135) becomes

$$\frac{l^2}{8\rho a} = 1 + \sqrt{\frac{4}{27} \frac{(1 - m)^3}{m^2}}.$$

Using expression (136) for the curvature, the temperature t_1, at which

---

[1] A more general investigation of bending and buckling of bimetallic strips is given in the writer's paper, *J. Optical Soc. Amer.*, vol. 11, p. 233, 1925.

buckling of the strip in a downward direction occurs, is obtained from the equation

$$\frac{3}{16}\frac{l^2}{ah}(\epsilon_2 - \epsilon_1)(t_1 - t_0) = 1 + \sqrt{\frac{4}{27}\frac{(1 - m)^3}{m^2}}. \tag{137}$$

The temperature t_2, at which the strip buckles in an upward direction after cooling, is obtained from the first of the inequalities (k) of the previous article. Hence

$$\frac{3}{16}\frac{l^2}{ah}(\epsilon_2 - \epsilon_1)(t_2 - t_0) = 1 - \sqrt{\frac{4}{27}\frac{(1 - m)^3}{m^2}}. \tag{138}$$

Taking, for instance, $l/h = 100$, $\epsilon_2 - \epsilon_1 = 4 \times 10^{-6}$ and the values of $m = h^2/3a^2$ as given in the first line of Table 17 below, the ratios of the initial rise a of the strip to its thickness are as given in the second line of the table. The values of $t_1 - t_0$, calculated from Eq. (137), and $t_2 - t_0$, calculated from Eq. (138), in °C., are in the third and fourth lines of the table, respectively.

TABLE 17.—NUMERICAL DATA ON BUCKLING OF BIMETALLIC STRIPS

m	$\frac{2}{3}$	$\frac{1}{2}$	$\frac{1}{3}$	$\frac{1}{4}$
a/h	0.707	0.814	1.000	1.154
$t_1 - t_0$	104°	137°	217°	307°
$t_2 - t_0$	83°	79°	50°	0°

It is seen from this table that the temperature t_1 of buckling increases with the increase of the initial curvature and that at the same time the temperature t_2 decreases, so that the sensitivity of the thermostat, given by the difference $t_1 - t_2$, decreases rapidly with the increase of the temperature of action t_1. The conditions can be improved by introducing elastic supports for the bimetallic strip.

If, under the action of the thrust H, the distance between the supports increases by some quantity βH, proportional to H, the equation for calculating the thrust becomes

$$\frac{Hl}{AE} + \beta H = \frac{1}{2}\int_0^l \left(\frac{dy}{dx}\right)^2 dx - \frac{1}{2}\int_0^l \left(\frac{dy_2}{dx}\right)^2 dx$$

and, instead of equation (g) of the previous article, we obtain

$$(1 - u)^2 = (1 - m_1\alpha)(1 - \alpha)^2, \tag{d}$$

in which

$$m_1 = m\left(1 + \frac{\beta AE}{l}\right). \tag{e}$$

It is seen that the operation of a bimetallic strip with elastic supports can be investigated in the same manner as before. It is only necessary to introduce, instead of the quantity m, a new quantity m_1 depending on the elasticity of supports. By a suitable adjustment of this elasticity the desired sensitivity of the thermostat can be obtained.[1]

[1] *Ibid.*

CHAPTER V

LATERAL BUCKLING OF BEAMS

46. Lateral Buckling of a Strip Submitted to Pure Bending in Its Plane.—A strip with a narrow rectangular cross section, if bent in its plane by couples M applied at the ends (Fig. 142), may prove unstable and at a certain *critical* value of M buckle sideways as shown in the figure. Such lateral buckling accompanied by twist may be of practical importance and should be

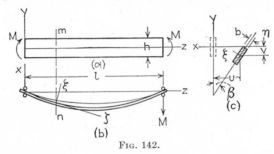

Fig. 142.

considered in the case of beams without lateral support if the flexural rigidity of the beam in the plane of bending is very large in comparison with its lateral rigidity.[1] In calculating the critical value of M, the same methods previously applied can be used. We assume that, under the action of the couples M in the vertical plane, a small lateral deflection occurs, and from the equations of equilibrium we determine the smallest value of M which is necessary to keep the strip in this slightly buckled shape. This smallest value of the bending couples is the critical value M_{cr}.

In deriving the differential equations of equilibrium of the buckled strip, we use the system of fixed coordinate axes x, y, z directed as shown in the figure. We take also at the centroid

---

[1] The first problems of this kind were discussed by L. Prandtl in his dissertation, "Kipperscheinungen," Nuremberg, 1899; and by A. G. M. Michell, *Phil. Mag.*, vol. 48, 1899.

of any cross section mn of the strip the system of coordinate axes ξ, η, ζ, such that ξ and η are in the directions of the principal axes of the cross section and ζ is in the direction of the tangent to the center line of the strip after buckling. The deformation of the strip is defined by the two components u and v of the displacement of the centroid of the cross section in the x- and y-directions and by the angle β through which the cross section rotates. Between the positive directions of the coordinate axes and the positive directions of rotations we take the same relations as exist between translation and rotation in a right-hand screw and consider β positive when rotation is in the direction from the x- to the y-axis as shown in the figure. In our further derivations the expressions for the cosines of the angles between the coordinate axes ξ, η, ζ and x, y, z will be needed. Considering the quantities u, v, β as very small and neglecting small quantities of higher order, the required cosines have the values given in the table below.

	x	y	z
ξ	1	β	$-du/dz$
η	$-\beta$	1	$-dv/dz$
ζ	du/dz	dv/dz	1

The numerical values of the curvatures of the center line of the strip, shown in Fig. 142, in the xz- and yz-planes are d^2u/dz^2 and d^2v/dz^2, respectively. For a very small angle β we can assume that curvatures of the same values will exist in the $\xi\zeta$ and $\eta\zeta$ planes. The angle of twist per unit length of the center line will be $d\beta/dz$. Having the expressions for curvatures and twist, we can write now in the usual way the differential equations of equilibrium:

$$\left.\begin{aligned}
B_1\frac{d^2u}{dz^2} &= M_\eta; \\
B_2\frac{d^2v}{dz^2} &= -M_\xi; \\
C\frac{d\beta}{dz} &= M_\zeta.
\end{aligned}\right\} \tag{139}$$

In these equations B_1 and B_2 are the principal *flexural rigidities* of the strip in the xz- and yz-planes, respectively, and C is the *torsional rigidity* of the strip. For a narrow rectangular cross section of width b and depth h, these quantities[1] are

$$B_1 = \frac{hb^3}{12}E; \qquad B_2 = \frac{bh^3}{12}E; \qquad C = \frac{hb^3}{3}\left(1 - 0.630\frac{b}{h}\right)G. \qquad (140)$$

The quantities M_ξ, M_η and M_ζ denote the moments with respect to ξ, η and ζ axes of the forces acting on the portion of the strip to the right of the cross section mn. These moments are taken positive when they are acting in the same directions as was designated for positive rotations with respect to the ξ, η and ζ axes. It is from this rule that the signs used in Eqs. (139) have been obtained.

For calculating M_ξ, M_η and M_ζ, we represent the couple M acting on the right end of the strip by a vector as shown in Fig. 142b. Projecting this vector onto the ξ, η and ζ axes and using the table of cosines, given above, we obtain

$$M_\xi = -M; \qquad M_\eta = \beta M; \qquad M_\zeta = -\frac{du}{dz}M.$$

Substituting these values in Eqs. (139) gives the following system of differential equations defining the deflections u and v and the angle of twist β:

$$\left.\begin{aligned} B_1\frac{d^2u}{dz^2} &= \beta M; \\ B_2\frac{d^2v}{dz^2} &= M; \\ C\frac{d\beta}{dz} &= -\frac{du}{dz}M. \end{aligned}\right\} \qquad (a)$$

Differentiating the third of these equations with respect to z and eliminating d^2u/dz^2 by using the first of Eqs. (a), we obtain for the angle of twist β the following differential equation:

$$\frac{d^2\beta}{dz^2} + \frac{M^2}{B_1C}\beta = 0. \qquad (b)$$

This equation is of the same kind as that obtained before for the buckling of a compressed strut (see **Art. 12**). Using the notation

$$k^2 = \frac{M^2}{B_1C}, \qquad (c)$$

[1] See author's "Theory of Elasticity," p. 249.

the general solution of Eq. (*b*) becomes

$$\beta = A \sin kz + B \cos kz. \qquad (d)$$

At the ends of the strip ($z = 0$ and $z = l$) the angle β must be equal to zero (Fig. 142). These conditions will be satisfied by taking $B = 0$ and putting

$$\sin kl = 0. \qquad (e)$$

The smallest root of Eq. (*e*), substituted in Eq. (*c*), gives

$$M_{cr} = \frac{\pi\sqrt{B_1 C}}{l}. \qquad (141)$$

The corresponding buckled form of equilibrium is shown in Fig. 142. By taking greater roots of Eq. (*e*) we shall find larger values of M, for which the corresponding deflection curves of the buckled strip will have one or more inflection points. In practical applications we are usually interested in the smallest value of M at which buckling occurs; this is given by expression (141). It is seen that the magnitude of M_{cr} depends on the product of the torsional rigidity C and the smallest flexural rigidity B_1 of the strip, and is independent of the flexural rigidity B_2 in the plane of the strip. This conclusion is obtained as a result of the assumption that the deflections of the strip in its plane are small, which assumption is justifiable in the case of a narrow rectangular cross section, *i.e.*, when the ratio b/h is small. If this ratio is not very small, the effect of bending in the plane of the strip may be of importance and should be considered.[1] Some numerical results of more elaborate calculations in which this bending is considered will be given later.

Formula (141) is analogous to Euler's formula for buckling of a compressed strut. It gives a correct value of M_{cr} only so long as the maximum bending stress is within the elastic limit. Beyond this limit the critical value of the moment is smaller than the value given by Eq. (141). The deflection of the buckled strip, as is seen from the derivation given above, remains indeterminate as long as we are using the simplified differential Eqs. (*a*).

[1] This question has been discussed by H. Reissner, *Sitzungsb. Berl. Math. Ges.*, 1904, p. 53. See also A. N. Dinnik, *Bull. Don. Polytech. Inst., Novotcherkassk*, vol. 2, 1913; and K. Federhofer, *Sitzungsb. Akad. Wiss., Wien*, vol. 140, Abt. IIa, p. 237, 1931.

The deflection of the strip can be obtained if we proceed as in the case of a compressed strut and use for the curvature of the deflection curve the complete expression (see Art. 13).[1]

If the strip is bent by two equal and opposite eccentrically applied forces P (Fig. 143), and if we proceed as before, we obtain, instead

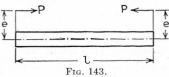

Fig. 143.

of the first and the third of Eqs. (a), the following differential equations of equilibrium for the buckled strip:

$$B_1 \frac{d^2u}{dz^2} = \beta M - Pu; \left.\begin{array}{c} \\ \\ \\ \\ \end{array}\right\} \qquad (f)$$
$$C \frac{d\beta}{dz} = -\frac{du}{dz}M,$$

in which $M = Pe$ is the bending moment at the ends of the strip. Eliminating β from these equations, we obtain

$$\frac{d^3u}{dz^3} + \frac{M^2}{B_1C}\left(1 + \frac{PC}{M^2}\right)\frac{du}{dz} = 0. \qquad (g)$$

Integrating this equation as before, we conclude from the conditions at the ends that the smallest value of the force P at which buckling of the strip occurs is determined from the equation

$$\frac{M^2}{B_1C}\left(1 + \frac{PC}{M^2}\right) = \frac{\pi^2}{l^2}. \qquad (h)$$

If the eccentricity e is very large, the force P, necessary to produce buckling, is small and the conditions of buckling approach those shown in Fig. 142, for which the critical value of M approaches the value (141). In Eq. (h) the second term in the parenthesis is, in this case, a small quantity and can be calculated with sufficient accuracy by using for M the value given by expression (141). Then

$$\frac{PC}{M^2} = \frac{C}{Me} = \frac{l}{\pi e}\sqrt{\frac{C}{B_1}},$$

[1] An investigation of this kind has been made by K. Federhofer, *Z. angew. Math. Mech.*, vol. 6, p. 43, 1926.

and the critical value of the bending moment is, from (h),

$$M_{cr} = \frac{\pi\sqrt{B_1 C}}{l\sqrt{1 + \frac{l}{\pi e}\sqrt{\frac{C}{B_1}}}}. \tag{142}$$

Comparing this result with formula (141), it can be concluded that the critical value of the bending moment in the case under consideration is smaller than in the case of pure bending in the ratio

$$\frac{1}{\sqrt{1 + \frac{l}{\pi e}\sqrt{\frac{C}{B_1}}}}. \tag{i}$$

By taking Poisson's ratio equal to 0.3, we find from (140) for the case of a very narrow rectangle:

$$\frac{C}{B_1} = \frac{4G}{E} = 1.54, \tag{143}$$

and the ratio (i) becomes

$$\frac{1}{\sqrt{1 + 0.395\frac{l}{e}}}. \tag{j}$$

This is sufficiently accurate only if it does not differ much from unity, *i.e.*, when the eccentricity e is large in comparison with the length l of the strip.

Let us consider now another extreme case, where the eccentricity e is very small and the conditions approach those of compression of a strut. Representing Eq. (h) in the form

$$\frac{P}{B_1}\left(1 + \frac{Pe^2}{C}\right) = \frac{\pi^2}{l^2} \tag{k}$$

and substituting $P = \pi^2 B_1/l^2$ in the second term in the parenthesis, we find

$$P_{cr} = \frac{\pi^2 B_1}{l^2} \cdot \frac{1}{1 + 6.4\frac{e^2}{l^2}}. \tag{144}$$

It is seen that in the case of a narrow rectangular cross section a considerable eccentricity in the plane of the strip produces only a small reduction in critical value of the force necessary to produce buckling in the lateral direction. Assuming, for instance, that $e = 0.1l$, we find from (144) that the critical value of the compressive force is only about 6 per cent smaller than that given by Euler's formula.

It was assumed in the case represented in Fig. 142 that during buckling the ends of the strip can rotate freely with respect to the vertical axes. If the ends of the strip are built in, the deflected center line of the buckled strip is tangent to the z-axis at the ends as shown in Fig. 144. The middle

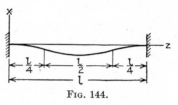

FIG. 144.

portion of the strip of length $l/2$ between the two inflection points of the center line is in the same condition as the strip shown in Fig. 142. Hence, in this case also, the calculation of the critical value of the couples can be made by formula (141). It is only necessary to substitute in this formula $l/2$ instead of l. Then

$$M_{cr} = \frac{2\pi\sqrt{B_1 C}}{l}. \tag{145}$$

That is, in the case of built-in ends the magnitude of the critical couple is twice that for the case of simply supported ends.

47. Lateral Buckling of a Cantilever Beam of Narrow Rectangular Cross Section.—We begin with the case where the

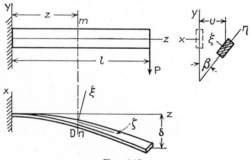

FIG. 145.

cantilever is bent by a force P applied at the centroid of the end and acting in the plane of the web. By increasing the load we finally arrive at the condition where the deflection form in the plane of the web becomes unstable and buckling occurs as shown in Fig. 145. For calculating the critical value of the load we assume, as before, that a small lateral buckling has occurred and then determine from the equations of equilibrium of the buckled cantilever the smallest value of the load which can keep it in this slightly buckled shape. This will be the critical load. We take the system of fixed coordinate axes x, y, z at the left end and the system ξ, η, ζ, at any cross section mn of the cantilever in the same manner as in the previous article, and use for defining the deformation the components u and v of the deflections and the angle of twist β. Considering the portion of the cantilever to the right of the cross section mn and calculating the moments of the vertical load P with respect to axes parallel to x, y, z through the centroid D of the cross section, we obtain

$$M_x = P(l - z); \qquad M_y = 0; \qquad M_z = -P(\delta - u).[1]$$

Projecting these moments onto the ξ, η and ζ axes by using the tables of cosines (see p. 240) and neglecting small quantities of higher order than the first, we obtain

$$M_\xi = P(l - z); \qquad M_\eta = -\beta P(l - z);$$
$$M_\zeta = P(l - z)\frac{du}{dz} - P(\delta - u).$$

The following equations are obtained by substituting these moments into Eqs. (139):

$$\left. \begin{array}{l} B_1 \dfrac{d^2u}{dz^2} = -\beta P(l - z); \\[2mm] B_2 \dfrac{d^2v}{dz^2} = -P(l - z); \\[2mm] C \dfrac{d\beta}{dz} = P(l - z)\dfrac{du}{dz} - P(\delta - u). \end{array} \right\} \qquad (a)$$

Differentiating the third of these equations with respect to z and eliminating d^2u/dz^2 by using the first of the equations, we finally obtain, for determining β, the following equation:

$$\frac{d^2\beta}{dz^2} + \frac{P^2}{B_1 C}(l - z)^2\beta = 0. \qquad (b)$$

Using, as before, the notation $P^2/B_1 C = k^2$ and introducing the new variable

$$w = l - z,$$

---

[1] δ and u are negative in the case shown in Fig. 145.

Eq. (*b*) becomes

$$\frac{d^2\beta}{dw^2} + k^2 w^2 \beta = 0. \qquad (c)$$

For the solution of this equation with variable coefficients, we use the method of infinite series (see p. 116). In this way we obtain

$$\beta = A\left(1 - \frac{k^2}{3\cdot 4}w^4 + \frac{k^4}{3\cdot 4\cdot 7\cdot 8}w^8 - \frac{k^6}{3\cdot 4\cdot 7\cdot 8\cdot 11\cdot 12}w^{12} + \right.$$
$$\left. \cdots \right) + B\left(w - \frac{k^2}{4\cdot 5}w^5 + \frac{k^4}{4\cdot 5\cdot 8\cdot 9}w^9 - \right.$$
$$\left. \frac{k^6}{4\cdot 5\cdot 8\cdot 9\cdot 12\cdot 13}w^{13} + \cdots \right), \quad (d)$$

where *A* and *B* are the constants of integration which are to be determined from the conditions at the ends. In the case represented in Fig. 145, these conditions are: At the built-in end the angle of twist is zero; hence

$$\beta = 0 \qquad \text{for} \qquad w = l. \qquad (e)$$

At the loaded end the torque M_ξ becomes zero; hence

$$\frac{d\beta}{dz} = 0 \qquad \text{for} \qquad w = 0. \qquad (f)$$

The condition (*f*) will be satisfied if we put $B = 0$ and take the expression for β in the form of the series

$$\beta = A\left(1 - \frac{k^2}{3\cdot 4}w^4 + \frac{k^4}{3\cdot 4\cdot 7\cdot 8}w^8 - \right.$$
$$\left. \frac{k^6}{3\cdot 4\cdot 7\cdot 8\cdot 11\cdot 12}w^{12} + \cdots \right).$$

The condition (*e*) at the built-in end requires that this expression become zero when $w = l$; hence

$$1 - \frac{(kl^2)^2}{3\cdot 4} + \frac{(kl^2)^4}{3\cdot 4\cdot 7\cdot 8} - \frac{(kl^2)^6}{3\cdot 4\cdot 7\cdot 8\cdot 11\cdot 12} + \cdots = 0. \quad (g)$$

A table of numerical values of the left side of Eq. (*g*) as a function of kl^2 has been calculated by L. Prandtl,[1] and it was shown

---

[1] *Loc. cit.*, p. 239. The general solution (*d*) can be expressed by Bessel's functions, the tables of which will be found in E. Jahnke and F. Emde, "Funktionentafeln mit Formeln und Kurven," Berlin, 1909. The new edition of the same book with German and English texts, Berlin, 1933.

that Eq. (g) has an infinite number of roots. The smallest of these roots, which determines the critical value of the load, is

$$kl^2 = 4.013.$$

Substituting for k its value $P/\sqrt{B_1C}$, we obtain

$$P_{cr} = \frac{4.013\sqrt{B_1C}}{l^2}. \tag{146}$$

The buckling shown in Fig. 145 corresponds to this value of the load. By taking larger roots of Eq. (g) we obtain deflection curves with one or more inflection points. These higher forms of unstable equilibrium are of no practical significance, since failure occurs when the load approaches the value given by (146).

Formula (146) gives the correct value of the critical load only within the elastic region. Beyond the elastic limit buckling occurs at a load smaller than that given by the formula. To establish the proportions of cantilevers for which formula (146) can be used, let us calculate the maximum bending stress in the cantilever. Observing that the maximum bending moment is $P_{cr}l$ and that the section modulus is $2B_2/hE$, we obtain

$$\sigma_{cr} = \frac{hEP_{cr}l}{2B_2} = 2.006\frac{h}{l}\sqrt{\frac{B_1}{B_2}\frac{C}{B_2}}E,$$

or, by using Eqs. (140) and taking Poisson's ratio equal to 0.3,

$$\sigma_{cr} = 2.487\frac{b^2}{hl}E\sqrt{1 - 0.630\frac{b}{h}}. \tag{h}$$

It is seen from this result that, for such material as steel, buckling in the elastic region may occur only if the quantity b^2/hl is very small.

Usually we need to consider lateral buckling only in the case of a very narrow rectangular cross section where b/h is a small quantity. Theoretically [see Eq. (h)] buckling may occur also in the case where b/h is not very small, but where the length l is very large. In this case a large deflection in the plane of the web will be produced before lateral buckling occurs and this deflection should be considered in the derivation of the equations of equilibrium (a). More elaborate investigations[1] by K. Federhofer and A. N. Dinnik show that in this case we obtain in formula (146), instead of the constant numerical factor 4.013, a variable factor the magnitude of

[1] *Loc. cit.*, p. 242.

which depends on the ratio b/h. Taking b/h equal to $\frac{1}{10}$, $\frac{1}{5}$ and $\frac{1}{3}$, we obtain values of this factor equal to 4.085, 4.324 and 5.030, respectively.

It was assumed in the previous discussion that the load P is applied at the centroid of the cross section. By using the same method of investigation as in the previous article, the effect on the magnitude of P_{cr} of having the point of application of the load above or below the centroid of the end cross section can be investigated.[1] If a denotes the distance of the point of application of the load vertically above the centroid (Fig. 145), the approximate formula for calculating the critical load can be put in the form

$$P_{cr} = \frac{4.013\sqrt{B_1 C}}{l^2}\left(1 - \frac{a}{l}\sqrt{\frac{B_1}{C}}\right). \tag{147}$$

It is seen that application of the load above the centroid diminishes its critical value. Formula (147) can be used also when the load is applied below the centroid. It is only necessary to change the sign of the displacement a.

If, instead of a load applied at the end, a distributed load is acting on the cantilever, the same phenomena of lateral buckling may occur when the load approaches a certain critical value. Assuming, that a uniform load of intensity q is distributed along the center line of the cantilever, the critical value of this load, as obtained from the equations of equilibrium of the buckled cantilever,[2] is

$$(ql)_{cr} = \frac{12.85\sqrt{B_1 C}}{l^2}. \tag{148}$$

Comparing this result with formula (146), it can be concluded that the critical value of the total uniformly distributed load is approximately three times larger than the critical value of the load applied at the end.

In the case of a distributed load, the intensity of which is given by the equation

$$q = q_0\left(1 - \frac{z}{l}\right)^n, \tag{i}$$

the critical value of the total load again can be represented by a formula analogous to formula (148).[3] It is only necessary to replace the numerical factor 12.85 by another factor, the value of which depends on the exponent n in Eq. (i). For $n = \frac{1}{4}$, $\frac{1}{2}$, $\frac{3}{4}$ and 1, these factors are 15.82, 19.08, 22.64 and 26.51, respectively.

The problem of buckling of a cantilever with a narrow rectangular cross section has been solved also for the case where the depth of the cross section

[1] Such an investigation has been made by the writer, *Bull. Polytech. Inst., Kiev*, 1910, and in a more complete form by A. Koroboff, *Bull. Polytech. Inst., Kiev*, 1911.

[2] This result has been obtained by L. Prandtl, *loc. cit.*, p. 239.

[5] Several cases of this kind have been investigated by A. N. Dinnik and K. Federhofer, *loc. cit.*, p. 242.

varies according to the law[1]

$$h = h_0\left(1 - \frac{z}{l}\right)^n.$$ (j)

In all cases the critical value of the total load can be represented by the formula

$$Q_{cr} = \frac{m\sqrt{B_1 C}}{l^2},$$ (k)

in which the numerical value of the factor m depends on the kind of loading and on the value of n in Eq. (j). B_1 and C are the flexural and torsional rigidities for the fixed end of the cantilever. Several values of m are given in the table below.

TABLE 18.—VALUES OF THE FACTOR m IN EQ. (k)

n	0	$\frac{1}{4}$	$\frac{1}{2}$	$\frac{3}{4}$	1
Uniform load	12.85	12.05	11.24	10.43	9.62
Load concentrated at the end	4.013	3.614	3.214	2.811	2.405

It is seen from this table that in the case of a cantilever, the depth of which decreases uniformly to zero at the free end [$n = 1$ in Eq. (j)], the critical value of the load concentrated at the end is approximately 60 per cent and the critical value of the uniformly distributed load is approximately 75 per cent of the load calculated for a cantilever of a constant cross section [$n = 0$ in Eq. (j)].

48. Lateral Buckling of a Simply Supported Beam of Narrow Rectangular Cross Section.—If a beam of narrow rectangular cross section is bent in its plane by a load P applied at the centroid of the middle cross section, the lateral buckling shown in Fig. 146 may occur at a certain value of the load. It is assumed that during deformation the ends can rotate freely with respect to the principal axes of inertia parallel to the x- and y-axes, while rotation with respect to the z-axis is prevented by some constraint (Fig. 146). Thus the lateral buckling is accompanied by some twisting of the beam. In calculating the critical value of the load, we assume, as before, that a small lateral buckling has occurred, and from the differential equations of equilibrium we determine the magnitude of the smallest load required to keep the beam in this slightly buckled form. Considering a portion of the beam to the right of any cross section mn, we see that the external forces acting on this portion reduce to one

[1] See K. Federhofer, *Reports Intern. Congr. Appl. Mech.*, Stockholm, 1930.

vertical force $P/2$ acting at the point B_1. The moments of this force, with respect to the axes having their origin at the centroid D of the cross section and parallel to the x-, y- and z-axes, are

$$M_x = -\frac{P}{2}\left(\frac{l}{2} - z\right); \qquad M_y = 0; \qquad M_z = \frac{P}{2}(\delta - u). \quad (a)$$

Here δ is the lateral deflection at the middle of the beam and u the deflection at any cross section. Both of these quantities

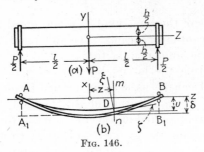

Fig. 146.

are taken positive when they are in the positive direction of the x-axis. Using the system of coordinate axes ξ, η and ζ as in the preceding articles, and projecting the moments (a) onto these axes by using the table of cosines (see p. 240), we obtain

$$M_\xi = -\frac{P}{2}\left(\frac{l}{2} - z\right); \qquad M_\eta = \frac{P}{2}\left(\frac{l}{2} - z\right)\beta;$$

$$M_\zeta = -\frac{P}{2}\left(\frac{l}{2} - z\right)\frac{du}{dz} + \frac{P}{2}(\delta - u). \quad (b)$$

Substituting expressions (b) in Eqs. (139), the following differential equations of equilibrium for the buckled beam (Fig. 146) are obtained:

$$\left.\begin{aligned}
B_1 \frac{d^2u}{dz^2} &= \frac{P}{2}\left(\frac{l}{2} - z\right)\beta; \\[2mm]
B_2 \frac{d^2v}{dz^2} &= \frac{P}{2}\left(\frac{l}{2} - z\right); \\[2mm]
C \frac{d\beta}{dz} &= -\frac{P}{2}\left(\frac{l}{2} - z\right)\frac{du}{dz} + \frac{P}{2}(\delta - u).
\end{aligned}\right\} \quad (c)$$

Eliminating u from the first and the third of these equations, we obtain

$$\frac{d^2\beta}{dz^2} + \frac{P^2}{4B_1C}\left(\frac{l}{2} - z\right)^2 \beta = 0. \qquad (d)$$

This equation is of the same type as Eq. (b) of the previous article and it can be integrated, as before, by the method of infinite series. By using the conditions at the ends of the beam, we obtain

$$P_{cr} = \frac{16.93\sqrt{B_1C}}{l^2}. \qquad (149)$$

This formula is of the same kind as we obtained in the previous article for a cantilever beam. The difference is only in the magnitude of the numerical factor.

In investigating the lateral buckling of a beam, the strain-energy method can be used to advantage in many cases.[1] As an example of the application of this method, let us consider again the case represented in Fig. 146. When the beam buckles sideways the strain energy increases since, to the bending in the plane of the web, a bending in the lateral direction and a twist about the longitudinal axis are added. At the same time the point of application of the load P lowers and the load produces certain work. The critical value of the load is now determined from the condition that this work is equal to the strain energy of lateral bending together with the strain energy of twist [see Eq. (64)]. Some small change of energy of bending of the beam in its plane, which occurs during buckling, can be neglected in applying the energy method. This is equivalent to the assumption previously made that the curvature in the plane of the web is infinitely small and can be neglected in deriving the differential equations of equilibrium. The result obtained in this way is correct when the rigidity of the beam in the plane of the web is infinitely large and it is accurate enough if this rigidity is very large in comparison with the rigidity in the lateral direction, which is practically always the case.

In calculating the strain energy of bending and torsion, the usual formulas can be applied. Then, by taking into consideration the symmetry of the buckled form of the beam (Fig. 146), the increase of strain energy due to buckling is

---

[1] Several examples of application of this method to the problem of lateral buckling of strips are given in writer's paper, *loc. cit.*, p. 82.

$$\Delta V = B_1 \int_0^{\frac{l}{2}} \left(\frac{d^2 u}{dz^2}\right)^2 dz + C \int_0^{\frac{l}{2}} \left(\frac{d\beta}{dz}\right)^2 dz. \quad (e)$$

For determining the lowering of the load P during lateral buckling, let us consider an element of the longitudinal axis of the beam at the point D (Fig. 146). Owing to bending of this element in the $\xi\zeta$ plane, and considering the cross section mn as fixed, the end B of the beam describes an infinitely small arc

$$\frac{d^2 u}{dz^2}\left(\frac{l}{2} - z\right)dz$$

in the $\xi\zeta$ plane, the vertical component of which is

$$\beta \frac{d^2 u}{dz^2}\left(\frac{l}{2} - z\right)dz. \quad (f)$$

Now, varying z from 0 to $l/2$ and summarizing such vertical components as given by (f), the lowering of the point of application of the load P due to lateral buckling of the beam is obtained in the form of the integral

$$\int_0^{\frac{l}{2}} \beta \frac{d^2 u}{dz^2}\left(\frac{l}{2} - z\right)dz, \quad (g)$$

and the equation for calculating the critical load becomes

$$P \int_0^{\frac{l}{2}} \beta \frac{d^2 u}{dz^2}\left(\frac{l}{2} - z\right)dz = B_1 \int_0^{\frac{l}{2}} \left(\frac{d^2 u}{dz^2}\right)^2 dz + C \int_0^{\frac{l}{2}} \left(\frac{d\beta}{dz}\right)^2 dz. \quad (h)$$

Substituting for $d^2 u/dz^2$ from the first of Eqs. (c), we obtain

$$\frac{P^2}{4B_1} \int_0^{\frac{l}{2}} \beta^2 \left(\frac{l}{2} - z\right)^2 dz = C \int_0^{\frac{l}{2}} \left(\frac{d\beta}{dz}\right)^2 dz. \quad (i)$$

To calculate the critical value of the load P, it is only necessary to take for the angle of twist β a suitable analytical expression satisfying the conditions at the ends of the beam and substitute this in Eq. (i). In the case shown in Fig. 146 the general expression for β, satisfying the end conditions, can be taken in the form of the trigonometric series

$$\beta = a_1 \cos\frac{\pi z}{l} + a_3 \cos\frac{3\pi z}{l} + a_5 \cos\frac{5\pi z}{l} + \cdots . \quad (j)$$

By taking for β, as the first approximation, only the first term of this series, substituting it into Eq. (i) and integrating, we obtain

$$P_{cr} = \frac{17.2\sqrt{B_1 C}}{l^2}.$$

Comparing this result with formula (149) it is seen that the error of the first approximation is about $1\frac{1}{2}$ per cent. If we take as the second approximation the first two terms of series (j) and adjust the constants a_1 and a_3 so as to make P_{cr} a minimum, the error is less than 0.1 of 1 per cent. Thus, it is seen from this example that the energy method can be successfully applied in studying lateral buckling of beams. By the use of this method a complicated integration of differential equations by infinite series is replaced by the calculation of simple integrals entering into Eq. (i), and a comparatively simple expression for β usually gives P_{cr} with an accuracy satisfactory for practical applications. As was explained before (see p. 81), such an approximate value of the critical load is always larger than its correct value.[1]

The magnitude of the critical load P depends on the position of its point of application. It is evident that application of the load above the centroid of the cross section diminishes its critical value, while its application below the centroid has an opposite effect. The extent of this effect can be easily obtained by using the energy method; it is necessary to take into consideration only the additional lowering of the load P during lateral buckling of the beam, due to rotation of the middle cross section. If β_0 is this angle of rotation and a is the vertical distance of the point of application of the load from the centroid of the cross section, positive when above, the additional lowering of the load is

$$a(1 - \cos \beta_0) \approx \frac{a\beta^2{}_0}{2}.$$

Then, instead of Eq. (i), we obtain

$$\frac{Pa\beta^2{}_0}{2} + \frac{P^2}{4B_1}\int_0^{\frac{l}{2}}\beta^2\left(\frac{l}{2} - z\right)^2 dz = C\int_0^{\frac{l}{2}}\left(\frac{d\beta}{dz}\right)^2 dz. \qquad (k)$$

[1] A method of successive approximations, analogous to that discussed in the chapter on columns (see Art. 16) can also be successfully used in investigating lateral buckling of beams. Examples of the application of such a method to beams under various load conditions have been communicated to the writer by Dr. Fritz Stüssi, Zürich. See also Stüssi's papers in *Schweiz. Bauzeitung*, vol. 105, p. 123, 1935, and in *Pub. Intern. Assoc. Bridge and Structural Eng.* vol. 3, p. 401, 1935.

If a is small, the first term on the left side of this equation is a small correction and we can substitute in it the value (149) for P. In this manner the following approximate formula is obtained:

$$P_{cr} = \frac{16.93\sqrt{B_1C}}{l^2}\left(1 - \frac{3.48a}{l}\sqrt{\frac{B_1}{C}}\right). \tag{150}$$

When the load P is not applied at the middle of the span, but at a distance c from one support, its critical value can be represented by the general formula

$$P_{cr} = \frac{m\sqrt{B_1C}}{l^2}, \tag{151}$$

in which the numerical value of the factor m depends on the value of the ratio c/l. Several values of m are given in Table 19.[1]

TABLE 19.—VALUES OF THE FACTOR m IN FORMULA (151)

c/l	0.50	0.45	0.40	0.35	0.30	0.25	0.20	0.15	0.10	0.05
m	16.93	17.15	17.82	19.04	21.01	24.10	29.11	37.88	56.01	111.6

It is seen that the value of the critical load increases when its point of application is to one side of the middle of the span. However, this effect is not large as long as the load remains within the middle third of the span.

The problem of lateral buckling of the beam shown in Fig. 146 has also been solved[2] for the case when the ends are built in and the load is acting at the centroid of the middle cross section. The critical value of the load in this case is

$$P_{cr} = \frac{26.6\sqrt{B_1C}}{l^2}. \tag{152}$$

If a beam with simply supported ends (Fig. 146) is carrying a load uniformly distributed along the center line, the critical value of the total load is given by the formula

$$(ql)_{cr} = \frac{28.3\sqrt{B_1C}}{l^2}. \tag{153}$$

It is seen that in all cases the formula for the critical load has the form (151); the difference between all these formulas is only in the magnitude of the numerical factor m.

These formulas can be applied only as long as the corresponding values of the maximum bending stress remain within the elastic region. Beyond the elastic limit the formulas give exaggerated values for the critical load; for a more satisfactory solution of the problem, bending beyond the elastic

[1] These values have been calculated by A. Koroboff, *loc. cit.*, p. 249. See also the paper by A. N. Dinnik, *loc. cit.*, p. 242.

[2] This solution and the following are due to L. Prandtl, *loc. cit.*, p. 239.

limit should be considered. This question will be discussed later in connection with the investigation of the lateral buckling of I-beams (see Art. 53).

49. Torsion of I-beams.—The formulas obtained in the previous articles for the critical values of the load for a beam of narrow rectangular cross section cannot be applied in the case of I-beams. The actual value of the critical load for an I-beam is always greater than that which would be obtained from the previously derived formulas by substituting in them for B_1 and C the lateral flexural rigidity and torsional rigidity of the I-beam. This result is due to the fact that the third of Eqs. (139) (see

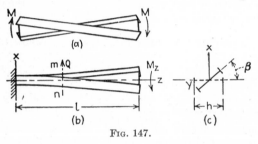

Fig. 147.

p. 240), giving the relation between the angle of twist and the torque, is not accurate enough for application to I-beams. It is derived for torsion of prisms, the cross sections of which are free to warp; if this warping is prevented[1] a bending deformation in addition to torsional deformation will be produced. This additional deformation is not of much practical importance in the case of beams of narrow rectangular cross section[2] but in the case of I-beams it may have a considerable effect on the angle of twist and should be considered in investigating lateral buckling.

In Fig. 147 two conditions of torsion of an I-beam are illustrated. When the cross sections are free to warp (Fig. 147a), the flanges of the twisted beam remain practically straight, and in calculating the angle of twist the third of Eqs. (139) can be used. When one end of the beam is built in so that free warping of the cross sections during torsion is prevented (Fig.

---

[1] From the condition of symmetry it can be concluded, for instance, that the middle cross sections of the strips shown in Figs. 142 and 146 remain plane during buckling.

[2] This question has been discussed by the writer, *Proc. London Math. Soc.*, series 2, vol. 20, p. 389, 1921. See also his "Theory of Elasticity," p. 275, 1934.

147*b*), the twisting of the beam is accompanied by bending of the flanges. At any cross section *mn* the external torque M_z is balanced partially by torsional stress and partially by shearing forces Q due to bending of flanges. Denoting by β the angle of twist, which varies along the length of the beam, the portion of the torque balanced by torsional stresses is equal to

$$C\frac{d\beta}{dz}. \qquad (a)$$

In calculating the second portion of the torque, the bending of the flanges must be considered. If h is the depth of the beam,[1] the deflection of the upper flange in Fig. 147*b* is

$$u = -\beta\frac{h}{2}. \qquad (b)$$

Denoting by D the flexural rigidity of one flange in the plane of the flange (which usually can be taken with sufficient accuracy equal to $\frac{1}{2}B_1$), the usual formula for shearing force Q (Fig. 147*b*), gives

$$Q = D\frac{d^3u}{dz^3} = -\frac{Dh}{2}\frac{d^3\beta}{dz^3}.$$

A force Q of the opposite sign will be obtained for the lower flange, and both these forces together give a couple

$$Qh = -\frac{Dh^2}{2}\frac{d^3\beta}{dz^3}. \qquad (c)$$

The two portions (*a*) and (*c*) together give the magnitude of the external torque M_z. Hence the following relation between the angle of twist β and the torque is obtained[2]

$$C\frac{d\beta}{dz} - D\frac{h^2}{2}\frac{d^3\beta}{dz^3} = M_z. \qquad (154)$$

[1] It is assumed in this calculation that the thickness of the flange is small in comparison with the depth of the beam, and the depth h is taken instead of the distance between the centroids of the cross sections of the flanges.

[2] This equation has been derived by the writer and proved to be in good agreement with experiments, see *Bull. Polytech. Inst., St. Petersburg*, vols. 4 and 5, 1905, 1906. See also his paper in *Z. Math. Physik*, vol. 58, p. 361, 1910. Further literature on this subject is given in the papers by C. Weber, *Z. angew. Math. Mech.*, vol. 6, p. 85, 1926, and by A. Ostenfeld, *Laboratorium Baustatik tech. Hochschule, Mitteilung*, no. 6, 1931, Copenhagen.

This equation, instead of the third of Eqs. (139), should be used in discussing lateral buckling of I-beams.

The general solution of Eq. (154) is

$$\beta = A_0 + A_1 e^{\frac{z}{a}} + A_2 e^{-\frac{z}{a}} + \frac{M_z z}{C}, \qquad (d)$$

in which

$$a^2 = \frac{Dh^2}{2C}. \qquad (155)$$

The constants of integration in each particular case are to be determined from the conditions at the ends.

Taking the case represented in Fig. 147b, these conditions are:

$$\beta = 0, \qquad \frac{d\beta}{dz} = 0, \qquad \text{for} \qquad z = 0;$$

$$\frac{d^2\beta}{dz^2} = 0, \qquad \text{for} \qquad z = l.$$

The last condition follows from the fact that there is no bending of the flanges at the free end of the beam. The above conditions are satisfied if we take for the constants of integration in solution (d) the following values:

$$A_0 = -\frac{M_z}{C} a \tanh \frac{l}{a}; \qquad A_1 = -\frac{M_z}{C} a \frac{e^{-\frac{l}{a}}}{2 \cosh \frac{l}{a}}; \qquad A_2 = \frac{M_z}{C} a \frac{e^{\frac{l}{a}}}{2 \cosh \frac{l}{a}}.$$

Substituting in (d), we find that the angle of twist at the end is

$$(\beta)_{z=l} = \frac{M_z}{C} l \left(1 - \frac{a}{l} \tanh \frac{l}{a} \right). \qquad (156)$$

Comparing this result with the usual formula for the angle of twist, it can be concluded that the magnitude of the correction due to bending of the flanges depends on the value of the ratio l/a. This ratio is usually much larger than unity and we can take with sufficient accuracy

$$\tanh \frac{l}{a} \approx 1.$$

Then, from Eq. (156), we conclude that bending of the flanges produces, on the magnitude of the angle of twist, an effect equivalent to that which would be produced by a shortening of the length of the beam by the amount a.

The ratio l/a, on which the resistance to twist of an I-beam depends, can be readily calculated from the dimensions of the beam. By using notation (155) we obtain

$$\frac{l^2}{a^2} = \frac{2C}{D} \frac{l^2}{h^2}. \qquad (157)$$

The flexural rigidity D of a flange can be taken equal to half of the flexural rigidity of the I-beam in the lateral direction and can be calculated in each particular case by using tables for I-beam cross sections. In calculating the torsional rigidity C, we may assume that an I-section consists of three narrow rectangles and we can use the approximate formula[1]

$$C = G(\tfrac{2}{3}bt^3 + \tfrac{1}{3}ht^3_1), \tag{158}$$

in which b is the width of the flanges, t is the average thickness of the flanges, h is the depth of the beam and t_1 is the thickness of the web.

Let us take, as a numerical example, $l = 20$ ft., $h = 24$ in., $b = 7$ in., $t = \tfrac{1}{2}(0.60 + 1.14) = 0.87$ in., $t_1 = 0.5$ in. Then, from the tables, $B_1 = 42.9E$, $B_2 = 2,090E$, and, from Eq. (158), $C = 4.07G$. Substituting in (157) and taking $E = 2.6G$, we obtain

$$\frac{l^2}{a^2} = \frac{4 \cdot 4.07 \cdot 100}{42.7 \cdot 2.6} = 14.7;$$

$$\frac{l}{a} = 3.83; \qquad \frac{a}{l} = 0.261.$$

From Eq. (156) we conclude that in this case, owing to bending of the flanges, the angle of twist of the beam with one end built in (Fig. 147b) is 26 per cent smaller than in the case when both ends are free to warp (Fig. 147a).

50. Lateral Buckling of I-beams Subjected to Pure Bending.[2]

If an I-beam is bent by two couples applied at the ends and acting in the plane of the web of the beam (Fig. 142), the critical value of these couples can be determined in the same manner as in the case of a beam of narrow rectangular cross section, discussed in Art. 46. It is necessary only to replace the left side of the third of the Eqs. (a) of that article with the left side

[1] For derivation of this formula see writer's "Strength of Materials," vol. I, p. 78, 1930. An experimental verification of the formula is given in the paper by A. Föppl, *Sitzungsb. math.-physik. Klasse bayer. Akad. Wiss.*, *München*, 1921, p. 295. See also *Bauingenieur* (5), vol. 3, p. 42, 1922. A more detailed calculation of the torsional rigidity of I-beams in which the effect of fillets between the web and flanges is considered has been made by C. Weber; see "Föppl-Festschrift," Berlin, 1924. It is shown in this way that the actual torsional rigidity for rolled I-beams is about 25 per cent larger than is given by formula (158). It should be noted that a considerable error in the calculation of the magnitude of C has only a small effect on the magnitude of the critical stresses. See writer's paper in *Trans. Am. Soc. Civil Eng.*, vol. 87, p. 1247, 1924. Recently a series of tests of structural beams in torsion has been made by J. Lyse and B. G. Johnston, *Proc. A.S.C.E.*, vol. 61, p. 469, 1935.

[2] Various cases of buckling of I-beams have been discussed by the writer, *loc. cit.*, p. 257. For applications of the energy method to the same kind of problems, see writer's paper, *loc. cit.*, p. 82.

of Eq. (154). Hence the equations for determining u and β are

$$\left.\begin{array}{r}B_1 \dfrac{d^2u}{dz^2} = \beta M; \\[2ex] C \dfrac{d\beta}{dz} - D\dfrac{h^2}{2} \dfrac{d^3\beta}{dz^3} = -\dfrac{du}{dz}\, M.\end{array}\right\} \qquad (a)$$

Differentiating the second of these equations with respect to z and eliminating d^2u/dz^2 by using the first equation, we obtain

$$\frac{d^4\beta}{dz^4} - \frac{1}{a^2}\frac{d^2\beta}{dz^2} - \frac{1}{d^4}\beta = 0, \qquad (b)$$

where a has the meaning given by Eq. (155) and

$$\frac{1}{d^4} = \frac{2M^2}{DB_1h^2}. \qquad (c)$$

Equation (b) is a linear differential equation with constant coefficients and its general solution can be represented in the following form:

$$\beta = C_1 \sin mz + C_2 \cos mz + C_3 e^{nz} + C_4 e^{-nz}, \qquad (d)$$

in which,

$$m = \sqrt{ -\frac{1}{2a^2} + \sqrt{\frac{1}{4a^4} + \frac{1}{d^4}}}; \qquad (e)$$

$$n = \sqrt{ \frac{1}{2a^2} + \sqrt{\frac{1}{4a^4} + \frac{1}{d^4}}}.$$

The constants of integration must be determined in each particular case from the conditions at the ends of the beam. Assuming that the ends of the beam during buckling can rotate freely with respect to their principal axes but cannot rotate with respect to the z-axis, as shown in Fig. 142, the conditions at the ends are:

$$(1)\ \beta = 0, \qquad (2)\ \frac{d^2\beta}{dz^2} = 0, \qquad \text{for} \qquad z = 0;$$

$$(3)\ \beta = 0, \qquad (4)\ \frac{d^2\beta}{dz^2} = 0, \qquad \text{for} \qquad z = l.$$

From the first two conditions it can be concluded that

$$C_2 = 0; \qquad C_3 = -C_4,$$

and the angle of twist β can be represented in the following form:

$$\beta = C_1 \sin mz + 2C_3 \sinh nz.$$

The last two conditions require that

$$C_1 \sin ml + 2C_3 \sinh nl = 0;$$
$$-C_1 m^2 \sin ml + 2C_3 n^2 \sinh nl = 0.$$

These conditions are satisfied by taking

$$C_3 = 0 \qquad \text{and} \qquad \sin ml = 0.$$

The smallest root of the obtained trigonometric equation is

$$m = \frac{\pi}{l}.$$

Using Eq. (e), we obtain

$$-\frac{l^2}{2a^2} + \sqrt{\frac{l^4}{4a^4} + \frac{l^4}{d^4}} = \pi^2,$$

from which, by using notation (c) and (155),

$$M_{cr} = \frac{\pi \sqrt{B_1 C}}{l} \sqrt{1 + \pi^2 \frac{a^2}{l^2}}. \tag{159}$$

Comparing this result with formula (141) obtained for a beam of narrow rectangular cross section (see p. 242), we note that it differs from (141) by the last factor, which is always larger than unity and which approaches unity when the ratio a/l becomes very small, *i.e.*, in the case of very long beams, where the effect of bending of the flanges becomes negligible. For the numerical example discussed in the previous article (see p. 259) we have $a^2/l^2 = 1/14.7$, and Eq. (159) gives

$$M_{cr} = 1.29 \frac{\pi \sqrt{B_1 C}}{l}.$$

That is, as a result of the resistance of flanges to bending, the critical value of the couples is 29 per cent larger than if calculated from formula (141), derived for a strip. With a decrease of the length l of the beam, the effect of bending of the flanges and the difference between formulas (141) and (159) increase.

In general, formula (159) can be presented in the form

$$M_{cr} = \frac{m \sqrt{B_1 C}}{l}, \tag{160}$$

in which m is a numerical factor, the value of which depends on the magnitude of the ratio l^2/a^2. Several values of this factor are given in the second line of the table below.

TABLE 20.—VALUES OF THE FACTOR m IN EQ. (160) AND CRITICAL STRESSES IN POUNDS PER SQUARE INCH, FOR I-BEAMS IN PURE BENDING HAVING $B_1 h^2/B_2 l^2 = 0.0001$, $E = 30 \cdot 10^6$ POUNDS PER SQUARE INCH

l^2/a^2	0.1	1.0	2.0	4.0	6.0	8.0	10	12
m	31.4	10.36	7.66	5.85	5.11	4.70	4.43	4.24
σ_{cr}	7,440	7,770	8,120	8,780	9,400	9,980	10,500	11,020

l^2/a^2	16	20	24	28	32	36	40	100
m	4.00	3.83	3.73	3.66	3.59	3.55	3.51	3.29
σ_{cr}	12,000	12,840	13,700	14,500	15,220	15,970	16,650	24,700

It is seen that as the ratio l^2/a^2 increases the factor m approaches the value π, which was obtained for a beam of narrow rectangular cross section. When $l^2/a^2 = 100$, the factor m differs from π by about 5 per cent. Hence for values of l^2/a^2 larger than 100, formula (141), derived for a strip, can also be applied with sufficient accuracy to I-beams.

When the critical value of the bending moment is calculated from (160), the corresponding value of the maximum bending stress is found from the equation

$$\sigma_{cr} = M_{cr} \frac{h}{2} \frac{E}{B_2} = \frac{m\sqrt{B_1 C}}{l} \frac{hE}{2B_2}$$

or, by using notation (155) and taking $D \approx \frac{1}{2} B_1$,

$$\sigma_{cr} = \frac{m}{4} \frac{l}{a} E \frac{h^2}{l^2} \frac{B_1}{B_2}. \tag{161}$$

We see that, for a beam with a known value of the ratio l/a, calculated from (157), the maximum bending stress is proportional to the quantity $h^2 B_1/l^2 B_2$. In the third line of Table 20 this stress is given for the case where $E = 30 \cdot 10^6$ lb. per square inch and $h^2 B_1/l^2 B_2 = 0.0001$. If, for a given beam,

$$\frac{h^2 B_1}{l^2 B_2} = \alpha, \tag{f}$$

the values of the critical stress in Table 20 must be multiplied by $\alpha \cdot 10^4$. Taking, for instance, the numerical example discussed on page 259, we have $l^2/a^2 = 14.7$ and

$$h^2 B_1/l^2 B_2 = 2.04 \cdot 10^{-4}.$$

From the third line of the table, for $l^2/a^2 = 14.7$, we obtain, by interpolation, a critical stress equal to 11,680 lb. per square inch. The actual critical stress is

$$\sigma_{cr} = 11,680 \cdot 2.04 = 23,800 \text{ lb. per square inch}$$

It should be noted, as before, that the calculated stress represents the true value of the critical stress only if it does not exceed the proportional limit of the material.

51. Lateral Buckling of a Cantilever Beam of I-section.—If a cantilever of I-section is loaded by a force P applied at the centroid of the free end (Fig. 145), the differential equations of the buckled form of equilibrium can be derived in the same manner as in the case of a cantilever of narrow rectangular section (see Art. 47). Using Eqs. (a) for a strip (p. 246) and replacing the left side of the third of these equations with the left side of Eq. (154), the following differential equations for determining u and β are obtained:

$$\left. \begin{array}{l} B_1 \dfrac{d^2u}{dz^2} = -\beta P(l - z); \\[2mm] C \dfrac{d\beta}{dz} - D\dfrac{h^2}{2} \dfrac{d^3\beta}{dz^3} = P(l - z)\dfrac{du}{dz} - P(\delta - u). \end{array} \right\} \qquad (a)$$

Differentiating the second of these equations with respect to z and eliminating d^2u/dz^2 by using the first equation, we obtain

$$\frac{d^4\beta}{dz^4} - \frac{1}{a^2} \frac{d^2\beta}{dz^2} - \frac{2P^2}{B_1 D h^2}(l - z)^2\beta = 0, \qquad (b)$$

in which the same notations as in the previous article are used. This equation can be integrated by using the method of infinite series. From the conditions at the ends, a transcendental equation for calculating the critical value of the load P can be obtained. The solution of this equation can be represented in the form

$$P_{cr} = \frac{m\sqrt{B_1 C}}{l^2}, \qquad (162)$$

in which m is a numerical factor, the magnitude of which depends on the value of the ratio l^2/a^2. Several values of m are given in the second line of Table 21. We see that, as the ratio l^2/a^2 increases, the factor m diminishes and approaches as a limit the value $m = 4.01$ as obtained before for a beam of narrow rectangular cross section (see Art. 47). For l^2/a^2 larger than 40,

TABLE 21.—VALUES OF THE FACTOR m IN EQ. (162) AND THE CRITICAL STRESSES, IN POUNDS PER SQUARE INCH, FOR A CANTILEVER WITH $B_1h^2/B_2l^2 = 0.0001$ AND $E = 30 \cdot 10^6$ POUNDS PER SQUARE INCH

l^2/a^2	0.1	1	2	3	4	6	8
m	44.3	15.7	12.2	10.7	9.76	8.69	8.03
σ_{cr}	10,500	11,780	12,900	13,900	14,600	15,900	17,000

l^2/a^2	10	12	14	16	24	32	40
m	7.58	7.20	6.96	6.73	6.19	5.87	5.64
σ_{cr}	18,000	18,700	19,500	20,200	22,700	24,900	26,700

a very satisfactory approximate value of m may be obtained by using the formula

$$m = \frac{4.01}{\left(1 - \dfrac{a}{l}\right)^2}, \tag{163}$$

which is obtained by substituting for the length of the cantilever in formula (146), derived for a strip, a reduced length $l\left(1 - \dfrac{a}{l}\right)$ (see p. 258).

Having the value of the critical load, from Eq. (162), the corresponding value of the critical stress is obtained from the equation

$$\sigma_{cr} = \frac{m\sqrt{B_1C}}{l}\frac{hE}{2B_2} = \frac{m}{4}\frac{l}{a}E\frac{h^2}{l^2}\frac{B_1}{B_2}, \tag{c}$$

which coincides with Eq. (161), obtained before for pure bending (see p. 262). Values of the critical stress, calculated for the case where $E = 30 \cdot 10^6$ lb. per square inch and $h^2B_1/l^2B_2 = 0.0001$, are given in the third line of Table 21.

Taking for the cantilever the same dimensions as in the numerical example on page 259, we have $l^2/a^2 = 14.7$, and $h^2B_1/l^2B_2 = 2.04 \cdot 10^{-4}$. The critical stress from Table 21, by interpolation, is 19,700 lb. per square inch. The actual critical stress is

$$\sigma_{cr} = 19,700 \cdot 2.04 = 40,200 \text{ lb. per square inch.}$$

We assume here that this stress is below proportional limit of the material. Otherwise, bending of the cantilever beyond the proportional limit must be considered (see Art. 53).

52. Lateral Buckling of I-beams Simply Supported at the Ends. *Beam Loaded at the Middle.*—Let us begin with the case where a load P is applied at the centroid of the middle cross section and the end cross sections are free to rotate with respect to their axes of symmetry (Fig. 146). Using Eqs. (c) of Art. 48

and making the necessary changes in the equation for torsion, we obtain the following equations for determining the quantities u and β:

$$B_1 \frac{d^2u}{dz^2} = \frac{P}{2}\left(\frac{l}{2} - z\right)\beta;$$

$$C\frac{d\beta}{dz} - D\frac{h^2}{2}\frac{d^3\beta}{dz^3} = -\frac{P}{2}\left(\frac{l}{2} - z\right)\frac{du}{dz} + \frac{P}{2}(\delta - u). \qquad \left.\right\} \quad (a)$$

Eliminating u from these two equations, an equation of the fourth order and of the same type as Eq. (b) of the previous article can be obtained. Integrating this equation by infinite series and using the conditions at the ends, it can be shown that the critical value of the load is represented by Eq. (162) and the values of the numerical factor m can be calculated. Several values of this factor are given in Table 22.

Instead of integrating Eqs. (a), the energy method can be used to good advantage for calculating the critical value of the load. Proceeding as in the case of a beam with narrow rectangular cross section (see Art. 48), it can be concluded that P_{cr} is that value of the load at which the work done by it during lateral buckling is equal to the increase in strain energy of the beam. In calculating the strain energy of lateral bending, we observe that, owing to twisting of the beam, the lateral deflections of the flanges are equal to $u \pm \frac{1}{2}(\beta h)$. Hence the energy of the lateral bending of the beam is

$$(B_1 - 2D)\int_0^{\frac{l}{2}}\left(\frac{d^2u}{dz^2}\right)^2 dz + D\int_0^{\frac{l}{2}}\left(\frac{d^2u}{dz^2} + \frac{h}{2}\frac{d^2\beta}{dz^2}\right)^2 dz +$$

$$D\int_0^{\frac{l}{2}}\left(\frac{d^2u}{dz^2} - \frac{h}{2}\frac{d^2\beta}{dz^2}\right)^2 dz = B_1\int_0^{\frac{l}{2}}\left(\frac{d^2u}{dz^2}\right)^2 dz + \frac{Dh^2}{2}\int_0^{\frac{l}{2}}\left(\frac{d^2\beta}{dz^2}\right)^2 dz. \quad (b)$$

The first term in this expression is the same as in the case of a strip (see p. 253). The second term represents the additional energy of bending in the flanges due to twist of the I-beam. To get the complete increase of strain energy during lateral buckling, the energy of torsion, equal to

$$C\int_0^{\frac{l}{2}}\left(\frac{d\beta}{dz}\right)^2 dz, \qquad (c)$$

must be added to the energy of bending (b).

The expression for the work done by the load P during lateral buckling is the same as in the case of a strip [see Eq. (g), p. 253]. Hence the equation for determining the critical value of the load is [see Eq. (h), p. 253]

$$P\int_0^{\frac{l}{2}}\beta\frac{d^2u}{dz^2}\left(\frac{l}{2}-z\right)dz = B_1\int_0^{\frac{l}{2}}\left(\frac{d^2u}{dz^2}\right)^2 dz + \frac{Dh^2}{2}\int_0^{\frac{l}{2}}\left(\frac{d^2\beta}{dz^2}\right)^2 dz +$$
$$C\int_0^{\frac{l}{2}}\left(\frac{d\beta}{dz}\right)^2 dz, \quad (d)$$

or, substituting for d^2u/dz^2 its expression from the first of Eqs. (a), we obtain

$$\frac{P^2}{4B_1}\int_0^{\frac{l}{2}}\beta^2\left(\frac{l}{2}-z\right)^2 dz = C\int_0^{\frac{l}{2}}\left(\frac{d\beta}{dz}\right)^2 dz + \frac{Dh^2}{2}\int_0^{\frac{l}{2}}\left(\frac{d^2\beta}{dz^2}\right)^2 dz. \quad (e)$$

Comparing this result with Eq. (i) for a strip (see p. 253), we see that the effect of bending of the flanges due to twist is represented by the last term in Eq. (e).

To determine the critical value of the load, it is necessary to assume for β a suitable expression, satisfying the conditions at the ends of the beam, and substitute it in Eq. (e). Taking this expression with one or several parameters *and adjusting these parameters in such a way as to make the expression for P, as obtained from Eq. (e), a minimum, the value of P_{cr} can be calculated with great accuracy.

If the conditions of constraint are as shown in Fig. 146, we can take the angle of twist β in the form of a trigonometric series

$$\beta = a_1 \cos\frac{\pi z}{l} + a_2 \cos\frac{3\pi z}{l} + \cdots, \quad (f)$$

in which each term together with its second derivative vanishes at the ends of the beam as required by the conditions of constraint. By taking one, two or more terms of the series (f), calculating the corresponding value of P_{cr} from Eq. (e) and comparing with the results obtained by the integration of Eqs. (a), the accuracy of the energy method can be investigated. In this manner it may be shown that, by taking only the first term of the series (f), the critical load, as obtained from Eq. (e), is only one-half of 1 per cent in error. By taking two terms of the series (f), the critical load is obtained with an error of less than one-tenth of 1 per cent. Thus the energy method, simplifying considerably the calculation of the critical load, gives an accuracy sufficient for practical applications.

TABLE 22.—VALUES OF THE FACTOR m IN EQ. (162) FOR I-BEAMS LOADED AT THE MIDDLE, AND CRITICAL STRESSES IN POUNDS PER SQUARE INCH FOR $B_1h^2/B_2l^2 = 0.0001$ AND $E = 30 \cdot 10^6$ POUNDS PER SQUARE INCH

l^2/a^2	0.4	4.0	8.0	16.0	24.0	32.0	48.0
m	86.4	31.9	25.6	21.8	20.3	19.6	18.8
σ_{cr}	10,200	12,000	13,600	16,400	18,700	20,800	24,400
σ'_{cr}	6,080	7,580	9,000	11,600	13,800	15,800	19,200
σ''_{cr}	17,300	18,800	20,300	22,800	25,100	27,000	30,500

l^2/a^2	64.0	80.0	96.0	160	240	320	400
m	18.3	18.1	17.9	17.5	17.4	17.2	17.2
σ_{cr}	27,400	30,300	32,800	41,500	50,500	57,700	64,500
σ'_{cr}	22,400	25,100	27,600	36,300	45,000	52,500	59,100
σ''_{cr}	33,600	36,300	38,700	47,400	56,100	63,600	70,200

Having the value of P_{cr}, the corresponding value of the critical stress is obtained from the equation

$$\sigma_{cr} = \frac{P_{cr}l}{4} \frac{hE}{2B_2} = \frac{m}{16} \frac{l}{a} E \frac{h^2}{l^2} \frac{B_1}{B_2}. \qquad (g)$$

Values of this stress, calculated for $E = 30 \cdot 10^6$ lb. per square inch and $B_1h^2/B_2l^2 = 0.0001$, are given in the third line of Table 22. By interpolation, the value of σ_{cr} for an I-beam of any proportions can be obtained without difficulty. Taking the numerical example discussed on page 259, we have

$$\frac{l^2}{a^2} = 14.7; \qquad \frac{l}{a} = 3.83; \qquad \frac{B_1h^2}{B_2l^2} = 2.04 \cdot 10^{-4},$$

and from Table 22, by interpolation, we find for the critical stress 15,900 lb. per square inch. The actual critical stress is

$$\sigma_{cr} = 15,900 \cdot 2.04 = 32,400 \text{ lb. per square inch.}$$

It is assumed in the previous derivations that the load P is applied at the centroid of the middle cross section. Obviously, the critical value of the load will be decreased by raising its point of application and increased by lowering the same point.

This effect of the position of the point of application of the load on its critical value can be investigated by using the energy method as was explained in Art. 48, p. 254. Considering two conditions: (1) when the load is applied at the upper flange of the beam, and (2) when the load is attached to the lower flange of the beam, the values of the critical stresses given in the fourth and fifth lines of Table 22 are obtained. It is seen that this raising or lowering of the point of application of the load has the greater effect on the critical stresses for the shorter beams, where l^2/a^2 is small.

Uniformly Loaded Beam.—The method used above for the case of a concentrated load at the middle can be applied also in the case of a load uniformly distributed along the center line of the beam. The critical value of this load can be represented by the formula

$$(ql)_{cr} = \frac{m\sqrt{B_1 C}}{l^2}, \tag{164}$$

in which, as before, the numerical value of the factor m depends on the value of the ratio l^2/a^2. This ratio in each particular case can be readily calculated from the proportions of the beam by using Eqs. (157) and (158). Several values of the factor m are given in Table 23.

TABLE 23.—VALUES OF THE FACTOR m IN EQ. (164) FOR A UNIFORMLY LOADED I-BEAM SUPPORTED AT THE ENDS, AND CRITICAL STRESSES IN POUNDS PER SQUARE INCH FOR $B_1 h^2/B_2 l^2 = 0.0001$ AND $E = 30 \cdot 10^6$ POUNDS PER SQUARE INCH

l^2/a^2	0.4	4.0	8.0	16.0	24.0	32.0	48.0
m	143	53.0	42.6	36.3	33.8	32.6	31.5
σ_{cr}	8,480	9,930	11,300	13,600	15,500	17,300	20,400
σ'_{cr}	5,510	6,810	8,070	10,300	12,200	13,800	16,800
σ''_{cr}	13,200	14,500	15,800	18,000	20,000	21,500	24,500

l^2/a^2	64	80	128	200	280	360	400
m	30.5	30.1	29.4	29.0	28.8	28.6	28.6
σ_{cr}	22,800	25,200	31,200	38,500	45,200	50,900	53,600
σ'_{cr}	19,400	21,600	27,600	35,000	41,600	47,400	50,000
σ''_{cr}	27,200	29,400	35,300	42,600	49,200	55,100	57,600

It is seen from this table that, as the ratio l^2/a^2 increases, the value of the factor m approaches the value obtained before for a beam of narrow rectangular cross section [see Eq. (153), p. 255].

Having the critical value of the load, the corresponding value of the stress is obtained from the equation

$$\sigma_{cr} = \frac{(ql)_{cr}l}{8}\frac{hE}{2B_2} = \frac{m}{32}\frac{l}{a}E\frac{h^2}{l^2}\frac{B_1}{B_2}. \tag{h}$$

The values of this stress, calculated for the case where $E = 30 \cdot 10^6$ lb. per square inch and $h^2B_1/l^2B_2 = 0.0001$, are given in the third line of Table 23. From this table the value of the critical stress for any other proportions of the beam can readily be obtained. Taking again the numerical example discussed before (see p. 259), we have $l^2/a^2 = 14.7$, and we obtain, from Table 23, by interpolation, a critical stress of 13,100 lb. per square inch. Taking into account that in our case $h^2B_1/l^2B_2 = 2.04 \cdot 10^{-4}$, the actual critical stress is

$$\sigma_{cr} = 13,100 \cdot 2.04 = 26,700 \text{ lb. per square inch.}$$

In investigating the lateral buckling of I-beams, the compressed flange of the beam is sometimes considered as a strut and the dimensions are determined in such a manner as to have a sufficient factor of safety against lateral buckling of such a strut.[1] On account of the fact that for uniform load the compressive force in the flange follows the parabolic law, the reduced length $L = 0.696l$, instead of the length l of the beam (see p. 128), must be taken in our example when considering the upper flange as a strut. Thus

$$L = 0.699 \cdot 240 = 167 \text{ in.}$$

Assuming that the cross-sectional area of the flanges is equal to 12.2 square inches, the radius of gyration of the cross section of a flange with respect to the vertical axis is

$$r \approx \sqrt{\frac{42.7}{12.2}} = 1.87 \text{ in.}$$

and we obtain $L/r = 167/1.87 \approx 90$.

For mild steel columns with pin ends, the straight-line formula (see p. 184) gives

$$\sigma_{cr} = 48,000 - 210\frac{L}{r} = 29,100 \text{ lb. per square inch,}$$

[1] Such a method is recommended, for instance, by R. Fleming, *Eng. News*, vol. 75, 1916. Some reduction of working stress, depending on the magnitude of the ratio of the length of the beam to the width of the flange, is usually required by specifications for structural design. See, for instance, American Institute Steel Construction, standard specifications.

which is higher than the critical stress derived above on the basis of a more exact investigation of lateral buckling of I-beams.

In calculating the critical stresses, given in the third line of Table 23, it was assumed that the load is distributed along the center line of the beam. When the load is applied to the upper or lower flange, its critical value changes and can be calculated as was explained before. The critical stresses σ'_{cr} and σ''_{cr} calculated for these two load conditions are given in the fourth and fifth lines of Table 23.

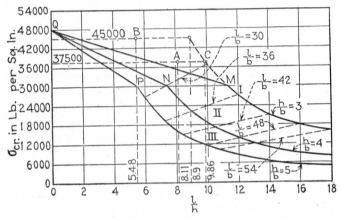

FIG. 148.

In order to show how the critical stress for an I-beam decreases with an increase of the ratios l/h and h/b, let us consider, as an example, a theoretical I-section, in which $t:t_1 = 2$ and $b:t = 10$.[1] The values of the critical stresses σ_{cr} calculated by the use of Table 23 for the three different ratios $h/b = 3, 4, 5$ are shown in Fig. 148 by the curves I, II and III.[2] The points with constant values of the ratio l/b are connected in the figure by the dotted lines. These lines indicate clearly that for a given value of the ratio l/b the critical stress decreases as the ratio l/h decreases. It is seen also that for a given value of l/h the critical stress decreases as the ratio h/b increases. Several values of σ_{cr}, taken from the curve I in Fig. 148, are given in the second line of Table 24; for comparison the values of the critical stresses calculated by using the column formula,[3] as explained above (see p. 269), are also given. It is seen that the critical stresses calculated from the column formula are always larger than the actual critical stress. With

[1] We use the same notations as on p. 259. G is taken equal to $0.40E$ in this calculation.

[2] Figures for the construction of curve I are given in Table 29, p. 276.

[3] For $L/r > 100$, Euler's formula was used. For $L/r < 100$ the straight-line formula was used.

increase of the ratio h/b, as is seen from the curves in Fig. 148, the discrepancy between the two methods of calculating σ_{cr} increases.

TABLE 24.—COMPARISON OF ACTUAL CRITICAL STRESSES IN POUNDS PER SQUARE INCH WITH THOSE OBTAINED BY USING THE COLUMN FORMULA

l/b	54	48	42	36
From Table 23, σ_{cr}	15,900	18,400	22,100	27,700
From column formula, σ_{cr}	17,600	22,300	29,200	29,900

Additional Constraints.—To increase the stability of an I-beam against buckling in the lateral direction, various kinds of lateral constraints are used. The effect of these constraints on the magnitude of the critical stress can be investigated by using the same methods as before. Take the case where, owing to an additional constraint, the middle cross section of a beam

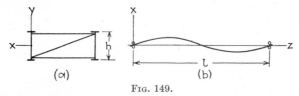

(a)   (b)

FIG. 149.

is prevented from rotation with respect to the center line of the beam. Such a condition is obtained when two parallel beams are braced at the middle as shown in Fig. 149. Owing to this bracing the deflection curve of the beam buckled in the lateral direction must have an inflection point, as shown in Fig. 149b. Assuming that the beam undergoes pure bending in the yz-plane and has a narrow rectangular cross section, the critical value of the bending moment can be obtained from the differential equation (b) of Art. 46 (see p. 241). To take account of the lateral constraint, it will be necessary in discussing the transcendental equation (e) (see p. 242) to take the root $kl = 2\pi$ instead of the smallest root $kl = \pi$, which was taken before for the beam without lateral constraint at the middle. In this manner we obtain

$$M_{cr} = \frac{2\pi\sqrt{B_1 C}}{l}.$$

Hence, owing to lateral constraint, the critical value of the bending moment is doubled in this case. In an analogous way the problem of lateral buckling of a beam with a constraint at the middle can be treated for the case of I-sections and for other kinds of loading.

If a load P is applied at the centroid of the middle cross section of the I-beam shown in Fig. 149, Eq. (162) must be used for calculating the critical value of the load. The values of the numerical factor m in this equation are larger than in the case of a beam without lateral constraint and are given in Table 25.

TABLE 25.—VALUES OF THE FACTOR m IN EQ. (162) FOR THE BEAM SHOWN IN FIG. 149 LOADED AT THE MIDDLE. CRITICAL STRESSES ARE IN POUNDS PER SQUARE INCH FOR $B_1h^2/B_2l^2 = 0.0001$ AND $E = 30 \cdot 10^6$ POUNDS PER SQUARE INCH

l^2/a^2	0.4	4.0	8.0	16.0	32.0	96.0	128	200	400
m	466	154	114	86.4	69.2	54.5	52.4	49.8	47.4
σ_{cr}	55,200	57,600	60,500	64,800	73,500	100,000	111,000	132,000	178,000

The corresponding values of the critical stress are found as before [see Eq. (g), p. 267] from the equation

$$\sigma_{cr} = \frac{m}{16}\frac{l}{a}E\frac{h^2}{l^2}\frac{B_1}{B_2}.$$

The values of the critical stress calculated for $B_1h^2/B_2l^2 = 0.0001$ and $E = 30 \cdot 10^6$ lb. per square inch are given in the third line of Table 25.

If the beam is uniformly loaded, the critical value of the total load is given by Eq. (164). The numerical values of the factor m in this equation for the case where the load is distributed along the center line of the beam are given in Table 26.

TABLE 26.—VALUES OF THE FACTOR m IN EQ. (164) FOR THE BEAM SHOWN IN FIG. 149 UNIFORMLY LOADED. CRITICAL STRESSES ARE IN POUNDS PER SQUARE INCH FOR $B_1h^2/B_2l^2 = 0.0001$ AND $E = 30 \cdot 10^6$ POUNDS PER SQUARE INCH

l^2/a^2	0.4	4.0	8.0	16	64	96	128	200
m	673	221	164	126	101	79.5	76.4	72.8
σ_{cr}	39,900	41,600	43,500	47,000	53,300	72,900	81,000	96,600
σ'_{cr}	34,800	36,500	38,400	42,000	48,300	67,800	75,900	91,500
σ''_{cr}	45,900	47,300	49,200	52,800	59,100	78,600	86,600	102,000

The corresponding values of the critical stress σ_{cr}, calculated from the equation

$$\sigma_{cr} = \frac{m}{32}\frac{l}{a}E\frac{h^2}{l^2}\frac{B_1}{B_2}$$

for the case when $h^2B_1/l^2B_2 = 0.0001$ and $E = 30 \cdot 10^6$ lb. per square inch, are given in the third line of the same table. In the fourth and fifth lines of the table the critical stresses are given for the cases where the uniform load is applied to the upper or lower flange of the beam.

If the ends of the beam are prevented from rotating with respect to their vertical axes of symmetry during buckling, the deflection curve of the axis of the beam in the lateral direction has two inflection points as shown in

Fig. 150.[1] Considering the case of a load P applied at the centroid of the middle cross section, the critical value of the load will be given by Eq. (162). The values of the numerical factor m and of the critical stresses calculated for $h^2 B_1/l^2 B_2 = 0.0001$ and $E = 30 \cdot 10^6$ lb. per square inch are given in Table 27.

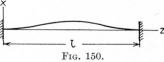

FIG. 150.

Comparing the figures of this table with those of Table 22 (see p. 267), it is seen that the effect of lateral constraint is larger in the case of short beams than in the case of long beams.

In Table 28 are given data for a beam uniformly loaded along the center line and having lateral constraint as in Fig. 150.

TABLE 27.—VALUES OF THE FACTOR m IN EQ. (162) FOR THE BEAM, SHOWN IN FIG. 150, LOADED AT THE MIDDLE. CRITICAL STRESSES ARE IN POUNDS PER SQUARE INCH FOR $B_1 h^2/B_2 l^2 = 0.0001$ AND $E = 30 \cdot 10^6$ POUNDS PER SQUARE INCH

l^2/a^2	0.4	4.0	8.0	16.0	24.0	32.0	64.0	128	200	320
m	268	88.8	65.5	50.2	43.6	40.2	34.1	30.7	29.4	28.4
σ_{cr}	31,800	33,300	34,800	37,500	40,200	42,600	51,300	65,100	78,000	95,400

TABLE 28.—VALUES OF THE FACTOR m IN EQ. (164) FOR THE BEAM SHOWN IN FIG. 150, UNIFORMLY LOADED. CRITICAL STRESSES ARE IN POUNDS PER SQUARE INCH FOR $B_1 h^2/B_2 l^2 = 0.0001$ AND $E = 30 \cdot 10^6$ POUNDS PER SQUARE INCH

l^2/a^2	0.4	4.0	8.0	16.0	32.0	96.0	128	200	400
m	488	161	119	91.3	73.0	58.0	55.8	53.5	51.2
σ_{cr}	29,000	30,200	31,500	34,200	38,700	53,300	59,100	70,800	96,000

By using the tables of this article the critical stress for an I-beam of any proportions can be readily calculated provided the value of the calculated stress is below the proportional limit of the material. The calculation of the critical stress beyond the proportional limit will be discussed in the next article.

53. Lateral Buckling of I-beams Stressed beyond the Proportional Limit.—If an I-beam is bent beyond the proportional limit of the material, the critical load can be calculated by using

[1] It is assumed that there are no constraints preventing the ends from rotating in the plane of the web and the beam is simply supported when bending in this plane is considered.

the reduced modulus E_r, varying with the stress, instead of the constant modulus of elasticity E. The method is analogous to that used before in investigating buckling of columns beyond the elastic limit (see Art. 29). It has been shown that the critical stress for lateral buckling within the elastic region depends on the magnitude of the lateral flexural rigidity B_1, which is proportional to the modulus E in tension, and also on the magnitude of the torsional rigidity C, which is proportional to the modulus of shear G. Beyond the proportional limit the lateral flexural rigidity diminishes in the ratio E_r/E. We assume in the following discussion that the torsional rigidity diminishes also in the same proportion.[1] Then the ratio l^2/a^2, defined by Eq. (157) (see p. 258), remains unchanged.

Let us begin with pure bending, in which case the stress in the flanges is constant along the span; hence the reduced modulus is the same for all cross sections of the beam bent beyond the proportional limit and the same differential equations of equilibrium as in the elastic region can be used. It is necessary only to replace the flexural and torsional rigidities of the beam by their *reduced values*. The critical value of the bending moment is then given by the equation

$$M_{cr} = \frac{\pi \sqrt{B'_1 C'}}{l} \sqrt{1 + \pi^2 \frac{a^2}{l^2}}, \qquad (165)$$

which has the same form as Eq. (159) except that, instead of B_1 and C, the reduced values

$$B'_1 = B_1 \frac{E_r}{E} \quad \text{and} \quad C' = C \frac{E_r}{E} \qquad (a)$$

are introduced.

Since the ratio a^2/l^2 remains unchanged beyond the proportional limit, it can be concluded from (165) that the critical value of the moment is less than the value of the same moment cal-

---

[1] While there are very few experimental data regarding variation of the torsional rigidity C of a bar when stressed longitudinally beyond the proportional limit of the material, the assumption made may be considered as on the safe side: the lateral rigidity is due practically to the rigidity of the flanges only; hence it diminishes beyond the proportional limit in the ratio E_r/E, while torsional rigidity depends also on the rigidity of the web, a portion of which remains always elastic and retains its initial rigidity; hence we can expect that it diminishes in a proportion smaller than E_r/E.

culated on the assumption of perfect elasticity, in the ratio E_r/E. If the magnitude of this ratio for each value of the stress is known—for instance, if it is given by a curve analogous to that in Fig. 113—the critical bending moment for each value of the stress can be easily calculated by the trial-and-error method. We assume a certain value for M_{cr}, calculate the value of the maximum bending stress and take the corresponding value of the reduced modulus E_r. With this modulus the critical value of the bending moment is obtained from Eq. (165). If the value calculated in this way coincides with the assumed value, it represents the true value of M_{cr}. Otherwise a new assumption regarding M_{cr} should be made and calculations repeated. Such calculations should be repeated as many times as is necessary to obtain a satisfactory agreement between the assumed value of M_{cr} and that calculated from Eq. (165).

In the case of bending of beams by concentrated or distributed loads, the bending moment and the stress in the flanges vary along the span of the beam. Hence, beyond the proportional limit, the reduced modulus E_r will also vary along the span and the differential equations of equilibrium for lateral buckling will be of the same kind as for beams of variable cross section. To simplify this problem and obtain an approximate value for the critical stress, we take a constant value for E_r, namely, the value corresponding to the maximum bending moment, and substitute it in the differential equations of equilibrium of the buckled beam. In this way the critical load will be obtained in the same form as before [see Eqs. (162) and (164)], it being only necessary to use for the flexural and torsional rigidities their reduced values (a). It is evident that in calculating critical stresses in this way we shall always be on the safe side since we reduce the lateral and torsional rigidities of the beam along the span in the constant proportion E_r/E, while this amount of reduction actually takes place only in the cross section with the maximum bending moment. In other cross-sections, stressed beyond the proportional limit, the reduction will be smaller, and there will be no reduction at all in portions of the beam where the stresses are below the proportional limit. With the above assumption made, the critical value of the load can be obtained by the trial-and-error method in the same manner as was explained for the case of pure bending.

In practical applications it is preferable to work with critical stresses, instead of critical loads. Assuming, in the case of I-sections, that beyond the elastic limit the stresses in the flanges can be obtained with satisfactory accuracy by dividing the maximum bending moment by the section modulus of the cross section, equations for calculating σ_{cr}, analogous to Eqs. (*g*) and (*h*) of the previous article, will be obtained, and the tables for σ_{cr} given in that article can be used for calculating critical stresses that are beyond the proportional limit. It is evident that with the above assumption we shall always be on the safe side, since beyond the elastic limit the actual stress in the flanges and the actual reduction of the lateral and torsional rigidities of the beam will be smaller than assumed.

The calculation of σ_{cr} beyond the proportional limit will be illustrated now by an example. Take an I-section consisting of three narrow rectangles, for which $t/t_1 = 2$, $b/t = 10$ and $h/b = 3$ (see p. 270). Then, by using Eqs. (157) and (158) and the dimensions of the beam, the results shown in the second and third lines of Table 29 are obtained.[1] Assuming that the beam carries the load uniformly distributed along the center line, and using Table 23 (see p. 268), the critical stresses shown in the fourth line of Table 29 are obtained for the case when buckling occurs within the elastic limit and $E = 30 \cdot 10^6$ lb. per square inch. These stresses are given by curve I in Fig. 148 (see p. 270).

TABLE 29.—DATA FOR UNIFORMLY LOADED I-BEAMS WITH $t/t_1 = 2$, $b/t = 10$, $h/b = 3$, $E = 30 \cdot 10^6$ POUNDS PER SQUARE INCH

l/h	4	6	8	10	12	14	16	18	20
l^2/a^2	1.22	2.74	4.86	7.60	10.9	14.9	19.4	24.6	30.4
$10^4 \dfrac{B_1 h^2}{B_2 l^2}$	20.4	9.06	5.10	3.26	2.26	1.66	1.27	1.01	0.815
σ_{cr}	181,000	85,600	52,200	36,400	27,700	22,100	18,400	15,900	13,900

Applying this table in the case of structural steel for which the proportional limit is 30,000 lb. per square inch, it is seen that for $l/h \lessgtr 10$ the figures in the fourth line of the table are beyond the proportional limit; hence they give exaggerated values for the critical stress. To take into account the plastic deformation of the material, the information regarding the reduced modulus E_r beyond the proportional limit should be given. Let us assume[2] for this numerical example that for compressive stresses 37,500 lb. per square inch and 45,000 lb. per square inch the ratio E_r/E has the values $\frac{32}{49}$ and $\frac{4}{9}$, respectively. To determine what ratio l/h the beam should have if the critical stress is 37,500 lb. per square inch, we note that on curve I (Fig. 148) the point C corresponds to this stress, and from the figure we obtain

[1] $G = 0.4E$ is assumed in these calculations.

[2] The true values of the ratio $E_r : E$ can be obtained only by using the stress-strain tensile-test diagram for the given material as has been explained in Art. 29.

$l/h = 9.86$. It is known, however, that curve I gives exaggerated values of σ_{cr} beyond the elastic limit. The true value of σ_{cr}, for $l/h = 9.86$, will be less than 37,500 and the ratio l/h corresponding to $\sigma_{cr} = 37,500$ will be less than 9.86. Its value will be found now by trial and error. Assume, for instance, that this true value is $l/h = 8$. Then from Table 29 $l^2/a^2 = 4.86$, and we obtain from Table 23 (p. 268), by interpolation,

$$\sigma_{cr} = 9,950 + \frac{1,350 \cdot 0.86}{4} \approx 10,200 \text{ lb. per square inch}$$

This is the critical stress for the case where $B_1 h^2/B_2 l^2 = 0.0001$. In our case, from the third line of Table 29, $B_1 h^2/B_2 l^2 = 5.10 \cdot 10^{-4}$. Using now the reduced modulus $E_r = \frac{36}{49} E$, we obtain

$$10^4 \frac{B'_1 h^2}{B_2 l^2} = 5.10 \cdot \frac{36}{49} \approx 3.75,$$

and the critical stress is

$$\sigma_{cr} = 10,200 \cdot 3.75 \approx 38,400 \text{ lb. per square inch.}$$

This stress is somewhat larger than the assumed stress 37,500 lb. per square inch. Hence the true value of the ratio l/h is larger than the assumed value 8. As a second trial, we assume $l/h = 8.2$. Then, from Table 29,

$$\frac{l^2}{a^2} = 4.86 \left(\frac{8.2}{8} \right)^2 = 5.10; \qquad 10^4 \frac{B_1 h^2}{B_2 l^2} = 5.10 \left(\frac{8}{8.2} \right)^2 = 4.86$$

and Table 23 gives, for $B_1 h^2/B_2 l^2 = 0.0001$, by interpolation,

$$\sigma_{cr} = 9,950 + \frac{1,350 \cdot 1.10}{4} \approx 10,300 \text{ lb. per square inch.}$$

Hence in our case

$$\sigma_{cr} = 10,300 \frac{B'_1 h^2}{B_2 l^2} 10^4 = 10,300 \cdot 4.86 \cdot \frac{36}{49} = 36,800 \text{ lb. per square inch}$$

This stress is now somewhat smaller than the assumed stress 37,500 lb. per square inch. Hence the true value of the ratio l/h is smaller than 8.2. From these two trials we conclude that the true value of the ratio l/h lies between 8 and 8.2. By linear interpolation we obtain

$$\frac{l}{h} = 8 + \frac{0.2}{1,600} \cdot 900 = 8.11.$$

This result is represented in Fig. 148 by the point A, which is much below the curve I, giving the critical stresses on the assumption of perfect elasticity.

As a second example we make calculations for the same beam by assuming the critical stress equal to 45,000 lb. per square inch, in which case $E_r/E = \frac{4}{9}$. From the curve I (Fig. 148) we have for this case $l/h = 8.9$. The true value of this ratio, owing to plastic deformation, is much smaller. Assuming $l/h = 5.6$ and proceeding as before, we obtain

$$\frac{l^2}{a^2} = 2.39; \qquad 10^4 \frac{B_1 h^2}{B_2 l^2} = 10.40,$$

and Table 23 gives for σ_{cr} the value, 9320 lb. per square inch. Hence the critical stress for the case when $10^4 \dfrac{B'_1 h^2}{B_2 l^2} = 10.40 \cdot \dfrac{4}{9} = 4.62$ is

$$9{,}320 \cdot 4.62 = 43{,}100 \text{ lb. per square inch,}$$

which is smaller than the assumed value; the true value of the ratio l/h is smaller than 5.6. Taking, as the second trial, $l/h = 5.4$, we find for the critical stress the value 46,100 lb. per square inch. From these two trials we find, by interpolation, $l/h = 5.48$. This result is shown in Fig. 148 by the point B.

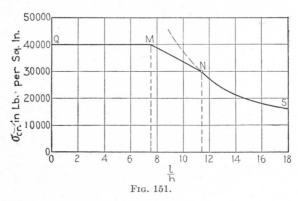

FIG. 151.

In the same manner the value of l/h can be found for any other assumed value of the critical stress beyond the elastic limit. Thus the curve representing the relation between σ_{cr} and the ratio l/h can be constructed provided the ratio E_r/E is known for any value of the stress σ_{cr}.

To simplify the calculations of critical stresses beyond the proportional limit in practical application, the curve representing the relation between σ_{cr} and the ratio l/h can be replaced by a straight line; a straight-line formula, analogous to that applied for columns (see p. 184), can also be used in the case of lateral buckling of beams. Assuming that the elastic limit of structural steel is 30,000 lb. per square inch, we find that the curves I, II and III of Fig. 148 can be used only below the points M, N and P. For higher stresses the straight lines MQ, NQ and PQ should be used. These lines are obtained by taking the highest stress (for $l/h = 0$) equal to 48,000 lb. per square inch as in the case of the straight-line formula for columns.

Curves analogous to those shown in Fig. 148 can be readily constructed by using Tables 22 and 23 for an I-beam of any cross section; thus the problem of determining critical stresses can be solved for any value of the ratio l/h.

Instead of straight lines MQ, NQ and PQ, as in Fig. 148, a diagram analogous to that represented in Fig. 114 (see p. 182) can be used in calculating critical stresses for lateral buckling of I-beams. To obtain such a diagram, we construct first the curve NS of critical stresses, assuming perfect elasticity (Fig. 151). This curve can be used up to the point N, corresponding to the proportional limit of the material. Then we draw a horizontal line QM corresponding to the yield point of the material, which gives critical stresses for short beams. For beams of intermediate length we use, for calculating critical stresses, the inclined line MN, which joins the point N, mentioned before, with a point M arbitrarily chosen on the horizontal yield-point line. In our diagram this point is taken so that the corresponding span of the beam is equal to 0.6 of the span at which the critical stress is equal to the proportional limit of the material. Having such a diagram and using a variable factor of safety, as in the case of columns, the safe stresses for any span of the beam of a given cross section can be readily obtained.[1]

54. Lateral Buckling of a Strip with Circular Axis.—The lateral buckling of a strip bent in the plane of its greatest rigidity,

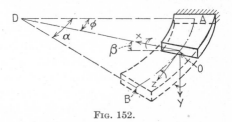

FIG. 152.

which has been discussed in the case of a straight strip (see Arts. 46–48), may occur also if the longitudinal axis of the strip is curved. To establish the formulas for critical load in such cases, let us consider first bending of a curved strip out of its plane of initial curvature and let us develop the necessary differential equations for such bending.[2]

A simple problem of this kind is shown in Fig. 152. A curved bar AB with its center line in the horizontal plane DAB is built in at A and is bent by a load distributed in some way along the axis AB. If the deflections are small, the deformed shape of the bar is completely determined by the displacement of the centroid of each cross section and the rotation of each cross section about the tangent to the center line. For any cross section of the bar defined by an angle ϕ, we take a system of rectangular coordinates

---

[1] A calculation of the allowable load on the basis of an assumed initial lateral curvature of the I-beam has been made by F. Stüssi, *loc. cit.*, p. 254.

[2] The theory of small deformation of naturally curved bars was developed by Saint-Venant; see series of papers in *Compt. rend.*, Paris, vol. 17, 1843. See also A. E. H. Love, "Mathematical Theory of Elasticity," 4th ed., p. 444, 1927.

with the origin at the centroid O and the axes so directed that x and y coincide with the principal axes of the cross section, while z coincides with the tangent to the center line. It is assumed that initially the plane xz coincides with the plane of the curvature of the bar; the positive direction of x is toward the center of curvature; z is taken positive in the direction corresponding to an increase of the angle ϕ; the arc s of the center line is measured from the built-in end A. The displacement of the centroid O is resolved into three components, u, v and w, in the directions of the x-, y- and z-axes, respectively. The angle of rotation of the cross section about the z-axis is called β and is taken positive when rotation is in the direction indicated in the figure. The deformation of an element of the curved strip cut out by two adjacent cross sections consists, generally of bending in each of the two principal planes xz and yz, and of twist about the z-axis. Let $1/r_1$ and $1/r_2$ be the curvatures of the center line at O after deformation in the principal planes yz and xz, respectively, and θ the angle of twist per unit length at the same point. Then, if $1/r_0$ denotes the initial curvature of the center line of the strip, the equations for calculating the curvatures and the twist are

$$\frac{B_1}{r_1} = M_x; \qquad B_2\left(\frac{1}{r_2} - \frac{1}{r_0}\right) = M_y; \qquad C\theta = M_z; \qquad (a)$$

in which M_x, M_y and M_z are the moments on the cross section at O about the x-, y- and z-axes, respectively, positive as shown in the figure; B_1 and B_2 are the two principal flexural rigidities; and C is the torsional rigidity of the strip.

To obtain the differential equations for calculating the displacements u, v, w and the angle β, it is necessary to establish the expressions for the curvatures and the twist as functions of u, v, w and β and to substitute these expressions in Eqs. (a). In the case of small displacements, we may consider separately each component of the displacements and obtain the final change in curvature and twist by summing up the effects produced by the individual components.

The components u and w represent displacements in the plane of initial curvature of the bar. They produce only a change of curvature in the plane xz, which was discussed in Art. 38. From that discussion we have

$$\frac{1}{r_2} = \frac{1}{r_0} + \frac{u}{r^2_0} + \frac{d^2u}{ds^2}. \tag{b}$$

Let us consider now the angular displacement β. It may be seen at once that this displacement produces a twist

$$\theta = \frac{d\beta}{ds}. \tag{c}$$

It produces also certain bending in the principal plane yz. Owing to the rotation β the surface of the strip becomes a conical surface, the curvature of which is

$$\frac{\sin \beta}{r_0} \approx \frac{\beta}{r_0}. \tag{d}$$

The displacement v produces a curvature in the principal plane yz of the amount

$$-\frac{d^2v}{ds^2} \tag{e}$$

analogous to that for a straight bar. The minus sign follows from our assumption regarding the positive signs of moments and

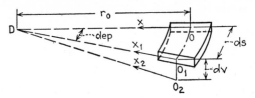

Fig. 153.

curvatures as given by Fig. 152 and by Eqs. (a). It will be seen from these that for a positive M_x and a positive $1/r_1$ there is bending in the yz-plane concave upward, and positive values of d^2v/ds^2 correspond to bending with concavity downward. Hence the minus sign in expression (e).

It may be seen also, from Fig. 153, that the displacement v produces a certain amount of twist. This figure represents an element of the curved strip between two adjacent cross sections O and O_1 a distance ds apart. Owing to the displacements v, this element rotates with respect to the axis Ox through the angle dv/ds. Because of this rotation, the axis O_1x_1 of the adjacent cross section O_1 comes into the position O_2x_2. The angle between

O_1x_1 and O_2x_2 is equal to dv/r_0. Hence, the twist per unit length, equal to

$$\frac{1}{r_0}\frac{dv}{ds},\qquad (f)$$

occurs owing to the displacements v if the angle β is kept equal to zero along the length of the bar.

Summing up the results given by formulas (b), (c), (d), (e) and (f), the curvatures and the twist of a curved strip after

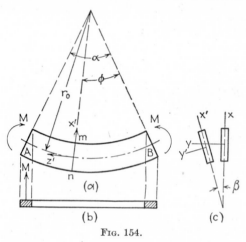

Fig. 154.

deformation are given, in the general case, by the following equations:

$$\left.\begin{aligned}
\frac{1}{r_1} &= \frac{\beta}{r_0} - \frac{d^2v}{ds^2};\\
\frac{1}{r_2} &= \frac{1}{r_0} + \frac{u}{r^2_0} + \frac{d^2u}{ds^2};\\
\theta &= \frac{d\beta}{ds} + \frac{1}{r_0}\frac{dv}{ds}.
\end{aligned}\right\}\qquad (166)$$

Substituting these into Eqs. (a), three equations for determining displacements are obtained.

Having these equations, let us consider the problem of buckling of a strip with a circular axis submitted to bending by two equal and opposite couples acting in the plane of the strip (Fig. 154).[1] The conditions at the ends of the strip are taken the same as

[1] See writer's paper in *Bull. Polytech. Inst., Kiev*, 1910.

in the case of the rectilinear strip, represented in Fig. 142. The ends can rotate freely with respect to their principal axes of inertia but they cannot rotate with respect to tangents at A and B to the center line of the strip. In calculating the critical value of the bending moment M, we assume that a small lateral buckling has occurred and we determine the value of M necessary to keep the strip in such a buckled form. Taking any cross section mn, which rotates during buckling through an angle β, as shown in Fig. 154c, so that the axes x, y and z take the directions x', y' and z', and considering the portion of the strip to the left of this cross section, the projections on the x', y' and z' axes of the vector M, applied at the left end of the strip and perpendicular to the initial plane of the strip, are, respectively,

$$M_{x'} = M\beta; \qquad M_{y'} = M; \qquad M_{z'} = M\frac{dv}{ds}.$$

Using these expressions with Eqs. (a) and using Eqs. (166), we obtain

$$\left. \begin{aligned} \beta M &= B_1\left(\frac{\beta}{r_0} - \frac{d^2v}{ds^2}\right); \\ M &= B_2\left(\frac{u}{r^2_0} + \frac{d^2u}{ds^2}\right); \\ M\frac{dv}{ds} &= C\left(\frac{d\beta}{ds} + \frac{1}{r_0}\frac{dv}{ds}\right). \end{aligned} \right\} \qquad (g)$$

Eliminating v from the first and third of these equations, we obtain the following equation for the angle β:

$$B_1C\frac{d^2\beta}{ds^2} - \left(M - \frac{C}{r_0}\right)\left(\frac{B_1}{r_0} - M\right)\beta = 0. \qquad (h)$$

In the case where $r_0 = \infty$, Eq. (h) coincides with Eq. (b) (see p. 241), as obtained before for a rectilinear strip. Using the notation

$$\left(M - \frac{C}{r_0}\right)\left(\frac{B_1}{r_0} - M\right) = -k^2B_1C, \qquad (i)$$

Eq. (h) becomes

$$\frac{d^2\beta}{ds^2} + k^2\beta = 0$$

and we obtain

$$\beta = A \sin ks + B \cos ks \qquad (j)$$

From the conditions at the ends, we conclude that

$$(\beta)_{s=0} = 0 \qquad \text{and} \qquad (\beta)_{s=\alpha r_0} = 0.$$

Hence $B = 0$ and

$$\sin k\alpha r_0 = 0. \qquad (k)$$

From this trigonometric equation the critical value of M is obtained. The smallest root of this equation, different from zero, is

$$k\alpha r_0 = \pi,$$

from which, by using notation (i), we obtain the following equation for calculating M_{cr}:

$$M^2{}_{cr} - \frac{B_1 + C}{r_0}M_{cr} + \frac{B_1C}{r^2{}_0}\left(1 - \frac{\pi^2}{\alpha^2}\right) = 0.$$

The two real roots of this equation are

$$M_{cr} = \frac{B_1 + C}{2r_0} \pm \sqrt{\left(\frac{B_1 - C}{2r_0}\right)^2 + \frac{B_1C}{r^2{}_0}\frac{\pi^2}{\alpha^2}}. \qquad (167)$$

Substituting in this solution $r_0 = \infty$ and $r_0\alpha = l$, we obtain

$$M_{cr} = \pm\frac{\pi}{l}\sqrt{B_1C},$$

which coincides with formula (141) obtained for a rectilinear strip.

When the angle α and the initial curvature of the center line of the strip (Fig. 154) are small, the first term under the radical in formula (167) can be neglected in comparison with the second term; then, by substituting $\alpha r_0 = l$, we obtain

$$M_{cr} = \frac{B_1 + C}{2r_0} \pm \frac{\pi}{l}\sqrt{B_1C}. \qquad (167')$$

The plus sign in this formula corresponds to the directions of moments shown in Fig. 154 and the minus sign to the reversed directions of the moments. Thus a slight curvature in the direction indicated in the figure increases the value of the critical moment as compared with that for a straight strip of the same length. A curvature in the opposite direction decreases the critical value of the moment.

When $\alpha = \pi$, one of the two values of the moment given by formula (167) becomes zero. This result corresponds to the freedom of a semicircular strip to rotate about the diameter joining the ends. For $\alpha > \pi$ both values of M_{cr} from formula (167) become positive; for obtaining negative values of M_{cr} the higher roots of Eq. (k) should be considered.

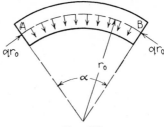

Fig. 155.

The problem of lateral buckling of a strip with a circular axis can also be solved without much difficulty[1] if the strip is submitted to the action of a continuous load of the intensity q uniformly distributed along the center line and radially directed (Fig. 155). If the ends of the strip are free to rotate with respect to their principal axes, but cannot rotate with respect to the tangents at A and B to the center line of the strip, the critical value of the compressive force in the strip, at which lateral buckling occurs, is given by the following formula:

$$q_{cr}r_0 = \frac{B_1}{r^2_0} \frac{(\pi^2 - \alpha^2)^2}{\alpha^2\left(\pi^2 + \alpha^2\frac{B_1}{C}\right)}. \tag{168}$$

In the derivation of this formula it is assumed that the directions of the loads q do not change during lateral buckling, and that they are displaced laterally only, remaining parallel to their initial direction. We denote by α the central angle of the strip, by B_1 its smallest flexural rigidity and by C its torsional rigidity.

When α is very small and we put $\alpha r_0 = l$, formula (168) gives

$$q_{cr}r_0 = \frac{\pi^2 B_1}{l^2},$$

i.e., we obtain the known Euler formula. When $\alpha = \pi/2$, we obtain, from (168),

$$q_{cr}r_0 = \frac{B_1}{r^2_0} \frac{9}{4 + \frac{B_1}{C}}. \tag{169}$$

This represents the critical compressive force for a complete ring which buckles under the action of radial pressure in four half-waves so that each half-wave corresponds to $\alpha = \pi/2$.

[1] See writer's paper in *Z. angew. Math. Mech.*, vol. 3, p. 358, 1923.

When $\alpha = \pi$, the critical load becomes zero since in this case the strip can rotate freely with respect to the diameter joining the ends of the strip.

If we assume that during buckling of the strip the loads q change their direction slightly so that they always are directed toward the center of the initial curvature of the strip, the critical value of the compressive force is

$$q_{cr}r_0 = \frac{\pi^2 B_1}{r^2_0} \frac{(\pi^2 - \alpha^2)}{\alpha^2 \left(\pi^2 + \alpha^2 \dfrac{B_1}{C}\right)}. \tag{170}$$

In the case of a complete circular ring buckling into four half-waves ($\alpha = \pi/2$), this formula gives[1]

$$q_{cr}r_0 = \frac{B_1}{r^2_0} \frac{12}{4 + \dfrac{B_1}{C}}. \tag{171}$$

It is seen that, owing to the assumed slight changing in the direction of the loads, the stability of the ring increases considerably.

If the ends of the strip (Fig. 155) are built in and if the loads retain their direction during buckling, as assumed in the first case, the critical value of the compressive force is given by the formula

$$q_{cr}r_0 = m\frac{B_1}{r^2_0}, \tag{172}$$

in which m is a numerical factor depending on the magnitude of the angle α. Several values of this factor are given in Table 30.

TABLE 30.—VALUES OF THE FACTOR m IN EQ. (172)

α	0.250π	0.500π	π	1.063π	1.10π	1.24π	1.50π	2π
m	60.1	12.6	1.85	1.54	1.40	1.00	0.69	0.60

If α is smaller than $\pi/2$, formula (172) can be replaced by the following approximate formula:

$$q_{cr}r_0 = \frac{B_1}{r^2_0} \frac{(4\pi^2 - \alpha^2)^2}{\alpha^2 \left(4\pi^2 + \alpha^2 \dfrac{B_1}{C}\right)}.$$

In the case where α is very small, this formula gives the Euler value of the critical load for a bar with built-in ends.

In treating problems of buckling of a strip with a circular axis, the energy method can also be used in the calculation of critical loads. It can be applied, for instance, in an approximate investigation of stability of a strip having an I cross section, in which case the integration of the differential equations of equilibrium, analogous to Eqs. (g), becomes very complicated.

[1] This formula was obtained by H. Hencky, *Z. angew. Math. Mech.*, vol. 1, p. 451, 1921.

CHAPTER VI

BENDING OF THIN PLATES

55. Pure Bending of Plates.—In the case of pure bending of
a prismatical bar, a rigorous solution for stress distribution is
obtained by assuming that cross sections of the bar remain plane
during bending and rotate only
with respect to their neutral
axes so as to be always normal
to the deflection curve. Combination of such bending in two
perpendicular directions brings
us to pure bending of plates.
Let us begin with pure bending
of a rectangular plate by

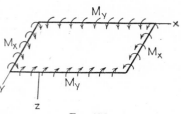

Fig. 156.

moments that are uniformly distributed along the sides of
the plate as shown in Fig. 156. The plane midway between
the faces of the plate, the so-called *middle plane* of the plate,
we take as the xy-plane and we direct the x- and y-axes
along the edges as shown. The z-axis is taken perpendicular
to the middle plane positive in a downward direction. By M_x we
denote the bending moment per unit length of the edges parallel
to the y-axis and by M_y the moment per unit length of the edges

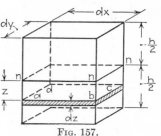

Fig. 157.

parallel to the x-axis. These moments we consider positive when
they produce compression at the
upper surface of the plate and tension at the lower. The thickness of
the plate we denote by h and we
consider it small in comparison with
the other dimensions.

Let us consider an element cut
out of the plate by two pairs of
planes parallel to the xz- and yz-planes as shown in Fig. 157.
Assuming that during bending of the plate the lateral sides of

this element remain plane and rotate about the neutral axes *n-n* so as to remain normal to the deflection surface, it can be concluded that the middle plane of the plate does not undergo any deformation during this bending and is therefore a *neutral surface.* Let $1/r_x$ and $1/r_y$ denote the curvatures[1] of this neutral surface in sections parallel to the *zx-* and *yz-*planes, respectively; then the unit elongations in the *x* and *y* directions of an elemental lamina *abcd* (Fig. 157), at a distance *z* from the neutral surface, are found, as in the case of a beam, and are equal to

$$\epsilon_x = \frac{z}{r_x}; \qquad \epsilon_y = \frac{z}{r_y}. \tag{a}$$

Using now Hooke's law,

$$\epsilon_x = \frac{1}{E}(\sigma_x - \nu\sigma_y); \qquad \epsilon_y = \frac{1}{E}(\sigma_y - \nu\sigma_x), \tag{b}$$

the corresponding stresses in the lamina *abcd* are

$$\left. \begin{aligned} \sigma_x &= \frac{Ez}{1-\nu^2}\left(\frac{1}{r_x} + \nu\frac{1}{r_y}\right); \\ \sigma_y &= \frac{Ez}{1-\nu^2}\left(\frac{1}{r_y} + \nu\frac{1}{r_x}\right). \end{aligned} \right\} \tag{c}$$

They are proportional to the distance *z* of the lamina *abcd* from the neutral surface and depend on the magnitude of curvatures of the bent plate.

These normal stresses distributed over the lateral sides of the element in Fig. 157 can be reduced to couples, which must be equal to external moments.   In this way we obtain the equations:

$$\left. \begin{aligned} \int_{-\frac{h}{2}}^{\frac{h}{2}} \sigma_x z \, dy \, dz &= M_x \, dy; \\ \int_{-\frac{h}{2}}^{\frac{h}{2}} \sigma_y z \, dx \, dz &= M_y \, dx. \end{aligned} \right\} \tag{d}$$

Substituting expressions (c) for σ_x and σ_y, we obtain

$$M_x = D\left(\frac{1}{r_x} + \nu\frac{1}{r_y}\right); \tag{173}$$

$$M_y = D\left(\frac{1}{r_y} + \nu\frac{1}{r_x}\right); \tag{174}$$

[1] Curvatures are taken positive if bending is convex down.

where

$$D = \frac{E}{1 - \nu^2} \int_{-\frac{h}{2}}^{\frac{h}{2}} z^2 \, dz = \frac{Eh^3}{12(1 - \nu^2)}. \tag{175}$$

This quantity is called the *flexural rigidity of the plate.*

Our assumption that there is no strain in the middle plane of a plate during bending is usually sufficiently accurate as long as the deflections of the plate are small in comparison with its thickness h. If this condition is not satisfied, some deformation in the middle surface of the plate usually will be produced[1] and should be considered in investigating the stress distribution in the plate. This more complicated problem of bending of plates will be discussed later (see Art. 61).

Denoting the deflection by w, the approximate formulas for curvatures of the plate, analogous to the known formula for curvature of a beam, are

$$\frac{1}{r_x} = -\frac{\partial^2 w}{\partial x^2} \quad \text{and} \quad \frac{1}{r_y} = -\frac{\partial^2 w}{\partial y^2}$$

Substituting in Eqs. (173) and (174), we obtain

$$M_x = -D\left(\frac{\partial^2 w}{\partial x^2} + \nu\frac{\partial^2 w}{\partial y^2}\right); \tag{176}$$

$$M_y = -D\left(\frac{\partial^2 w}{\partial y^2} + \nu\frac{\partial^2 w}{\partial x^2}\right). \tag{177}$$

These equations define the deflection surface of the plate provided the moments M_x and M_y are given. In the particular case where $M_y = 0$, the rectangular plate (Fig. 156) is bent as a beam. From Eq. (177) we have for this case

$$\frac{\partial^2 w}{\partial y^2} = -\nu\frac{\partial^2 w}{\partial x^2}.$$

The plate has two curvatures in opposite directions, *i.e.*, it is bent into an *anticlastic* surface.[2]

When $M_x = M_y = M$, the curvatures of the deflection surface in two perpendicular directions are equal and the surface is

---

[1] Considerable deflections without strain in the middle surface of the plate are possible only if the deflection surface is a developable surface, as, for instance, a cylindrical or conical surface.

[2] See author's "Theory of Elasticity," p. 225.

spherical. The curvature of the sphere, from Eq. (173), is

$$\frac{1}{r} = \frac{M}{D(1 + \nu)}. \tag{178}$$

Let us consider now, in the case of a bent plate, the stresses acting on a section parallel to the z-axis and inclined to the x- and y-axes. If *acd* (Fig. 158) represents a portion of the thin lamina *abcd* (Fig. 157), cut by such a section, the stress acting on the side *ac* can be found from equations of statics. Resolving this stress into a normal component σ_n and a shearing component

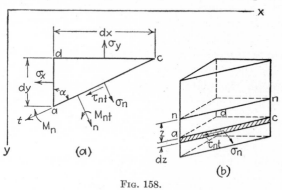

FIG. 158.

τ_{nt}, the magnitudes of these components are given by the known equations

$$\left.\begin{array}{l} \sigma_n = \sigma_x \cos^2 \alpha + \sigma_y \sin^2 \alpha; \\ \tau_{nt} = \tfrac{1}{2}(\sigma_y - \sigma_x) \sin 2\alpha; \end{array}\right\} \tag{e}$$

in which α is the angle between the normal n and the x-axis, or between the direction t and the y-axis (Fig. 158a). This angle is considered positive if measured in a clockwise direction.

Considering all laminae, such as *acd*, over the thickness of the plate (Fig. 158b), the normal stresses σ_n give us the bending moment acting on the section *ac* of the plate, the magnitude of which per unit length along *ac* is

$$M_n = \int_{-\frac{h}{2}}^{\frac{h}{2}} \sigma_n z \, dz = M_x \cos^2 \alpha + M_y \sin^2 \alpha. \tag{179}$$

The shearing stresses τ_{nt} give us the twisting moment acting on the section *ac* of the plate, the magnitude of which per unit length of *ac* is

$$M_{nt} = -\int_{-\frac{h}{2}}^{\frac{h}{2}} \tau_{nt}z \, dz = \tfrac{1}{2}\sin 2\alpha(M_x - M_y). \tag{180}$$

The signs of M_n and M_{nt} are chosen in such a manner that the positive values of these moments are represented by vectors in the positive directions of n and t if the rule of the right-hand screw is used as shown in Fig. 158a. When α is zero or π, Eq. (179) gives $M_n = M_x$. For $\alpha = \pi/2$ or $3\pi/2$, we obtain $M_n = M_y$. The moments M_{nt} become zero for these values of α. Thus we obtain the conditions shown in Fig. 156.

Equations (179) and (180) are similar to Eqs. (e), and by using them the bending and twisting moments can be calculated easily for any value of α. We can solve also without any difficulty the problem in which M_n and M_{nt} are given for two sections perpendicular to each other and it is required to find the two values of α defining the *principal planes*, *i.e.* the planes on which only bending moments M_x and M_y act and on which the twisting moment is zero.

Let us represent now M_n and M_{nt} as functions of deflections w of the plate. From the assumption that the sides of such an element, as shown in Fig. 157, remain plane during bending of the plate and rotate only with respect to the neutral axes n-n, remaining normal to the deflection surface, it follows that every linear element, perpendicular to the middle plane, remains straight during bending and becomes normal to the deflection surface of the plate. The unit elongations of the fibers parallel to n and t (Fig. 158a) and at a distance z from the middle plane are expressed by the equations

$$\epsilon_n = \frac{z}{r_n}; \qquad \epsilon_t = \frac{z}{r_t}, \tag{f}$$

in which r_n and r_t denote the radii of curvature of the deflection surface in the nz- and tz-planes. Equations (f) are analogous to Eqs. (a); using them, together with Hooke's law [see Eqs. (b)], we obtain

$$\sigma_n = \frac{Ez}{1 - \nu^2}\left(\frac{1}{r_n} + \nu\frac{1}{r_t}\right).$$

Substituting this in Eq. (179), we find

$$M_n = D\left(\frac{1}{r_n} + \nu\frac{1}{r_t}\right),$$

or, by using approximate expressions for the curvatures,

$$M_n = -D\left(\frac{\partial^2 w}{\partial n^2} + \nu \frac{\partial^2 w}{\partial t^2}\right). \tag{181}$$

This is an equation analogous to Eqs. (176) and (177) obtained before. We arrive at the same result also by substituting expressions (176) and (177) for M_x and M_y in Eq. (179) and by

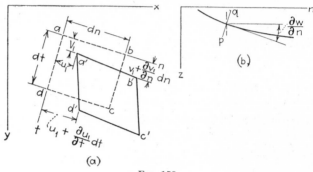

(a)

(b)

Fig. 159.

using the known relations between the curvatures of a surface in two perpendicular directions:

$$\left.\begin{aligned}\frac{1}{r_n} &= \frac{1}{r_x} \cos^2 \alpha + \frac{1}{r_y} \sin^2 \alpha; \\ \frac{1}{r_t} &= \frac{1}{r_x} \sin^2 \alpha + \frac{1}{r_y} \cos^2 \alpha.\end{aligned}\right\} \tag{g}$$

To get an expression for the twisting moment M_{nt}, let us consider the distortion of a thin lamina $abcd$ with the sides ab and ad parallel to the n and t directions and at a distance z from the middle plane (Fig. 159a). During bending of the plate the points a, b, c and d undergo some small displacements. The components of the displacement of the point a in the n- and t-directions we denote by u_1 and v_1. Then the displacement of the adjacent point d in the n-direction is $u_1 + \frac{\partial u_1}{\partial t} dt$ and the displacement of the point b in the t-direction is $v_1 + \frac{\partial v_1}{\partial n} dn$. Owing to these displacements, we obtain for the shearing strain

$$\gamma_{nt} = \frac{\partial u_1}{\partial t} + \frac{\partial v_1}{\partial n}. \tag{h}$$

The corresponding shearing stress is

$$\tau_{nt} = G\left(\frac{\partial u_1}{\partial t} + \frac{\partial v_1}{\partial n}\right). \tag{i}$$

From Fig. 159b, representing the section of the deflection surface made by a vertical plane through the n-axis, it may be seen that the angle of rotation in this plane of an element pq, which initially was perpendicular to the xy-plane, is equal to $\partial w/\partial n$. Owing to this rotation a point of the element at a distance z from the neutral surface has a displacement in the n-direction equal to

$$u_1 = -z\,\frac{\partial w}{\partial n}.$$

Considering the section of the plate made by a vertical plane through the t-axis, it can be shown that the same point has a displacement in the t-direction equal to

$$v_1 = -z\,\frac{\partial w}{\partial t}.$$

Substituting these values of the displacements u_1 and v_1 in expression (i), we find

$$\tau_{nt} = -2Gz\,\frac{\partial^2 w}{\partial n\,\partial t} \tag{182}$$

and the expression (180) for the twisting moment becomes

$$M_{nt} = -\int_{-\frac{h}{2}}^{\frac{h}{2}} \tau_{nt} z\, dz = \frac{Gh^3}{6}\,\frac{\partial^2 w}{\partial n\,\partial t} = D(1-\nu)\frac{\partial^2 w}{\partial n\,\partial t}. \tag{183}$$

The expressions (181) and (183) for bending and twisting moments will be used later in discussion of more general cases of bending of plates.

In the above discussion of pure bending of plates, we started with the case of a rectangular plate along the edges of which uniformly distributed bending moments act. To obtain a general case of pure bending of plates, let us imagine that a portion of any shape is cut out from the above-considered plate by a cylindrical surface perpendicular to the plate. The conditions of bending of this portion will remain unchanged provided the bending and twisting moments of the amounts given by

Eqs. (179) and (180) will be distributed along the boundary of the isolated portion of the plate. Thus we arrive at the case of pure bending of a plate of any shape and we conclude that pure bending of a plate is always produced if along the edges of the plate bending moments M_n and twisting moments M_{nt} are distributed in such a manner as given by formulas (179) and (180). Taking, for instance, a particular case $M_x = M_y = M$, it can be concluded from Eqs. (179) and (180) that a plate of any shape will be bent to a spherical surface if along the edge uniformly distributed bending moments M are acting. Another particular case we obtain by taking $M_x = -M_y = M$. Cutting out from the plate shown in Fig. 156 a rectangular plate the sides of which make angles of 45° with the x- and y-axes, and substituting $\alpha = \pi/4$ or $3\pi/4$ in Eqs. (179) and (180), we obtain $M_n = 0$ for both directions; $M_{nt} = M$ for $\alpha = \pi/4$, and $M_{nt} = -M$ for $\alpha = 3\pi/4$. Hence in this case we produce pure bending in a rectangular plate by applying twisting moments uniformly distributed along the edges.

Regarding the stresses in a plate undergoing pure bending, it can be concluded from the first of Eqs. (*e*) that the maximum normal stress acts on those sections parallel to the xz- or yz-planes. The magnitudes of these stresses are obtained from Eqs. (*c*) by substituting $z = h/2$ and by using Eqs. (173), (174) and (175). In this way we find

$$(\sigma_x)_{\text{max.}} = \frac{6M_x}{h^2}; \qquad (\sigma_y)_{\text{max.}} = \frac{6M_y}{h^2}. \tag{184}$$

If these stresses are of opposite signs, the maximum shearing stress acts in the plane bisecting the angle between the xz- and yz-planes and is equal to

$$\tau_{\text{max.}} = \frac{1}{2}(\sigma_x - \sigma_y) = \frac{3(M_x - M_y)}{h^2}.$$

If the stresses (184) are of the same sign, the maximum shear acts in the plane bisecting the angle between the xy- and xz-planes or in that bisecting the angle between the xy- and yz-planes, and is equal to $\frac{1}{2}(\sigma_y)_{\text{max.}}$ or $\frac{1}{2}(\sigma_x)_{\text{max.}}$ depending on which of the two normal stresses $(\sigma_y)_{\text{max.}}$ or $(\sigma_x)_{\text{max.}}$ is greater.

56. Bending of Plates by Distributed Lateral Load.—In considering the case of bending of a plate by a distributed load acting perpendicular to its middle plane, let us assume that this middle plane is horizontal and contains the x- and y-axes while the z-axis is directed vertically downward. We denote by q the intensity of the load, which, in general, may vary along the surface of the plate and which is considered as a function of x and y. Cutting an element from the plate by two pairs of planes parallel to the xz- and yz-planes (Fig. 160), it can be concluded from statics that, owing to the action of the load q,

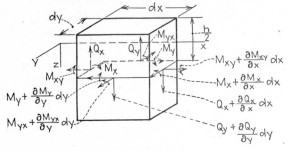

Fig. 160.

there will be produced on the lateral sides of this element not only bending and twisting moments, as discussed in the previous article, but also vertical shearing forces, the magnitude of which per unit of length will be defined by the following formulas:

$$Q_x = \int_{-\frac{h}{2}}^{\frac{h}{2}} \tau_{xz}\, dz; \qquad Q_y = \int_{-\frac{h}{2}}^{\frac{h}{2}} \tau_{yz}\, dz. \qquad (a)$$

The variation of τ_{xz} and τ_{yz} along the small distances dy and dx can be neglected, and it will be assumed that the resultant shearing forces $Q_x\, dy$ and $Q_y\, dx$ pass through the centroids of the sides of the element. For the bending and twisting moments per unit length, we take the same definitions as in the previous article and assume

$$M_x = \int_{-\frac{h}{2}}^{\frac{h}{2}} \sigma_x z\, dz; \qquad M_y = \int_{-\frac{h}{2}}^{\frac{h}{2}} \sigma_y z\, dz; \qquad (b)$$

$$M_{xy} = -\int_{-\frac{h}{2}}^{\frac{h}{2}} \tau_{xy} z\, dz; \qquad M_{yx} = \int_{-\frac{h}{2}}^{\frac{h}{2}} \tau_{yx} z\, dz. \qquad (c)$$

The shearing forces (a), bending moments (b) and twisting moments (c) are all functions of the coordinates x and y. Hence, in using notations Q_x, M_x and M_{xy} for the left side of the element in Fig. 160, we shall have for the right side of the element, distant dx from the left side, the corresponding quantities equal to $Q_x + \dfrac{\partial Q_x}{\partial x}\, dx$, $M_x + \dfrac{\partial M_x}{\partial x}\, dx$ and $M_{xy} + \dfrac{\partial M_{xy}}{\partial x}\, dx$ as shown in the figure. An analogous conclusion will be obtained also for the sides of the element parallel to the xz-plane.

In considering the conditions of equilibrium of the element, we observe that all forces acting on it are parallel to the z-axis and that the couples are represented by vectors perpendicular to the z-axis. Hence we have only three equations of statics to discuss—the projections of all forces on the z-axis and the moments of all forces with respect to the x- and y-axes. Noting the directions of forces indicated in Fig. 160, their projections on the z-axis give us the equation

$$\frac{\partial Q_x}{\partial x}\, dx\, dy + \frac{\partial Q_y}{\partial y}\, dy\, dx + q\, dx\, dy = 0,$$

or, after simplification,

$$\frac{\partial Q_x}{\partial x} + \frac{\partial Q_y}{\partial y} + q = 0. \tag{d}$$

The weight of the plate itself can be considered as included in the value of q. By taking the moments of all forces acting on the element with respect to the x-axis, and observing the directions indicated in the figure, we obtain

$$\frac{\partial M_{xy}}{\partial x}\, dx\, dy - \frac{\partial M_y}{\partial y}\, dy\, dx + Q_y\, dx\, dy = 0.$$

The moment of the load q and the moment due to change in the force Q_y are neglected in deriving this equation since they are small quantities of a higher order than those which we retain. After simplification, the equation becomes

$$\frac{\partial M_{xy}}{\partial x} - \frac{\partial M_y}{\partial y} + Q_y = 0. \tag{e}$$

In the same way, by taking moments with respect to the y-axis, we obtain

$$\frac{\partial M_{yx}}{\partial y} + \frac{\partial M_x}{\partial x} - Q_x = 0. \tag{f}$$

Determining Q_x and Q_y from Eqs. (f) and (e) and substituting in Eq. (d), we obtain

$$\frac{\partial^2 M_x}{\partial x^2} + \frac{\partial^2 M_{yx}}{\partial x\,\partial y} + \frac{\partial^2 M_y}{\partial y^2} - \frac{\partial^2 M_{xy}}{\partial x\,\partial y} = -q.$$

Observing that $M_{yx} = -M_{xy}$, in virtue of $\tau_{xy} = \tau_{yx}$, we finally obtain the following equation of equilibrium:

$$\frac{\partial^2 M_x}{\partial x^2} - \frac{2\partial^2 M_{xy}}{\partial x\,\partial y} + \frac{\partial^2 M_y}{\partial y^2} = -q. \tag{g}$$

Neglecting the effect of shearing forces Q_x and Q_y on the curvatures of the plate[1] and using Eqs. (181) and (183), developed for the case of pure bending, we obtain the following expressions for bending and twisting moments:

$$M_x = -D\left(\frac{\partial^2 w}{\partial x^2} + \nu\frac{\partial^2 w}{\partial y^2}\right); \qquad M_y = -D\left(\frac{\partial^2 w}{\partial y^2} + \nu\frac{\partial^2 w}{\partial x^2}\right); \tag{185}$$

$$M_{xy} = -M_{yx} = D(1 - \nu)\frac{\partial^2 w}{\partial x\,\partial y}. \tag{186}$$

Substituting in Eq. (g), we obtain

$$\frac{\partial^4 w}{\partial x^4} + 2\frac{\partial^4 w}{\partial x^2\,\partial y^2} + \frac{\partial^4 w}{\partial y^4} = \frac{q}{D}. \tag{187}$$

Thus the determination of the deflection surface of a plate is reduced to the integration of Eq. (187).

If, for a particular case, the solution of this equation is found, the bending and twisting moments will be calculated from Eqs. (185) and (186). The shearing forces will now be found from Eqs. (e) and (f). Substituting in these equations for bending and twisting moments their expressions (185) and (186), we obtain

$$Q_x = \frac{\partial M_x}{\partial x} + \frac{\partial M_{yx}}{\partial y} = -D\frac{\partial}{\partial x}\left(\frac{\partial^2 w}{\partial x^2} + \frac{\partial^2 w}{\partial y^2}\right), \tag{188}$$

$$Q_y = \frac{\partial M_y}{\partial y} - \frac{\partial M_{xy}}{\partial x} = -D\frac{\partial}{\partial y}\left(\frac{\partial^2 w}{\partial x^2} + \frac{\partial^2 w}{\partial y^2}\right). \tag{189}$$

[1] We know that in the case of a beam this effect is small if the depth of the beam is small in comparison with the span. An analogous conclusion can be made also in the case of a plate if the thickness of the plate is small in comparison with other dimensions. A more exact theory of bending of plates, in which the effect of shearing stresses on deflections is considered, has been developed by J. H. Michell, *Proc. London Math. Soc.*, vol. 31, 1900, and by A. E. H. Love, "Theory of Elasticity," 4th ed., p. 465, 1927.

Having the bending and twisting moments, the normal stresses $(\sigma_x)_{\max.}$ and $(\sigma_y)_{\max.}$ are obtained from Eqs. (184). Shearing stresses parallel to the x- and y-axes are obtained from Eq. (182) by taking n and t in the x- and y-directions, respectively. Shearing stresses parallel to the z-axis are obtained by assuming that the shearing forces Q_x and Q_y are distributed along the thickness of the plate following the parabolic law, as in the case of beams of rectangular cross sections. Then

$$(\tau_{xz})_{\max.} = \frac{3}{2h}(Q_x)_{\max.}, \qquad (\tau_{yz})_{\max.} = \frac{3}{2h}(Q_y)_{\max.}.$$

Thus all stresses can be calculated provided the deflection surface of the plate is known.

The determination of the deflection surface of a plate requires in each particular case the integration of the partial differential equation (187) for a given distribution of the load q and for given conditions at the boundary of the plate. In the following discussion we will be occupied principally with rectangular plates and the various boundary conditions for such plates will now be considered.

Built-in Edge.—If the edge of a plate is built in, the deflection along this edge is zero and the tangent plane to the deflection surface along this edge coincides with the initial position of the middle plane of the plate. Taking in the middle plane of the plate x- and y-axes in the directions of the two edges of the plate, and assuming that the edge coinciding with the x-axis is built in, the boundary conditions along this edge will be

$$(w)_{y=0} = 0; \qquad \left(\frac{\partial w}{\partial y}\right)_{y=0} = 0. \tag{190}$$

Simply Supported Edge.—If the edge $y = 0$ of the plate is simply supported, the deflection w along this edge must be zero. At the same time this edge can rotate freely with respect to the x-axis, *i.e.*, there are no bending moments M_y along this edge. This kind of support is represented in Fig. 161. The analytical expressions of the boundary conditions in this case are

$$(w)_{y=0} = 0; \qquad \left(\frac{\partial^2 w}{\partial y^2} + \nu\frac{\partial^2 w}{\partial x^2}\right)_{y=0} = 0. \tag{191}$$

Free Edge.—If an edge of a plate, say the edge $x = a$ (Fig. 162), is entirely free, it is natural to assume that along this edge there will be no bending and twisting moments and also no vertical shearing forces, *i.e.*,

$$(M_x)_{x=a} = 0; \qquad (M_{xy})_{x=a} = 0; \qquad (Q_x)_{x=a} = 0.$$

In such form the boundary conditions were discussed by Poisson.[1] But later, Kirchhoff[2] proved that three boundary conditions

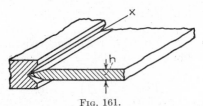

Fig. 161.

are too many and that two conditions are sufficient for the complete determination of deflections w. He showed also that two of Poisson's requirements regarding twisting moment and shearing force can be replaced by one boundary condition. The physical meaning of this reduction in the number of boundary conditions has been explained by Thomson and Tait.[3] These authors point out that bending of the plate will not be changed if the horizontal forces giving the twisting couple $M_{xy} \, dy$ acting on an element of the length dy of the edge $x = a$ are replaced by

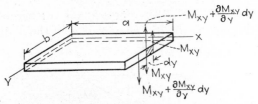

Fig. 162.

two vertical forces M_{xy}, dy apart, as shown in Fig. 162. Such a replacement does not change the magnitude of twisting moments and produces only local changes in stress distribution at the edge of the plate, leaving the stress condition of the rest of the plate unchanged. Proceeding with the above replacement of

---

[1] See discussion of this subject in J. Todhunter and K. Pearson, "History of the Theory of Elasticity," vol. 1, p. 250. See also Saint Venant's discussion in "Théorie de l'élasticité des corps solides" by Clebsch, final note to §73, p. 689.

[2] See *J. de Crelle*, vol. 40, 1850.

[3] See "Natural Philosophy," vol. 1, part 2, p. 188, 1883.

twisting couples along the edge of the plate, we will find, as can be seen from a consideration of the two adjacent elements indicated in the figure, that the distribution of twisting moments M_{xy} is statically equivalent to the distribution of shearing forces of the intensity

$$(Q'_x)_{x=a} = -\left(\frac{\partial M_{xy}}{\partial y}\right)_{x=a}.$$

Hence the joint requirement regarding twisting moments and shearing forces along the free edge $x = a$ becomes

$$\left(Q_x - \frac{\partial M_{xy}}{\partial y}\right)_{x=a} = 0. \tag{h}$$

Substituting for Q_x and M_{xy} their expressions (188) and (186), we finally get for a free edge, $x = a$:

$$\left[\frac{\partial^3 w}{\partial x^3} + (2 - \nu)\frac{\partial^3 w}{\partial x\,\partial y^2}\right]_{x=a} = 0. \tag{192}$$

The condition that bending moment along the free edge is zero requires

$$\left(\frac{\partial^2 w}{\partial x^2} + \nu\frac{\partial^2 w}{\partial y^2}\right)_{x=a} = 0. \tag{193}$$

Equations (192) and (193) represent the two necessary boundary conditions along the free edge, $x = a$, of the plate.

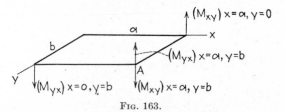

Fig. 163.

Transforming the twisting couples as explained in the above discussion and shown in Fig. 162, we obtain not only shearing forces Q'_x distributed along the edge $x = a$ but also two concentrated forces at the ends of that edge, as indicated in Fig. 163. The magnitudes of these forces are equal to the magnitudes of the twisting couple M_{xy} at the corresponding corners of the plate. Making the analogous transformation of twisting couples M_{yx} along the edge $y = b$, we will find that in this case again, in addition to the distributed shearing forces, there will be concentrated forces M_{yx} at the corners. This indicates that a rectangular plate supported in some way along the edges and laterally loaded will usually produce not only pressures distributed along the boundary but also concentrated pressures at the corners. Regarding the directions of concentrated pressures, a conclusion can be made if the general shape of the deflection surface is known. Take, for instance, a uniformly loaded square plate simply supported along the edges. The general shape of the deflection

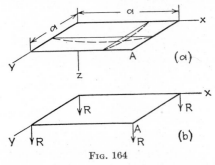

Fig. 164

surface is indicated in Fig. 164a by dotted lines representing the sections of the deflection surface by planes parallel to the xz- and yz-coordinate planes. Considering these lines it is seen that near the corner A the derivative $\partial w/\partial x$, representing the slope of the deflection surface in the x direction, is negative and numerically decreases with increasing y. Hence $\partial^2 w/\partial x\,\partial y$ is positive at the corner A; from Eq. (186) we conclude that M_{xy} is positive and that M_{yx} is negative. From this and from the directions of M_{xy} and M_{yx} (Fig. 160), it follows that both concentrated forces, indicated at the corner A in Fig. 163, have a downward direction. From symmetry we conclude also that at all four corners of the plate the forces have the same direction and magnitude. Hence the conditions will be as indicated in Fig. 164b in which $R = 2D(1 - \nu)\dfrac{\partial^2 w}{\partial x\,\partial y}$. When a square plate is uniformly loaded, the corners have the tendency to rise and this is prevented by concentrated reactions at the corners as indicated in the figure.

Elastically Supported and Elastically Built-in Edge.—If the edge, $x = a$, of a rectangular plate is rigidly joined together with a supporting beam

(Fig. 165), the deflection along this edge is not zero and is equal to deflection of the beam. Also rotation of the edge is equal to the twisting of the beam. Let B be the flexural and C the torsional rigidity of the beam. The pressure

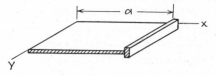

Fɪɢ. 165.

transmitted from the plate to the supporting beam, from Eq. (h) (see p. 300), is

$$-\left(Q_x - \frac{\partial M_{xy}}{\partial y}\right)_{x=a} = D\frac{\partial}{\partial x}\left[\frac{\partial^2 w}{\partial x^2} + (2 - \nu)\frac{\partial^2 w}{\partial y^2}\right]_{x=a}$$

and the differential equation of the deflection curve of the beam is

$$B\left(\frac{\partial^4 w}{\partial y^4}\right)_{x=a} = D\frac{\partial}{\partial x}\left[\frac{\partial^2 w}{\partial x^2} + (2 - \nu)\frac{\partial^2 w}{\partial y^2}\right]_{x=a}. \tag{194}$$

This equation represents one of the boundary conditions of the plate along the edge $x = a$.

To obtain the second condition, twisting of the beam should be considered. The angle of rotation of any cross section of the beam is $-(\partial w/\partial x)_{x=a}$, the rate of change of this angle along the edge is

$$-\left(\frac{\partial^2 w}{\partial x\,\partial y}\right)_{x=a}$$

and the twisting moment in the beam is $-C(\partial^2 w/\partial x\,\partial y)_{x=a}$. This moment varies along the edge since the plate, rigidly connected with the beam, transmits twisting moments to the beam. The magnitude of these moments per unit length must be equal and opposite to the bending moment M_x in the plate. Hence, from the consideration of twist of the supporting beam, we obtain

$$-C\frac{\partial}{\partial y}\left(\frac{\partial^2 w}{\partial x\,\partial y}\right)_{x=a} = -(M_x)_{x=a},$$

or, substituting for M_x its expression (185),

$$-C\frac{\partial}{\partial y}\left(\frac{\partial^2 w}{\partial x\,\partial y}\right)_{x=a} = D\left(\frac{\partial^2 w}{\partial x^2} + \nu\frac{\partial^2 w}{\partial y^2}\right)_{x=a} \tag{195}$$

This is the second boundary condition at the edge $x = a$ of the plate.

57. Combined Bending and Tension or Compression of Plates.—In our previous discussion it has been assumed that the plate is bent by lateral load and that deflections are so small that the stretching of the middle plane of the plate can be neglected; thus this plane has been considered as the neutral plane of the plate. If in addition to lateral load there are forces acting in the middle plane of the plate, they produce stretching of this plane and the corresponding stresses should be considered. We shall distinguish two possible cases. (1) These stresses are small[1] and we can neglect their effect on bending of the plate and assume that total stresses are obtained with sufficient accuracy by superposing the stresses due to stretching of the middle plane on the stresses produced by lateral load. (2) The stresses in the middle plane of the plate are not small and their effect on bending of the plate should be considered. In deriving the corresponding differential equation of the deflection surface for this latter case, we consider again the equilibrium of a small element cut out from the plate by two pairs of planes parallel to the *xz*- and *yz*-coordinate planes. In addition to the forces considered in the previous article

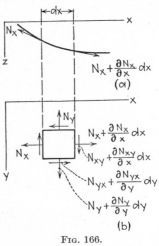

Fig. 166.

(see Fig. 160), we shall now have forces acting in the middle plane of the plate, the notations for which per unit length are shown in Fig. 166. Projecting these forces on the *x*- and *y*-axes and assuming that there are no body forces acting in those directions, we obtain the following equations of equilibrium:

$$\left.\begin{array}{l} \dfrac{\partial N_x}{\partial x} + \dfrac{\partial N_{yx}}{\partial y} = 0; \\[2mm] \dfrac{\partial N_y}{\partial y} + \dfrac{\partial N_{xy}}{\partial x} = 0. \end{array}\right\} \qquad (196)$$

It may be seen that these equations are entirely independent of the three equations of equilibrium considered in the previous article and can be treated separately as will be shown later (see Art. 61).

In considering the projection of the forces, shown in Fig. 166, on the *z*-axis, we must take into account the deflection of the

---

[1] We mean here that they are small in comparison with *critical* stresses which may produce buckling of the plate. The values of these critical stresses in various particular cases will be discussed in the next chapter.

plate.   Owing to curvature of the plate in the xz-plane (Fig. 166a), the projection of the normal forces N_x on the z-axis gives

$$-N_x\, dy\frac{\partial w}{\partial x} + \left(N_x + \frac{\partial N_x}{\partial x}dx\right)\left(\frac{\partial w}{\partial x} + \frac{\partial^2 w}{\partial x^2}dx\right)dy.$$

After simplification and neglecting the small quantities of higher order, this projection will be

$$N_x\frac{\partial^2 w}{\partial x^2}dx\, dy + \frac{\partial N_x}{\partial x}\frac{\partial w}{\partial x}dx\, dy. \qquad (a)$$

In the same way the projection on the z-axis of the normal forces N_y gives

$$N_y\frac{\partial^2 w}{\partial y^2}dx\, dy + \frac{\partial N_y}{\partial y}\frac{\partial w}{\partial y}dx\, dy. \qquad (b)$$

In discussing the projection on the z-axis of the shearing forces N_{xy}, let us consider the deflection of an element $dx\, dy$ of the

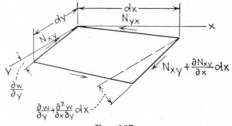

Fig. 167.

middle plane shown in Fig. 167.   It is seen that, owing to the angles $\dfrac{\partial w}{\partial y}$ and $\dfrac{\partial w}{\partial y} + \dfrac{\partial^2 w}{\partial x\, \partial y}dx$, shown in the figure, the shearing forces N_{xy} have the projection on the z-axis equal to

$$N_{xy}\frac{\partial^2 w}{\partial x\, \partial y}dx\, dy + \frac{\partial N_{xy}}{\partial x}\frac{\partial w}{\partial y}dx\, dy.$$

An analogous expression is obtained for the projection on the z-axis of the shearing forces $N_{yx} = N_{xy}$ and the final expression for the projection of all shearing forces on the z-axis is

$$2N_{xy}\frac{\partial^2 w}{\partial x\, \partial y}dx\, dy + \frac{\partial N_{xy}}{\partial x}\frac{\partial w}{\partial y}dx\, dy + \frac{\partial N_{xy}}{\partial y}\frac{\partial w}{\partial x}dx\, dy. \qquad (c)$$

Adding expressions (a), (b) and (c) to the load $q\, dx\, dy$ acting on the element and using Eqs. (196), we obtain, instead of Eq. (g)

of the previous article (see p. 297), the following equation of equilibrium:

$$\frac{\partial^2 M_x}{\partial x^2} - 2\frac{\partial^2 M_{xy}}{\partial x \, \partial y} + \frac{\partial^2 M_y}{\partial y^2} =$$
$$-\left(q + N_x\frac{\partial^2 w}{\partial x^2} + N_y\frac{\partial^2 w}{\partial y^2} + 2N_{xy}\frac{\partial^2 w}{\partial x \, \partial y}\right).$$

Substituting for M_x, M_y and M_{xy} their expressions (185) and (186), we obtain[1]

$$\frac{\partial^4 w}{\partial x^4} + 2\frac{\partial^4 w}{\partial x^2 \, \partial y^2} + \frac{\partial^4 w}{\partial y^4} =$$
$$\frac{1}{D}\left(q + N_x\frac{\partial^2 w}{\partial x^2} + N_y\frac{\partial^2 w}{\partial y^2} + 2N_{xy}\frac{\partial^2 w}{\partial x \, \partial y}\right). \quad (197)$$

This differential equation, instead of Eq. (187), should be used in determining the deflection surface of a plate if the forces N_x, N_y and N_{xy} are not small in comparison with the critical values of these forces.

If there are body forces acting in the middle plane of the plate, the differential equations of equilibrium of the element represented in Fig. 166 become

$$\left.\begin{array}{l} \dfrac{\partial N_x}{\partial x} + \dfrac{\partial N_{xy}}{\partial y} + X = 0, \\[2mm] \dfrac{\partial N_{xy}}{\partial x} + \dfrac{\partial N_y}{\partial y} + Y = 0. \end{array}\right\} \quad (196')$$

Here X and Y represent the two components of the body force per unit area of the middle plane of the plate.

Adding as before expressions (a), (b) and (c) to the load $q \, dx \, dy$ and using Eqs. (196') instead of Eqs. (196), we obtain, instead of Eq. (197), the following equation:

$$\frac{\partial^4 w}{\partial x^4} + 2\frac{\partial^4 w}{\partial x^2 \, \partial y^2} + \frac{\partial^4 w}{\partial y^4} = \frac{1}{D}\left(q + N_x\frac{\partial^2 w}{\partial x^2} + N_y\frac{\partial^2 w}{\partial y^2} +\right.$$
$$\left.2N_{xy}\frac{\partial^2 w}{\partial x \, \partial y} - X\frac{\partial w}{\partial x} - Y\frac{\partial w}{\partial y}\right). \quad (197')$$

This differential equation should be used, instead of Eq. (197), when there are body forces to be considered.

58. Strain Energy in Bending of Plates.—In investigating the stability of thin plates, the energy method (see Art. 14)

---

[1] This differential equation has been derived by Saint Venant, see final note, §73, in Saint Venant's translation of Clebsch, "Théorie de l'élasticité des corps solides," p. 704, 1883.

frequently can be used to advantage.   We will derive here expressions for strain energy of a bent plate under various conditions of loading.

Pure Bending.—If a plate is bent by uniformly distributed bending moments M_x and M_y (Fig. 156), the strain energy accumulated in an element, such as shown in Fig. 157, is obtained by calculating the work done by the moments $M_x \, dy$ and $M_y \, dx$ on the element during bending of the plate.   Since the sides of the element remain plane, the work done by moments $M_x \, dy$ is obtained by taking half of the product of the moment and the angle between the corresponding sides of the element after bending.   Since $-\partial^2 w/\partial x^2$ represents approximately the curvature of the plate in the xz-plane, the angle corresponding to the moments $M_x \, dy$ is $-(\partial^2 w/\partial x^2)dx$ and the work done by these moments is

$$-\frac{1}{2}M_x\frac{\partial^2 w}{\partial x^2}dx \, dy.$$

An analogous expression is obtained also for the work produced by the moments $M_y \, dx$.   Then the total work, equal to the potential energy of the element, is

$$dV = -\frac{1}{2}\left(M_x\frac{\partial^2 w}{\partial x^2} + M_y\frac{\partial^2 w}{\partial y^2}\right)dx \, dy.$$

Substituting for the moments their expressions (**176**) and (**177**), the strain energy of the element will be represented in the following form:

$$dV = \frac{1}{2}D\left[\left(\frac{\partial^2 w}{\partial x^2}\right)^2 + \left(\frac{\partial^2 w}{\partial y^2}\right)^2 + 2\nu\,\frac{\partial^2 w}{\partial x^2}\frac{\partial^2 w}{\partial y^2}\right]dx \, dy. \qquad (a)$$

The total strain energy of the plate will then be obtained by integration of expression (a):

$$V = \frac{1}{2}D \int \int \left[\left(\frac{\partial^2 w}{\partial x^2}\right)^2 + \left(\frac{\partial^2 w}{\partial y^2}\right)^2 + 2\nu\,\frac{\partial^2 w}{\partial x^2}\frac{\partial^2 w}{\partial y^2}\right]dx \, dy, \quad (198)$$

where the integration must be extended over the entire surface of the plate.

Bending of a Plate by Lateral Load.—Considering again an element of the plate, such as shown in Fig. 160, and neglecting the strain energy due to shearing forces Q_x and Q_y, we find that the strain energy of the element is equal to the work done on the element by the bending moments $M_x dy$ and $M_y dx$ and by the twisting moments $M_{xy} dy$ and $M_{yx} dx$. Since we neglect the effect of vertical shearing forces on the curvature of the deflection surface, the strain energy due to bending moments will be represented by the expression (198) above derived for the case of pure bending.

In deriving the expression for the strain energy due to twisting moments $M_{xy}\, dy$, we note that the corresponding angle of twist (Fig. 167) is $(\partial^2 w/\partial x\, \partial y)dx$; hence the strain energy due to $M_{xy}\, dy$ is

$$\frac{1}{2}M_{xy}\frac{\partial^2 w}{\partial x\, \partial y}dx\, dy = \frac{1}{2}D(1 - \nu)\left(\frac{\partial^2 w}{\partial x\, \partial y}\right)^2 dx\, dy.$$

The same amount of energy will be produced also by the couples $M_{yx}\, dx$ so that the strain energy due to both twisting couples is

$$D(1 - \nu)\left(\frac{\partial^2 w}{\partial x\, \partial y}\right)^2 dx\, dy.$$

Since the twist does not affect the work produced by the bending moments, the total strain energy of an element of a plate is obtained by adding together the energy of bending and the energy of twist. Thus we obtain

$$dV = \frac{1}{2}D\left[\left(\frac{\partial^2 w}{\partial x^2}\right)^2 + \left(\frac{\partial^2 w}{\partial y^2}\right)^2 + 2\nu\frac{\partial^2 w}{\partial x^2}\frac{\partial^2 w}{\partial y^2}\right]dx\, dy +$$
$$D(1 - \nu)\left(\frac{\partial^2 w}{\partial x\, \partial y}\right)^2 dx\, dy. \quad (b)$$

The strain energy of the entire plate is now obtained by integration

$$V = \frac{1}{2}D \int \int \left[\left(\frac{\partial^2 w}{\partial x^2}\right)^2 + \left(\frac{\partial^2 w}{\partial y^2}\right)^2 + 2\nu\frac{\partial^2 w}{\partial x^2}\frac{\partial^2 w}{\partial y^2} + \right.$$
$$\left. 2(1 - \nu)\left(\frac{\partial^2 w}{\partial x\, \partial y}\right)^2\right]dx\, dy$$

or

$$V = \frac{1}{2}D \int \int \left\{\left(\frac{\partial^2 w}{\partial x^2} + \frac{\partial^2 w}{\partial y^2}\right)^2 - \right.$$
$$\left. 2(1 - \nu)\left[\frac{\partial^2 w}{\partial x^2}\frac{\partial^2 w}{\partial y^2} - \left(\frac{\partial^2 w}{\partial x\, \partial y}\right)^2\right]\right\}dx\, dy. \quad (199)$$

Combined Bending and Tension or Compression of Plates.—If, in addition to bending, the plate is submitted to the action of forces in the middle plane of the plate, the total strain energy is obtained by adding together the energy of bending, represented by formula (199), and the energy of stretching of the middle plane.

Before we go into the derivation of the complete expression for strain energy of a plate in this case, let us consider a simple

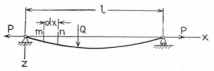

Fɪɢ. 168.

example of a prismatical bar submitted to the simultaneous action of bending and axial tension (Fig. 168). In calculating the strain energy of this bar we assume that the tensile forces P are applied to the initially straight bar. The corresponding strain energy is

$$\frac{P^2l}{2AE},\qquad(c)$$

where l is the span and A the cross-sectional area of the bar. By applying now lateral load Q deflection of the bar will be produced. Let u and w be the components in the x- and z-directions, respectively, of the displacement of any point of the center line of the bar during bending. The unit elongation of an element mn of the center line due to displacements u is du/dx. The unit elongation of the same element due to displacements w is $\frac{1}{2}(dw/dx)^2$. Thus the total unit elongation is

$$\frac{du}{dx} + \frac{1}{2}\left(\frac{dw}{dx}\right)^2.$$

Considering the tensile force at each cross section as constant during bending and equal to P, the additional tensile strain energy in the element will be

$$P\left[\frac{du}{dx} + \frac{1}{2}\left(\frac{dw}{dx}\right)^2\right]dx$$

and the corresponding energy of the entire bar is

$$\int_0^l P\left[\frac{du}{dx} + \frac{1}{2}\left(\frac{dw}{dx}\right)^2\right]dx. \tag{d}$$

The energy of bending of the bar will be represented by the usual formula

$$\frac{EI}{2}\int_0^l \left(\frac{d^2w}{dx^2}\right)^2 dx, \tag{e}$$

in which EI is the flexural rigidity of the bar. The total energy of the bar will now be obtained by summing up the expressions (c), (d) and (e). Since the portion (c) remains constant during bending, only the sum of expressions (d) and (e) should be considered in calculating deflections. This latter sum can be represented in the form

$$\int_0^l P\frac{du}{dx}\,dx + \frac{1}{2}\int_0^l P\left(\frac{dw}{dx}\right)^2 dx + \frac{EI}{2}\int_0^l \left(\frac{d^2w}{dx^2}\right)^2 dx. \tag{f}$$

Integrating the first term of this expression and denoting by λ the value of u for the movable support of the bar (Fig. 168), we obtain

$$\int_0^l P\frac{du}{dx}\,dx = P\left.u\right|_0^l = P\lambda,$$

i.e., the first term in expression (f) represents the work done during bending by the axial forces P. The two other terms of the same expression must then represent the work done by the lateral load Q.

This conclusion holds also for a more general case when there are axial forces distributed along the length of the bar and when the tensile force P is a function of x. Integrating by parts we obtain in such case

$$\int_0^l P\frac{du}{dx}\,dx = \left.\left|P\,u\right.\right|_0^l - \int_0^l u\frac{dP}{dx}\,dx.$$

The first term on the right side represents the work of forces applied at the ends of the bar and the second term represents the work produced by loads distributed along the axis of the bar. This latter conclusion is easily obtained if we observe that $(dP/dx)dx$ is the difference of the axial force in two adjacent cross sections of the bar. Hence $-(dP/dx)dx$ is the body force applied between the above two cross sections.

Using T_h for the work produced by the axial forces and T_v for the work produced by the lateral forces, we conclude that

$$T_h = \int_0^l P \frac{du}{dx}\, dx; \qquad (g)$$

$$T_v = \frac{1}{2}\int_0^l P\left(\frac{dw}{dx}\right)^2 dx + \frac{EI}{2}\int_0^l \left(\frac{d^2w}{dx^2}\right)^2 dx. \qquad (h)$$

We assumed in the derivation that the force P remains constant during bending; then the strain of the center line of the bar does not change during bending and we have

$$\frac{du}{dx} = -\frac{1}{2}\left(\frac{dw}{dx}\right)^2.$$

Hence

$$\frac{1}{2}\int_0^l P\left(\frac{dw}{dx}\right)^2 dx = -\int_0^l P \frac{du}{dx}\, dx = -T_h$$

and Eq. (h) can be put in the following form:

$$T_v = -T_h + \frac{EI}{2}\int_0^l \left(\frac{d^2w}{dx^2}\right)^2 dx. \qquad (i)$$

If the deflection curve of the bar is represented by the trigonometrical series

$$w = \sum_{n=1}^{n=\infty} a_n \sin \frac{n\pi x}{l}$$

and the three terms of Eq. (i) are represented as functions of the coefficients $a_1, a_2, \ldots$, then the value of any coefficient a_n is obtained by using the principle of virtual displacements

$$\frac{\partial T_v}{\partial a_n}\, \delta a_n + \frac{\partial T_h}{\partial a_n}\, \delta a_n = \frac{EI}{2}\frac{\partial}{\partial a_n}\int_0^l \left(\frac{\partial^2w}{\partial x^2}\right)^2 dx\, \delta a_n.$$

Such an equation we have used before (see Art. 7) in investigating deflections of an axially compressed bar.

In the case of bending of a plate submitted to the simultaneous action of transverse loads and of forces applied in the middle plane of the plate, we assume that the forces in the middle plane are applied first. In this way we obtain a two-dimensional problem. Solving this problem, we determine the forces N_x, N_y and N_{xy} (Fig. 166) and the components of strain

$$\epsilon_x = \frac{1}{hE}(N_x - \nu N_y); \qquad \epsilon_y = \frac{1}{hE}(N_y - \nu N_x);$$

$$\gamma_{xy} = \frac{N_{xy}}{hG}.$$

Then the energy, due to stretching of the middle plane of the plate by the forces applied in this plane, is

$$V = \frac{1}{2}\int\int (N_x\epsilon_x + N_y\epsilon_y + N_{xy}\gamma_{xy})dx\,dy =$$

$$\frac{1}{2hE}\int\int [N^2{}_x + N^2{}_y - 2\nu N_x N_y + 2(1 + \nu)N^2{}_{xy}]dx\,dy. \quad (200)$$

This portion of energy remains constant during bending and we do not need to consider it in the following discussion.

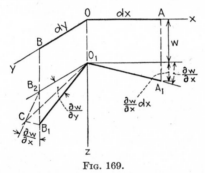

Fig. 169.

Let us apply now lateral load, producing bending of the plate. The three components in the x-, y- and z-directions of the displacement of any point in the middle surface of the plate during bending, we denote by u, v and w, respectively. Then, proceeding as above in the case of a beam, the strains in the x- and y-directions are

$$\left.\begin{aligned} \epsilon_x &= \frac{\partial u}{\partial x} + \frac{1}{2}\left(\frac{\partial w}{\partial x}\right)^2; \\ \epsilon_y &= \frac{\partial v}{\partial y} + \frac{1}{2}\left(\frac{\partial w}{\partial y}\right)^2 \end{aligned}\right\} \qquad (j)$$

The shearing strain due to displacements u and v will be found from Eq. (h) (p. 292). For the determination of shearing strain due to displacements w, we take two infinitely small linear elements OA and OB in the x- and y-directions, as shown in Fig. 169. Because of displacements w these elements come to the positions O_1A_1 and O_1B_1. The difference between the angle $A_1O_1B_1$ and $\pi/2$ is the shearing strain corresponding to displacements w. To determine this difference we consider the right angle $B_2O_1A_1$. Rotating this angle with respect to O_1A_1 by the angle $\partial w/\partial y$, we bring the plane $B_2O_1A_1$ into coincidence with the plane $B_1O_1A_1{}^1$ and the point B_2 takes the position C. The displacement B_2C is equal to $\dfrac{\partial w}{\partial y}\,dy$ and is inclined to the vertical B_2B_1 by the angle $\partial w/\partial x$. Then CB_1 is equal to $\dfrac{\partial w}{\partial x}\dfrac{\partial w}{\partial y}\,dy$, and the angle CO_1B_1, representing the shearing strain corresponding to displacements w, is $(\partial w/\partial x)(\partial w/\partial y)$. Adding this to the shear due to displacements u and v, we obtain

$$\gamma_{xy} = \frac{\partial u}{\partial y} + \frac{\partial v}{\partial x} + \frac{\partial w}{\partial x}\frac{\partial w}{\partial y}. \tag{k}$$

Assuming that the forces N_x, N_y and N_{xy} remain constant during bending, the strain energy of the plate due to stretching of the middle surface is

$$\iint (N_x\epsilon_x + N_y\epsilon_y + N_{xy}\gamma_{xy})dx\,dy.$$

Adding to this the energy of bending represented by Eq. (199) and substituting for ϵ_x, ϵ_y and γ_{xy} their expressions (j) and (k), the total change in strain energy of the plate during bending can be represented in the following form:

$$V = \int\int\left[N_x\frac{\partial u}{\partial x} + N_y\frac{\partial v}{\partial y} + N_{xy}\left(\frac{\partial u}{\partial y} + \frac{\partial v}{\partial x}\right)\right]dx\,dy +$$
$$\frac{1}{2}\int\int\left[N_x\left(\frac{\partial w}{\partial x}\right)^2 + N_y\left(\frac{\partial w}{\partial y}\right)^2 + 2N_{xy}\frac{\partial w}{\partial x}\frac{\partial w}{\partial y}\right]dx\,dy +$$
$$\frac{1}{2}D\int\int\left\{\left(\frac{\partial^2 w}{\partial x^2} + \frac{\partial^2 w}{\partial y^2}\right)^2 - 2(1-\nu)\left[\frac{\partial^2 w}{\partial x^2}\frac{\partial^2 w}{\partial y^2} - \left(\frac{\partial^2 w}{\partial x\,\partial y}\right)^2\right]\right\}dx\,dy.$$
$$\tag{l}$$

It can be shown, integrating by parts, that the first integral on the right side represents the work done during bending by the forces acting in the middle plane of the plate. Taking a rectangular plate, as shown in Fig. 164a, we obtain

---

[1] We consider the angles $\partial w/\partial y$ and $\partial w/\partial x$ as very small.

$$\int_0^b \int_0^a \left[N_x \frac{\partial u}{\partial x} + N_y \frac{\partial v}{\partial y} + N_{xy}\left(\frac{\partial u}{\partial y} + \frac{\partial v}{\partial x}\right) \right] dx\, dy =$$

$$\int_0^b \left(\left| N_x u \right|_0^a + \left| N_{xy} v \right|_0^a \right) dy + \int_0^a \left(\left| N_y v \right|_0^b + \left| N_{xy} u \right|_0^b \right) dx -$$

$$\int_0^b \int_0^a u \left(\frac{\partial N_x}{\partial x} + \frac{\partial N_{xy}}{\partial y} \right) dx\, dy - \int_0^b \int_0^a v \left(\frac{\partial N_{xy}}{\partial x} + \frac{\partial N_y}{\partial y} \right) dx\, dy.$$

The first two integrals on the right side of this expression represent the work done by the forces applied at the boundary of the plate and acting in its middle plane. The last two integrals vanish if Eqs. (196) hold, *i.e.*, if there are no body forces acting in the middle plane of the plate. Otherwise these integrals represent the work of the body forces during bending of the plate [see Eqs. (196′)].

If the first integral of expression (*l*) represents the work of forces acting in the middle plane of the plate, then the rest of the same expression must be equal to the work produced by the load normal to the plate. Using notations T_h and T_v for the work of the above two systems of forces, expression (*l*) gives

$$T_h = \int \int \left[N_x \frac{\partial u}{\partial x} + N_y \frac{\partial v}{\partial y} + N_{xy}\left(\frac{\partial u}{\partial y} + \frac{\partial v}{\partial x}\right) \right] dx\, dy;$$

$$T_v = \frac{1}{2} \int \int \left[N_x \left(\frac{\partial w}{\partial x}\right)^2 + N_y \left(\frac{\partial w}{\partial y}\right)^2 + 2N_{xy}\frac{\partial w}{\partial x}\frac{\partial w}{\partial y} \right] dx\, dy +$$

$$\frac{1}{2} D \int \int \left\{ \left(\frac{\partial^2 w}{\partial x^2} + \frac{\partial^2 w}{\partial y^2}\right)^2 - 2(1 - \nu)\left[\frac{\partial^2 w}{\partial x^2}\frac{\partial^2 w}{\partial y^2} - \left(\frac{\partial^2 w}{\partial x\, \partial y}\right)^2 \right] \right\} dx\, dy.$$

$$(m)$$

In the case of small deflections which we are considering, the stretching of the middle plane of the plate is negligible and from expressions (*j*) and (*k*) we conclude

$$\frac{1}{2}\left(\frac{\partial w}{\partial x}\right)^2 = -\frac{\partial u}{\partial x}; \qquad \frac{1}{2}\left(\frac{\partial w}{\partial y}\right)^2 = -\frac{\partial v}{\partial y};$$

$$\frac{\partial w}{\partial x}\frac{\partial w}{\partial y} = -\frac{\partial u}{\partial y} - \frac{\partial v}{\partial x}.$$

From this it follows that the work of the forces acting in the middle plane of the plate can be represented in the following form:[1]

[1] The work of the forces acting in the middle plane of the plate was first used in this form by G. H. Bryan, *Proc. London Math. Soc.*, vol. 22, p. 54,

$$T_h = -\frac{1}{2} \int \int \left[N_x \left(\frac{\partial w}{\partial x}\right)^2 + N_y \left(\frac{\partial w}{\partial y}\right)^2 + 2N_{xy} \frac{\partial w}{\partial x} \frac{\partial w}{\partial y} \right] dx\,dy. \quad (201)$$

Then Eq. (m) becomes

$$T_v + T_h = \frac{1}{2} D \int \int \left\{ \left(\frac{\partial^2 w}{\partial x^2} + \frac{\partial^2 w}{\partial y^2}\right)^2 - 2(1-\nu) \left[\frac{\partial^2 w}{\partial x^2} \frac{\partial^2 w}{\partial y^2} - \left(\frac{\partial^2 w}{\partial x\,\partial y}\right)^2 \right] \right\} dx\,dy. \quad (202)$$

By using expression (202), together with the principle of virtual displacement, the deflections of the plate can be obtained in the same manner as in the case of beams (see Art. 7). Several examples of the application of this method will be discussed in the next two articles.

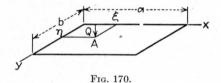

Fig. 170.

59. Deflections of Rectangular Plates with Simply Supported Edges.—In the case of a rectangular plate with simply supported edges (Fig. 170), the deflection surface can be represented by the double series

$$w = \sum_{m=1}^{\infty} \sum_{n=1}^{\infty} a_{mn} \sin \frac{m\pi x}{a} \sin \frac{n\pi y}{b}. \quad (203)$$

Each term of this series vanishes for $x = 0$, $x = a$ and also for $y = 0$, $y = b$. Hence the deflection w is zero along the boundary as is required. Calculating the derivatives $\partial^2 w/\partial x^2$ and $\partial^2 w/\partial y^2$, we find again that each term of the calculated series becomes zero at the boundary. From this it can be concluded that bending moments (185) are zero along the boundary as they should be in the case of simply supported edges (see p. 298). Thus expression (203) satisfies all boundary conditions. The expression for the potential energy of bending for this case is [Eq. (199)]

1891. Further discussion of this expression has been given by H. Reissner, *Z. angew. Math. Mech.*, vol. 5, p. 475, 1925.

$$V = \frac{1}{2}D \int_0^a \int_0^b \left\{ \left(\frac{\partial^2 w}{\partial x^2} + \frac{\partial^2 w}{\partial y^2} \right)^2 - 2(1 - \nu) \left[\frac{\partial^2 w}{\partial x^2} \frac{\partial^2 w}{\partial y^2} - \left(\frac{\partial^2 w}{\partial x \, \partial y} \right)^2 \right] \right\} dx \, dy.$$

Substituting for w expression (203), it can be shown that the integral of the term in the brackets vanishes and we obtain

$$V = \frac{1}{2}D \int_0^a \int_0^b \left\{ \sum_{m=1}^{\infty} \sum_{n=1}^{\infty} a_{mn} \left(\frac{m^2 \pi^2}{a^2} + \frac{n^2 \pi^2}{b^2} \right) \sin \frac{m\pi x}{a} \sin \frac{n\pi y}{b} \right\}^2 dx \, dy.$$

Only the squares of terms of the infinite series in the parenthesis give integrals different from zero (see p. 28). Then observing that

$$\int_0^a \int_0^b \sin^2 \frac{m\pi x}{a} \sin^2 \frac{n\pi y}{b} dx \, dy = \frac{ab}{4},$$

we obtain

$$V = \frac{ab}{8}D \sum_{m=1}^{\infty} \sum_{n=1}^{\infty} a^2_{mn} \left(\frac{m^2 \pi^2}{a^2} + \frac{n^2 \pi^2}{b^2} \right)^2. \tag{204}$$

Having this expression for V, the deflection of the plate for any kind of loading can be obtained by using the principle of virtual displacements exactly in the same manner as in the case of bending of beams (see Art. 7). Assume, for instance, that a concentrated force Q is acting at a point A with coordinates ξ and η (Fig. 170). To determine any coefficient a_{mn} of the series (203) in this case, we give to this coefficient a small increase δa_{mn}. The corresponding virtual deflection of the plate is

$$\delta a_{mn} \sin \frac{m\pi x}{a} \sin \frac{n\pi y}{b}.$$

The work done by the load Q during this displacement is

$$Q \delta a_{mn} \sin \frac{m\pi \xi}{a} \sin \frac{n\pi \eta}{b}$$

and from the principle of virtual displacements we obtain the following equation:

$$Q \delta a_{mn} \sin \frac{m\pi \xi}{a} \sin \frac{n\pi \eta}{b} = \frac{\partial V}{\partial a_{mn}} \delta a_{mn} = \frac{ab}{4} D a_{mn} \left(\frac{m^2 \pi^2}{a^2} + \frac{n^2 \pi^2}{b^2} \right)^2 \delta a_{mn},$$

$$\tag{a}$$

from which

$$a_{mn} = \frac{4Q \sin \dfrac{m\pi\xi}{a} \sin \dfrac{n\pi\eta}{b}}{abD\pi^4 \left(\dfrac{m^2}{a^2} + \dfrac{n^2}{b^2}\right)^2}. \tag{b}$$

Substituting this in expression (203), the deflection of the plate produced by a concentrated load Q is obtained.

Having this deflection and using the principle of superposition, the deflections for any kind of loading can be determined. Let us consider, as an example, the deflection produced by a load uniformly distributed over the surface of the plate. If q is the intensity of the load, $qd\xi d\eta$ will be the load acting on an elemental area $d\xi\, d\eta$ at point A. Substituting this load for Q in expression (b) and integrating it, we obtain the value of the coefficient a_{mn} for the case when the uniform load covers the entire plate

$$a_{mn} = \frac{4q}{abD\pi^4 \left(\dfrac{m^2}{a^2} + \dfrac{n^2}{b^2}\right)^2} \int_0^a \int_0^b \sin \frac{m\pi\xi}{a} \sin \frac{n\pi\eta}{b}\, d\xi\, d\eta =$$

$$\frac{16q}{\pi^6 Dmn} \frac{1}{\left(\dfrac{m^2}{a^2} + \dfrac{n^2}{b^2}\right)^2},$$

if m and n are both odd numbers. Otherwise $a_{mn} = 0$. Substituting these values of the coefficients in expression (203), the deflection surface for the uniform load becomes

$$w = \frac{16q}{\pi^6 D} \sum_{m=1,\,3,\,5,\,\cdots}^{\infty} \sum_{n=1,\,3,\,5,\,\cdots}^{\infty} \frac{1}{mn\left(\dfrac{m^2}{a^2} + \dfrac{n^2}{b^2}\right)^2} \sin \frac{m\pi x}{a} \sin \frac{n\pi y}{b}. \tag{c}$$

The deflection at the middle is obtained by substituting $x = a/2$, $y = b/2$. Then

$$(w)_{x=\frac{a}{2},\, y=\frac{b}{2}} = \frac{16q}{\pi^6 D} \sum_{m=1,\,3,\,5,\,\cdots}^{\infty} \sum_{n=1,\,3,\,5,\,\cdots}^{\infty} \frac{(-1)^{\frac{m+n-2}{2}}}{mn\left(\dfrac{m^2}{a^2} + \dfrac{n^2}{b^2}\right)^2}. \tag{d}$$

This is a rapidly converging series. In the case of a square plate, $a = b$, the summation of the series gives,[1] with $\nu = 0.3$,

[1] See "Strength of Materials," vol. 2, p. 507.

$$w_{\text{max.}} = 0.0443 \frac{qa^4}{Eh^3}.$$

By taking the first term of (d) only, we obtain, instead of the factor 0.0443 in the above expression, the factor 0.0454. Thus the error of the first approximation is less than 3 per cent.

If the plate of Fig. 170 is uniformly compressed in x direction, the same method as above can again be used in calculating deflections. It is necessary in applying the principle of virtual displacements to consider not only the work done by the transverse load but also the work done by the compressive forces. From Eq. (201), by assuming that the compressive force per unit length of the edges $x = 0$ and $x = a$ is equal to N_x, we obtain

$$T_h = \frac{1}{2} \int_0^a \int_0^b N_x \left(\frac{\partial w}{\partial x}\right)^2 dx\ dy$$

or, substituting for w its expression (203),

$$T_h = \frac{ab}{8} N_x \sum_{m=1}^{\infty} \sum_{n=1}^{\infty} a^2_{mn} \frac{m^2 \pi^2}{a^2}. \tag{e}$$

Giving to a coefficient a_{mn} an increase δa_{mn}, the corresponding work of the compressive forces is

$$\frac{\partial T_h}{\partial a_{mn}} \delta a_{mn} = \frac{\pi^2 b N_x}{4a} m^2 a_{mn}\ \delta a_{mn}.$$

Adding this work to the left side of Eq. (a), we find that, in the case of bending of the compressed plate by a concentrated force Q, the coefficients a_{mn} in the general expression (203) for deflection are determined from the following formula:

$$a_{mn} = \frac{4Q \sin \dfrac{m\pi \xi}{a} \sin \dfrac{n\pi \eta}{b}}{abD\pi^4 \left[\left(\dfrac{m^2}{a^2} + \dfrac{n^2}{b^2}\right)^2 - \dfrac{m^2 N_x}{\pi^2 a^2 D} \right]}. \tag{f}$$

Comparing this with the expression (b), it can be concluded that, owing to the compressive forces N_x, all the coefficients increase; hence deflections of a compressed plate are larger than those of the equally loaded identical plate without compression in the middle plane. It is seen also that by a gradual increase of compression we will arrive at a value of N_x for which one of the coefficients (f) becomes infinity. The smallest of these values of N_x is called the *critical value*. It is determined from the equation

$$\left(\frac{m^2}{a^2} + \frac{n^2}{b^2}\right)^2 - \frac{m^2 N_x}{\pi^2 a^2 D} = 0, \qquad (g)$$

from which

$$N_x = \frac{\pi^2 D}{a^2}\left(m + \frac{n^2}{m}\frac{a^2}{b^2}\right)^2. \qquad (h)$$

To get the *critical value* of N_x, i.e., the smallest value satisfying Eq. (g), it is necessary to take $n = 1$ and to take for m such an integer as to make the parenthesis in expression (h) a minimum. For instance, in the case of a square plate we must take $m = 1$ to make expression (h) a minimum. Then

$$N_{cr} = \frac{4\pi^2 D}{a^2}. \qquad (205)$$

This formula is analogous to Euler's formula for buckling of struts. Since N_{cr} is the compressive load for a strip of unit width and D is the flexural rigidity of such strip, it can be concluded that, owing to continuity of the plate, each longitudinal strip can carry a load four times larger than Euler's load for an isolated strip. The question of lateral buckling of compressed plates will be fully discussed in the next chapter.

In the above discussion it was assumed that compressive forces are acting on the plate. If, instead of compression, we have tensile forces N_x, the expression (f) for coefficients a_{mn} can be used again. It is only necessary to substitute in it $-N_x$ instead of N_x. It is seen that tensile forces decrease the deflection of the plate.

If there is a more general case, in which normal forces N_x and N_y and shearing forces N_{xy} are acting on the boundary of the plate, the same general method can be used in calculating deflections. There will be no difficulty in such calculations provided the forces are uniformly distributed along the edges of the plate. If the distribution is not uniform, there may be difficulty in solving the corresponding two-dimensional problem[1] and determining N_x, N_y and N_{xy} as functions of x and y. But if the two-dimensional problem is solved and the forces N_x, N_y and N_{xy} are determined, we can use the same expression (203) for the

---

[1] For two-dimensional problems see "Theory of Elasticity," Chap. 2.

deflection surface of the plate and can determine the coefficients a_{mn} by applying the principle of virtual displacements in exactly the same manner as is shown in the above example.

60. Bending of Plates with a Small Initial Curvature.[1]— Assume that a plate has some initial warp of the middle surface so that at any point there is initial deflection of the magnitude w_0, which is small in comparison with the thickness of the plate. If such a plate is submitted to the action of transverse loading, some additional deflection w_1 will be produced and the total deflection at any point of the middle surface of the plate will be $w_0 + w_1$. In calculating the deflection w_1 we use Eq. (187) derived before for flat plates. This procedure is justifiable if the initial deflection w_0 is small, since we may consider it as produced by some fictitious lateral load and can use the principle of superposition.[2]

If in addition to lateral load there are forces acting in the middle plane of the plate, the effect of these forces on bending depends not only on w_1 but also on w_0. To take this into account in using Eq. (197), we take on the right side of this equation the total deflection $w = w_0 + w_1$. The left side of the same equation is obtained from the expressions for bending moments and, since these moments depend not on the total curvature but only on the change in curvature of the plate, the deflection w_1, instead of w, should be used on that side. Hence Eq. (197) for the case of an initially curved plate becomes

$$\frac{\partial^4 w_1}{\partial x^4} + 2\frac{\partial^4 w_1}{\partial x^2 \, \partial y^2} + \frac{\partial^4 w_1}{\partial y^4} = \frac{1}{D}\Bigg[q + N_x \frac{\partial^2(w_0 + w_1)}{\partial x^2} +$$
$$N_y \frac{\partial^2(w_0 + w_1)}{\partial y^2} + 2N_{xy} \frac{\partial^2(w_0 + w_1)}{\partial x \, \partial y} \Bigg]. \quad (206)$$

It is seen that the effect of an initial curvature on deflection is equivalent to the effect of a fictitious lateral load of the intensity

$$N_x \frac{\partial^2 w_0}{\partial x^2} + N_y \frac{\partial^2 w_0}{\partial y^2} + 2N_{xy} \frac{\partial^2 w_0}{\partial x \, \partial y}.$$

Thus a plate will undergo bending under the action of forces in the xy-plane alone provided there is an initial curvature.

---

[1] See writer's paper in *Memoirs of the Institute of Ways of Communication*, St. Petersburg, vol. 89, 1915 (Russian).

[2] In the case of large deflections the magnitude of deflections is no longer proportional to the load and the principle of superposition is not applicable.

Take as an example the case of a simply supported rectangular plate (Fig. 170) and assume that the initial deflection of the plate is defined by the equation

$$w_0 = a_{11} \sin \frac{\pi x}{a} \sin \frac{\pi y}{b}. \tag{a}$$

If on the edges $x = 0$ and $x = a$ of this plate uniformly distributed compressive forces N_x are acting, Eq. (206) becomes

$$\frac{\partial^4 w_1}{\partial x^4} + 2 \frac{\partial^4 w_1}{\partial x^2 \, \partial y^2} + \frac{\partial^4 w_1}{\partial y^4} =$$
$$\frac{1}{D}\left(N_x \frac{a_{11}\pi^2}{a^2} \sin \frac{\pi x}{a} \sin \frac{\pi y}{b} - N_x \frac{\partial^2 w_1}{\partial x^2} \right). \tag{b}$$

Let us take the solution of this equation in the form

$$w_1 = A \sin \frac{\pi x}{a} \sin \frac{\pi y}{b}. \tag{c}$$

Substituting this value of w_1 in Eq. (b), we obtain

$$A = \frac{a_{11}N_x}{\dfrac{\pi^2 D}{a^2}\left(1 + \dfrac{a^2}{b^2}\right)^2 - N_x}$$

With this value of A expression (c) gives the deflection of the plate produced by compressive forces N_x. Adding this deflection to the initial deflection (a), we obtain for the total deflection of the plate the following expression:

$$w = w_0 + w_1 = \frac{a_{11}}{1 - \alpha} \sin \frac{\pi x}{a} \sin \frac{\pi y}{b}, \tag{d}$$

in which

$$\alpha = \frac{N_x}{\dfrac{\pi^2 D}{a^2}\left(1 + \dfrac{a^2}{b^2}\right)^2}. \tag{e}$$

The maximum deflection will be at the center and we obtain

$$w_{\text{max.}} = \frac{a_{11}}{1 - \alpha}. \tag{f}$$

This formula is analogous to formula (46) (see p. 29) derived for the deflection of an initially curved beam.

In a more general case we can take the initial deflection surface of the rectangular plate in the form of the following series:

$$w_0 = \sum_{m=1}^{\infty} \sum_{n=1}^{\infty} a_{mn} \sin \frac{m\pi x}{a} \sin \frac{n\pi y}{b}. \tag{g}$$

Substituting this series in Eq. (206), we find that the additional deflection of any point of the plate is

$$w_1 = \sum_{m=1}^{\infty} \sum_{n=1}^{\infty} b_{mn} \sin \frac{m\pi x}{a} \sin \frac{n\pi y}{b}, \tag{h}$$

in which

$$b_{mn} = \frac{a_{mn} N_x}{\dfrac{\pi^2 D}{a^2}\left(m + \dfrac{n^2}{m}\dfrac{a^2}{b^2}\right)^2 - N_x}. \tag{i}$$

It is seen that all coefficients b_{mn} increase with the increase of N_x; when N_x approaches the critical value, the term in the series (h) which corresponds to the shape of lateral buckling of the plate [see Eq. (h) of Art. 59] obtains the preponderant value. We have here a complete analogy with the case of bending of initially curved compressed bars (see Art. 8). Hence, in experimental determinations of critical values of compressive forces, the method recommended by Southwell (see p. 177) can be used.

The problem can be handled in the same manner if, instead of compression, we have tension in the middle plane of the plate. In such case it will be necessary only to change the sign of N_x in the previous equations. Without any difficulty we can obtain the deflection also in the case when there are not only forces N_x but also forces N_y and N_{xy} uniformly distributed along the edges of the plate.

61. Large Deflection of Plates.—If the deflection of a plate is not small, the assumption regarding the inextensibility of the middle surface of the plate holds only if the deflection surface is a *developable* surface. In the general case large deflections of a plate are accompanied by some stretching of the middle surface. To give some idea regarding the magnitude of stresses due to this stretching, it can be mentioned that in the case of pure bending of a circular plate for the maximum deflection equal to $0.6h$ the maximum stress due to stretching of the middle plane is about 18 per cent of the maximum bending stress.[1] For a uniformly loaded circular plate with clamped edges and with maximum deflection equal to h, the maximum

[1] See writer's paper in Memoirs of the Institute of Ways of Communication, vol. 89, 1915.

stress due to stretching is about 23 per cent of the maximum bending stress calculated by neglecting stretching.[1] Thus, in these cases, it is only for small deflections, not exceeding, say, $0.4h$, that the stretching of the middle surface can be neglected without a substantial error in the magnitude of maximum stresses.

In considering large deflection[2] of plates, we can continue to use Eq. (197), derived from the condition of equilibrium of an element in the direction normal to the plate, but the forces N_x, N_y and N_{xy} depend now, not only on the external forces applied in the xy-plane, but also on the stretching of the middle surface of the plate due to bending. Assuming that there are no body forces in the xy-plane, the equations of equilibrium in this plane are [see Eqs. (196)]

$$\left. \begin{aligned} \frac{\partial N_x}{\partial x} + \frac{\partial N_{xy}}{\partial y} &= 0; \\ \frac{\partial N_y}{\partial y} + \frac{\partial N_{xy}}{\partial x} &= 0. \end{aligned} \right\} \tag{a}$$

The third equation for determining N_x, N_y and N_{xy} will be obtained from the consideration of strain in the middle surface of the plate during bending. The corresponding strain components are (see pp. 311 and 312)

$$\left. \begin{aligned} \epsilon_x &= \frac{\partial u}{\partial x} + \frac{1}{2}\left(\frac{\partial w}{\partial x}\right)^2; \\ \epsilon_y &= \frac{\partial v}{\partial y} + \frac{1}{2}\left(\frac{\partial w}{\partial y}\right)^2; \\ \gamma_{xy} &= \frac{\partial u}{\partial y} + \frac{\partial v}{\partial x} + \frac{\partial w}{\partial x}\frac{\partial w}{\partial y}. \end{aligned} \right\} \tag{b}$$

By differentiating these expressions, it can be shown that

$$\frac{\partial^2 \epsilon_x}{\partial y^2} + \frac{\partial^2 \epsilon_y}{\partial x^2} - \frac{\partial^2 \gamma_{xy}}{\partial x\,\partial y} = \left(\frac{\partial^2 w}{\partial x\,\partial y}\right)^2 - \frac{\partial^2 w}{\partial x^2}\frac{\partial^2 w}{\partial y^2}. \tag{c}$$

By substituting for the strain components their expressions in terms of the stresses, the third equation in terms of N_x, N_y and N_{xy} is obtained.

The solution of these three equations can be greatly simplified by introducing a *stress function*.[3] It is seen that Eqs. (a) are identically satisfied by taking

$$N_x = h\frac{\partial^2 F}{\partial y^2}; \qquad N_y = h\frac{\partial^2 F}{\partial x^2}; \qquad N_{xy} = -h\frac{\partial^2 F}{\partial x\,\partial y}, \tag{d}$$

where F is a function of x and y.

---

[1] WAY, STEWART, *Trans. Am. Soc. Mech. Eng.*, 1934, p. 627.

[2] That is, deflections which are no longer small in comparison with the thickness, but which are at the same time small enough to justify the application of simplified formulas for curvatures of a plate (see p. 289).

[3] See "Theory of Elasticity," p. 24.

With these expressions for forces, the strain components become

$$\epsilon_x = \frac{1}{hE}(N_x - \nu N_y) = \frac{1}{E}\left(\frac{\partial^2 F}{\partial y^2} - \nu\frac{\partial^2 F}{\partial x^2}\right);$$
$$\epsilon_y = \frac{1}{hE}(N_y - \nu N_x) = \frac{1}{E}\left(\frac{\partial^2 F}{\partial x^2} - \nu\frac{\partial^2 F}{\partial y^2}\right); \qquad (e)$$
$$\gamma_{xy} = \frac{1}{hG}N_{xy} = -\frac{2(1 + \nu)}{E}\frac{\partial^2 F}{\partial x\,\partial y}.$$

Substituting these expressions in Eq. (c), we obtain

$$\frac{\partial^4 F}{\partial x^4} + 2\frac{\partial^4 F}{\partial x^2\,\partial y^2} + \frac{\partial^4 F}{\partial y^4} = E\left[\left(\frac{\partial^2 w}{\partial x\,\partial y}\right)^2 - \frac{\partial^2 w}{\partial x^2}\frac{\partial^2 w}{\partial y^2}\right]. \qquad (207)$$

By using expressions (d), Eq. (197) becomes

$$\frac{\partial^4 w}{\partial x^4} + 2\frac{\partial^4 w}{\partial x^2\,\partial y^2} + \frac{\partial^4 w}{\partial y^4} = \frac{h}{D}\left(\frac{q}{h} + \frac{\partial^2 F}{\partial y^2}\frac{\partial^2 w}{\partial x^2} + \frac{\partial^2 F}{\partial x^2}\frac{\partial^2 w}{\partial y^2} - 2\frac{\partial^2 F}{\partial x\,\partial y}\frac{\partial^2 w}{\partial x\,\partial y}\right). \qquad (208)$$

Equations (207) and (208), together with boundary conditions, determine the two functions F and w.[1] Having the stress function F, we determine the stresses in the middle surface of a plate by using Eqs. (d). From the function w, defining the deflection surface of the plate, the bending and shearing stresses are obtained by using the same formulas as in the case of plates with small deflections (see Art. 56). Thus the investigation of large deflection of plates reduces to the solution of the two Eqs. (207) and (208). Some approximate solutions of these equations have been obtained only for simplest cases, namely, for uniformly loaded long rectangular plates and for uniformly loaded circular plates.

[1] These two equations for large deflections of plates were derived by Th. v. Kármán, "Encyklopädie der Mathematischen Wissenschaften," vol. IV₄, p. 349, 1910.

CHAPTER VII

BUCKLING OF THIN PLATES

62. Methods of Calculation of Critical Loads.—In calculating *critical values* of forces applied in the middle plane of a plate at which the flat form of equilibrium becomes unstable and the plate begins to buckle, the same methods as in the case of compressed bars can be used.

From the discussion of the previous chapter (see Arts. 59 and 60) it may be seen that the critical values of the forces acting in the middle plane of a plate can be obtained by assuming that from the beginning the plate has some initial curvature or some lateral loading. Then those values of the forces in the middle plane at which deflections tend to become infinitely large are usually the critical values.

Another way of investigating such stability problems is to assume that the plate buckles slightly under the action of forces applied in its middle plane and then to calculate the magnitudes that the forces must have in order to keep the plate in such a slightly buckled shape. The differential equation of the deflection surface in this case is obtained from Eq. (197) by putting $q = 0$, *i.e.*, by assuming that there is no lateral load. If there are no body forces,[1] the equation for the buckled plate then becomes

$$\frac{\partial^4 w}{\partial x^4} + 2\frac{\partial^4 w}{\partial x^2\,\partial y^2} + \frac{\partial^4 w}{\partial y^4} =$$
$$\frac{1}{D}\left(N_x\frac{\partial^2 w}{\partial x^2} + N_y\frac{\partial^2 w}{\partial y^2} + 2N_{xy}\frac{\partial^2 w}{\partial x\,\partial y}\right). \quad (209)$$

The simplest case is obtained when the forces N_x, N_y and N_{xy} are constant throughout the plate. Assuming that there are given ratios between these forces so that $N_y = \alpha N_x$ and $N_{xy} = \beta N_x$, and solving Eq. (209) for the given boundary

---

[1] In the case of body forces acting in the middle plane of the plate, Eq. (197′) must be used.

conditions, we will find that the assumed buckling of the plate is possible only for certain definite values of N_x. The smallest of these values determines the desired critical value.

If the forces N_x, N_y and N_{xy} are not constant, the problem becomes more complicated, since Eq. (209) has in this case variable coefficients, but the general conclusion remains the same. In such cases we can assume that the expressions for the forces N_x, N_y and N_{xy} have a common factor γ, so that a gradual increase of loading is obtained by an increase of this factor. From the investigation of Eq. (209), together with the given boundary conditions, it will be concluded that curved forms of equilibrium are possible only for certain values of the factor γ and that the smallest of these values will define the critical loading.

The energy method also can be used in investigating buckling of plates. This method is especially useful in those cases where a rigorous solution of Eq. (209) is unknown and where it is required to find only an approximate value of the critical load. In applying this method we proceed as in the case of buckling of bars (see Art. 14) and assume that the plate, which is stressed by forces acting in its middle plane, undergoes some small lateral bending consistent with given boundary conditions. Such limited bending can be produced without stretching of the middle plane and we need consider only the energy of bending and the corresponding work done by the forces acting in the middle plane of the plate. If the work done by these forces is smaller than the strain energy of bending for every possible shape of lateral buckling, the flat form of equilibrium of the plate is stable. If the same work becomes larger than the energy of bending for any shape of lateral deflection, the plate is unstable and buckling occurs. Denoting by ΔT_h the above-mentioned work of external forces and by ΔV the energy of bending, the critical values of forces are found from the equation

$$\Delta T_h = \Delta V. \qquad (a)$$

Substituting for the work ΔT_h expression (201) and for ΔV expression (199), we obtain

$$-\frac{1}{2}\int\int\left[N_x\left(\frac{\partial w}{\partial x}\right)^2 + N_y\left(\frac{\partial w}{\partial y}\right)^2 + 2N_{xy}\frac{\partial w}{\partial x}\frac{\partial w}{\partial y}\right]dx\,dy =$$
$$\frac{D}{2}\int\int\left\{\left(\frac{\partial^2 w}{\partial x^2} + \frac{\partial^2 w}{\partial y^2}\right)^2 - 2(1-\nu)\left[\frac{\partial^2 w}{\partial x^2}\frac{\partial^2 w}{\partial y^2} - \left(\frac{\partial^2 w}{\partial x\,\partial y}\right)^2\right]\right\}dx\,dy. \qquad (210)$$

Assuming that forces N_x, N_y and N_{xy} are represented by certain expressions with a common factor γ, so that

$$N_x = \gamma N'_x; \qquad N_y = \gamma N'_y; \qquad N_{xy} = \gamma N'_{xy}, \tag{b}$$

a simultaneous increase of these forces is obtained by increasing γ. The critical value of this factor is then obtained from Eq. (210), from which

$$\gamma = -\frac{D\iint\left\{\left(\frac{\partial^2 w}{\partial x^2}+\frac{\partial^2 w}{\partial y^2}\right)^2 -2(1-\nu)\left[\frac{\partial^2 w}{\partial x^2}\frac{\partial^2 w}{\partial y^2}-\left(\frac{\partial^2 w}{\partial x\,\partial y}\right)^2\right]\right\}dx\,dy}{\iint\left[N'_x\left(\frac{\partial w}{\partial x}\right)^2+N'_y\left(\frac{\partial w}{\partial y}\right)^2+2N'_{xy}\frac{\partial w}{\partial x}\frac{\partial w}{\partial y}\right]dx\,dy}. \tag{211}$$

For the calculation of γ it is necessary to find, in each particular case, an expression for w which satisfies the given boundary conditions and makes expression (211) a minimum, *i.e.*, the variation of the fraction (211) must be zero. Denoting the numerator by I_1 and the denominator by I_2, the variation of expression (211) is

$$\delta\gamma = -\frac{(I_2\delta I_1 - I_1\delta I_2)}{I^2_2},$$

which, when equated to zero, gives

$$\frac{1}{I_2}(\delta I_1 - \gamma\delta I_2) = 0. \tag{c}$$

By calculating the indicated variations and assuming that there are no body forces, we will arrive at Eq. (209). Thus the energy method brings us in this way to the integration of the same equation, which we have discussed before.

For an approximate calculation of critical loads by the energy method, we will proceed as in the case of struts (see p. 82) and assume w in the form of a series

$$w = a_1f_1(xy) + a_2f_2(xy) + \cdots , \tag{d}$$

in which the functions $f_1(xy)$, $f_2(xy)$ . . . satisfy the boundary conditions for w and are chosen so as to be suitable for the representation of the buckled surface of the plate. In each particular case we will be guided in choosing these functions by experimental data regarding the shape of a buckled plate. The coefficients a_1, a_2, . . . of the series must now be chosen so as to make the expression (211) a minimum. Using this condition of minimum and proceeding as in the derivation of Eq. (c) above, we obtain the following equations:

$$\left.\begin{aligned}
\frac{\partial I_1}{\partial a_1} - \gamma\frac{\partial I_2}{\partial a_1} &= 0; \\
\frac{\partial I_1}{\partial a_2} - \gamma\frac{\partial I_2}{\partial a_2} &= 0; \\
\cdots\cdots\cdots\cdots \\
\cdots\cdots\cdots\cdots
\end{aligned}\right\} \tag{212}$$

It may be seen from Eq. (211) that expressions for I_1 and I_2, after integration, will be represented by homogeneous functions of second degree in terms of

$a_1, a_2, \ldots$ Hence Eqs. (212) will be a system of homogeneous linear equations in $a_1, a_2, \ldots$ Such equations may yield for $a_1, a_2, \ldots$ solutions different from zero only if the determinant of these equations is zero. Putting this determinant equal to zero, an equation for determining the critical value for γ will be obtained. This method of calculation of critical loads will be illustrated by several examples in the following articles.

63. Buckling of Simply Supported Rectangular Plates Uniformly Compressed in One Direction.[1]—Assume that a rectangular plate (Fig. 171) is compressed in its middle plane by forces uniformly distributed along the sides $x = 0$ and $x = a$.

Let the magnitude of this compressive force per unit length of edge be denoted by N_x. By gradually increasing N_x we arrive at the condition where the flat form of equilibrium of the compressed plate becomes unstable and buckling occurs. The cor-

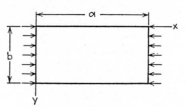

Fig. 171.

responding critical value of the compressive force can be found in this case from a consideration of the energy of the system. The deflection surface of the buckled plate can be represented, in the case of simply supported edges, by the double series (203) (see p. 314)

$$w = \sum_{m=1}^{\infty} \sum_{n=1}^{\infty} a_{mn} \sin \frac{m\pi x}{a} \sin \frac{n\pi y}{b}. \qquad (a)$$

The strain energy of bending in this case, from expression (204), is

$$\Delta V = \frac{\pi^4 ab}{8} D \sum_{m=1}^{\infty} \sum_{n=1}^{\infty} a^2{}_{mn} \left(\frac{m^2}{a^2} + \frac{n^2}{b^2} \right)^2. \qquad (b)$$

The work done by compressive forces during buckling of the plate, from Eq. (201) and Eq. (*e*) (p. 317), will be

$$\frac{1}{2} N_x \int_0^a \int_0^b \left(\frac{\partial w}{\partial x} \right)^2 dx \, dy = \frac{\pi^2 b}{8a} N_x \sum_{m=1}^{\infty} \sum_{n=1}^{\infty} m^2 a^2{}_{mn}. \qquad (c)$$

[1] Solution of this problem was given by G. H. Bryan, *Proc. London Math. Soc.*, vol. 22, p. 54, 1891.

Thus Eq. (210), for determining the critical value of compressive forces, becomes

$$\frac{\pi^2 b}{8a} N_x \sum_{m=1}^{\infty} \sum_{n=1}^{\infty} m^2 a^2{}_{mn} = \frac{\pi^4 ab}{8} D \sum_{m=1}^{\infty} \sum_{n=1}^{\infty} a^2{}_{mn} \left(\frac{m^2}{a^2} + \frac{n^2}{b^2}\right)^2,$$

from which

$$N_x = \frac{\pi^2 a^2 D \sum_{m=1}^{\infty} \sum_{n=1}^{\infty} a^2{}_{mn} \left(\dfrac{m^2}{a^2} + \dfrac{n^2}{b^2}\right)^2}{\sum_{m=1}^{\infty} \sum_{n=1}^{\infty} m^2 a^2{}_{mn}}. \qquad (d)$$

By the same reasoning as in the case of compressed bars (see p. 83) it can be shown that expression (d) becomes a minimum if all coefficients a_{mn}, except one, are taken equal to zero. Then

$$N_x = \frac{\pi^2 a^2 D}{m^2} \left(\frac{m^2}{a^2} + \frac{n^2}{b^2}\right)^2.$$

It is obvious that the smallest value of N_x will be obtained by taking n equal to 1. The physical meaning of this is that a plate buckles in such a way that there can be several half-waves in the direction of compression but only one half-wave in the perpendicular direction. Thus the expression for the critical value of the compressive force becomes

$$(N_x)_{cr} = \frac{\pi^2 D}{a^2} \left(m + \frac{1}{m} \frac{a^2}{b^2}\right)^2. \qquad (e)$$

The first factor in this expression represents the Euler load for a strip of unit width and of length a. The second factor indicates in what proportion the stability of the continuous plate is greater than the stability of an isolated strip. The magnitude of this factor depends on the magnitude of the ratio a/b and also on the number m, which gives the number of half-waves into which the plate buckles. If a is smaller than b, the second term in the parenthesis of expression (e) is always smaller than the first and the minimum value of the expression is obtained by taking $m = 1$, *i.e.*, by assuming that the plate buckles in one half-wave and that the deflection surface has the form

$$w = a_{11} \sin \frac{\pi x}{a} \sin \frac{\pi y}{b}. \qquad (f)$$

The maximum deflection a_{11} remains indefinite provided we consider it small and neglect stretching of the middle plane of the plate during buckling. The method of calculation of this deflection when it is not small will be discussed later (see Art. 72).

The critical load, with $m = 1$, in expression (e), can be finally represented in the following form

$$(N_x)_{cr} = \frac{\pi^2 D}{b^2} \left(\frac{b}{a} + \frac{a}{b} \right)^2. \qquad (g)$$

If we keep the width of the plate constant and gradually change the length a, the factor before the parenthesis in expression (g) remains constant and the factor in parenthesis changes with the change of the ratio a/b. It may be seen that this factor acquires its minimum value when $a = b$, i.e., for a plate of a given width the critical value of the load is the smallest if the plate is square. In this case

$$(N_x)_{cr} = \frac{4\pi^2 D}{b^2}. \qquad (h)$$

This is the same result obtained before (see p. 318) in considering the simultaneous action on a plate of both bending and compression. For other proportions of the plate the expression (g) can be represented in the form

$$(N_x)_{cr} = k \frac{\pi^2 D}{b^2}, \qquad (213)$$

in which k is a numerical factor, the magnitude of which depends on the ratio a/b. This factor is represented in Fig. 172 by the curve marked $m = 1$. We see that it is large for small values of a/b and decreases as a/b increases, becoming a minimum for $a = b$ and then increasing again.

Let us assume now that the plate buckles into two half-waves and that the deflection surface is represented by the expression

$$w = a_{21} \sin \frac{2\pi x}{a} \sin \frac{\pi y}{b}.$$

We have an inflection line dividing the plate in halves and each half is in exactly the same condition as a simply supported plate of length $a/2$. For calculating the critical load we can again use Eq. (g) by substituting in it $a/2$ instead of a. Then

$$(N_x)_{cr} = \frac{\pi^2 D}{b^2}\left(\frac{2b}{a} + \frac{a}{2b}\right)^2.\qquad (i)$$

The second factor in this expression, depending on the ratio a/b, is represented in Fig. 172 by the curve $m = 2$. It may be seen that the curve $m = 2$ is readily obtained from the curve $m = 1$ by keeping the ordinates unchanged and doubling the abscissas. Proceeding further in the same way and assuming

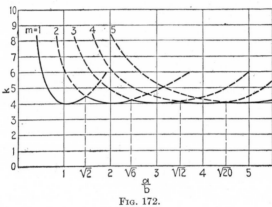

Fig. 172.

$m = 3$, $m = 4$ and so on, we obtain the series of curves shown in Fig. 172. Having these curves, the critical load and the number of half-waves for any value of the ratio a/b can be easily determined. It is only necessary to take the corresponding point on the axis of abscissas and to choose the curve having the smallest ordinate for that point. In Fig. 172 the portions of the curves defining the critical values of the load are shown by full lines. It is seen that for very short plates the curve $m = 1$ gives the smallest ordinates, *i.e.*, the smallest values of k in Eq. (213). Beginning with the point of intersection of the curves $m = 1$ and $m = 2$, the second curve has the smallest ordinates, *i.e.*, the plate buckles into two half-waves and this holds up to the point of intersection of the curves $m = 2$ and $m = 3$. Beginning from this point, the plate buckles in three half-waves, and so on. The transition from m to $m + 1$ half-waves evidently occurs when the two corresponding curves in Fig. 172 have equal ordinates, *i.e.*, when

$$\frac{mb}{a} + \frac{a}{mb} = \frac{(m+1)b}{a} + \frac{a}{(m+1)b}.$$

From this equation we obtain

$$\frac{a}{b} = \sqrt{m(m+1)}. \qquad (j)$$

Substituting $m = 1$, we obtain

$$\frac{a}{b} = \sqrt{2} = 1.41.$$

At this ratio we have transition from one to two half-waves. By taking $m = 2$ we find that transition from two or three half-waves occurs when

$$\frac{a}{b} = \sqrt{6} = 2.45.$$

It is seen that the number of half-waves increases with the ratio a/b, and for very long plates m is a large number. Then, from (j), we obtain

$$\frac{a}{b} \approx m,$$

i.e., a very long plate buckles in half-waves, the lengths of which approach the width of the plate. Thus a buckled plate subdivides approximately into squares.

After the number of half-waves m in which a plate buckles has been determined from Fig. 172 or from Eq. (j), the critical load is calculated from Eq. (g). It is only necessary to substitute in Eq. (g) the length a/m of one half-wave, instead of a.

To simplify this calculation, Table 31 can be used; the values of the factor k in Eq. (213) are given for various values of the ratio a/b.

From Eq. (213) the critical value of the compressive stress is

$$\sigma_{cr} = \frac{(N_x)_{cr}}{h} = \frac{k\pi^2 E}{12(1 - \nu^2)}\frac{h^2}{b^2}. \qquad (214)$$

For a given ratio a/b the coefficient k is constant, and σ_{cr} is proportional to the modulus of the material and to the square of the ratio h/b. In the third line of Table 31 the critical stresses are given for steel plates, assuming $E = 30 \cdot 10^6$ lb. per square inch, $\nu = 0.3$ and $h/b = 0.01$. For any other material with a modulus

TABLE 31.—VALUES OF FACTOR k IN EQ. (213) FOR UNIFORMLY COMPRESSED, SIMPLY SUPPORTED RECTANGULAR PLATES AND σ_{cr} IN POUNDS PER SQUARE INCH FOR $E = 30 \cdot 10^6$ POUNDS PER SQUARE INCH, $b/h = 100$, $\nu = 0.3$

a/b	0.2	0.3	0.4	0.5	0.6	0.7	0.8
k	27.0	13.2	8.41	6.25	5.14	4.53	4.20
σ_{cr}	73,200	35,800	22,800	16,900	13,900	12,300	11,400
a/b	0.9	1.0	1.1	1.2	1.3	1.4	1.41
k	4.04	4.00	4.04	4.13	4.28	4.47	4.49
σ_{cr}	11,000	10,800	11,000	11,200	11,600	12,100	12,200

E_1 and any other value of the ratio h/b, the critical stress is obtained by multiplying the values in the table by the factor[1]

$$\frac{E_1}{30 \cdot 10^2} \left(\frac{h}{b}\right)^2.$$

Comparing steel and duralumin plates of the same dimensions a and b, it is interesting to note that for the same weight the duralumin plate will be about three times thicker than the steel plate; since the modulus of elasticity of duralumin is about one-third that of steel, it can be concluded from Eq. (214) that the critical stress for the duralumin plate will be about three times larger and the critical load about nine times larger than for a steel plate of the same weight. From this comparison it may be seen how important is the use of light aluminum alloy sheets in such structures as airplanes where the weight of the structure is of primary importance.

The critical values of σ_x, calculated by the use of Table 31, represent the true critical stresses provided they are below the proportional limit of the material. Above this limit formula (214) gives an exaggerated value for σ_{cr} and the true value of this stress can be obtained only by taking into consideration the plastic deformation of the material (see Art. 71). In each particular case, assuming that formula (214) is accurate enough up to the yield point of the material, the limiting value of the ratio h/b, up to which formula (214) can be applied, is obtained by substituting in it $\sigma_{cr} = \sigma_{Y.P.}$. Taking, for instance, steel

[1] It is assumed that Poisson's ratio ν can be considered as a constant.

for which $\sigma_{\text{Y.P.}} = 40,000$ lb. per square inch, $E = 30 \cdot 10^6$ lb. per square inch and $\nu = 0.3$ and assuming that the plate is long enough so that $k \approx 4$, we find from Eq. (214) that $b/h \approx 52$.

Below this value of the ratio b/h the material begins to yield before the critical stress given by formula (214) is obtained.

The edge conditions assumed in the problem discussed above are realized in the case of uniform compression of a thin tube of square cross section (Fig. 173). When compressive

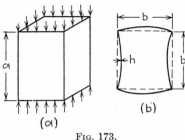

Fig. 173.

stresses become equal to their critical value (214), buckling begins and the cross sections of the tube become curved as shown in Fig. 173*b*. There will be no bending moments acting between the sides of the buckled tube along the corners and each side is in the con-

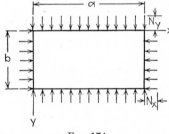

Fig. 174.

dition of a compressed rectangular plate with simply supported edges.

64. Buckling of Simply Supported Rectangular Plates Compressed in Two Perpendicular Directions.—If a rectangular plate (Fig. 174) with simply supported edges is submitted to the action of uniformly distributed compressive forces N_x and N_y, the same expression for the deflection w can be used as in the previous article, and it can be proved again that only one term in the double series for w should be considered in calculating the critical values of N_x and N_y. Applying the energy method, Eq. (210) then becomes

$$N_x \frac{m^2\pi^2}{a^2} + N_y \frac{n^2\pi^2}{b^2} = D\left(\frac{m^2\pi^2}{a^2} + \frac{n^2\pi^2}{b^2}\right)^2, \tag{a}$$

in which m determines the number of half-waves in the x direction and n the number in the y-direction. Dividing Eq. (a) by the thickness of the plate and introducing the notation

$$\frac{\pi^2 D}{a^2 h} = \sigma_e, \tag{b}$$

we obtain

$$\sigma_x m^2 + \sigma_y n^2 \frac{a^2}{b^2} = \sigma_e\left(m^2 + n^2 \frac{a^2}{b^2}\right)^2. \tag{c}$$

Taking any integer for m and n, the corresponding deflection surface of the buckled plate is given by the equation

$$w_{mn} = a_{mn} \sin \frac{m\pi x}{a} \sin \frac{n\pi y}{b}$$

and the corresponding values of σ_x and σ_y are such as to satisfy Eq. (c). Taking σ_x and σ_y as rectangular coordinates, Eq. (c) will be represented by a straight line. Several lines of this kind for various values of m and n and for the case of a square plate $(a = b)$ are shown in Fig. 175. The values of m and n are indicated on these lines and positive values of σ_x and σ_y indicate compressive stresses. Since we seek the smallest values of σ_x and σ_y at

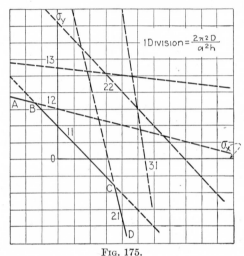

Fig. 175.

which buckling may occur, we need to consider only the portions of the straight lines shown in the figure by full lines and forming the polygon $ABCD$. By preparing a figure analogous to Fig. 175 for any given ratio a/b, the corresponding critical values of σ_x and σ_y can be obtained from that figure. It may be seen that the point of intersection of the line BC with the axis of abscissas gives the critical value of σ_x for the case where $\sigma_y = 0$, discussed in the previous article. The intersection of the same line with the vertical axis gives $(\sigma_y)_{cr}$, when $\sigma_x = 0$.

When $\sigma_x = \sigma_y = \sigma$, we draw through the origin 0 a line which makes an angle of 45° with the horizontal axis. Then the intersection of this line with the line BC determines the critical value of σ in this case.

Equation (c) in this case becomes

$$\sigma = \sigma_e\left(m^2 + n^2\frac{a^2}{b^2}\right).$$

The smallest value of σ is obtained by taking $m = n = 1$. Hence

$$\sigma_{cr} = \sigma_e\left(1 + \frac{a^2}{b^2}\right). \tag{215}$$

In the particular case of a square plate

$$\sigma_{cr} = 2\sigma_e,$$

i.e., the critical stress in this case is just half that for the case of compression of a square plate in one direction only.

For any value of σ_x the critical value of σ_y is obtained by drawing a vertical line through the corresponding point on the axis of abscissas. The ordinate of the point of intersection of this line with the polygon $ABCD$ (Fig. 175) gives the value of $(\sigma_y)_{cr}$. If, in the case of a square plate, σ_x is larger than $4\sigma_e$, $(\sigma_y)_{cr}$ becomes negative. This shows that the plate can stand a compressive stress larger than the critical value for the case of simple compression (Art. 63), provided an adequate tensile stress acts in the perpendicular direction.

In practical applications of Eq. (*c*) it is advantageous to know the coordinates of such points as B and C in Fig. 175 representing the apexes of the polygon $ABCD$. The largest value of σ_x up to which we can use the line $BC(m = 1, n = 1)$ in determining the critical value of σ_y is defined by the abscissa of the point C, which is the point of intersection of the lines 11 and 21. Equations of these lines, by using Eq. (*c*), are

$$\sigma_x + \sigma_y \frac{a^2}{b^2} = \sigma_e\left(1 + \frac{a^2}{b^2}\right)^2, \qquad m = 1, \qquad n = 1;$$

$$4\sigma_x + \sigma_y \frac{a^2}{b^2} = \sigma_e\left(4 + \frac{a^2}{b^2}\right)^2, \qquad m = 2, \qquad n = 1.$$

Solving these equations, the upper limit for σ_x, up to which the line 11 can be used, is

$$\sigma_x = \sigma_e\left(5 + 2\frac{a^2}{b^2}\right). \qquad (d)$$

In the same manner the lower limit for σ_x is obtained from equations

$$\sigma_x + \sigma_y \frac{a^2}{b^2} = \sigma_e\left(1 + \frac{a^2}{b^2}\right)^2, \qquad m = 1, \qquad n = 1;$$

$$\sigma_x + 4\sigma_y \frac{a^2}{b^2} = \sigma_e\left(1 + \frac{4a^2}{b^2}\right)^2, \qquad m = 1, \qquad n = 2,$$

from which

$$\sigma_x = \sigma_e\left(1 - 4\frac{a^4}{b^4}\right). \qquad (e)$$

Hence the line $m = 1, n = 1$ should be used in calculating $(\sigma_y)_{cr}$ if the following inequality for σ_x holds:

$$\sigma_e\left(1 - 4\frac{a^4}{b^4}\right) < \sigma_x < \sigma_e\left(5 + 2\frac{a^2}{b^2}\right). \qquad (f)$$

Let us take $a = 0.5b$ and $\sigma_x = \sigma_e$ and determine the corresponding critical value of σ_y. Substituting $a/b = 0.5$ in the inequality (*f*), we find

$$0.75\sigma_e < \sigma_x < 5.5\sigma_e.$$

Since the given value of σ_x is within these limits, we substitute $m = n = 1$ in Eq. (*c*). Then

$$\sigma_x + \sigma_y \frac{a^2}{b^2} = \sigma_e\left(1 + \frac{a^2}{b^2}\right)^2,$$

and by taking $a/b = 0.5$ and $\sigma_x = \sigma_e$ we obtain

$$(\sigma_y)_{cr} = 2.25\sigma_e = 2.25\frac{\pi^2 D}{a^2 h}.$$

If the given value of σ_x is larger than the limiting value (d), it is necessary to consider straight lines obtained from Eq. (c) by taking $n = 1$ and putting $m = 2, 3, 4, \ldots$. Consider the line for which $n = 1$ and $m = i$. The lower limit for σ_x for which this line should be used is defined by the point of intersection of this line with the line for which $m = i - 1$, $n = 1$. The equations of these lines, from Eq. (c), are

$$\sigma_x i^2 + \sigma_y \frac{a^2}{b^2} = \sigma_e\left(i^2 + \frac{a^2}{b^2}\right)^2;$$

$$\sigma_x(i - 1)^2 + \sigma_y \frac{a^2}{b^2} = \sigma_e\left[(i - 1)^2 + \frac{a^2}{b^2}\right]^2,$$

from which the lower limit of σ_x is

$$\sigma_x = \sigma_e\left(2i^2 - 2i + 1 + 2\frac{a^2}{b^2}\right).$$

In the same manner the intersection point of the lines for which $m = i$, $n = 1$ and $m = i + 1$, $n = 1$ determines the upper limit for σ_x which is

$$\sigma_x = \sigma_e\left(2i^2 + 2i + 1 + 2\frac{a^2}{b^2}\right).$$

Thus the line $m = i$, $n = 1$ must be used for determining the critical value of σ_y if the given value of σ_x is within the following limits:

$$\sigma_e\left(2i^2 - 2i + 1 + 2\frac{a^2}{b^2}\right) < \sigma_x < \sigma_e\left(2i^2 + 2i + 1 + 2\frac{a^2}{b^2}\right). \qquad (g)$$

In the same manner, if σ_x is smaller than the limiting value (e), the lines for which $m = 1$, $n = 2, 3, 4, \ldots$ must be considered. Proceeding as in the previous case, we will find that the line defined by $m = 1$, $n = i$ must be used if the following inequality[1] holds:

$$\sigma_e\left[1 - i^2(i - 1)^2\frac{a^4}{b^4}\right] > \sigma_x > \sigma_e\left[1 - i^2(i + 1)^2\frac{a^4}{b^4}\right]. \qquad (h)$$

Let us consider, as an example, the case where $a/b = 0.5$ and let us assume $\sigma_x = 7\sigma_e$. Since σ_x is larger than the value (d), we use the general inequality (g) which will be satisfied by taking $i = 2$. Hence, substituting $m = 2$, $n = 1$ in Eq. (c), the straight line which must be used in this case is

$$4\sigma_x + \sigma_y \frac{a^2}{b^2} = \sigma_e\left(4 + \frac{a^2}{b^2}\right)^2.$$

Substituting in this equation $\sigma_x = 7\sigma_e$ and $a = 0.5b$, we find

$$(\sigma_y)_{cr} = -39.75\sigma_e.$$

[1] Compressive stresses here must be considered as positive.

This indicates that a tensile stress larger than $39.75\sigma_e$ must act in the y-direction to prevent buckling of the plate under the action of the given value of the compressive stress σ_x.

If to the same plate there is applied a tensile stress in the x-direction of magnitude $\sigma_x = -11\sigma_e$, we must use the inequality (h) which will be satisfied by taking $i = 4$. The corresponding critical value of σ_y will be determined from the following equation:

$$\sigma_x + 16\sigma_y\frac{a^2}{b^2} = \sigma_e\left(1 + 16\frac{a^2}{b^2}\right)^2.$$

Substituting in this equation $\sigma_x = -11\sigma_e$ and $a = 0.5b$, we find

$$\sigma_{cr} = 9\sigma_e.$$

65. Buckling of Uniformly Compressed Rectangular Plates Simply Supported along Two Opposite Sides Perpendicular to the Direction of Compression and Having Various Edge Conditions along the Other Two Sides.—In the discussion of this problem both methods, the method of energy and the method of integration of the differential equation for the deflected plate, can be used.[1] In applying the

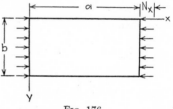

FIG. 176.

method of integration we use Eq. (209), which for the case of uniform compression along the x-axis (see Fig. 176), and with N_x considered positive for compression, becomes

$$\frac{\partial^4 w}{\partial x^4} + 2\frac{\partial^4 w}{\partial x^2\,\partial y^2} + \frac{\partial^4 w}{\partial y^4} = -\frac{N_x}{D}\frac{\partial^2 w}{\partial x^2}. \qquad (a)$$

Assuming that under the action of compressive forces the plate buckles in m sinusoidal half-waves, we take the solution of Eq. (a) in the form

$$w = f(y)\sin\frac{m\pi x}{a}, \qquad (b)$$

in which $f(y)$ is a function of y alone, which is to be determined later. Expression (b) satisfies the boundary conditions along the

[1] The method of integration was used by the writer in the paper published in the *Bull. Polytech. Inst., Kiev*, 1907. See also *Z. Math. Physik*, vol. 58, p. 343, 1910. The use of the energy method was shown in the paper published in *Ann. ponts chaussées*, 1913, IV, p. 372. Some of the problems of this article have been discussed, independently of the writer, by H. Reissner, *Zentr. Bauverwaltung*, 1909, p. 93.

simply supported sides $x = 0$ and $x = a$ of the plate, since

$$w = 0 \quad \text{and} \quad \frac{\partial^2 w}{\partial x^2} + \nu \frac{\partial^2 w}{\partial y^2} = 0$$

$$\text{for } x = 0 \text{ and } x = a.$$

Substituting (b) in Eq. (a), we obtain the following ordinary differential equation for determining the function $f(y)$:

$$f'''' - \frac{2m^2\pi^2}{a^2} f'' + \left(\frac{m^4\pi^4}{a^4} - \frac{N_x}{D} \frac{m^2\pi^2}{a^2} \right) f = 0. \tag{c}$$

Noting that, owing to some constraints along the sides $y = 0$ and $y = b$, we always have

$$\frac{N_x}{D} > \frac{m^2\pi^2}{a^2},$$

and, using the notations

$$\alpha = \sqrt{\frac{m^2\pi^2}{a^2} + \sqrt{\frac{N_x}{D} \frac{m^2\pi^2}{a^2}}}; \quad \beta = \sqrt{-\frac{m^2\pi^2}{a^2} + \sqrt{\frac{N_x}{D} \frac{m^2\pi^2}{a^2}}}, \tag{d}$$

the general solution of Eq. (c) can be represented in the following form:

$$f(y) = C_1 e^{-\alpha y} + C_2 e^{\alpha y} + C_3 \cos \beta y + C_4 \sin \beta y. \tag{e}$$

The constants of integration in this solution must be determined in each particular case from the conditions of constraint along the sides $y = 0$ and $y = b$. Several particular cases of constraint along these sides will now be discussed.

The side $y = 0$ is simply supported; the side $y = b$ is free (Fig. 176). From these conditions it follows [see Eqs. (191 and 192)] that

$$w = 0, \quad \frac{\partial^2 w}{\partial y^2} + \nu \frac{\partial^2 w}{\partial x^2} = 0, \quad \text{for} \quad y = 0; \tag{f}$$

$$\frac{\partial^2 w}{\partial y^2} + \nu \frac{\partial^2 w}{\partial x^2} = 0, \quad \frac{\partial^3 w}{\partial y^3} + (2 - \nu) \frac{\partial^3 w}{\partial x^2 \, \partial y} = 0, \quad \text{for} \quad y = b. \tag{g}$$

The boundary conditions (f) will be satisfied if we take in the general solution (e)

$$C_1 = -C_2 \quad \text{and} \quad C_3 = 0.$$

The function $f(y)$ can be written then in the form

$$f(y) = A \sinh \alpha y + B \sin \beta y,$$

in which A and B are constants. From the boundary conditions (g) it follows that

$$
\left.\begin{aligned}
A\left(\alpha^2 - \nu\frac{m^2\pi^2}{a^2}\right) \sinh \alpha b - B\left(\beta^2 + \nu\frac{m^2\pi^2}{a^2}\right) \sin \beta b &= 0; \\
A\alpha\left[\alpha^2 - (2 - \nu)\frac{m^2\pi^2}{a^2}\right] \cosh \alpha b - \\
B\beta\left[\beta^2 + (2 - \nu)\frac{m^2\pi^2}{a^2}\right] \cos \beta b &= 0.
\end{aligned}\right\} \quad (h)
$$

These equations can be satisfied by taking $A = B = 0$. Then the deflection at each point of the plate is zero and we obtain the flat form of equilibrium of the plate. The buckled form of equilibrium of the plate becomes possible only if Eqs. (h) yield for A and B solutions different from zero, which requires that the determinant of these equations becomes zero, *i.e.*,

$$
\beta\left(\alpha^2 - \nu\frac{m^2\pi^2}{a^2}\right)^2 \tanh \alpha b = \alpha\left(\beta^2 + \nu\frac{m^2\pi^2}{a^2}\right)^2 \tan \beta b. \quad (i)
$$

Since α and β contain N_x [see notations (d)], Eq. (i) can be used for the calculation of the critical value of N_x if the dimensions of the plate and the elastic constants of the material are known. These calculations show that the smallest value of N_x is obtained by taking $m = 1$, *i.e.*, by assuming that the buckled plate has only one half-wave. The magnitude of the corresponding critical compressive stress can be represented by the formula

$$
(\sigma_x)_{cr} = \frac{(N_x)_{cr}}{h} = k\frac{\pi^2 D}{b^2 h}, \quad (j)
$$

in which k is a numerical factor depending on the magnitude of the ratio a/b. Several values of this factor, calculated from Eq. (i) for $\nu = 0.25$, are given in the second line of Table 32.

TABLE 32.—NUMERICAL VALUES OF k IN EQ. (j) WHEN THE SIDE $y = 0$ IS SIMPLY SUPPORTED AND THE SIDE $y = b$ IS FREE (FIG. 176)

a/b	0.50	1.0	1.2	1.4	1.6	1.8	2.0	2.5	3.0	4.0	5.0
k	4.40	1.440	1.135	0.952	0.835	0.755	0.698	0.610	0.564	0.516	0.506
$(\sigma_x)_{cr}$	11,600	3,790	2,990	2,500	2,200	1,990	1,840	1,600	1,480	1,360	1,330

For long plates it can be assumed with sufficient accuracy that

$$k = \left(0.456 + \frac{b^2}{a^2}\right).$$

In the third line of Table 32 the critical stresses in pounds per square inch are given, calculated on the assumption that $E = 30 \cdot 10^6$ lb. per square inch, $\nu = 0.25$ and $h/b = 0.01$. For any other material with a modulus E_1 and any other value of the ratio h/b, the critical stress is obtained by multiplying the numbers of the table by the factor

$$\frac{E_1}{30 \cdot 10^2}\left(\frac{h}{b}\right)^2.$$

Edge conditions similar to those assumed above are realized in the case of compression of an angle as shown in Fig. 177. When

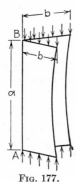

FIG. 177.

the compressive stresses, uniformly distributed over the width of the sides of the angle, become equal to the critical stress given by formula (j), the free longitudinal edges of the angle buckle, as shown in the figure, while the line AB remains straight and the edge conditions along this line are the same as along a simply supported edge. Experiments made with compression of angles[1] are in good agreement with the theory. In the case of comparatively short angles buckling occurs as shown in Fig. 177. For a long strut with such an angular cross section, Euler's critical compressive stress may become smaller than that given by formula (j), in which case the strut buckles like a compressed column.

The buckling of eccentrically compressed struts of L-and other thin profile sections, such as used in airplane construction, has been discussed by H. Wagner,[2] who pointed out that in such struts the torsional rigidity is very small in comparison with flexural rigidities and that a buckling connected with torsion

---

[1] See paper by F. J. Bridget, C. C. Jerome and A. B. Vosseller, *Trans. Am. Soc. Mech. Eng.*, 1934, p. 569. See also Dissertation by C. F. Kollbrunner, Zürich, 1935.

[2] See paper in Festschrift "Fünfundzwanzig Jahre Technische Hochschule Danzig," p. 329.

is likely to occur at a compressive load which is smaller than Euler's load.

The side $y = 0$ is built in; the side $y = b$ is free (Fig. 176). In this case the edge conditions for determining the constants in the general solution (e) are

$$w = 0, \qquad \frac{\partial w}{\partial y} = 0 \qquad \text{for} \qquad y = 0; \qquad (k)$$

$$\frac{\partial^2 w}{\partial y^2} + \nu \frac{\partial^2 w}{\partial x^2} = 0, \quad \frac{\partial^3 w}{\partial y^3} + (2 - \nu) \frac{\partial^3 w}{\partial x^2 \, \partial y} = 0 \quad \text{for} \quad y = b. \quad (l)$$

From the conditions (k) it follows that

$$C_1 = -\frac{\alpha C_3 - \beta C_4}{2\alpha}; \qquad C_2 = -\frac{\alpha C_3 + \beta C_4}{2\alpha}$$

and the function $f(y)$ can be represented in the form

$$f(y) = A(\cos \beta y - \cosh \alpha y) + B(\sin \beta y - \frac{\beta}{\alpha} \sinh \alpha y).$$

Substituting this expression in the conditions (l), two homogeneous equations linear in A and B are obtained. The critical value of the compressive stress is now determined by equating to zero the determinant of these equations, which gives

$$2ts + (s^2 + t^2) \cos \beta b \cosh \alpha b = \frac{1}{\alpha\beta}(\alpha^2 t^2 - \beta^2 s^2) \sin \beta b \sinh \alpha b$$

$$(m)$$

where

$$t = \beta^2 + \nu \frac{m^2\pi^2}{a^2}; \qquad s = \alpha^2 - \nu \frac{m^2\pi^2}{a^2}.$$

For a given value of the ratio a/b and a given value of ν the critical value of compressive stress can be calculated from the transcendental equation (m) and can be represented by Eq. (j). Calculations show that for a comparatively short length a the plate buckles in one-half wave and we must take $m = 1$ in our calculations. Several values of the numerical factor k in Eq. (j) for various values of the ratio a/b are given in Table 33. The same values are also represented in Fig. 178 by the curve $m = 1$. It is seen that at the beginning the values of k decrease with an increase in the ratio a/b. The minimum value of k ($k = 1.328$) is obtained for $a/b = 1.635$ and, beginning from this value, k increases with the ratio a/b. Having the curve for $m = 1$, the curves for $m = 2$, $m = 3$, $\cdots$ can be constructed, as explained in Art. 63. By using such curves the number of half-waves in any particular case can be determined readily.

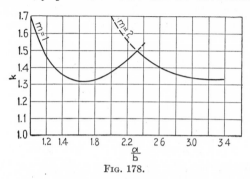

Fig. 178.

In the case of a comparatively long plate we can take with sufficient accuracy $k = 1.328$ in Eq. (j).

TABLE 33.—NUMERICAL VALUES OF k IN EQ. (j) WHEN THE SIDE $y = 0$ IS BUILT IN AND THE SIDE $y = b$ IS FREE (FIG. 176); $\nu = 0.25$

a/b	1.0	1.1	1.2	1.3	1.4	1.5	1.6	1.7	1.8	1.9	2.0	2.2	2.4
k	1.70	1.56	1.47	1.41	1.36	1.34	1.33	1.33	1.34	1.36	1.38	1.45	1.47
$(\sigma_x)_{cr}$	4,470	4,110	3,870	3,710	3,580	3,520	3,500	3,500	3,520	3,580	3,630	3,820	3,870

In the third line of Table 33 are given the values of the critical stresses in pounds per square inch, calculated from Eq. (j) assuming $E = 30 \cdot 10^6$ lb. per square inch, $\nu = 0.25$ and $h/b = 0.01$. By using these figures the critical stresses for any other proportions of the plate and any value of the modulus can be easily calculated.

The side $y = 0$ is elastically built in and the side $y = b$ is free (Fig. 176). In the previous discussions two extreme assumptions for the constraint along the side $y = 0$ have been considered, namely, a simply supported edge and a built-in edge. In practical cases we will usually have some intermediate condition of constraint. Take, for instance, the case of a compression member of a T cross section (Fig. 179). While the upper edge of the vertical web cannot be assumed to rotate freely during buckling, neither can it be considered as rigidly built in since during buckling of the web some rotation of the horizontal flange will take place. We may consider in this case the upper edge of the plate as *elastically built in*, since the bending moments that appear during buckling along this edge are proportional at each point to the angle of rotation of the edge. To show this, let us consider torsion of the flange of the member shown in Fig. 179. The angle of rotation of this flange during buckling of the web is equal to $\partial w/\partial y$ and the rate of change of this angle is $\partial^2 w/\partial x\,\partial y$; hence the twisting moment at any cross section of the flange along the x-axis is

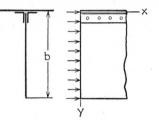

FIG. 179.

$$C\,\frac{\partial^2 w}{\partial x\,\partial y},$$

where C is the torsional rigidity of the flange.[1] The rate of change of this twisting moment is numerically equal to the bending moment M_y per unit length of the upper edge of the web. The signs of these two moments, with the assumed rule regarding the positive direction of M_y (see p. 287) are also the same. Hence the corresponding boundary condition along the upper edge of the web is

$$-D\!\left(\frac{\partial^2 w}{\partial y^2} + \nu\,\frac{\partial^2 w}{\partial x^2}\right) = C\,\frac{\partial^3 w}{\partial x^2\,\partial y}.$$

Using for w expression (b), and observing that along the upper edge of the web $w = 0$,[2] the above boundary condition can be put in the following form:[3]

$$D\frac{\partial^2 w}{\partial y^2} = C\frac{\pi^2}{a^2}\frac{\partial w}{\partial y}, \qquad \text{for } y = 0. \tag{n}$$

That is, the bending moments M_y along the upper edge of the buckled web are proportional to the angle of rotation $\partial w/\partial y$ as stated before.

From the condition (n), together with the condition that $w = 0$ for $y = 0$, we find the following relations between the constants in expression (e):

$$C_1 = \frac{C_3(\alpha^2 + \beta^2 - r\alpha)}{2r\alpha} + \frac{C_4\beta}{2\alpha};$$

$$C_2 = -\frac{C_3(\alpha^2 + \beta^2 + r\alpha)}{2r\alpha} - \frac{C_4\beta}{2\alpha},$$

where

$$r = \frac{C}{D}\frac{\pi^2}{a^2}. \tag{o}$$

---

[1] This rigidity can be calculated in each particular case with sufficient accuracy by considering the cross section of the flange as consisting of narrow rectangles; see "Theory of Elasticity," p. 257. The center of twist is assumed to coincide with the edge of the web.

[2] We assume here that the flexural rigidity of the flange in the xz-plane is very large and we neglect deflection of the flange in that plane.

[3] It is assumed that $m = 1$, *i.e.*, that there is only one half-wave formed by the buckled web.

With these relations between the constants, we obtain

$$f(y) = C_3\left(\cos \beta y - \cosh \alpha y - \frac{\alpha^2 + \beta^2}{r\alpha} \sinh \alpha y\right) +$$
$$C_4\left(\sin \beta y - \frac{\beta}{\alpha} \sinh \alpha y\right).$$

Substituting this in the expression (b) for w and in the boundary conditions (l) along the free edge of the web, we obtain the following equations:

$$\left.\begin{array}{l} C_3(t \cos \beta b + s \cosh \alpha b + qs \sinh \alpha b) + C_4\left(t \sin \beta b + \dfrac{\beta}{\alpha} s \sinh \alpha b\right) = 0; \\ C_3(-\beta s \sin \beta b + \alpha t \sinh \alpha b + q\alpha t \cosh \alpha b) + \\ \qquad\qquad C_4(\beta s \cos \beta b + \beta t \cosh \alpha b) = 0, \end{array}\right\} \quad (p)$$

where

$$s = \alpha^2 - \nu\frac{\pi^2}{a^2}; \qquad t = \beta^2 + \nu\frac{\pi^2}{a^2}; \qquad q = \frac{\alpha^2 + \beta^2}{\alpha r}.$$

Assuming that the torsional rigidity of the flange is very large and taking $q = 0$, Eqs. (p) coincide with those for a plate rigidly built in along the edge $y = 0$.

The critical values of the compressive forces will be found by setting the determinant of the Eqs. (p) equal to zero. In this way we find again that the critical values of the compressive stress can be represented by the formula (j). The values of the factor k in this formula will evidently depend on the magnitude of the *coefficient of fixity* r. The results of calculations made for $rb = 2$ and $rb = 8$ and for $\nu = 0.25$ are given in Table 34.

TABLE 34.—NUMERICAL VALUES OF k IN EQ. (j) WHEN THE SIDE $y = 0$ IS ELASTICALLY BUILT IN AND THE SIDE $y = b$ IS FREE; $\nu = 0.25$

a/b	1	1.3	1.5	1.8	2.0	2.3	2.5	2.7	3.0	4.0
$rb = 2$	1.49	1.13	1.01	0.92	0.90	0.89	0.90	0.93	0.98	0.90
$rb = 8$	1.58	1.25	1.16	1.11	1.12	1.18	1.23	1.30	1.16	1.12

It is seen that with the increase of r the factor k increases, and for $rb = 8$ the values of k approach the values given in Table 33, calculated for a rigidly built-in edge. It can be seen also that with the increase of r the ratio a/b, at which k becomes a minimum, decreases. This means that in the case of long plates the length of waves in which the plate subdivides during buckling decreases as r increases. By using the values of k given in Table 34, curves analogous to those shown in Fig. 178 can be constructed and from such curves the number of half-waves in which a plate subdivides at buckling can be determined in the same manner as explained before.

Both sides $y = 0$ *and* $y = b$ *are built in.* In this case the boundary conditions are

$$w = 0, \qquad \frac{\partial w}{\partial y} = 0, \qquad \text{for} \qquad y = 0 \qquad \text{and} \qquad y = b.$$

Proceeding as in the previous cases, we find for the calculation of the critical value of the compressive forces the following transcendental equation:

$$(\cos \beta b - \cosh \alpha b)^2 =$$
$$-\left(\sin \beta b - \frac{\beta}{\alpha} \sinh \alpha b\right)\left(\sin \beta b + \frac{\alpha}{\beta} \sinh \alpha b\right).$$

The critical values of the compressive stress again are given by Eq. (j). Several values of the numerical factor k, calculated for various values of the ratio a/b, are given in Table 35.

TABLE 35.—NUMERICAL VALUES OF k IN EQ. (j) WHEN BOTH SIDES $y = 0$
AND $y = b$ ARE BUILT IN; $\nu = 0.25$

a/b	0.4	0.5	0.6	0.7	0.8	0.9	1.0
k	9.44	7.69	7.05	7.00	7.29	7.83	7.69

It is seen that the smallest value of k is obtained when

$$0.6 < \frac{a}{b} < 0.7.$$

That is, a long compressed plate buckles in this case in compara-

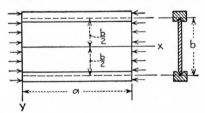

FIG. 180.

tively short waves. The number of half-waves can be determined as before by plotting curves analogous to those shown in Fig. 178.

Both sides $y = 0$ and $y = b$ are supported by elastic beams. Taking the coordinate axes as shown in Fig. 180, we assume that the conditions at the edges $x = 0$ and $x = a$ of the plate are the same as before. Along the edges $y = b/2$ and $y = -b/2$ the plate is free to rotate during buckling but deflections of the plate at these edges are resisted by the two equal elastic supporting beams. The condition of freedom of rotation requires that

$$\frac{\partial^2 w}{\partial y^2} + \nu \frac{\partial^2 w}{\partial x^2} = 0 \qquad \text{for} \qquad y = \pm \frac{b}{2}. \tag{q}$$

To get an expression for the second condition, bending of the supporting beams must be considered. We assume that these beams are simply supported at the ends, that they have the same modulus of elasticity as the plate and that they are compressed together with the plate so that the compressive forces on each are equal to $A\sigma_x$, where A is the cross-sectional area of one beam. Denoting by EI the flexural rigidity of the beam, the differential equation of its deflection curve is

$$EI\,\frac{\partial^4 w}{\partial x^4} = q - A\sigma_x\,\frac{\partial^2 w}{\partial x^2},$$

where q is the intensity of the load transmitted from the plate to the beam. From expressions for shearing forces (see p. 300) this intensity is

$$q = D\left[\frac{\partial^3 w}{\partial y^3} + (2-\nu)\frac{\partial^3 w}{\partial x^2\,\partial y}\right], \qquad \text{for} \qquad y = \frac{b}{2};$$

$$q = -D\left[\frac{\partial^3 w}{\partial y^3} + (2-\nu)\frac{\partial^3 w}{\partial x^2\,\partial y}\right], \qquad \text{for} \qquad y = -\frac{b}{2}.$$

Substituting these values of q in the above equation for the deflection curve, the following boundary conditions are obtained:

$$\left.\begin{aligned}
EI\,\frac{\partial^4 w}{\partial x^4} &= D\left[\frac{\partial^3 w}{\partial y^3} + (2-\nu)\frac{\partial^3 w}{\partial x^2\,\partial y}\right] - A\sigma_x\,\frac{\partial^2 w}{\partial x^2}, \qquad \text{for} \qquad y = \frac{b}{2}; \\
EI\,\frac{\partial^4 w}{\partial x^4} &= -D\left[\frac{\partial^3 w}{\partial y^3} + (2-\nu)\frac{\partial^3 w}{\partial x^2\,\partial y}\right] - A\sigma_x\,\frac{\partial^2 w}{\partial x^2}, \qquad \text{for} \qquad y = -\frac{b}{2}.
\end{aligned}\right\} \quad (r)$$

By using the four boundary conditions (q) and (r) for determining the constants in expression (e) and by equating to zero the determinant of these equations, we obtain the transcendental equation for calculating the critical values of the compressive stresses. Assuming that during buckling both supporting beams deflect in the same direction and that the deflection surface of the plate is symmetrical with respect to the x-axis (Fig. 180), the equation for determining the critical stress σ_{cr} becomes[1]

$$\beta\left(1 - \nu + \frac{a}{m\pi}\sqrt{\frac{h\sigma_{cr}}{D}}\right)^2 \tan\frac{\beta b}{2} + \alpha\left(1 - \nu - \frac{a}{m\pi}\sqrt{\frac{h\sigma_{cr}}{D}}\right)^2 \tanh\frac{\alpha b}{2} =$$
$$\frac{2m\pi}{a}\sqrt{\frac{h\sigma_{cr}}{D}}\left(\frac{EI}{D} - \frac{a^2 A\sigma_{cr}}{m^2\pi^2 D}\right), \quad (s)$$

where α and β are given, as before, by the formulas (d).

If we assume that the supporting beams are deflecting during buckling in opposite directions, we obtain a transcendental equation which always

[1] The first calculations of critical stresses for a compressed plate supported by elastic beams were made for the writer by K. Cališev, *Memoirs of the Institute of Engineers of Ways of Communication*, St. Petersburg, 1914. The curves for calculating σ_{cr} given in this book are taken from the thesis of A. J. Miles, presented at the University of Michigan, January 1935. Independently of the writer the same problem was discussed by E. Melan, *Reports Intern. Cong. Appl. Mech.*, vol. 3, p. 59, 1930, and by L. Rendulič, *Ingenieur-Archiv*, vol. 3, p. 447, 1932.

gives for σ_{cr} larger values than those obtained from the assumption of symmetry. Thus, in this case, only the symmetrical case of buckling should be considered.

To simplify the solution of equations we introduce the following notations:

$$\frac{m\pi b}{a} = \phi; \qquad b\sqrt{\frac{h\sigma_{cr}}{D}} = \psi; \qquad \frac{EI}{bD} - \frac{A}{bh}\frac{\psi^2}{\phi^2} = \theta.$$

Then

$$\sqrt{\psi - \phi}[\psi + (1 - \nu)\phi]^2 \tan \tfrac{1}{2}\sqrt{\psi\phi - \phi^2} +$$
$$\sqrt{\psi + \phi}[\psi - (1 - \nu)\phi]^2 \tanh \tfrac{1}{2}\sqrt{\psi\phi + \phi^2} = 2\phi^{\frac{3}{2}}\psi\theta. \quad (t)$$

To further simplify the solution of this equation, curves representing ψ as a function of ϕ^2 for various numerical values of θ are plotted in Fig. 181. The

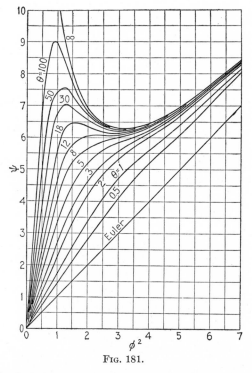

Fɪɢ. 181.

procedure of calculation in each particular case will then be as follows: we calculate EI/bD and A/bh by using the given dimensions of the plate and assume a certain value for the number of half-waves m. In this manner the quantity ϕ is determined and the quantity ψ can be found by trial and error by using the curves in Fig. 181. In the case of quite rigid supporting beams, we can take, as a first approximation, the same number of half-waves and the same value of σ_{cr} as for the case of a plate supported by absolutely rigid beams. To illustrate the application of the curves in Fig. 181, the critical stresses for the channels shown in Fig. 182 are calculated. Considering the web of the channel as a compressed rectangular plate and the flanges as the supporting beams, and varying the width d of the flanges, a variety of cases can be obtained. By taking $m = 1$ and assuming $d = 1$ in., 2 in., 3 in., the curves, with always decreasing ordinates, as shown in Fig. 182, are obtained. For comparison there is given also the curve $\theta = 0$ representing the case where the longitudinal edges of the plate are entirely free. For $d = 4$ in. the corresponding curve in Fig. 182 has a more complicated

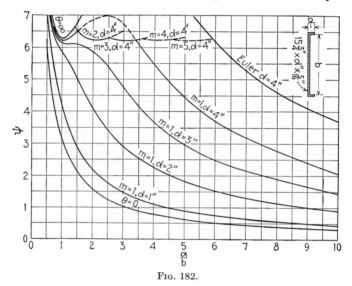

Fig. 182.

shape. It has a minimum for $a/b \approx 1$; then it goes up and has a maximum for $a/b \approx 2.5$, after which the ordinates begin to decrease continuously. By making calculations with $m = 2$ and $m = 3$ and by plotting the corresponding curves in Fig. 182, it is shown that in the region $1.5 < a/b < 3.4$ these curves have smaller ordinates than the curve $m = 1$; hence, in calculating σ_{cr}, these curves should be used as shown by the full lines in Fig. 182. For comparison there is shown also the curve $\theta = \infty$ giving buckling conditions for absolutely rigid supporting beams. It may be seen that, with $d = 4$ in. and for a comparatively short channel, the critical stresses are approximately the same as for a rigidly supported plate. For greater lengths the curve $m = 1$ should be used in calculating σ_{cr} and the buckling conditions approach those given by Euler's curve calculated for the channel considered as a strut.

It has been assumed in the above discussion that the flanges of the member do not resist twisting during buckling of the web (see Fig. 180). By taking into account the resistance to twisting, a more complicated transcendental equation, containing the ratio of the torsional rigidity C of flanges to the flexural rigidity D of the web, may be obtained,[1] and the effect of torsional rigidity on the magnitude of σ_{cr} can be calculated.

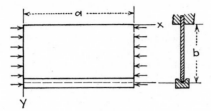

Fig. 183.

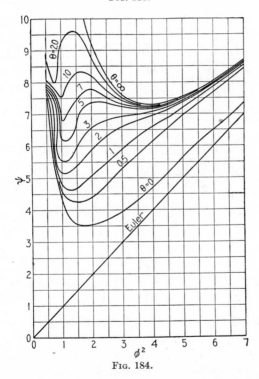

Fig. 184.

The edge $y = 0$ *is built in and the edge* $y = b$ *is supported by an elastic beam* (Fig. 183). Proceeding as in the previous case and using the same notations as before, we obtain for critical stresses the following transcendental equation:

[1] This case has been discussed in the paper by E. Chwalla, *Ingenieur-Archiv*, vol. 5, p. 54, 1934.

$$\theta\psi\phi^2(\sqrt{\psi\phi - \phi^2}\ \tanh\ \sqrt{\psi\phi + \phi^2} - \sqrt{\psi\phi + \phi^2}\ \tan\ \sqrt{\psi\phi - \phi^2}) =$$
$$\sqrt{\psi^2 - \phi^2}\left[\frac{\psi^2 - \phi^2(1 - \nu)^2}{\cos\sqrt{\psi\phi - \phi^2}\ \cosh\sqrt{\psi\phi + \phi^2}} + \psi^2 + \phi^2(1 - \nu)^2\right] +$$
$$\phi[\psi^2(1 - 2\nu) - \phi^2(1 - \nu)^2]\ \tan\ \sqrt{\psi\phi - \phi^2}\ \tanh\ \sqrt{\psi\phi + \phi^2}.$$

To simplify the solution of this equation, curves representing ψ as a function of ϕ^2 for various numerical values of θ are plotted in Fig. 184. To illustrate the application of these curves, the case represented in Fig. 185 has been calculated. By using the curves in Fig. 184, curves representing ψ as functions of the ratio a/b for various values of the width d of the flange have

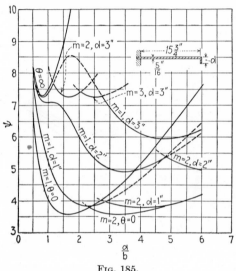

Fig. 185.

been plotted in Fig. 185. It may be seen that for $d = 3$ in. and a comparatively short plate, the conditions approach those of a plate rigidly supported ($\theta = \infty$) along the edge $y = b$ (Fig. 183).

66. Buckling of a Simply Supported Rectangular Plate under Combined Bending and Compression.[1]—Let us consider a simply supported rectangular plate (Fig. 186) along whose sides $x = 0$ and $x = a$ distributed forces, acting in the middle plane of the plate, are applied, their intensity being given by the equation

$$N_x = N_0\left(1 - \alpha\frac{y}{b}\right),\qquad (a)$$

[1] See writer's paper, *loc. cit.*, p. 337. See also J. Boobnoff, "Theory of Structure of Ships," vol. 2, p. 515, St. Petersburg, 1914.

where N_0 is the intensity of compressive force at the edge $y = 0$ and α is a numerical factor. By changing α, various particular cases can be obtained. For example, by taking $\alpha = 0$ we obtain the case of uniformly distributed compressive force as discussed in Art. 63. Again for $\alpha = 2$ we obtain the case of pure bending. If α is less than 2, we have a combination of bending and compression as indicated in Fig. 186. If $\alpha > 2$, there will be a similar combination of bending and tension.

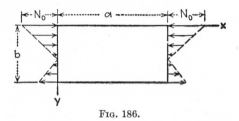

Fig. 186.

The deflection of the buckled plate simply supported on all sides can be taken, as before, in the form of the double trigonometric series

$$w = \sum_{m=1}^{\infty} \sum_{n=1}^{\infty} a_{mn} \sin \frac{m\pi x}{a} \sin \frac{n\pi y}{b}. \tag{b}$$

For calculating the critical value of the compressive force N_0 we will use the energy method. Then for the strain energy of bending due to deflections (b) we use the previously derived expression (see p. 327)

$$\Delta V = \frac{D}{2} \frac{ab\pi^4}{4} \sum_{m=1}^{m=\infty} \sum_{n=1}^{n=\infty} a^2{}_{mn} \left(\frac{m^2}{a^2} + \frac{n^2}{b^2}\right)^2. \tag{c}$$

The work done by external forces during buckling of the plate is [see Eq. (201)]

$$\Delta T = \frac{1}{2} \int_0^a \int_0^b N_0 \left(1 - \alpha \frac{y}{b}\right) \left(\frac{\partial w}{\partial x}\right)^2 dx \, dy. \tag{d}$$

Substituting expression (b) for w and observing that

$$\int_0^b y \sin \frac{i\pi y}{b} \sin \frac{j\pi y}{b}\, dy = \frac{b^2}{4}, \qquad \text{for} \qquad i = j;$$

$$\int_0^b y \sin \frac{i\pi y}{b} \sin \frac{j\pi y}{b}\, dy = 0, \qquad \text{for} \qquad i \neq j \qquad \text{and}$$

$$i \pm j \text{ is an even number;}$$

$$\int_0^b y \sin \frac{i\pi y}{b} \sin \frac{j\pi y}{b}\, dy = -\frac{4b^2}{\pi^2} \frac{ij}{(i^2 - j^2)^2}, \qquad \text{for} \qquad i \neq j \qquad \text{and}$$

$$i \pm j \text{ is an odd number,}$$

we obtain, for the work done by external forces, the following expression:

$$\Delta T = \frac{N_0}{2} \frac{ab}{4} \sum_{m=1}^{m=\infty} \sum_{n=1}^{n=\infty} a^2{}_{mn} \frac{m^2\pi^2}{a^2} - $$
$$\frac{N_0}{2} \frac{\alpha a}{2b} \sum_{m=1}^{m=\infty} \frac{m^2\pi^2}{a^2} \left[\frac{b^2}{4} \sum_{n=1}^{n=\infty} a^2{}_{mn} - \frac{8b^2}{\pi^2} \sum_{n=1}^{n=\infty} \sum_i^{\infty} \frac{a_{mn} a_{mi} ni}{(n^2 - i^2)^2} \right],$$

where for i only such numbers are taken that $n \pm i$ is always odd.

Equating this work to the strain energy of bending (c), we obtain for the critical value of N_0 the equation

$$(N_0)_{cr} = \frac{\pi^4 D \displaystyle\sum_{m=1}^{m=\infty} \sum_{n=1}^{n=\infty} a^2{}_{mn} \left(\frac{m^2}{a^2} + \frac{n^2}{b^2} \right)^2}{\displaystyle\sum_{m=1}^{m=\infty} \sum_{n=1}^{n=\infty} a^2{}_{mn} \frac{m^2\pi^2}{a^2} - \frac{\alpha}{2} \sum_{m=1}^{m=\infty} \frac{m^2\pi^2}{a^2} \left[\sum_{n=1}^{n=\infty} a^2{}_{mn} - \frac{32}{\pi^2} \sum_{n=1}^{n=\infty} \sum_i^{\infty} \frac{a_{mn} a_{mi} ni}{(n^2 - i^2)^2} \right]} . \qquad (e)$$

The coefficients a_{mn} must be adjusted now so as to make the obtained expression for $(N_0)_{cr}$ a minimum. By taking the derivatives of this expression with respect to each coefficient a_{mn} and equating these derivatives to zero, we finally obtain a system of linear equations of the following form:

$$Da_{mn}\pi^4\left(\frac{m^2}{a^2} + \frac{n^2}{b^2}\right)^2 =$$

$$(N_0)_{cr}\left\{a_{mn}\frac{m^2\pi^2}{a^2} - \frac{\alpha}{2}\frac{m^2\pi^2}{a^2}\left[a_{mn} - \frac{16}{\pi^2}\sum_{i}^{\infty}\frac{a_{mi}ni}{(n^2-i^2)^2}\right]\right\}. \quad (f)$$

Let us collect all equations with a certain value of the number m. These equations will contain coefficients a_{m1}, a_{m2}, a_{m3}, ... All other coefficients we take equal to zero, *i.e.*, instead of the general expression (b) we take, for the deflection of the plate, the expression

$$w = \sin\frac{m\pi x}{a}\sum_{n=1}^{n=\infty} a_{mn}\sin\frac{n\pi y}{b},$$

which is equivalent to the assumption that the buckled plate is subdivided along the x-axis into m half-waves.[1]

We can consider one half-wave between two nodal lines as a simply supported plate which is buckled into one half-wave. Substituting $m = 1$ in Eqs. (f) and using the notation

$$\sigma_{cr} = \frac{(N_0)_{cr}}{h},$$

we obtain a system of equations of the following kind:

$$a_{1n}\left[\left(1 + n^2\frac{a^2}{b^2}\right)^2 - \sigma_{cr}\frac{a^2h}{\pi^2D}\left(1 - \frac{\alpha}{2}\right)\right] -$$

$$8\alpha\sigma_{cr}\frac{a^2h}{\pi^4D}\sum_{i}^{\infty}\frac{a_{1i}ni}{(n^2-i^2)^2} = 0, \quad (g)$$

where the summation is taken over all numbers i such that $n \pm i$ is an odd number.

These are homogeneous linear equations in a_{11}, a_{12}, . . . which will be satisfied by putting a_{11}, a_{12}, . . . equal to zero, which corresponds to the flat form of equilibrium of the plate.

[1] This assumption is justified since the system of Eqs. (f) can be subdivided into groups, each of which has a definite value of m, *i.e.*, represents a buckling of the plate into a number of half-waves with nodal lines parallel to the y-axis. The determinant of the entire system of Eqs. (f) becomes zero if the determinant of one of these groups is zero.

To get for the coefficients a_{11}, a_{12}, . . . solutions different from zero, which indicates the possibility of buckling of the plate, the determinant of the Eqs. (g) must be zero. In this way an equation for calculating the critical values of compressive stresses is obtained. The calculation can be made by successive approximations. We begin by taking only the first of the Eqs. (g) and assuming that all coefficients, except a_{11}, are zero. In this way we obtain

$$\left(1 + \frac{a^2}{b^2}\right)^2 - \sigma_{cr}\frac{a^2h}{\pi^2D}\left(1 - \frac{\alpha}{2}\right) = 0,$$

from which

$$\sigma_{cr} = \frac{\pi^2D}{a^2h}\left(1 + \frac{a^2}{b^2}\right)^2 \frac{1}{1 - \dfrac{\alpha}{2}} = \frac{\pi^2D}{b^2h}\left(\frac{b}{a} + \frac{a}{b}\right)^2 \frac{1}{1 - \dfrac{\alpha}{2}}. \qquad (h)$$

This first approximation gives a satisfactory result only for small values of α, *i.e.*, in the cases when bending stresses are small in comparison with the uniform compressive stress [see Eq. (a)]. In the case of $\alpha = 0$, the expression (h) coincides with expression for the critical stress of a uniformly compressed plate (see p. 329).

To obtain a second approximation, two equations of the system (g) with coefficients a_{11} and a_{12} should be taken, and we obtain

$$a_{11}\left[\left(1 + \frac{a^2}{b^2}\right)^2 - \sigma_{cr}\frac{a^2h}{\pi^2D}\left(1 - \frac{\alpha}{2}\right)\right] - 8\alpha\sigma_{cr}\frac{a^2h}{\pi^4D}\frac{2}{9}a_{12} = 0;$$

$$-8\alpha\sigma_{cr}\frac{a^2h}{\pi^4D}\frac{2}{9}a_{11} + \left[\left(1 + 4\frac{a^2}{b^2}\right)^2 - \sigma_{cr}\frac{a^2h}{\pi^2D}\left(1 - \frac{\alpha}{2}\right)\right]a_{12} = 0.$$

Equating to zero the determinant of these equations, we obtain

$$\left(\frac{\sigma_{cr}a^2h}{\pi^2D}\right)^2\left[\left(1 - \frac{\alpha}{2}\right)^2 - \left(\frac{8\alpha}{\pi^2}\frac{2}{9}\right)^2\right] - \frac{\sigma_{cr}a^2h}{\pi^2D}\left(1 - \frac{\alpha}{2}\right)\left[\left(1 + \frac{a^2}{b^2}\right)^2 + \right.$$
$$\left.\left(1 + 4\frac{a^2}{b^2}\right)^2\right] + \left(1 + \frac{a^2}{b^2}\right)^2\left(1 + 4\frac{a^2}{b^2}\right)^2 = 0. \quad (i)$$

From this equation the second approximation for σ_{cr} can be calculated. The accuracy of this approximation decreases as α increases; for pure bending, when $\alpha = 2$, and for a square plate ($a = b$) the error is about 8 per cent, so that the calculation

of a further approximation is necessary to obtain a more satisfactory accuracy. By taking three equations of the system
(g) and assuming $\alpha = 2$, we obtain

$$\left(1 + \frac{a^2}{b^2}\right)^2 a_{11} - 16\sigma_{cr}\frac{a^2 h}{\pi^4 D}\frac{2}{9}a_{12} = 0;$$

$$-16\sigma_{cr}\frac{a^2 h}{\pi^4 D}\frac{2}{9}a_{11} + \left(1 + 4\frac{a^2}{b^2}\right)^2 a_{12} - 16\sigma_{cr}\frac{a^2 h}{\pi^4 D}\frac{6}{25}a_{13} = 0;$$

$$-16\sigma_{cr}\frac{a^2 h}{\pi^4 D}\frac{6}{25}a_{12} + \left(1 + 9\frac{a^2}{b^2}\right)^2 a_{13} = 0.$$

Equating to zero the determinant of these equations, an equation
for calculating the third approximation is obtained which is
sufficiently accurate for the case of pure bending.[1]

The final expression for σ_{cr} can be again represented by the
equation

$$\sigma_{cr} = k\frac{\pi^2 D}{b^2 h}. \qquad (j)$$

Several values of the numerical factor k for various values of
the ratio a/b and for various values of α are given in Table 36.
For the case of pure bending the third approximation was used;
in other cases Eq. (i), representing the second approximation,
was used in calculating σ_{cr}.

TABLE 36.—NUMERICAL VALUES OF THE FACTOR k IN EQ. (j)

α \\ a/b	0.4	0.5	0.6	0.667	0.75	0.8	0.9	1.0	1.5
2	29.1	25.6	24.1	23.9	24.1	24.4	25.6	25.6	24.1
$\frac{4}{3}$	18.7	....	12.9	......	11.5	11.2	....	11.0	11.5
1	15.1	....	9.7	......	8.4	8.1	....	7.8	8.4
$\frac{4}{5}$	13.3	....	8.3	......	7.1	6.9	....	6.6	7.1
$\frac{2}{3}$	10.8	....	7.1	......	6.1	6.0	....	5.8	6.1

It is seen from the table that in the case of pure bending ($\alpha = 2$)
the value of σ_{cr} becomes a minimum when $a/b = \frac{2}{3}$. With the
decrease of α the ratio a/b, at which σ_{cr} is a minimum, increases
and approaches unity as obtained before for a uniformly com-

[1] Calculation of a fourth approximation for the case of pure bending
shows that the difference between the third and the fourth approximation
is only about one-third of 1 per cent.

pressed plate.   The values of k for pure bending are shown in the Fig. 187 by the curve $m = 1$.

It is assumed in the preceding discussion that the plate is buckled into one half-wave, but the results obtained can be

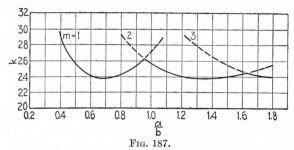

FIG. 187.

applied also for the case of several half-waves, it being necessary only to construct the curves $m = 2$, $m = 3$, $\cdots$ as explained in Art. 63.   The portions of these curves, shown in Fig. 187 by a full line, should be used in calculating σ_{cr} and in determining the number of half-waves into which a buckled plate is subdivided by nodal lines.   It is seen that a long plate will buckle in such a way that the length of each half-wave will be approximately equal to $\frac{2}{3}b$.   Curves analogous to those shown in Fig. 187 can be constructed also for other values of α, $i.e.$, for various combinations of compressive and bending stresses.

If, in addition to bending stresses, uniformly distributed compressive stresses σ_y act on the plate in a perpendicular direction (Fig. 188), the critical

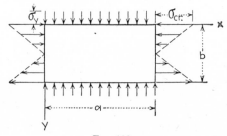

FIG. 188.

value of the maximum bending stress σ_{cr} will be reduced and can be calculated on the basis of our preceding derivation by adding to the work done by bending stresses [see expression (d)] the work done by compressive stresses σ_y.   Calculations show that the effect of σ_y on the magnitude of σ_{cr} depends on the ratios $\sigma_y : 4\pi^2 D/b^2 h$ and $a : b$.   Taking, for instance,

$$\frac{\sigma_y b^2 h}{4\pi^2 D} = \frac{1}{3} \qquad \text{and} \qquad a = b,$$

the critical stress σ_{cr} becomes about 25 per cent smaller than in the case when bending stresses are acting alone.[1]

67. Buckling of Rectangular Plates under the Action of Shearing Stresses.—We begin with a simply supported rectangular plate submitted to the action of shearing forces N_{xy} uniformly distributed along the edges[2] (Fig. 189). In calculating the critical value of shearing stress τ_{cr} at which buckling of the plate occurs, we use again the energy method. The boundary conditions at the supported edges are satisfied by

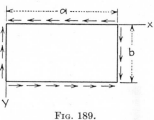

FIG. 189.

taking for the deflection surface of the buckled plate the previously used expression in the form of the double series

$$w = \sum_{m=1}^{m=\infty} \sum_{n=1}^{n=\infty} a_{mn} \sin \frac{m\pi x}{a} \sin \frac{n\pi y}{b}. \tag{a}$$

Then for the strain energy of bending of the buckled plate we will have the expression (see p. 315)

$$\Delta V = \frac{D}{2} \frac{\pi^4 ab}{4} \sum_{m=1}^{m=\infty} \sum_{n=1}^{n=\infty} a^2_{mn}\left(\frac{m^2}{a^2} + \frac{n^2}{b^2}\right)^2. \tag{b}$$

The work done by external forces during buckling of the plate is [see Eq. (201)]

$$\Delta T = -N_{xy}\int_0^a \int_0^b \frac{\partial w}{\partial x} \frac{\partial w}{\partial y}\ dx\ dy. \tag{c}$$

Substituting expression (a) for w and observing that

[1] Several examples of such calculations are given in the writer's paper, *loc. cit.*, p. 337.

[2] See writer's paper in *Memoirs of the Institute of Engineers of Ways of Communication*, vol. 89, p. 23, 1915, and in *Der Eisenbau*, vol. 12, p. 147, 1921.

$$\int_0^a \sin \frac{m\pi x}{a} \cos \frac{p\pi x}{a} \, dx = 0, \quad \text{if} \quad m \pm p \text{ is an even number;}$$

$$\int_0^a \sin \frac{m\pi x}{a} \cos \frac{p\pi x}{a} \, dx = \frac{2a}{\pi} \frac{m}{m^2 - p^2}, \quad \text{if}$$

$$m \pm p \text{ is an odd number,}$$

we obtain

$$\Delta T = -8N_{xy} \sum_m \sum_n \sum_p \sum_q a_{mn} a_{pq} \frac{mnpq}{(m^2 - p^2)(q^2 - n^2)}, \quad (d)$$

in which m, n, p, q are such integers that $m \pm p$ and $n \pm q$ are odd numbers.

Equating the work (d) produced by external forces to the strain energy (b), we obtain, for determining the critical value of shearing forces, the following expression:

$$N_{xy} = -\frac{abD}{64} \frac{\displaystyle\sum_{m=1}^{m=\infty} \sum_{n=1}^{n=\infty} a^2{}_{mn}\left(\frac{m^2\pi^2}{a^2} + \frac{n^2\pi^2}{b^2}\right)^2}{\displaystyle\sum_m \sum_n \sum_p \sum_q a_{mn} a_{pq} \frac{mnpq}{(m^2 - p^2)(q^2 - n^2)}}. \quad (e)$$

It is necessary now to select such a system of constants a_{mn} and a_{pq} as to make N_{xy} a minimum. Proceeding as before and equating to zero the derivatives of the expression (e) with respect to each of the coefficients a_{mn}, . . . , we obtain a system of homogeneous linear equations in a_{mn}, ... This system can be divided into two groups, one containing constants a_{mn} for which $m + n$ are odd numbers and the other for which $m + n$ are even numbers. Calculations show that this second group of equations gives for $(N_{xy})_{cr}$ the smallest value. Hence only this group should be considered.

Using the notations

$$\beta = \frac{a}{b}; \quad \lambda = -\frac{\pi^2}{32\beta} \frac{\pi^2 D}{b^2 h \tau_{cr}}, \quad (f)$$

we can write this group of equations in the following form:[1]

---

[1] For simplification we write only the factors with which the constants shown in the first row should be multiplied.

a_{11}	a_{22}	a_{13}	a_{31}	a_{33}	a_{42}	
$\dfrac{\lambda(1+\beta^2)^2}{\beta^2}$	$\dfrac{4}{9}$	0	0	0	$\dfrac{8}{45}$	$=0$
$\dfrac{4}{9}$	$\dfrac{16\lambda(1+\beta^2)^2}{\beta^2}$	$-\dfrac{4}{5}$	$-\dfrac{4}{5}$	$\dfrac{36}{25}$	0	$=0$
0	$-\dfrac{4}{5}$	$\dfrac{\lambda(1+9\beta^2)^2}{\beta^2}$	0	0	$-\dfrac{24}{75}$	$=0$
0	$-\dfrac{4}{5}$	0	$\dfrac{\lambda(9+\beta^2)^2}{\beta^2}$	0	$\dfrac{24}{21}$	$=0$
0	$\dfrac{36}{25}$	0	0	$\dfrac{\lambda(9+9\beta^2)^2}{\beta^2}$	$-\dfrac{72}{35}$	$=0$
$\dfrac{8}{45}$	0	$-\dfrac{24}{75}$	$\dfrac{24}{21}$	$-\dfrac{72}{35}$	$\dfrac{\lambda(16+4\beta^2)^2}{\beta^2}$	$=0$

$$(g)$$

The equation for calculating τ_{cr} will now be obtained by equating to zero the determinant of the above system of equations. The calculation can be made by successive approximations. Limiting calculations to two equations with two constants a_{11} and a_{22} and equating to zero the determinant of these equations, we obtain

$$\lambda = \pm\frac{1}{9}\frac{\beta^2}{(1+\beta^2)^2}$$

or, by using notations (f),

$$\tau_{cr} = \pm\frac{9\pi^2}{32}\frac{(1+\beta^2)^2}{\beta^3}\frac{\pi^2 D}{b^2 h}. \qquad (h)$$

The two signs indicate that in this case the critical value of the shearing stress does not depend on the direction of the stress.

The approximation (h) is not sufficiently accurate since the error is about 15 per cent for square plates and increases as the ratio a/b increases. To get a more satisfactory approximation, a larger number of equations in the system (g) must be considered.

By taking five equations and equating to zero their determinant, we obtain

$$\lambda^2 = \frac{\beta^4}{81(1+\beta^2)^4}\left[1 + \frac{81}{625} + \frac{81}{25}\left(\frac{1+\beta^2}{1+9\beta^2}\right)^2 + \frac{81}{25}\left(\frac{1+\beta^2}{9+\beta^2}\right)^2\right]. \quad (i)$$

Calculating λ and substituting it in Eq. (f), we obtain

$$\tau_{cr} = k\frac{\pi^2 D}{b^2 h}, \qquad (j)$$

where k is a constant depending on the ratio $a/b = \beta$. For a square plate we obtain in this manner $k = 9.4$.   Calculations made with a larger number of equations of the system (g)[1] show that the exact value of k is about 9.34, so that in this case the error of the approximation represented by Eq. (i) is less than 1 per cent.   Equation (i) gives a satisfactory approximation for k if the shape of the plate does not differ much from a square, say $a/b \lessgtr 1.5$.   For larger values of the ratio a/b a larger number of equations of the system (g) must be considered. In Table 37 the results of calculations with six equations are given.

TABLE 37.—NUMERICAL VALUES FOR k IN EQ. (j)

a/b	1.0	1.2	1.4	1.5	1.6	1.8	2.0	2.5	3
k	9.4	8.0	7.3	7.1	7.0	6.8	6.6	6.3	6.1

The accuracy of values of k given in this table decreases as the ratio a/b increases.   To get more accurate results for long narrow plates, let us consider a limiting case of an infinitely long plate with simply supported edges.   An approximate solution of the problem is obtained by taking for the deflection surface of the plate the following expression:

$$w = A \sin \frac{\pi y}{b} \sin \frac{\pi}{s}(x - \alpha y). \qquad (k)$$

This expression gives zero deflections for $y = 0$, $y = b$ and also along nodal lines, for which $(x - \alpha y)$ is a multiple of s.   Here s represents the length of half-waves of the buckled plate and the factor α is the slope of nodal lines.   The exact solution of the problem[2] shows that the nodal lines are not straight and that the deflection surface of the buckled plate has the form shown in Fig. 190.   Expression (k) does not satisfy the boundary conditions regarding equality to zero of the bending moments along the longitudinal edges of the plate since $\partial^2 w / \partial y^2$ is not zero along these edges; however, it can be used for an approximate

---

[1] Recently several authors have made such calculations.   See, for instance, St. Bergmann and H. Reissner, *Z. Flugtech. Motorluftsch.*, vol. 23, p. 6, 1932, and E. Seydel, *Ingenieur-Archiv*, vol. 4, 1933, p. 169.

[2] Exact solution of this problem has been given by R. V. Southwell, *Phil. Mag.*, vol. 48, p. 540, 1924, and also *Proc. Roy. Soc., London*, series A, vol. 105, p. 582.

solution of the problem. Substituting expression (k) in Eq. (199) for strain energy of bending of the buckled plate and also in the

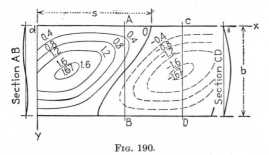

equation for the work done by external forces,[1] and equating these two quantities, we obtain

$$\tau_{cr} = \frac{\pi^2 D}{2\alpha b^2 h}\left[6\alpha^2 + 2 + \frac{s^2}{b^2} + \frac{b^2}{s^2}(1 + \alpha^2)^2 \right]. \qquad (l)$$

The smallest value for τ_{cr} is obtained by taking

$$s = b\sqrt{1 + \alpha^2} \qquad \text{and} \qquad \alpha = \frac{1}{\sqrt{2}}.$$

Then

$$\tau_{cr} = 5.7\frac{\pi^2 D}{b^2 h}. \qquad (m)$$

The exact solution of the problem for an infinitely long strip with simply supported edges gives

$$\tau_{cr} = 5.35\frac{\pi^2 D}{b^2 h}, \qquad (216)$$

so that the error of the approximate solution in this case is about $6\frac{1}{2}$ per cent.

Having the exact value for k in Eq. (j) for an infinitely long plate and a very accurate value of k for a square plate, a parabolic curve given by the equation $k = 5.35 + 4(b/a)^2$ and shown in Fig. 191 can be taken to approximate values of k for other proportions of plates.[2] For comparison there are shown also points corresponding to the figures given in Table 37. It is

---

[1] The strain energy and the work done per wave should be considered.

[2] This is only a rough approximation since the exact values of k are defined by a system of intersecting curves similar to those in Fig. 172.

seen that for longer plates the values of k given in the table are always above the curve. The values obtained from the curve can be used for practical applications.

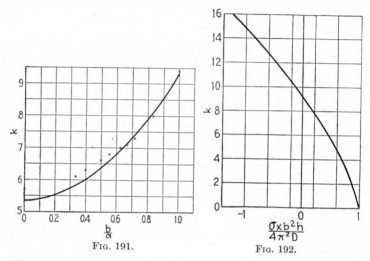

FIG. 191.   FIG. 192.

The problem of buckling of an infinitely long plate under uniform shear has been solved also for the case of clamped edges[1] and the following value found for the critical stress:

$$\tau_{cr} = 8.98 \frac{\pi^2 D}{b^2 h}. \qquad (217)$$

The combination of a pure shear with a uniform longitudinal compression or tension σ_x was also studied by R. V. Southwell and the corresponding values of k, which must be substituted in Eq. (j) for determining τ_{cr}, are given by the curve in Fig. 192. It is seen that any compressive stress

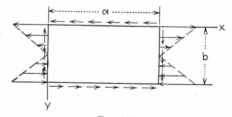

FIG. 193.

reduces the stability of a plate submitted to shear, while any tension increases this stability. For $\sigma_x = 0$ the value $k = 8.98$, given before [see Eq. (217)], is obtained from the curve.

[1] See paper by R. V. Southwell, *loc. cit.*, p. 360.

The case of combined shearing and bending stresses (Fig. 193) is also of practical interest and has been investigated in the case of a plate with simply supported edges by taking for the deflection surface the expression (*a*) and using the energy method. The results of this investigation[1] are represented

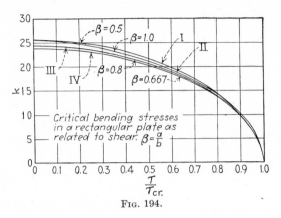

Fig. 194.

by the curves I, II, III and IV in Fig. 194.[2] As abscissas in plotting these curves, the ratios of the actual shearing stress to the critical shearing stress determined by using Table 37 have been taken. The ordinates are the values of the factor k which must be substituted in Eq. (*j*) (see p. 355) for the critical value of the bending stresses. It is seen that for small values of τ/τ_{cr}, say $(\tau/\tau_{cr}) < 0.4$, the effect of shearing stress on the critical value of bending stress is small. When τ/τ_{cr} approaches unity, the curves I, II, III and IV become steep, which indicates that some bending stresses can be added to pure shear without producing a substantial reduction in the critical value of the shearing stress.

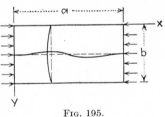

Fig. 195.

The case of shearing stress combined with tension or compression in two perpendicular directions has been discussed by H. Wagner.[3]

68. Other Cases of Buckling of Rectangular Plates.—*A rectangular plate clamped at two opposite sides and simply supported along the other two sides*

[1] See writer's paper presented at the meeting of the A.S.C.E. and the A.S.M.E., Chicago, June, 1933, published in *Engineering*, vol. 138, p. 207, 1934. See also paper by O. Stein, *Stahlbau*, vol. 7, p. 57, 1934. In the latter paper a smaller number of terms in expression (*a*) was used than in our calculations represented in Fig. 194, and thus the results are less accurate.

[2] These curves were calculated for the writer by S. Way. Eight equations of the system (*g*) were used in these calculations.

[3] H. Wagner, *Jb. Wiss. Ges. Luftf.*, 1928, p. 113.

uniformly compressed in the direction of the supported sides[1] (Fig. 195). A method, analogous to that used in Art. 65 can be used here also. The critical value of compressive stress is given by the equation

$$\sigma_{cr} = k\frac{\pi^2 D}{b^2 h},\tag{a}$$

in which k is a numerical factor depending on the ratio a/b of the sides of the plate. Several values of this factor are given in Table 38.

TABLE 38.—VALUES OF THE FACTOR k IN EQ. (a)

a/b	0.6	0.8	1.0	1.2	1.4	1.6	1.7	1.73	1.8	2.0	2.5	2.83	3.0
k	13.38	8.73	6.74	5.84	5.45	5.34	5.33	5.33	5.18	4.85	4.52	4.50	4.41

Up to the value $a/b = 1.73$ the plate buckles into one half-wave. From $a/b = 1.73$ to $a/b = 2.83$ there will be two half-waves and the shape of the buckled plate is as indicated in Fig. 195. Generally the transition from m to $m + 1$ half-waves occurs when $a/b = \sqrt{m(m + 2)}$. It may be seen that the effect of clamping the edges on the magnitude of the σ_{cr} decreases as the ratio a/b increases; for $a/b = 3$ the value of k in Table 38 is only 10 per cent higher than the value 4 obtained for a plate with all four edges simply supported.

A rectangular plate with clamped edges under pressure in two perpendicular directions. Taking the coordinate axes as shown in Fig. 195, and assuming that the shape of the plate does not differ much from a square and that the stresses σ_x and σ_y are about equal, we can expect that the deflection surface of the buckled plate is represented with sufficient accuracy by the equation

$$w = \frac{\delta}{4}\left(1 - \cos\frac{2\pi x}{a}\right)\left(1 - \cos\frac{2\pi y}{b}\right),$$

which satisfies the boundary conditions. With this expression for deflections, the strain energy of bending is

$$\Delta V = \frac{\pi^4 \delta^2 D}{8} ab\left(\frac{3}{a^4} + \frac{3}{b^4} + \frac{2}{a^2 b^2}\right).$$

The work done by compressive forces during buckling of the plate is

$$\Delta T = \frac{\sigma_x h}{2}\int_0^a\int_0^b\left(\frac{\partial w}{\partial x}\right)^2 dx\, dy + \frac{\sigma_y h}{2}\int_0^a\int_0^b\left(\frac{\partial w}{\partial y}\right)^2 dx\, dy = \frac{3}{32}\pi^2\delta^2 h\frac{b}{a}\left(\sigma_x + \frac{a^2}{b^2}\sigma_y\right).$$

Equating this work to the strain energy of bending, we obtain the following equation for calculating critical values of the compressive stresses σ_x and σ_y:

$$\left(\sigma_x + \frac{a^2}{b^2}\sigma_y\right)_{cr} = \frac{4}{3}\frac{\pi^2 D a^2}{h}\left(\frac{3}{a^4} + \frac{3}{b^4} + \frac{2}{a^2 b^2}\right).\tag{218}$$

[1] SCHLEICHER, F., *Mitt. Forschungsanstalt. Gutehoffnungshütte Konzerns,* vol. 1, 1931.

In the particular case of a square plate submitted to the action of uniform thrust, we obtain from the above equation

$$\sigma_{cr} = 5.33 \frac{\pi^2 D}{a^2 h}.$$

It is interesting to note that for this case we have another solution of the problem[1] which gives as a lower limit for σ_{cr} the value

$$\sigma_{cr} = 5.30 \frac{\pi^2 D}{a^2 h}. \tag{219}$$

Thus the approximate solution is very accurate in this case.

In the case of rectangular plates compressed longitudinally, the buckling of the plate with one or several nodal lines perpendicular to the length of the plate should be considered. The solution of this problem was recently discussed by O. H. Faxen.[2] By using Taylor's method mentioned above he found that if the plate is uniformly compressed along the x-axis the factor k in Eq. (a) has the numerical values 18.3, 10.1, 8.3 and 7.9 for a/b equal to .5, 1.0, 1.5 and 2 respectively. For a plate of considerable length the critical value of compressive stresses must approach that obtained from Table 35 for $a/b = 0.7$.

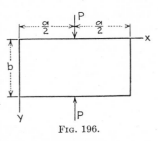

Fig. 196.

A simply supported rectangular plate compressed by two equal and opposite forces (Fig. 196).[3] An approximate solution of this problem is obtained by taking for the deflection surface of the buckled plate the following series:

$$w = \sin \frac{\pi y}{b} \sum_{m=1,\,3,\,5,\,\cdots}^{\infty} a_m \sin \frac{m\pi x}{a}. \tag{b}$$

The expression for strain energy of bending becomes

$$\Delta V = \frac{abD}{8} \sum_{m=1,\,3,\,5,\,\cdots}^{\infty} a^2{}_m \left(\frac{m^2 \pi^2}{a^2} + \frac{\pi^2}{b^2} \right)^2. \tag{c}$$

The work done by the compressive forces during buckling is

$$\Delta T = \frac{P}{2} \int_0^b \left(\frac{\partial w}{\partial y} \right)^2_{x=\frac{a}{2}} dy = \frac{\pi^2 P}{4b} (a_1 - a_3 + a_5 - \cdots)^2. \tag{d}$$

Equating this work to the strain energy of bending (c), we obtain for the critical value of compressive forces

[1] TAYLOR, G. I., *Z. angew. Math. Mech.*, vol. 13, p. 147, 1933. See also A. Weinstein, *Compt. rend.*, 1935.

[2] *Z. angew. Math. Mech.*, vol. 15, p. 268, 1935.

[3] See A. Sommerfeld, *Z. Math. Physik*, vol. 54, 1906, and the writer, *Z. Math. Physik*, vol. 58, p. 357, 1910.

$$P_{cr} = \frac{\pi^2 Dab^2}{2} \frac{\sum_{m=1,\,3,\,5,\,\cdots} a^2{}_m \left(\dfrac{m^2}{a^2} + \dfrac{1}{b^2}\right)^2}{(a_1 - a_3 + a_5 - \cdots)^2}. \tag{e}$$

Equating to zero the derivatives of this expression with respect to each coefficient a_n, we obtain a system of linear equations of the following form:

$$a_n = \frac{2P_{cr}}{\pi^2 Dab^2} \frac{(-1)^{\frac{n-1}{2}} \sum_{m=1,\,3,\,5\,\cdots}^{\infty} a_m (-1)^{\frac{m-1}{2}}}{\left(\dfrac{n^2}{a^2} + \dfrac{1}{b^2}\right)^2}. \tag{f}$$

Multiplying each of these equations by $(-1)^{\frac{n-1}{2}}$ and adding them together, we obtain

$$P_{cr} = \frac{\pi^2 Dab^2}{2} \frac{1}{\displaystyle\sum_{n=1,\,3,\,5,\,\cdots}^{\infty} \frac{1}{\left(\dfrac{n^2}{a^2} + \dfrac{1}{b^2}\right)^2}} \tag{g}$$

or, by using notation $a/b = \beta$,

$$P_{cr} = \frac{\pi^2 D}{2b} \frac{1}{\beta^3 \displaystyle\sum_{n=1,\,3,\,5,\,\cdots}^{\infty} \frac{1}{(\beta^2 + n^2)^2}}. \tag{h}$$

For summation of the series in the denominator we note that

$$\frac{e^{\frac{\pi z}{2}} + e^{-\frac{\pi z}{2}}}{2} = (1 + z^2)\left(1 + \frac{z^2}{9}\right)\left(1 + \frac{z^2}{25}\right) \cdots.$$

Taking the logarithm of each side and differentiating, we obtain

$$\frac{\pi}{4} \tanh \frac{\pi z}{2} = z \sum_{m=1,\,3,\,5,\,\cdots}^{\infty} \frac{1}{m^2 + z^2} \tag{i}$$

The second differentiation gives

$$\frac{\pi^2}{8} \frac{1}{\cosh^2 \dfrac{\pi z}{2}} = \sum_{m=1,\,3,\,5,\,\cdots}^{\infty} \frac{1}{m^2 + z^2} - \sum_{m=1,\,3,\,5,\,\cdots}^{\infty} \frac{2z^2}{(m^2 + z^2)^2}.$$

Multiplying this by z and using Eq. (i), we obtain

$$z^3 \sum_{m=1,\,3,\,5,\,\cdots}^{\infty} \frac{1}{(m^2 + z^2)^2} = \frac{\pi}{8}\left(\tanh \frac{\pi z}{2} - \frac{\pi z/2}{\cosh^2 \dfrac{\pi z}{2}}\right).$$

The left side of this equation is the same series that we had in Eq. (h) and it is seen that the sum of this series can be readily calculated for each value of the ratio $\beta = a/b$ by using tables of hyperbolic functions. With increasing β the sum rapidly approaches the limiting value $\pi/8$ (for $a/b = 2$, this sum is $0.973\pi/8$), and for long plates we can assume

$$P_{cr} = \frac{4\pi D}{b}. \tag{220}$$

If the sides $y = 0$ and $y = b$ of the plate are clamped, we take the deflection surface of the buckled plate in the form of the following series:

$$w = \left(1 - \cos \frac{2\pi y}{b}\right) \sum_{m = 1, 3, 5, \, \cdots}^{\infty} a_m \sin \frac{m\pi x}{a}.$$

Then proceeding as in the previous case, we obtain for long plates

$$P_{cr} = \frac{8\pi D}{b}. \tag{221}$$

69. Buckling of Circular Plates.[1]—Let us begin with the simple

case of a circular plate with clamped edges (Fig. 197). To determine the critical value of the compressive forces N_r uniformly distributed around the edge of the plate, we assume that a slight buckling has taken place and we use the differential equation of the deflection surface of the plate. Assuming that the deflection surface is a surface of revolution and denoting by

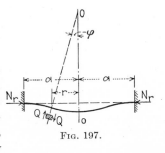

FIG. 197.

ϕ the angle between the axis of revolution and any normal to the plate, the required equation is[2]

$$r^2 \frac{d^2\phi}{dr^2} + r\frac{d\phi}{dr} - \phi = -\frac{Qr^2}{D}. \tag{a}$$

Here r is the distance of any point measured from the center of the plate and Q is the shearing force per unit of length, the positive direction of which is shown in Fig. 197. Since there are no lateral loads acting on the plate, we have

$$Q = N_r\phi, \tag{b}$$

and, using the notation

$$\frac{N_r}{D} = \alpha^2, \tag{c}$$

[1] See G. H. Bryan, *Proc. London Math. Soc.*, vol. 22, p. 54, 1891. See also A. Nadai, *Z. Ver. deut. Ing.*, vol. 59, p. 169, 1915.

[2] See "Strength of Materials," vol. 2, p. 490, 1930.

we obtain

$$r^2 \frac{d^2\phi}{dr^2} + r \frac{d\phi}{dr} + (\alpha^2 r^2 - 1)\phi = 0. \qquad (d)$$

Let us introduce now a new variable

$$u = \alpha r, \qquad (e)$$

by the use of which Eq. (d) becomes

$$u^2 \frac{d^2\phi}{du^2} + u \frac{d\phi}{du} + (u^2 - 1)\phi = 0. \qquad (f)$$

Integrating this equation by series (see p. **116**), we obtain a particular solution in the following form:[1]

$$\phi = C \frac{u}{2} \left[1 - \frac{1}{1 \cdot 2} \left(\frac{u}{2} \right)^2 + \frac{1}{1 \cdot 2 \cdot 2 \cdot 3} \left(\frac{u}{2} \right)^4 - \cdots \right], \qquad (g)$$

in which C is a constant; the function of u, with which it is multiplied, is the known Bessel's function of the first order, usually denoted by $J_1(u)$ so that

$$\phi = C J_1(u) = C J_1(\alpha r). \qquad (h)$$

At the center of the plate we have $r = u = 0$; thus the angle ϕ, from Eq. (g), is zero as it should be from symmetry. To satisfy the condition at the clamped edge of the plate, we must have

$$(\phi)_{r=a} = 0.$$

Hence

$$J_1(\alpha a) = 0. \qquad (i)$$

There are numerical tables[2] for the function $J_1(\alpha a)$, by using which the smallest value of α satisfying Eq. (i) and the smallest value of N_r in Eq. (c) at which buckling of the plate occurs can be calculated. In this way we find that the smallest root of Eq. (i) is

$$\alpha a = 3.832.$$

Substituting this into Eq. (c) we obtain

$$(N_r)_{cr} = \frac{(3.832)^2 D}{a^2} = \frac{14.68 D}{a^2}. \qquad (222)$$

---

[1] The second particular solution of the Eq. (f) becomes infinity at the center of the plate; hence it should not be considered in the case of a plate without a hole at the center.

[2] See, for instance, E. Jahnke and F. Emde, "Funktionentafeln," **1933**.

For comparison we note that the critical compressive force for a strip of unit width with clamped ends, and having the length equal to the diameter of the plate, is

$$\frac{\pi^2 D}{a^2}.$$

Thus for producing buckling of the plate compressive stresses about 50 per cent higher than for the strip should be applied.

Solution (g) can be used also for the case of buckling of a compressed circular plate with simply supported edge. The bending moment along the edge in this case must be zero. Hence[1]

$$\left(\frac{d\phi}{dr} + \nu \frac{\phi}{r} \right) = 0. \qquad (j)$$

The derivative dJ_1/du can be calculated by differentiation of the series (g) and can be represented in the following form

$$\frac{dJ_1}{du} = J_0 - \frac{J_1}{u}, \qquad (k)$$

in which

$$J_0 = 1 - \left(\frac{u}{2}\right)^2 + \frac{1}{(2 \cdot 1)^2} \left(\frac{u}{2}\right)^4 - \frac{1}{(3 \cdot 2 \cdot 1)^2} \left(\frac{u}{2}\right)^6 + \cdots .$$

This is Bessel's function of zero order. Using Eq. (k) the boundary condition (j) becomes

$$\alpha a J_0(\alpha a) - (1 - \nu) J_1(\alpha a) = 0. \qquad (l)$$

Taking $\nu = 0.3$ and using the tables of functions J_0 and J_1, the smallest root of the transcendental Eq. (l) is found to be 2.05. Then, from Eq. (c),

$$(N_r)_{cr} = \frac{2.05^2 D}{a^2} = \frac{4.20 D}{a^2}. \qquad (223)$$

That is, the critical compressive stress in this case is about three and a half times smaller than in the case of a plate with clamped edge.

In the case of a plate with a hole at the center,[2] the compressive stresses produced by forces N_r, uniformly distributed along the

[1] See "Strength of Materials," vol. 2, p. 489, 1930.

[2] This case was discussed by E. Meissner, *Schweiz. Bauzeitung*, vol. 101, p. 87, 1933.

outer boundary of the plate, are no longer constant and are determined by the known Lamé's formula.   Assuming a buckling of the plate symmetrical with respect to the center, the differential equation for the deflection surface of the plate can again be integrated by Bessel's function and the expression for $(N_r)_{cr}$ is

$$(N_r)_{cr} = k\frac{D}{a^2}, \qquad (m)$$

in which k is a numerical factor, the magnitude of which depends on the ratio b/a, where b is the radius of the hole.   The values

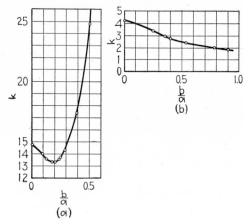

Fig. 198.

of k for various values of b/a are given in Fig. 198a for a clamped plate and in Fig. 198b for a plate supported along the outer boundary.   It is assumed in both cases that the boundary of the hole is free from forces.[1]   It is seen that in the case of a plate with clamped edge the factor k is a minimum for b/a approximately equal to 0.2, and for the ratio b/a larger than 0.2 it increases rapidly with this ratio and becomes larger than for a plate without a hole.   It must be noted, however, that in this discussion buckling symmetrical with respect to the center of the plate is assumed, while for b/a approaching unity the conditions for a compressed ring with outer boundary clamped are analogous to those of a long compressed rectangular plate clamped along one side and free along the other.   Such a plate buckles in many waves (see p. 341); we should expect that in the case of a narrow

[1] Poisson's ratio ν is taken equal to $\frac{1}{3}$ in this problem.

ring also several waves along the circumference would be formed during buckling and that the values of k obtained on the assumption of symmetrical buckling would give exaggerated values for $(N_r)_{cr}$.

Buckling of plates into several waves with radial and circular nodal lines has been discussed in the case of a plate without a hole, and it has been shown that the critical value of the compressive forces is always given by Eq. (m). Using these results, the problem of buckling of plates supported along two radii and two concentric circles can be solved.[1]

The problem of buckling of a uniformly compressed equilateral triangular plate with simply supported edges also has been discussed[2] and it was found that the critical value of the compressive forces is

$$N_{cr} = \frac{4\pi^2 D}{a^2}, \tag{224}$$

where a is the altitude of the triangle. It is seen that the critical stress in this case is about the same as for a simply supported and uniformly compressed circular plate whose boundary is an inscribed circle to the equilateral triangle of altitude a.

70. Stability of Plates Reinforced by Ribs.[3]—In all cases of buckling of plates, the critical values of normal or shearing forces are proportional to the flexural rigidity of the plates. Hence, for a rectangular plate with given boundary conditions and a given ratio a/b, the magnitude of the critical stress is proportional to (h/b).[2] The stability of the plate can always be increased by increasing its thickness, but such a design will not be economical in respect to the weight of material used. A more economical solution is obtained by keeping the thickness of the plate as small as possible and increasing the stability by introducing reinforcing ribs. In the case of a compressed plate, as shown in Fig. 199, its stability can be made about four times greater by adding a longitudinal rib of suitable cross section which bisects the width of the plate. The weight of such a rib usually will be much smaller than the additional weight introduced by an ade-

---

[1] GALERKIN, B., *Compt. rend.*, vol. 179, p. 1392, 1924.

[2] See S. Woinowsky-Krieger, *Ingenieur-Archiv*, vol. 4, p. 254, 1933.

[3] See writer's paper in *Memoirs of the Institute of Engineers of Ways of Communication*, St. Petersburg, vol. 89, 1915, and also in *Der Eisenbau*, vol. 12, p. 147, 1921.

quate increase in the thickness of the plate.   In practical design it is usually desirable to have such proportions of reinforcing ribs as to make the critical value of the stresses equal to the yield-

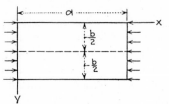

Fig. 199.

point stress of the material.   Then the strength of all the material is used to best advantage.[1]

The relation between the cross-sectional dimensions of ribs and the critical value of stresses in a plate can be obtained as before by using the energy method.   Several cases of stiffening of rectangular plates under compression and shear will now be considered.

Simply Supported Rectangular Plates with Longitudinal Ribs.— In this case we take the deflection surface of the buckled plate (Fig. 199) in the form of a double series

$$w = \sum_{m=1}^{m=\infty} \sum_{n=1}^{n=\infty} a_{mn} \sin \frac{m\pi x}{a} \sin \frac{n\pi y}{b}. \qquad (a)$$

The corresponding strain energy of bending of the plate is

$$\Delta V = \frac{\pi^4 D}{2} \frac{ab}{4} \sum_{m=1}^{m=\infty} \sum_{n=1}^{n=\infty} a^2_{mn} \left(\frac{m^2}{a^2} + \frac{n^2}{b^2} \right)^2. \qquad (b)$$

Assuming a general case of several longitudinal ribs, and denoting by B_i the flexural rigidity of a rib[2] at the distance c_i from the edge $y = 0$, the strain energy of bending of this rib, when buckled together with the plate, is

$$\Delta V_i = \frac{B_i}{2} \int_0^a \left(\frac{\partial^2 w}{\partial x^2} \right)^2_{y=c_i} dx =$$

$$\frac{\pi^4 B_i}{4a^3} \sum_{m=1}^{m=\infty} m^4 \left(a_{m1} \sin \frac{\pi c_i}{b} + a_{m2} \sin \frac{2\pi c_i}{b} + \cdots \right)^2. \qquad (c)$$

[1] The case of light structures in which the strength of plates is taken into account after buckling has occurred will be discussed later (see Art. 72).

[2] Since the rib is rigidly connected with the plate, a portion of the plate must be taken in calculating B_i (see pp. 377 and 399).

The work done during buckling by compressive forces N_x acting on the plate is

$$\Delta T = \frac{N_x}{2} \frac{ab}{4} \sum_{m=1}^{m=\infty} \sum_{n=1}^{n=\infty} \frac{m^2\pi^2}{a^2} a^2_{mn}. \tag{d}$$

The work done during buckling by the compressive force P_i acting on a rib is

$$\Delta T_i = \frac{P_i}{2} \int_0^a \left(\frac{\partial w}{\partial x}\right)^2_{y=c_i} dx = \frac{P_i}{2} \frac{\pi^2}{a^2} \frac{a}{2} \sum_{m=1}^{m=\infty} m^2 \left(a_{m1} \sin \frac{\pi c_i}{b} + a_{m2} \sin \frac{2\pi c_i}{b} + \cdots \right)^2. \tag{e}$$

The general equation for the calculation of critical stress is[1]

$$\Delta V + \Delta \sum_i V_i = \Delta T + \Delta \sum_i T_i, \tag{f}$$

in which the summation must be extended over all the stiffening ribs. Using notations

$$\frac{a}{b} = \beta; \qquad \frac{B_i}{bD} = \gamma_i; \qquad \frac{P_i}{bN_x} = \frac{A_i}{bh} = \delta_i, \tag{g}$$

where bh is the cross-sectional area of the plate and A_i that of one rib, we obtain from Eq. (f)

$$\sigma_{cr} =$$

$$\frac{\pi^2 D}{b^2 h \beta^2} \frac{\displaystyle\sum_{m=1}^{m=\infty} \sum_{n=1}^{n=\infty} a^2_{mn}(m^2+n^2\beta^2)^2 + 2\sum_i \gamma_i \sum_{m=1}^{m=\infty} m^4 \left(\sum_{n=1}^{n=\infty} a_{mn} \sin \frac{n\pi c_i}{b}\right)^2}{\displaystyle\sum_{m=1}^{m=\infty} \sum_{n=1}^{n=\infty} m^2 a^2_{mn} + 2\sum_i \delta_i \sum_{m=1}^{m=\infty} m^2 \left(\sum_{n=1}^{n=\infty} a_{mn} \sin \frac{n\pi c_i}{b}\right)^2}. \tag{h}$$

Proceeding as before and equating to zero the derivatives of this expression with respect to the coefficients a_{mn}, we obtain a system of homogeneous linear equations of the following type:

[1] The energy of twist of the rib, which occurs during buckling, is neglected in this discussion.

$$\frac{\pi^2 D}{b^2 h}\left[a_{mn}(m^2 + n^2\beta^2)^2 + 2\sum_i \gamma_i \sin\frac{n\pi c_i}{b}m^4 \sum_{p=1}^{p=\infty} a_{mp} \sin\frac{p\pi c_i}{b}\right] -$$

$$\beta^2\sigma_{cr}\left(m^2 a_{mn} + 2\sum_i \delta_i \sin\frac{n\pi c_i}{b}m^2 \sum_{p=1}^{p=\infty} a_{mp} \sin\frac{p\pi c_i}{b}\right) = 0. \quad (i)$$

By equating to zero the determinant of this system of equations, an equation for determining σ_{cr} is obtained.

Let us begin with the case of one longitudinal rib dividing the width of the plate in halves (Fig. 199); then $c_i = b/2$. Without limiting the generality of our conclusions, we can assume that the reinforced plate buckles into one half-wave and we can take $m = 1$. Then Eq. (i) can be represented in the following simplified form:[1]

$$\frac{\pi^2 D}{b^2 h \beta^2}[a_1(1 + \beta^2)^2 + 2\gamma(a_1 - a_3 + a_5 - \cdots)] -$$

$$\sigma_{cr}[a_1 + 2\delta(a_1 - a_3 + a_5 - \cdots)] = 0;$$

$$\frac{\pi^2 D}{b^2 h \beta^2}(1 + 4\beta^2)^2 a_2 - \sigma_{cr}a_2 = 0;$$

$$\frac{\pi^2 D}{b^2 h \beta^2}[a_3(1 + 9\beta^2)^2 - 2\gamma(a_1 - a_3 + a_5 - \cdots)] - \quad (j)$$

$$\sigma_{cr}[a_3 - 2\delta(a_1 - a_3 + a_5 - \cdots)] = 0;$$

$$\frac{\pi^2 D}{b^2 h \beta^2}(1 + 16\beta^2)^2 a_4 - \sigma_{cr}a_4 = 0;$$

. . . .

. . . .

We note that the equations of even order each contain only one coefficient. The corresponding values of σ_{cr} are the values for which the buckled plate has a nodal line coinciding with the rib and the rib remains straight during buckling of the plate. To establish the relation between the flexural rigidity of the rib and the critical value of the compressive stresses, the equations of odd order in the system (j) must be considered. The first approximation for σ_{cr} is obtained by taking the first equation of the system and assuming that only one coefficient a_1 is different

---

[1] The first subscript in coefficients a_{mn} is omitted in the following derivations.

from zero, *i.e.*, by taking only the first term in the double series (*a*) representing the surface of the buckled plate. Then

$$\sigma_{cr} = \frac{\pi^2 D}{b^2 h} \frac{(1 + \beta^2)^2 + 2\gamma}{\beta^2 (1 + 2\delta)}. \tag{225}$$

The following calculations, in which a larger number of Eqs. (*j*) is considered, show that this first approximation is a very accurate one for longer plates, say for $\beta > 2$. For shorter plates a larger number of Eqs. (*j*) must be considered. By taking the first and the third of those equations with coefficients a_1 and a_3 different from zero, and by equating to zero the determinant of these two equations, we obtain for the second approximation of σ_{cr} the following quadratic equation:

$$(k\beta^2)^2(1 + 4\delta) - k\beta^2[(1 + 2\delta)(c + d) - 8\gamma\delta] + cd - 4\gamma^2 = 0, \quad (k)$$

in which

$$k = \frac{\sigma_{cr} b^2 h}{\pi^2 D};$$
$$c = (1 + \beta^2)^2 + 2\gamma; \qquad d = (1 + 9\beta^2)^2 + 2\gamma.$$

By taking three equations of the system (*j*) with three coefficients a_1, a_3 and a_5 different from zero, we obtain for the third approximation of σ_{cr} a cubic equation. These calculations show that the difference between the second and the third approximations is small; hence Eq. (*k*) is accurate enough for calculating critical stresses in a compressed plate with one rib. These stresses always can be represented by the formula

$$\sigma_{cr} = k\frac{\pi^2 D}{b^2 h}, \tag{l}$$

in which the factor k depends on the proportions of the plate and of the rib which are defined by the ratios (*g*). Several values of this factor are given in Table 39. It is seen that for a definite value of γ and δ the factor k varies with the ratio a/b and becomes a minimum for a certain value of this ratio. This indicates that a long plate will usually buckle into several half-waves such that the ratio of the length of one half-wave to the width of the plate approaches the value at which k is a minimum. It can be seen from the table that the length of the half-waves increases as the flexural rigidity of the rib increases. By using for σ_{cr}

TABLE 39.—NUMERICAL VALUES OF k IN EQ. (l) FOR A PLATE STIFFENED BY ONE LONGITUDINAL RIB (FIG. 199)

β	$\gamma = 5$			$\gamma = 10$			$\gamma = 15$			$\gamma = 20$			$\gamma = 25$		
	$\delta = 0.05$	$\delta = 0.10$	$\delta = 0.20$	$\delta = 0.05$	$\delta = 0.10$	$\delta = 0.20$	$\delta = 0.05$	$\delta = 0.10$	$\delta = 0.20$	$\delta = 0.05$	$\delta = 0.10$	$\delta = 0.20$	$\delta = 0.05$	$\delta = 0.10$	$\delta = 0.20$
0.6	16.5	16.5	16.5	16.5	16.5	16.5	16.5	16.5	16.5	16.5	16.5	16.5	16.5	16.5	16.5
0.8	15.4	14.6	13.0	16.8	16.8	16.8	16.8	16.8	16.8	16.8	16.8	16.8	16.8	16.8	16.8
1.0	12.0	11.1	9.72	16.0	16.0	15.8	16.0	16.0	16.0	16.0	16.0	16.0	16.0	16.0	16.0
1.2	9.83	9.06	7.88	15.3	14.2	12.4	16.5	16.5	16.5	16.5	16.5	16.5	16.5	16.5	16.5
1.4	8.62	7.91	6.82	12.9	12.0	10.3	16.1	15.7	13.6	16.1	16.1	16.1	16.1	16.1	16.1
1.6	8.01	7.38	6.32	11.4	10.5	9.05	14.7	13.6	11.8	16.1	16.1	14.4	16.1	16.1	16.1
1.8	7.84	7.19	6.16	10.6	9.70	8.35	13.2	12.2	10.5	15.9	14.7	12.6	16.2	16.2	14.7
2.0	7.96	7.29	6.24	10.2	9.35	8.03	12.4	11.4	9.80	14.6	13.4	11.6	15.4	15.4	13.3
2.2	8.28	7.58	6.50	10.2	9.30	7.99	12.0	11.0	9.45	13.9	12.7	10.9	15.8	14.5	12.4
2.4	8.79	8.06	6.91	10.4	9.49	8.15	11.9	10.9	9.37	13.5	12.4	10.6	15.1	13.8	11.9
2.6	9.27	8.50	7.28	10.8	9.86	8.48	12.1	11.1	9.53	13.5	12.4	10.6	14.8	13.6	11.6
2.8	8.62	7.91	6.31	11.4	10.4	8.94	12.5	11.5	9.85	13.7	12.6	10.8	14.8	13.6	11.6
3.0	8.31	7.62	6.53	12.0	11.1	9.52	13.1	12.0	10.3	14.1	13.0	11.1	15.2	13.9	11.9
3.2	8.01	7.38	6.32	11.4	10.5	9.05	13.9	12.7	10.9	14.8	13.5	11.6	15.6	14.3	12.3
3.6	7.84	7.19	6.16	10.6	9.70	8.35	13.2	12.2	10.5	15.9	14.7	12.6	16.2	15.7	13.5
4.0	7.96	7.29	6.24	10.2	9.35	8.03	12.4	11.4	9.8	14.6	13.4	11.6	16.0	15.4	13.3

the first approximation (225), it can be readily shown that k becomes a minimum when

$$\beta^2 = \sqrt{1 + 2\gamma}.$$

The values of k above the horizontal lines, shown in the table, are the same as for a simply supported plate of width equal to $b/2$. It indicates those proportions of the rib and of the plate for which the rib remains straight when the plate buckles.

From Table 39 the critical compressive stress for a plate stiffened by one rib (Fig. 199) can be calculated without difficulty in each particular case. Let a compressed steel plate with simply supported edges have the following dimensions: $a = 48$ in., $b = 80$ in., $h = \frac{9}{16}$ in., $E = 30 \cdot 10^6$ lb. per square inch and $\nu = 0.3$. Then $\beta = a/b = 0.6$ and, for a plate without a stiffening rib, we obtain from Table 31 (see p. 332) $\sigma_{cr} = 6,900$ lb. per square inch. Let us assume now that an absolutely rigid rib subdivides the width of the plate in halves. In such case each half can be considered as a plate of the width $b/2 = 40$ in. For this plate, considered as simply supported, we find, by using Table 31 that $\sigma_{cr} = 22,100$ lb. per square inch. To decide what cross-sectional dimensions the rib must have in order to remain straight during buckling of the plate, we use Table 39. It is seen from this table that, for $a/b = 0.6$, such a condition is obtained by using a stiffener, for which $\gamma = B/bD = 5$ and $\delta = A/bh < 0.2$. In calculating the quantity B, note that the stiffener is riveted or welded to a plate of great width; this results in a considerable increase of flexural rigidity of the rib. By taking the stiffener in the form of a channel or a bar of Z-section, riveted to the plate by one flange, the centroid of the cross section, consisting of the stiffener and the plate, will be very near to the surface of the plate; the moment of inertia of the cross section of the stiffener with respect to the axis coinciding with the outer surface of the flange should be taken in calculating B. Taking for the rib a standard channel of 4 in. depth and 1.56 sq. in. cross-sectional area, we obtain $B = E(3.8 + 1.56 \cdot 4) = 10.0E$ lb. sq. inches, $\gamma = B/bD \approx 7.7$ and $\delta = A/bh \approx 0.034$. For such proportions, as we see from Table 39 for $\beta = 0.6$, the rib can be considered as absolutely rigid.

If the length of the plate is twice as great, we have $a/b = 1.2$ and it is seen from the table that to eliminate buckling of the stiffener the ratio γ must be larger than 10. Taking for the stiffener a standard channel of 5 in. depth and 1.95 sq. in. cross-sectional area, we obtain $B = (7.4 + 1.95 \cdot 2.5^2)E = 19.6E$ lb. sq. inches, $\gamma = 15$ and $\delta = .043$. For such proportions, as is seen from the table, the rib can be considered as absolutely rigid.

In the case of two equal longitudinal ribs dividing the width of the plate into three equal parts, the problem of stability can be analyzed in a similar way and we obtain as the first approximation from Eqs. (i)

$$\sigma_{cr} = \frac{\pi^2 D}{b^2 h} \frac{(1 + \beta^2)^2 + 3\gamma}{\beta^2(1 + 3\delta)}. \tag{226}$$

This formula has the same form as formula (l) given above for the case of one rib. Several values of the numerical factor k are given in Table 40.

TABLE 40.—VALUES OF THE FACTOR k IN EQ. (l) FOR THE CASE OF TWO LONGITUDINAL RIBS DIVIDING THE PLATE INTO THREE EQUAL PARTS

β	$\gamma = \frac{10}{3}$		$\gamma = 5$		$\gamma = \frac{20}{3}$		$\gamma = 10$	
	$\delta = 0.05$	$\delta = 0.10$	$\delta = 0.05$	$\delta = 0.10$	$\delta = 0.05$	$\delta = 0.10$	$\delta = 0.05$	$\delta = 0.10$
0.6	26.8	24.1	36.4	33.2	36.4	36.4	36.4	36.4
0.8	16.9	15.0	23.3	20.7	29.4	26.3	37.2	37.1
1.0	12.1	10.7	16.3	14.5	20.5	18.2	28.7	25.6
1.2	9.61	8.51	12.6	11.2	15.5	13.8	21.4	19.0
1.4	8.32	7.36	10.5	9.32	12.7	11.3	17.2	15.2
1.6	7.70	6.81	9.40	8.31	11.1	9.82	14.5	12.8
1.8	7.51	6.64	8.85	7.83	10.2	9.02	12.9	11.4
2.0	7.61	6.73	8.70	7.69	9.78	8.65	11.9	10.6

By using formula (226) we can establish in each particular case the value of β at which the factor k in Eq. (l) becomes a minimum and also the number of waves into which the plate will subdivide during buckling if the proportions of the stiffeners are chosen.

If the number of equidistant stiffening ribs is larger than two, the approximate expression for the critical stress, from Eq. (i), is

FIG. 200.

$$\sigma_{cr} = \frac{\pi^2 D}{b^2 h} \frac{(1 + \beta^2)^2 + 2\sum_i \gamma_i \sin^2 \frac{\pi c_i}{b}}{\beta^2 \left(1 + 2\sum_i \delta_i \sin^2 \frac{\pi c_i}{b}\right)}. \tag{227}$$

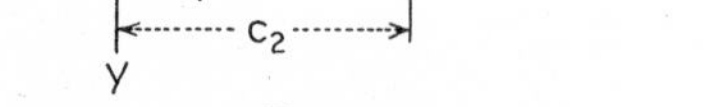

Simply Supported Compressed Plate with Transverse Stiffening Ribs (Fig. 200).—In this case we take the deflection surface of the plate in the form of the series[1]

$$w = \sum_{m=1}^{m=\infty} a_m \sin \frac{m\pi x}{a} \sin \frac{\pi y}{b}. \tag{m}$$

[1] There will be formed during buckling only one half-wave in the y-direction.

Proceeding as before and using notations (g), we obtain a system of homogeneous linear equations of the following kind:

$$a_m(m^2 + \beta^2)^2 + \sum_i 2\gamma_i\beta^3 \sin \frac{m\pi c_i}{a}\left(a_1 \sin \frac{\pi c_i}{a} + a_2 \sin \frac{2\pi c_i}{a} + \cdots\right) = \sigma_{cr}\frac{b^2h}{\pi^2D}\beta^2 m^2 a_m. \quad (n)$$

If there are many equidistant and comparatively flexible ribs of equal rigidity, so that there will be several ribs for each half-wave of the buckled plate, we can take only one term in expression m and assume

$$w = a_m \sin \frac{m\pi x}{a} \sin \frac{\pi y}{b}.$$

Equation (n) becomes

$$a_m(m^2 + \beta^2)^2 + a_m 2\gamma\beta^3 \sum_i \sin^2 \frac{m\pi c_i}{a} = \sigma_{cr}\frac{b^2h}{\pi^2D}\beta^2 m^2 a_m.$$

In this case an approximate formula for the critical stress is

$$\sigma_{cr} = \frac{\pi^2D}{b^2h}\frac{(m^2 + \beta^2)^2 + r\gamma\beta^3}{\beta^2 m^2}, \quad (228)$$

in which $r - 1$ represents the number of ribs and m the number of half-waves. In each particular case m should be chosen so as to make expression (228) a minimum. In the case of a comparatively short plate in which there is only one transverse rib bisecting the plate (Fig. 200), we assume that only the coefficient a_1 in expression (m) is different from zero, and from the first of Eqs. (n) we obtain as the first approximation

$$\sigma_{cr} = \frac{\pi^2D}{b^2h}\frac{(1 + \beta^2)^2 + 2\gamma\beta^3}{\beta^2}. \quad (229)$$

This formula shows how the critical stress is affected by the presence of the rib if the plate buckles into one half-wave.

A better approximation is obtained by taking a_1 and a_3 different from zero and using the first and third of Eqs. (n). By gradually increasing γ, we finally arrive at the condition where the plate buckles into two half-waves and the rib becomes the nodal line for the buckled plate. Several limiting values of γ, at which the rib remains straight during buckling of the plate, have been calculated for various values of β by using two of Eqs. (n); these are given in Table 41.

TABLE 41.—LIMITING VALUES OF γ IN THE CASE OF ONE TRANSVERSE RIB

β	0.50	0.60	0.70	0.80	0.90	1.0	1.2	1.41
γ	12.6	7.18	4.39	2.80	1.82	1.26	0.433	0

It is seen that the effect of the rib on the magnitude of the critical compressive stress depends on the proportions of the plate. Taking a square plate and using such a rib that $\gamma = 1.26$, we obtain two half-waves instead of one and the critical stress increases, as compared with that for the unstiffened plate (see Table 31) in the ratio 6.25:4. If the proportions of the plate are such that $\beta = 1.41$, the critical stress for the unstiffened plate is the same for buckling into one or two half-waves; hence in this case a transverse rib bisecting the plate has no effect whatsoever on the magnitude of the critical stress.

The case of stiffening the plate by using three equal and equidistant ribs can be discussed in a similar manner and the limiting values of γ, at which the ribs remain straight when the plate buckles into four equal half-waves, can be calculated. Several limiting values of γ for this case are given in Table 42.

TABLE 42.—LIMITING VALUES OF γ IN THE CASE OF THREE EQUAL AND EQUIDISTANT TRANSVERSE RIBS

β	0.60	0.80	1.0	1.2	1.4
γ	101	42.6	21.7	12.4	7.71

The method used above in calculating the stiffening effect of ribs can be applied also if it is desired to investigate the effect of rivet joints (Fig. 201)

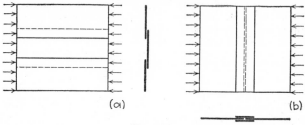

FIG. 201.

on critical stresses. Such a problem sometimes is encountered in the theory of ship structure.[1]

In the case of a large number of equal and equidistant ribs parallel to one of the sides of a compressed rectangular plate, we can consider the stiffened plate as a plate having two different flexural rigidities in the two perpendicular directions.[2] The general differential equation for the deflection surface of such a plate, if submitted to the action of forces in its middle plane, is

$$D_1 \frac{\partial^4 w}{\partial x^4} + 2D_3 \frac{\partial^4 w}{\partial x^2 \partial y^2} + D_2 \frac{\partial^4 w}{\partial y^4} = \left(N_x \frac{\partial^2 w}{\partial x^2} + N_y \frac{\partial^2 w}{\partial y^2} + 2N_{xy} \frac{\partial^2 w}{\partial x \partial y} \right). \quad (230)$$

[1] Several examples of this kind have been discussed by G. Schnadel, *Werft, Reederei, Hafen*, vol. 11, 1930.

[2] Bending of such plates was considered by M. T. Huber, *Bauingenieur*, 1923, p. 354, and also *Reports Intern. Cong. Appl. Mech.*, Zürich, 1926.

In this equation, $D_1 = \dfrac{(EI)_x}{1 - \nu_x \nu_y}$ is the average flexural rigidity of the stiffened plate corresponding to bending moments M_x; ν_x and ν_y are two values of Poisson's ratio corresponding to the directions x and y; $D_2 = \dfrac{(EI)_y}{1 - \nu_x \nu_y}$ is the average flexural rigidity corresponding to bending moments M_y; and

$$D_3 = \tfrac{1}{2}(\nu_x D_2 + \nu_y D_1) + 2(GI)_{xy},$$

where $2(GI)_{xy}$ is the average torsional rigidity [see Eqs. (o)]. Equation 230 can be derived by substituting in the equation of equilibrium (g) of Art. 56 (see p. 297) the following expressions for moments:

$$\left.\begin{aligned}
M_x &= -\frac{(EI)_x}{1 - \nu_x \nu_y}\left(\frac{\partial^2 w}{\partial x^2} + \nu_y \frac{\partial^2 w}{\partial y^2}\right); \\
M_y &= -\frac{(EI)_y}{1 - \nu_x \nu_y}\left(\frac{\partial^2 w}{\partial y^2} + \nu_x \frac{\partial^2 w}{\partial x^2}\right); \\
M_{xy} &= 2(GI)_{xy}\frac{\partial^2 w}{\partial x\,\partial y},
\end{aligned}\right\} \qquad (o)$$

which are obtained from the equations

$$\left.\begin{aligned}
\frac{\partial^2 w}{\partial x^2} &= -\frac{M_x}{(EI)_x} + \frac{\nu_y}{(EI)_y}M_y; \\
\frac{\partial^2 w}{\partial y^2} &= -\frac{M_y}{(EI)_y} + \frac{\nu_x}{(EI)_x}M_x; \\
\frac{\partial^2 w}{\partial x\,\partial y} &= \frac{1}{2(GI)_{xy}}M_{xy}.
\end{aligned}\right\} \qquad (p)$$

The quantities $(EI)_x$, $(EI)_y$, $(GI)_{xy}$, ν_x and ν_y can be determined by direct tests of stiffened plates by applying each time only one of the bending or torsional moments and measuring the corresponding deformation of the plate. Such tests[1] show that we usually can take ν_x and ν_y equal to zero in our calculations.

In the case of uniform compression of such a plate parallel to the x-axis (Fig. 171), if we denote the magnitude of the average compressive force per unit length by N_x, we obtain, from Eq. (230),

$$D_1 \frac{\partial^4 w}{\partial x^4} + 2D_3 \frac{\partial^4 w}{\partial x^2\,\partial y^2} + D_2 \frac{\partial^4 w}{\partial y^4} + N_x \frac{\partial^2 w}{\partial x^2} = 0. \qquad (231)$$

Assuming that the plate buckles into one half-wave and substituting in Eq. (231)

$$w = A \sin\frac{\pi x}{a} \sin\frac{\pi y}{b},$$

we obtain

$$\sigma_{cr} = \frac{\pi^2}{b^2 h}\left(D_1\frac{b^2}{a^2} + 2D_3 + D_2\frac{a^2}{b^2}\right).$$

[1] See, for instance, E. Seydel's paper in "Jahrbuch 1930 der deutschen Versuchsanstalt für Luftfahrt," p. 235, Berlin, 1930.

The smallest value for the critical stress is obtained when

$$\frac{a}{b} = \sqrt[4]{\frac{D_1}{D_2}}. \tag{232}$$

This value is

$$\sigma_{cr} = \frac{2\pi^2}{b^2 h}(\sqrt{D_1 D_2} + D_3). \tag{233}$$

From this we conclude that a long rectangular plate compressed longitudinally and stiffened by parallel longitudinal ribs buckles into many equal half-waves, the lengths of which satisfy Eq. (232). The critical stress is then determined from Eq. (233). For an isotropic plate $D_1 = D_2 = D_3$ and Eq. (233) coincides with Eq. (*h*) of Art. 63 (see p. 329).

Stiffening of Simply Supported Rectangular Plates under Shearing Stresses.—Several simple cases of this kind have been investigated. Let us begin

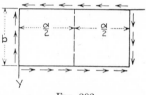

Fig. 202.

with a simply supported rectangular plate submitted to the action of uniformly distributed shearing stresses and stiffened by one rib bisecting the plate (Fig. 202). In studying the effect of ribs on the magnitude of critical shearing stresses the energy method can be used as before. It can be shown in this way that, if the rigidity of the stiffener is not sufficient, the inclined waves of the buckled plate run across the stiffener and buckling of the plate is accompanied by bending of the rib. By subsequent increase of the rigidity of the rib, we may finally arrive at a condition in which each half of the plate will buckle as a rectangular plate of dimensions $(a/2) \cdot b$ with simply supported edges and the rib will remain straight. The corresponding limiting value of the flexural rigidity B of the rib can be found from the consideration of strain energy of bending of the plate and of the rib. Several values of the ratio γ of this flexural rigidity to the rigidity Da of the plate if bent into a cylindrical surface are given in Table 43.

TABLE 43.—LIMITING VALUES OF THE RATIO γ IN THE CASE OF ONE RIB

a/b	2	1.5	1.25	1
$\gamma = B/Da$	0.83	2.9	6.3	15

If there are two ribs dividing the plate into three equal portions, the limiting value of γ at which the ribs remain straight when the plate buckles

TABLE 44.—LIMITING VALUES OF THE RATIO γ IN THE CASE OF TWO RIBS

a/b	3	2.5	2	1.5	1.2
$\gamma = B/Da$	0.64	1.37	3.53	10.7	22.6

can be determined in a similar manner. Several such values of γ are given in Table 44. Some applications of these results in determining the proper dimensions of stiffeners in the case of plate girders will be shown later (see Art. 75).

If a long rectangular plate is stiffened by several longitudinal ribs, an approximate value of the critical shearing stress can be obtained by using for the deflection surface of the buckled plate the expression (k) (see p. 360). Adding to the strain energy of bending of the buckled plate the strain energy of bending of the ribs and equating this sum to the work done by shearing forces, we obtain

$$\tau_{cr} = \frac{\pi^2 D}{b^2 h} \frac{1}{2\alpha} \left\{ 2 + 6\alpha^2 + \frac{s^2}{b^2} + \frac{b^2}{s^2} \left[\gamma + (1 + \alpha^2)^2 \right] \right\}, \qquad (234)$$

where

$$\gamma = \frac{2 \sum_i B_i \sin^2 \frac{\pi c_i}{b}}{Db}, \qquad (q)$$

in which B_i is the flexural rigidity of a rib at a distance c_i from the edge of the plate and where b is the width of the plate. For any assumed value of γ it is necessary to determine the quantities α and s so as to make expression (234) a minimum. In this way the critical value of shearing stress will be represented by the formula

$$\tau_{cr} = k \frac{\pi^2 D}{b^2 h}. \qquad (r)$$

Several values of the factor k are given in Table 45.

TABLE 45.—VALUES OF k IN EQ. (r)

γ	5	10	20	30	40	50	60	70	80	90	100
k	6.98	7.70	8.67	9.36	9.90	10.4	10.8	11.1	11.4	11.7	12.0

To appreciate the effect of stiffeners on the critical stress, the values of k given in this table should be compared with the approximate value 5.7 obtained for an unstiffened long plate (see p. 361).

Take, as an example, a long rectangular plate with $b = 84$ in. and $h = \frac{3}{8}$ in., stiffened by three equidistant ribs in the form of standard channels of depth 4 in. and cross-sectional area 1.56 sq. in. In such a case

$$B = E(3.8 + 1.56 \cdot 4) = 10E \text{ lb. sq. inches}$$

and we obtain from Eq. (q) $\gamma \approx 98$; hence k, in Eq. (r), is about 12.

In the case of a large number of parallel, equal and equidistant ribs, the stiffened plate can again be considered as a plate having two different flexural rigidities in the two perpendicular directions and Eq. (230) can be used. In this way buckling of corrugated plates has been discussed by

S. Bergman and H. Reissner.[1]   Assuming that the corrugation waves are parallel to one of the sides of a simply supported rectangular plate (Fig. 189) and using the notations

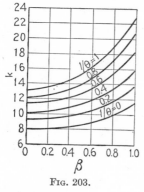

$$\theta = \frac{\sqrt{D_1 D_2}}{D_3} \qquad \text{and} \qquad \beta = \frac{b}{a}\sqrt[4]{\frac{D_1}{D_2}},$$

the critical value of the shearing force N_{xy} for $\theta > 1$ is obtained from the equation

$$(N_{xy})_{cr} = 4k\frac{\sqrt[4]{D_1 D_2^3}}{b^2}, \qquad (235)$$

in which k is a factor, depending on the values of θ and β, which can be taken from the curves[2] in Fig. 203.   In the case of an infinitely long isotropic plate $\beta = 0$, $\theta = 1$ and we obtain from Fig. 203 a value for k which brings Eq. (235) in agreement with Eq. (216) obtained

Fig. 203.

before.   For $\theta < 1$ the critical value of the shearing force is obtained from the equation

$$(N_{xy})_{cr} = 4k\frac{\sqrt{D_2 D_3}}{b^2}. \qquad (236)$$

Several values of k for an infinitely long plate are given in Table 46.

TABLE 46.—VALUES OF THE FACTOR k IN EQ. (236) FOR AN INFINITELY LONG PLATE

θ	0	0.2	0.5	1.0
k	11.7	11.8	12.2	13.17

Equations (235) and (236) can be used also in the case of a long plate with clamped edges, in which case the values of k must be taken from Table 47.

TABLE 47.—VALUES OF THE FACTOR k IN EQS. (235) AND (236) FOR AN INFINITELY LONG PLATE WITH CLAMPED EDGES

θ	0	0.2	0.5	1	2	3	5	10	20	40	∞
k	18.6	18.9	19.9	22.15	18.8	17.6	16.6	15.9	15.5	15.3	15.1

71. Buckling of Plates beyond Proportional Limit.—So far in our discussion of buckling of plates we have assumed that the stresses remain within the elastic range.   Beyond the propor-

[1] *Z. Flugtech. und Motorluftsch.*, vol. 20, p. 475, 1929.   See also E. Seydel's paper, *loc. cit.*, p. 381.

[2] See E. Seydel's paper in *Z. Flugtech. Motorluft.*, vol. 24, p. 78, 1933.

tional limit the formulas previously derived give exaggerated values for critical stresses, and in order to get more satisfactory results the behavior of the material beyond the proportional limit must be considered. Let us begin with the case of a rectangular plate simply supported along all edges and uniformly compressed parallel to one side (Fig. 171). The critical

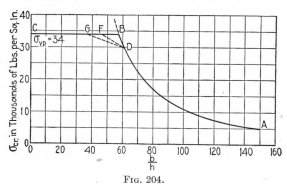

Fig. 204.

value of the compressive stress within the elastic limit and for buckling into one half-wave is given by the formula

$$\sigma_{cr} = \frac{\pi^2 D}{b^2 h}\left(\frac{a}{b} + \frac{b}{a}\right)^2. \qquad (a)$$

The smallest value of this stress, for a given value of the ratio h/b, is obtained in the case of a square plate for which

$$\sigma_{cr} = \frac{4\pi^2 D}{b^2 h} = \frac{\pi^2 E}{3(1 - \nu^2)}\frac{h^2}{b^2}. \qquad (b)$$

This value of σ_{cr} can be used also for long rectangular plates buckling into many waves. Taking the case of structural steel for which $E = 30 \cdot 10^6$ lb. per square inch and $\nu = 0.3$, we can represent σ_{cr} as a function of the ratio b/h by the curve AB shown in Fig. 204. This curve can be used for obtaining σ_{cr} within the elastic region.

Experiments show that, when the compressive stress reaches the yield point of the material, which in this case is assumed equal to 34,000 lb. per square inch, the plate buckles for any value of the ratio b/h. This is shown in the figure by the horizontal line BC. If the material has a sharply defined yield point and follows Hooke's law up to that point, the horizontal line BC, together with the curve BA, determines the value of the critical compressive stress for any value of the ratio b/h. In such a material as structural steel some permanent set usually takes place at a stress lower than the yield point. Assuming that point D in the figure corresponds to the proportional limit of the material, *i.e.*, to the stress at which the beginning of permanent set becomes noticeable, there must be in the figure, instead of a sharp corner at B, some intermediate curve joining the curve AD, corresponding to the region of perfect elasticity, with the horizontal line representing plastic flow. In the case of columns this curve can be readily constructed by introducing in Euler's formula the reduced modulus E_r instead of the modulus E (see Art. 29). There are also sufficient experimental data from which E_r can be determined for compressive stresses in the region of transition between the proportional limit and the yield point.

In the case of buckling of plates we have to deal with stresses acting in two perpendicular directions. There are not sufficient experimental data regarding stress-strain relations beyond the proportional limit for this case and it is necessary to make some arbitrary assumption regarding the curve of transition in Fig. 204. Considering the plate as subdivided (1) into strips parallel to the direction of compression (Fig. 171), or (2) into strips perpendicular to compression, it seems reasonable to assume that beyond the proportional limit the flexural rigidity of the first kind of strip is reduced in the ratio $E_r:E$, while the flexural rigidity of strips perpendicular to the direction of compression remains unchanged. Thus the problem of buckling beyond the proportional limit requires an investigation of bending of non-isotropic plates.[1] The differential equation of the deflection surface of the plate

$$D\left(\frac{\partial^4 w}{\partial x^4} + 2\frac{\partial^4 w}{\partial x^2\,\partial y^2} + \frac{\partial^4 w}{\partial y^4}\right) + N_x\frac{\partial^2 w}{\partial x^2} = 0, \qquad (c)$$

which has been used in the elastic region, must now be changed in accordance with the above assumption. Using the notation

$$\alpha = \frac{E_r}{E}, \qquad (d)$$

[1] See writer's paper in *Ann. ponts chaussées*, 1913, IV, p. 410, and also F. Bleich, "Theorie d. Eisernen Brücken," 1924, p. 216.

and noting that the first term of Eq. (c) corresponds to bending of longitudinal strips, we diminish this term in the ratio α. The third term of the equation, which corresponds to bending of strips perpendicular to the direction of compression, we leave unchanged. The second term of the equation is due principally to a twisting[1] action. Assuming that the torsional rigidity of each element of a plate, compressed beyond the proportional limit, is reduced in proportion to $\sqrt{\alpha}$, we diminish this second term in the same proportion. Thus finally we obtain for the case of bending of a plate, compressed beyond the proportional limit, the following equation:

$$D\left(\alpha\frac{\partial^4 w}{\partial x^4} + 2\sqrt{\alpha}\frac{\partial^4 w}{\partial x^2\,\partial y^2} + \frac{\partial^4 w}{\partial y^4}\right) + N_x\frac{\partial^2 w}{\partial x^2} = 0. \qquad (237)$$

Taking the solution of this equation for the case of simply supported edges in the form

$$w = a_1 \sin\frac{\pi x}{a} \sin\frac{\pi y}{b} \qquad (e)$$

and substituting it in the equation, we obtain

$$(N_x)_{cr} = \frac{\pi^2 D}{b^2}\left(\frac{b}{a}\sqrt{\alpha} + \frac{a}{b}\right)^2$$

and

$$\sigma_{cr} = \frac{\pi^2 D}{b^2 h}\left(\frac{b}{a}\sqrt{\alpha} + \frac{a}{b}\right)^2. \qquad (238)$$

The smallest value of this stress is obtained if

$$\frac{a}{b} = \sqrt[4]{\alpha} \qquad (f)$$

and is equal to

$$\sigma_{cr} = \frac{4\pi^2 D}{b^2 h}\sqrt{\alpha} = \frac{\pi^2 E}{3(1-\nu^2)}\frac{h^2}{b^2}\sqrt{\alpha}. \qquad (239)$$

This shows that a long plate compressed beyond the proportional limit subdivides during buckling into half-waves, the lengths of which are shorter than the width of the plate in the ratio $\sqrt[4]{\alpha}$. The corresponding critical stress is smaller than that obtained for a perfectly elastic plate in the proportion $\sqrt{\alpha}$. If a complete compression-test diagram for the material is

[1] See the derivation of the equation in Art. 56.

given, the value of E_r for any value of σ can be determined (see Art. 29). Taking a series of values for σ_{cr} and corresponding values of E_r and substituting them in Eq. (239), we find from this equation the corresponding values of b/h and can plot a curve for the intermediate range $\sigma_{\text{P.L.}} < \sigma_{cr} < \sigma_{\text{Y.P.}}$ in Fig. 204.

In calculating critical stresses for columns of structural steel in the region between the proportional limit ($l/r = 100$) and the yield point ($l/r = 60$), a straight-line formula is sometimes used (see Fig. 113). Assuming a steel for which $E = 30 \cdot 10^6$ lb. per square inch, $\sigma_{\text{Y.P.}} = 34,000$ lb. per square inch and $\sigma_{\text{P.L.}} = \pi^2 E/10^4 = 29,600$ lb. per square inch, the critical stress obtained from this straight-line formula is

$$\sigma_{cr} = 40,600 - 110\frac{l}{r}. \tag{g}$$

For $l/r = 100$ this formula gives $\sigma_{cr} = 40,600 - 11,000 = 29,600$ lb. per square inch $= \sigma_{\text{P.L.}}$, and for $l/r = 60$ it gives

$$\sigma_{cr} = 40,600 - 6,600 = 34,000 \text{ lb. per square inch} = \sigma_{\text{Y.P.}}.$$

Assuming Eq. (g) to apply, we can establish a certain relation between the ratio $\alpha = E_r/E$ and σ_{cr}, which can be expressed analytically by taking the modified Euler's formula

$$\sigma_{cr} = \frac{\pi^2 E_r r^2}{l^2} = \frac{\pi^2 E r^2}{l^2}\alpha \tag{h}$$

and eliminating l/r from this formula by the use of Eq. (g). In this manner we obtain

$$\alpha = \frac{\sigma_{cr}(40,600 - \sigma_{cr})^2}{\pi^2 E 110^2}. \tag{240}$$

Using this expression for α in studying the case of buckling of plates and substituting (240) in Eq. (239), we obtain

$$\frac{b^2}{h^2} = \frac{\pi(40,600 - \sigma_{cr})\sqrt{E}}{3(1 - \nu^2)110\sqrt{\sigma_{cr}}}. \tag{241}$$

From this equation the value of b/h for any value of σ_{cr} in the region of $\sigma_{\text{P.L.}} < \sigma_{cr} < \sigma_{\text{Y.P.}}$ can be calculated. Taking $\sigma_{cr} = \sigma_{\text{Y.P.}} = 34,000$ lb. per square inch, we obtain $b/h = 45.3$. For $\sigma_{cr} = \sigma_{\text{P.L.}} = 29,600$ lb. per square inch, Eq. (241) gives $b/h = 60.6$. Thus by using Eq. (241) the curve *FD*, shown in Fig. 204, is obtained.[1]

It was assumed in the derivation of Eq. (237) that compression of a plate beyond the proportional limit in one direction does not affect the elastic property of the material as regards stresses in the perpendicular direction. Another extreme assumption is that compression of a plate beyond the proportional limit in

[1] This curve differs only slightly from a straight line.

one direction affects the mechanical properties of the material in the same manner in all other directions, *i.e.*, that the plate remains isotropic.[1] If this second assumption is taken, the first three terms of Eq. (c) must all be diminished in the same ratio α if the plate is compressed beyond the proportional limit in the x-direction; thus we obtain

$$\alpha D\left(\frac{\partial^4 w}{\partial x^4} + 2\frac{\partial^4 w}{\partial x^2\,\partial y^2} + \frac{\partial^4 w}{\partial y^4}\right) + N_x\frac{\partial^2 w}{\partial x^2} = 0. \qquad (242)$$

Solving this equation as before, we obtain for the case of a square plate or that of a long plate with simply supported edges

$$\sigma_{cr} = \frac{\pi^2 E}{3(1 - \nu^2)}\frac{h^2}{b^2}\alpha. \qquad (243)$$

The shape of the buckled plate is the same as in the case of elastic buckling but the value of the critical stress is reduced in the ratio α.

In the case of structural steel, taking for α expression (240), we obtain, for $\sigma_{cr} = \sigma_{Y.P.} = 34{,}000$ lb. per square inch, $b/h = 36.4$; and, for $\sigma_{cr} = \sigma_{P.L.} = 29{,}600$ lb. per square inch, as before, $b/h = 60.6$. For the range of transition we obtain in this way the curve GD in Fig. 204. It may be seen that there is not much difference between the two curves FD and GD. In practical applications we will be on the safe side by taking the curve GD.

Both assumptions regarding the range of transition can be applied also in other cases of buckling of compressed plates; the critical value of σ is obtained with an accuracy sufficient for practical applications by multiplying the expressions for σ_{cr}, derived for the case of elastic buckling, by the factor $\sqrt{\alpha}$ or α, respectively. Taking the case of longitudinal compression of a long rectangular plate with the longitudinal edges built in, we obtain (see Table 35, p. 345)

$$\sigma_{cr} = \frac{7\pi^2 D}{b^2 h}\sqrt{\alpha} = \frac{7\pi^2 E}{12(1 - \nu^2)}\frac{h^2}{b^2}\sqrt{\alpha},$$

or

$$\sigma_{cr} = \frac{7\pi^2 D}{b^2 h}\alpha = \frac{7\pi^2 E}{12(1 - \nu^2)}\frac{h^2}{b^2}\alpha.$$

Applying these two formulas to the case of structural steel, considered before, and assuming $\sigma_{cr} = \sigma_{Y.P.}$, we obtain $b/h = 59.8$ and $b/h = 48$, respectively.

In the case of compression of a long plate, one of whose longitudinal sides is free while the other is simply supported, we can take (see p. 338)

[1] See E. Chwalla, *Reports 2d Intern. Cong. Bridge and Structural Eng.*, Vienna, p. 322, 1928. See also M. Roš and A. Eichinger, *Reports Intern. Cong. Bridge and Structural Eng.*, Paris, p. 144, 1932.

$$\sigma_{cr} = \frac{0.46\pi^2 D}{b^2 h}\sqrt{\alpha}, \qquad \text{or} \qquad \sigma_{cr} = \frac{0.46\pi^2 D}{b^2 h}\alpha,$$

and for structural steel, assuming $\sigma_{cr} = \sigma_{Y.P.}$, we obtain $b/h = 15.4$ and $b/h = 12.3$, respectively.

For the same plate, if one longitudinal side is free and the other is clamped (see p. 341), we have

$$\sigma_{cr} = \frac{1.33\pi^2 D}{b^2 h}\sqrt{\alpha} \qquad \text{or} \qquad \sigma_{cr} = \frac{1.33\pi^2 D}{b^2 h}\alpha,$$

and for structural steel, by taking $\sigma_{cr} = \sigma_{Y.P.}$, we obtain $b/h = 26.2$ and $b/h = 21.0$, respectively.

In the case of buckling of rectangular plates under the action of pure shear (Art. 67), it is reasonable to assume that beyond the proportional limit the mechanical properties change in the same manner in all the directions and that the plate remains isotropic. Then the critical values of the stress are obtained by multiplying by α the formulas derived for the cases of elastic buckling.

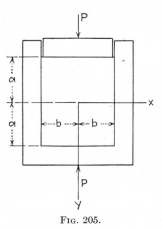

Fig. 205.

72. Large Deflections of Buckled Plates. So far in the calculation of critical stresses for various cases of buckling of plates we have assumed that the deflections are very small and that the strain in the middle plane of the plate due to buckling can be neglected. To investigate bending of plates when the stresses are above critical, the strain in the middle plane should be considered. The application of the general Eqs. (207) and (208) (p. 323) to this problem represents great difficulty since these equations are very complicated. To get an approximate solution let us use the expression for the strain energy of the buckled plate and determine its deflection from the condition of minimum of this energy.[1]

Let us begin with the case in which a simply supported plate is compressed in the y-direction and lateral expansion in x-direction is prevented by a rigid frame (Fig. 205). Taking the origin of coordinates as shown in the figure, an approximate expression for the deflection surface of the buckled plate, satisfying the boundary conditions, is

$$w = f \cos\frac{\pi x}{2b} \cos\frac{\pi y}{2a}. \qquad (a)$$

The components v and u of displacements in the middle plane of the plate, satisfying the boundary conditions, can be taken in the following form:

[1] Another method of solution of the problem has been given by G. Schnadel, *Reports 3d Intern. Cong. Appl. Mech.*, Stockholm, vol. 3, p. 73, 1930.

$$v = C_1 \sin \frac{\pi y}{a} \cos \frac{\pi x}{2b} - ey; \left.\begin{matrix}\\\\\end{matrix}\right\}$$

$$u = C_2 \sin \frac{\pi x}{b} \cos \frac{\pi y}{2a}, \tag{b}$$

where C_1, C_2 and e are constants. It is seen that the displacements u become zero at the edges $x = \pm b$. The displacements v at the boundaries $y = \pm a$ are equal to those due to the uniform compression strain e in the y-direction.

The components of strain in the middle plane of the plate are (see p. 322)

$$\epsilon_x = \frac{\partial u}{\partial x} + \frac{1}{2}\left(\frac{\partial w}{\partial x}\right)^2; \left.\begin{matrix}\\\\\\\\\\\end{matrix}\right\}$$

$$\epsilon_y = \frac{\partial v}{\partial y} + \frac{1}{2}\left(\frac{\partial w}{\partial y}\right)^2; \tag{c}$$

$$\gamma_{xy} = \frac{\partial v}{\partial x} + \frac{\partial u}{\partial y} + \frac{\partial w}{\partial x}\frac{\partial w}{\partial y}$$

and the corresponding strain energy of the plate is

$$V_1 = \frac{h}{2}\int_{-a}^{+a}\int_{-b}^{+b}(\sigma_x\epsilon_x + \sigma_y\epsilon_y + \tau_{xy}\gamma_{xy})dx\,dy =$$

$$\frac{Gh}{1-\nu}\int_{-a}^{+a}\int_{-b}^{+b}\left[\epsilon_x^2 + \epsilon_y^2 + 2\nu\epsilon_x\epsilon_y + \frac{1}{2}(1-\nu)\gamma_{xy}^2\right]dx\,dy.$$

Using for the displacements u, v and w expressions (a) and (b), and adding to the energy of strain V_1 of the middle plane the energy of bending

$$V_2 = \frac{\pi^4 abf^2D}{32}\left(\frac{1}{a^2} + \frac{1}{b^2}\right)^2,$$

we obtain

$$V = V_1 + V_2 = \frac{\pi^4 abf^2D}{32}\left(\frac{1}{a^2} + \frac{1}{b^2}\right)^2 + \frac{Gh}{1-\nu}\left[4abe^2 - \frac{\pi^2 f^2 be}{4a} + \right.$$

$$\frac{\pi^4 f^4}{1,024ab}\left(9\frac{a^2}{b^2} + 9\frac{b^2}{a^2} + 2\right) - C_1\frac{\pi^2 f^2}{6}\left(\frac{2b}{a^2} + \frac{1-3\nu}{2b}\right) -$$

$$C_2\frac{\pi^2 f^2}{6}\left(\frac{2a}{b^2} + \frac{1-3\nu}{2a}\right) + C_1^2\pi^2\left(\frac{b}{a} + \frac{1-\nu}{8}\frac{a}{b}\right) +$$

$$\left. C_2^2\pi^2\left(\frac{a}{b} + \frac{1-\nu}{8}\frac{b}{a}\right) + C_1C_2\frac{16}{9}(1+\nu) - \nu\frac{\pi^2 f^2 ae}{4b}\right]. \tag{d}$$

For a given unit compression e of the plate the constants C_1, C_2 and f in the expressions (a) and (b) will be found from the conditions that the strain energy V is a minimum; hence

$$\frac{\partial V}{\partial C_1} = 0; \qquad \frac{\partial V}{\partial C_2} = 0; \qquad \frac{\partial V}{\partial f} = 0. \tag{e}$$

Let us consider now the case of a square plate. Then $a = b$, $C_1 = C_2 = C$ and the first two of Eqs. (e) become

$$-\frac{\pi^2 f^2}{6a}\frac{5-3\nu}{2} + 2\pi^2 C\frac{9-\nu}{8} + \frac{16}{9}C(1+\nu) = 0,$$

from which, with $\nu = 0.3$, we obtain

$$C = 0.1418 \frac{f^2}{a}. \qquad (f)$$

Substituting this in the third of Eqs. (e), we obtain

$$f(4.058h^2 - 6.42a^2e + 5.688f^2) = 0. \qquad (g)$$

The solution $f = 0$ of this equation corresponds to the flat form of the compressed plate. The other solution giving the deflection of the buckled plate is obtained by equating to zero the parenthesis in Eq. (g). Then

$$f = \sqrt{\frac{6.42a^2e - 4.058h^2}{5.688}}. \qquad (h)$$

We obtain a real solution for f only if

$$6.42a^2e > 4.058h^2.$$

The limiting condition

$$6.42a^2e = 4.058h^2$$

gives

$$e_{cr} = 0.632 \frac{h^2}{a^2}, \qquad (i)$$

and the corresponding compressive stress is

$$\sigma_{cr} = \frac{e_{cr}E}{1 - \nu^2} = \frac{0.632h^2E}{(1 - \nu^2)a^2}. \qquad (j)$$

This stress is equal to the critical compressive stress $(\sigma_y)_{cr}$ for a rectangular plate compressed in two perpendicular directions as obtained from Eq. (c) (see p. 333) by taking $m = n = 1$, $a = b$, and $\sigma_x = \nu\sigma_y = 0.3\sigma_y$.

If we take for e a value n times larger than that given by (i), we obtain from (h)

$$f = 0.845h\sqrt{n - 1}. \qquad (k)$$

Taking $n = 10$, *i.e.*, making the compression of the plate 10 times larger than its critical value, given by (i), we find $f = 2.535h$, *i.e.*, deflection at the center is about 2.5 times larger than the thickness of the plate.

Substituting the values of the constants f and C from (k) and (f) in expressions (a) and (b) for the displacements, the corresponding strain in the middle plane of the plate can be found from expressions (c) and the corresponding stresses can be calculated. For $y = a$ we obtain in this way

$$(\sigma_x)_{y=a} = \nu(\sigma_y)_{y=a};$$

$$(\sigma_y)_{y=a} = \frac{E}{1 - \nu^2}[(\epsilon_y)_{y=a} + \nu(\epsilon_x)_{y=a}] =$$

$$0.714 \frac{E}{1 - \nu^2} \frac{h^2}{a^2}(n - 1) \cos \frac{\pi x}{2a}\left(\frac{\pi^2}{8} \cos \frac{\pi x}{2a} - 0.142\pi\right) - 0.632 \frac{E}{1 - \nu^2}n\frac{h^2}{a^2}.$$

The stresses at the edges of the plate calculated for $n = 10$ are shown in

Fig. 206. It is seen that for larger deflections of the plate the distribution of compressive stresses is no longer uniform and the larger portion of the load is taken by the portions of the plate near the edges.

For comparatively thin plates as used in airplane construction, for which the ultimate load may be many times larger than the critical load, we cannot expect this approximate solution to be sufficiently accurate. The solution can be improved by taking more terms in expressions (a) and (b) for the displacements, but in such case the amount of work required in calculation

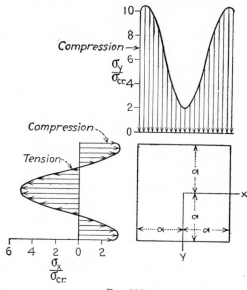

Fig. 206.

increases immensely. Calculations were made by adding one term to the expression (a) for deflections and taking

$$w = f \cos \frac{\pi y}{2a} \cos \frac{\pi x}{2b} + f_1 \cos \frac{3\pi y}{2a} \cos \frac{3\pi x}{2b}. \tag{l}$$

Then, retaining the previous expressions for u and v, we obtain a second approximation. These calculations show that the difference between the first and second approximations is small and that the difference in the magnitude of $(\sigma_y)_{\max}$ becomes noticeable only for a very large value of n (say $n > 50$), *i.e.*, when the acting load is many times larger than the critical load.

It was assumed in the previous discussion that the frame is absolutely rigid and that lateral displacements of the edges of the compressed plate are entirely suppressed. The problem can be discussed in an analogous manner for the case where the vertical bars of the frame, keeping the lateral edges of the plate straight, can move freely laterally when the plate is compressed. Taking

$$w = f \cos \frac{\pi x}{2b} \cos \frac{\pi y}{2a};$$

$$v = C_1 \sin \frac{\pi y}{a} \cos \frac{\pi x}{2b} - ey;$$

$$u = C_2 \sin \frac{\pi x}{b} \cos \frac{\pi y}{2a} + \alpha x,$$

(m)

we determine α from the condition that the sum of normal stresses along the vertical edges of the plate is equal to zero. This gives

$$\alpha = -\frac{\pi^2 f^2}{16b^2} + \frac{2C_2}{b} + \nu e. \qquad (n)$$

Substituting this in the third of expressions (m) and calculating the strain energy, we again use Eqs. (e) for determining f, C_1 and C_2. In the case of a square plate, with $\nu = 0.3$, we obtain from the first two of these equations

$$C_1 = 0.144 \frac{f^2}{a}; \qquad C_2 = 0.1215 \frac{f^2}{a} \qquad (o)$$

and the third of these equations becomes

$$f(0.411h^2 - 0.455ea^2 + 0.320f^2) = 0.$$

The deflection of the buckled plate is

$$f = \sqrt{\frac{0.455ea^2 - 0.411h^2}{0.320}}. \qquad (p)$$

By putting this deflection equal to zero, we obtain for the critical value of the longitudinal compression of the plate

$$e_{cr} = \frac{0.411}{0.455} \frac{h^2}{a^2} = 0.904 \frac{h^2}{a^2},$$

which coincides exactly with what we get for a square plate from Eq. (213). Using again the notation $n = e/e_{cr}$, Eq. (p) gives

$$f = 1.133h\sqrt{n - 1}. \qquad (q)$$

Substituting this in Eqs. (o) and using expressions (m), we obtain expressions for the stresses σ_x and σ_y in the plate. For the boundary these stresses are

$$(\sigma_x)_{x=a} = 1.41(n - 1)E\frac{h^2}{a^2}\left[\left(1.234 \cos \frac{\pi y}{2a} - 0.382\right) \cos \frac{\pi y}{2a} - 0.374\right];$$

$$(\sigma_y)_{y=a} = E\frac{h^2}{a^2}\left[1.74(n - 1)\left(\cos \frac{\pi x}{2a} - 0.366\right) \cos \frac{\pi x}{2a} - 1.062n + 0.158\right].$$

(r)

Distribution of these stresses for the particular case where $n = 59.7$ is shown in Fig. 207.

Assuming that the above expressions for stresses are accurate enough up to complete failure of the plate, we can determine the ultimate load that the complete plate can carry from the condition[1]

---

[1] We use here the maximum-shear theory in calculating the beginning of yielding.

$$\tau_{\text{max.}} = \tfrac{1}{2}(\sigma_x - \sigma_y)_{\text{max.}} = \tfrac{1}{2}\sigma_{\text{Y.P.}}. \qquad (s)$$

The maximum value of the shearing stress occurs at the points $x = \pm b$, $y = 0$ (Fig. 205) and is

$$\tau_{\text{max.}} = \frac{1}{2}(\sigma_x - \sigma_y) = E\frac{h^2}{2a^2}(1.38n - 0.473).$$

With this value of $\tau_{\text{max.}}$ we obtain from Eq. (s)

$$n = \frac{0.726}{E}\frac{a^2}{h^2}\sigma_{\text{Y.P.}} + 0.34.$$

Substituting this value of n in the second of the expressions (r), we obtain

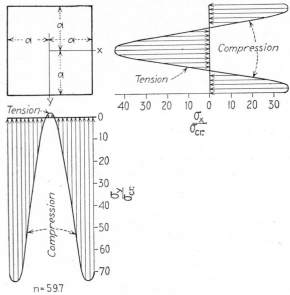

$$n = 59.7$$

Fig. 207.

for the ultimate load that the plate can carry

$$P_{\text{ult.}} = 2h\int_0^a \sigma_y \, dx = 0.867ah\sigma_{\text{Y.P.}} + 1.02E\frac{h^3}{a} =$$

$$A\left[0.434\sigma_{\text{Y.P.}} + 2.04E\frac{h^2}{(2a)^2}\right], \qquad (244)$$

where $A = 2ah$ is the cross-sectional area of the plate.

73. Ultimate Strength of Buckled Plates.—It is general practice in the design of metallic structures to determine the proportions of thin plates in such a way as to eliminate all possibility of buckling under service conditions. However, as we have seen from the discussion of the previous article, a plate after buckling may, in some cases, carry without failure a load many times larger than the critical load at which buckling begins. Thus it is logical in cases where the question of economy in weight is of primary importance, as in airplane construction, to consider not only the critical load but also the ultimate load that a plate may carry without complete failure.

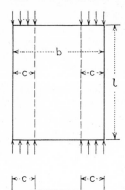

FIG. 208.

In the case of compression of a rectangular plate with simply supported edges, it can be assumed for a rough calculation of the ultimate load that the load transmitted to the plate by a rigid block (Fig. 205) is carried finally by two strips of width c, one on each side of the sheet, and that the load distribution is uniform across these strips (Fig. 208). Then the middle portion of the sheet can be disregarded and the two strips can be handled as a long simply supported rectangular plate of width $2c$.[1] The critical stress for such a plate is (see p. 331)

$$\sigma_{cr} = \frac{4\pi^2 D}{h(2c)^2} = \frac{\pi^2 E h^2}{12(1 - \nu^2)c^2}. \qquad (a)$$

Assuming that the ultimate load is obtained when σ_{cr} becomes equal to the yield-point stress $\sigma_{Y.P.}$ of the material, we find, from (a),

$$c = \frac{\pi h}{\sqrt{12(1 - \nu^2)}} \sqrt{\frac{E}{\sigma_{Y.P.}}}, \qquad (b)$$

and the ultimate load is

$$P_{\text{ult.}} = 2ch\sigma_{Y.P.} = \frac{\pi h^2}{\sqrt{3(1 - \nu^2)}} \sqrt{E\sigma_{Y.P.}}. \qquad (245)$$

It is seen that the ultimate load is independent of the width b of the sheet and is proportional to the square of its thickness. This result is different from that obtained in the previous article by assuming that the edges of the plate are kept straight during buckling. If there is not such a restraint, experiments (see

[1] Such an assumption has been proposed by Th. v. Kármán; see paper by Th. Kármán, E. E. Sechler and L. H. Donnell, *Trans. Am. Soc. Mech. Eng.*, vol. 54, p. 53, 1932.

Art. 74) are in good agreement with formula (245). A better agreement can be obtained by using in this formula instead of a constant factor $\pi/\sqrt{3(1 - \nu^2)} = 1.90$ (for $\nu = 0.3$) a factor C varying with the proportions of the plate and given by the curve in Fig. 213.

For comparison of formulas (244) and (245) with tests, we give below the results obtained with three kinds of duralumin plates.[1]

TABLE 48.—COMPARISON OF ULTIMATE LOADS FOR THREE COMPRESSED DURALUMIN PLATES

Thickness, h in.	Width, b in.	b/h	Length, a in.	E, lb. per square inch	$\sigma_{Y.P.}$, lb. per square inch	Ultimate load, lb.		
						Formula (244)	Formula (245)	Tests
0.0893	4.00	44.8	24	$10.6 \cdot 10^6$	41,000	10,200	9,990	7,300
0.0356	3.515	98.75	9	$10 \cdot 10^6$	45,000	2,700	1,620	1,175
0.0322	10.01	311	21	$10 \cdot 10^6$	45,000	6,375	1,310	1,270

It is seen that the formula (245) gives results which are in satisfactory agreement with experiments. Formula (244) gives exaggerated values for $P_{ult.}$, especially for small values of the ratio h/b. It should be noted, however, that the latter formula has been developed on the assumption that the edges of the plate remain straight during buckling, while no such constraints existed in the tests. In actual structures where rigid ribs are placed along the edges of the plates, the conditions may be closer to those assumed in the derivations of the previous article and formula (244) may prove more satisfactory.

In the case of compression tests of thin tubes of square cross section, the edges of the flat sides of the tubes remain straight during buckling of the sides and actual conditions approach those assumed in the derivation of formula (244). In Table 49 is given a comparison of ultimate loads as calculated by using formulas (244) and (245) and as obtained by direct tests of brass tubes.[2] It is seen that in this case formula (244) is in better agreement with tests than in the case of compression of plates in V-grooves. It is seen also that the agreement becomes less satisfactory as the ratio h/b decreases.

[1] The first plate is taken from the Bureau of Standards series of tests (see Art. 74) and the other two from the paper by E. E. Sechler, Guggenheim Aeronautics Laboratory, California Institute of Technology, Publication 27, 1933.

[2] These experimental data have been communicated to the author by L. H. Donnell and were obtained at the aeronautics laboratory, California Institute of Technology, Pasadena, 1933.

For very small values of h/b formula (244) always gives exaggerated values for ultimate loads.

TABLE 49.—COMPARISON OF ULTIMATE LOADS OF COMPRESSED BRASS SQUARE TUBES

Thickness, h in.	Width, b in.	Ratio, b/h	E, lb. per square inch	$\sigma_{Y.P.}$, lb. per square inch	Total ultimate load of tube, lb.		
					Formula (244)	Formula (245)	Tests
0.0065	1.0	154	$16.4 \cdot 10^6$	31,400	391	231	290
0.0056	1.0	178.5	$16.0 \cdot 10^6$	28,600	300	161	210
0.0065	2.0	308	$16.4 \cdot 10^6$	31,400	726	231	340

In discussing the ultimate strength of thin sheets submitted to the action of shearing stresses, let us consider a system consisting of three absolutely rigid bars with hinges at the joints (Fig. 209a). The field *abcd* between the bars is occupied by a very thin plate which cannot resist bending or compression. Under the action of the load P the condition will be analogous to that of a system with flexible diagonals (Fig. 209b). Under the action of the load P the diagonal in compression buckles sideways and only the diagonal *ac* in tension is working. Since the thin plate cannot sustain shearing stress, it buckles sideways and corrugations at 45° as indicated in the figure will be formed.[1] From the condition of equilibrium of the portion *nmbc*, the tensile stress σ is

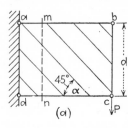

(a)

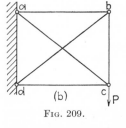

(b)

FIG. 209.

$$\sigma = \frac{2P}{dh},$$

in which d is the depth of the web and h the thickness of the plate. This stress is twice as great as that which would be produced in a rigid plate under pure shear. If extension and compression of the bars are taken into consideration, the angle α of the corrugations becomes somewhat different from 45°. For the proportions encountered in the design of airplanes, it can always be assumed with sufficient accuracy[2] that $\alpha = 40°$. By using this value of α, the stresses and the ultimate strength of a girder with a very thin web and with

[1] It is assumed that the bars are absolutely rigid. Then the maximum tensile strain defining the direction of the generators of corrugation occurs at 45° to the horizontal.

[2] See paper by H. Wagner, *Z. Flugtech. Motorluftsch.*, vol. 20, p. 200, 1929.

equidistant vertical stiffeners (Fig. 210) can easily be calculated. If σ is the tensile stress in the corrugated web, the load per unit length of horizontal bars is

$$q = \sigma h \sin \alpha. \qquad (c)$$

Resolving this into horizontal and vertical components we obtain

$$q_x = \sigma h \sin \alpha \cos \alpha; \qquad q_y = \sigma h \sin^2 \alpha. \qquad (d)$$

Here q_x represents the increase of force per unit length of the horizontal bar. From simple statical considerations we obtain

$$\frac{P}{d} = \sigma h \sin \alpha \cos \alpha,$$

from which

$$\sigma = \frac{2P}{dh \sin 2\alpha}. \qquad (e)$$

The compressive force S in the vertical stiffeners, equal to the load of inten-

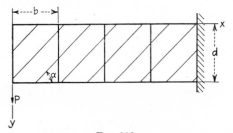

Fig. 210.

sity q_y distributed along the distance b between the stiffeners, is

$$S = \sigma h b \sin^2 \alpha. \qquad (f)$$

Taking for α the approximate value of 40°, we find the following approximate formulas

$$\sigma = \frac{2P}{dh}; \qquad S = \frac{0.9\,Pb}{d},$$

which can be used in calculating the ultimate strength of the girder. Failure takes place when σ becomes equal to $\sigma_{\text{Y.P.}}$ or when S becomes equal to Euler's load for a stiffener.[1]

The ultimate strength of a compressed thin rectangular plate, to which are attached stiffeners, running in the direction of the applied compressive load, can be calculated with sufficient accuracy by considering each stiffener, together with a portion of the plate, as a strut. The effective width of the plate which should be considered in calculating the slenderness ratio of a stiffener can be calculated from Eq. (b) by successive approximations. We

[1] Some further study of the behavior of thin sheet-metal panels in shear has been done by H. L. Cox, Aeronautical Research Committee Report and Memoranda, 1553, London, 1933.

begin by taking the stiffener alone and calculating the critical stress for it as for a strut. Substituting this critical stress in Eq. (b) for $\sigma_{Y.P.}$, the effective width $2c$ of the plate is obtained, which must be added to the stiffener in calculating σ_{cr}. With this new value for σ_{cr} we obtain from Eq. (b) the second approximation for the effective width $2c$, which is usually accurate enough for practical applications.[1]

74. Experiments on Buckling of Plates.—*Compression of Rectangular Plates.*—Usually in such experiments plates with simply supported edges are taken since the theoretical solution

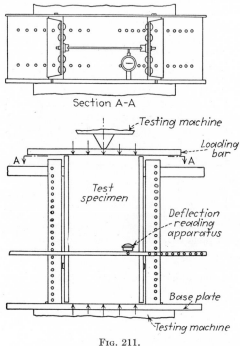

Section A-A

FIG. 211.

for this case is a very simple one. Experimentally, however, this case is a very complicated one since it is difficult in the experiment to realize the conditions of a simply supported edge. To realize, as nearly as possible, complete freedom of rotation of the edges, frames with V-notches are used[2] (Fig. 211). However,

[1] Experiments with stiffened compressed plates were made by E. E. Lundquist, *Nat. Advisory Comm. Aeronautics Tech. Note* 455.

[2] Figure 211 represents the testing apparatus used at the Bureau of Standards; see L. Schuman and G. Back, *Nat. Advisory Comm. Aeronautics Rep.* 356.

an unrounded edge of the plate is not entirely free to rotate in such a notch and any rotation during buckling is accompanied by some displacement of the middle plane perpendicular to the surface of the plate (Fig. 212). The loaded edges of the plate are sometimes made semicircular in order to realize the application of the load in the middle plane of the plate.[1]

Owing to initial curvature of plates and eccentricities in application of the load, lateral buckling usually begins at a very small load. To determine from the observed deflections the critical value of the load, it is advantageous to apply the method suggested by R. V. Southwell in testing columns.[2] In discussing bending of compressed plates with an initial curvature (see Art. 60), it was shown that, when the load P approaches its critical value, the corresponding term in the double series, representing deflections, becomes pre-

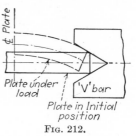

Fig. 212.

ponderant and increases with the load in such a way that, by plotting observed deflections δ against values of the ratio δ/P, a straight line is obtained. The slope of this line gives the true value of the critical load. The values obtained in this manner are usually in very satisfactory agreement with theoretical values. The wave formation obtained during buckling of compressed plates is also usually in good agreement with the theory.[3]

Most experiments on buckling of plates have been made with thin plates such as used in airplane structures, the principal interest being to establish the ultimate load that a compressed plate can carry. These experiments show that a thin sheet of metal of considerable width can carry a much larger load than the critical load predicted theoretically. This ultimate value of the load can be calculated with sufficient accuracy from the formula [see formula (245), p. 396]

$$P_{\text{ult.}} = Ch^2\sqrt{E\sigma_{\text{Y.P.}}}, \tag{246}$$

in which h is the thickness of the plate, E the modulus of elasticity

[1] See paper by E. E. Sechler, Guggenheim Aeronautics Laboratory, California Institute of Technology Publication 27.

[2] *Loc. cit.*, p. 177.

[3] See report by L. Schuman and G. Back, *loc. cit.*, p. 400.

of the material, $\sigma_{\text{Y.P.}}$ its yield-point stress and C a factor depending on the properties of the material and on the proportions of the plate. Experimental values[1] for this factor are shown in Fig. 213 and there is also given a curve for C which can be used in practical calculations of ultimate strength of thin compressed sheets of metal.

Compression of Angles.[2]—A compressed strut of ∟-section may fail in two entirely different manners: (1) as a column, or (2) owing to buckling of the flanges. Tests made with struts of symmetrical ∟-sections show that, when the widths of flanges

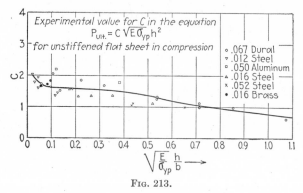

Fig. 213.

are small as compared with the length, the struts buckle as columns, while for wide flanges plate buckling occurs first. In order to obtain definite conditions for buckling of the strut and of its flanges, such end supports as shown in Fig. 214 were used. A $\frac{5}{8}$-in. steel ball was inserted in each end block, making the strut hinged about the centers of the balls. To eliminate initial eccentricities, a special arrangement was used providing for an adjustment whereby the ball could be moved along a line parallel to the axis of the greatest moment of inertia of the cross section of the strut, so that the effect of initial eccentricities could be removed and a very sharply defined buckling of the strut could be obtained. To obtain definite edge conditions for the flanges, each side of the angle section was camfered along its width at

[1] These values are taken from E. E. Sechler's experiments, *loc. cit*, p. 401.

[2] See paper by F. J. Bridget, C. C. Jerome and A. B. Vosseller, *Trans. Am. Soc. Mech. Eng.*, Applied Mechanics Division, vol. 56, p. 569, 1934. Buckling of compressed angles beyond yield point is described in the paper by C. F. Kollbrunner, *loc. cit.*, p. 340.

the ends to an angle of 60° and the end blocks each had two 120-degree V-grooves in which the ends of the strut were supported, thus insuring hinged edge conditions for the flanges.

The experimental results obtained thus with struts of 24 SRT aluminum alloy are shown in Fig. 215. The specimens tested were all 22 in. in length and of 0.025-in. thickness; the width of the sides varied from 0.405 to 2.025 in. It is seen that for struts with small width of sides the experimental results follow Euler's curve very closely. In the case of wider widths, in

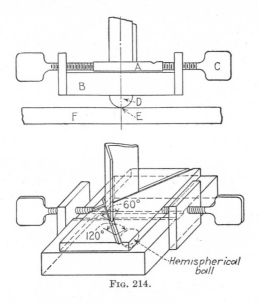

Fig. 214.

which plate buckling occurred before column buckling, the critical values of the load, given in the figure, were calculated by Southwell's method, and we have again a very satisfactory agreement with the theory.

Buckling of Plates under Shearing Forces.—Most experiments of this kind have been made with very long strips, the longitudinal sides of which were clamped.[1] For this case we have an exact solution (see p. 360) and experiments show that, regarding wave formation, there is satisfactory agreement with the theory. The

[1] See paper by F. Bollenrath, *Luftfahrtforschung*, vol. 6, p. 1, 1929. See also paper by H. J. Gough and H. L. Cox, *Proc. Royal Soc., London*, series A, vol. 137, p. 145, 1932.

magnitude of the critical load is also obtained with sufficient accuracy if the Southwell method is applied.

Some experiments have been made also with corrugated rectangular plates[1] subjected to the action of shear. The shearing forces were applied by the use of a hinged rectangular frame along one diagonal of which external tensile forces were acting (Fig. 216). The wave formation and the magnitude of the critical load are in satisfactory agreement with the theory

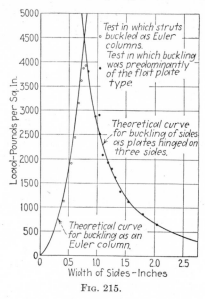

FIG. 215.

developed on the assumption that a corrugated plate can be considered as a plate of non-isotropic material.[2] It will be noted that in this case the direction of nodal lines made only a small angle with the direction of the sides parallel to corrugations instead of approximately 45° as in the case of unstiffened plates.

75. Practical Applications of the Theory of Buckling of Plates. *Applications in Design of Compression Members.*—In discussing buckling of columns it was shown that for practical proportions of compression members failure occurs when, in the weakest cross section, the maximum combined direct and bending stress becomes equal to the yield point stress of the material. Only

[1] See "Deutsche Versuchsanstalt für Luftfahrt E. V.," 1931.
[2] See the paper by H. Reissner and S. Bergman, *loc. cit.*, p. 384.

in the case of very slender struts can sufficient buckling occur within elastic limit to be equivalent to complete failure. This fact must be kept in mind in designing compression members

Fig. 216.

built up of comparatively thin sheets of metal. Take, for instance, the case of a compression member, the cross section of which is shown in Fig. 217. The two vertical web plates of width b and thickness h, with angles along the edges, are connected by diagonals and battens in horizontal planes as shown by dotted lines. To be on the safe side, we neglect the resistance to twist of the angles and consider the web plates as uniformly compressed rectangular plates with simply supported edges. Since the length of these plates is large in comparison with their width, the critical stress within the elastic limit is determined, for $\nu = 0.3$, by the formula (see p. 331)

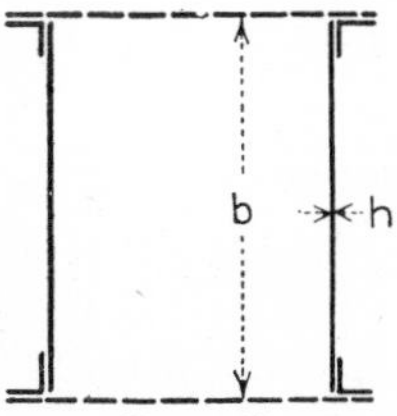

$$\sigma_{cr} = \frac{\pi^2 E}{2.73} \frac{h^2}{b^2}.$$

Fig. 217.

In the case of very slender struts, say $l/r > 150$, it is justifiable to take for the ratio b/h such a value that the critical stress for the plate is equal to the critical stress for the entire strut.   Then, using Euler's formula for the strut, the equation for determining the required value of the ratio b/h is

$$\frac{\pi^2 E}{2.73} \frac{h^2}{b^2} = \frac{\pi^2 E r^2}{l^2}, \qquad (a)$$

in which l/r is the slenderness ratio for the strut.   From this equation we obtain

$$\frac{b}{h} \approx 0.60 \frac{l}{r}. \qquad (b)$$

Thus, to have the factor of safety for buckling of the web equal to the factor of safety for buckling of a slender strut, the proportions of the web must satisfy condition (b).

If a compression member has proportions usual in structural engineering, failure occurs as a result of local yielding of the material in the weakest cross section.   Owing to various kinds of inaccuracy, this yielding may be produced while the average compressive stress in the strut is far below the yield-point stress.   Under this condition it is evident that a built-up strut can be expected to behave as a solid one only if the proportions of the plates are such that they will not buckle at a stress below the yield point of the material.

In discussing buckling of plates beyond the proportional limit, and assuming that beyond that limit their flexural rigidity is reduced in the ratio α (see p. 389), we have seen that, to eliminate the possibility of buckling at stresses below the yield point, long compressed plates of structural steel with simply supported edges must be of such proportions that $b/h \gtrless 36$. Since long compressed plates buckle in many waves, a local compression along one half-wave will have practically the same effect as a uniform compression of the entire plate.   Thus the same ratio

$$\frac{b}{h} = 36 \qquad (c)$$

can be recommended also in the case of a compression member like the one shown in Fig. 217.   It should be noted also that, owing to the local character of buckling of the web, the transverse diaphragms, which are usually placed at certain intervals along the length of compression members, will not increase the stability of the web.

If the vertical web plates of a compression member are rigidly connected with heavy horizontal plates (Fig. 218), it is justifiable to consider the vertical plates as built in at the longitudinal edges. In such case we can take (see p. 389)

$$\frac{b}{h} = 48. \qquad (d)$$

The conditions at the edges of the vertical webs of a compression member, the cross section of which is shown in Fig. 219,

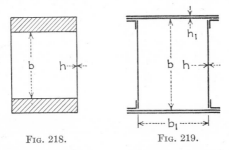

Fig. 218. Fig. 219.

are intermediate between simply supported and clamped edge conditions. Assuming that the degree of restraint depends approximately on the magnitude of the ratio

$$\frac{h^3 b_1}{h^3_1 b},$$

we obtain for partial restraint, by interpolation between (c) and (d),

$$\frac{b}{h} = 48\left(1 - \frac{h^3 b_1}{4h^3_1 b}\right), \qquad (e)$$

from which the required ratio b/h for any proportions of plates with $h_1{}^3 b > h^3 b_1$, can be calculated. When $h_1{}^3 b = h^3 b_1$ the critical compressive stress for horizontal plates is the same as for vertical webs, thus the latter are in condition of plates with simply supported edges. Equation (e) in such a case reduces to Eq. (c) given above.

In the cases shown in Fig. 220 each flange may be considered as a plate simply supported along one edge and entirely free along the other. In such cases, to eliminate the possibility of buckling at a stress below the yield point, we take for structural steel (see p. 390)

$$\frac{b}{h} = 12. \tag{f}$$

In the case shown in Fig. 221, assuming that the upper edges of the vertical web plates are built in, we obtain

$$\frac{b}{h} = 21. \tag{g}$$

In all these cases it has been assumed that structural steel has a yield-point stress equal to 34,000 lb. per square inch.

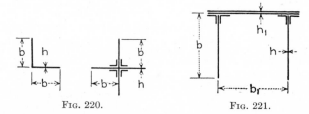

Fig. 220.   Fig. 221.

For materials with some other mechanical properties the ratio b/h should be changed in a proportion depending on the value of α at the yield-point stress (see Art. 71) for that material.

Applications in Design of Plate Girders.—The proportioning of plate girders is based at present to a great extent on empirical rules. Being the result of long experience, these rules usually give satisfactory proportions and at the same time are sufficiently flexible so that they leave considerable freedom for individual judgment. As a result of this we have a variety of dimensions of plate girders designed for the same span and the same load. Comparing, for instance, plate girders with a span of 100 ft. and depth of 10 ft., we find that the thickness of the web varies from $\frac{7}{16}$ to $\frac{5}{8}$ in.[1] A comparison[2] of two plate girders of 90-ft. span, one for an American railway and the other for a British railway, shows that in the American type the stiffeners comprise 25 per cent and in the British 40 per cent of the material in both web and stiffeners.

[1] Rode, H., *Der Eisenbau*, vol. 7, p. 217, 1916,

[2] Gibb, H. M., *Engineering*, vol. 90, 1910,

Such a variety of proportions indicates that the old problem of proportioning of plate girders cannot be considered as completely settled. If this is true for plate girders of common sizes, it must be much more so in the design of plate girders of exceptionally large dimensions for which a large experience is lacking. During recent years a number of plate girders of long spans were built,[1] sometimes exceeding 300 ft. In designing such girders the proper selection of the web thickness and stiffener spacing becomes an important problem which can be satisfactorily solved only on the basis of a rational theory or by using model tests.

The problem of determining this proper web thickness and stiffening of the web is essentially a stability problem. It is well-known that a web, if not sufficiently thick or not satisfactorily stiffened, may buckle sideways and act as a tie while the stiffeners are working as struts. To take into account the possibility of such buckling, several engineers have recommended[2] that a narrow strip of web making an angle of 45° with the longitudinal axis of the girder be considered as a column carrying a compressive stress over its cross section equal to the shearing stress at the neutral axis. The length of this column is taken as $h\sqrt{2}$, in which h is the unsupported depth of the web, the ends of the column being considered as built in. This assumption, as we shall see later, underestimates considerably the stability of the unstiffened webs.

To get a more reliable conclusion regarding the stability of the web, experiments on plate girders, together with the theory of buckling of a thin plate under the action of normal and shearing stresses in its plane, should be considered.

The first experiments with buckling of thin webs transmitting shearing and bending stresses were made by William Fairbairn in connection with the construction of the famous Britannia and Conway tubular bridges. Even up to the present time these classical experiments[3] have held great interest for engineers working with thin-walled structures. The Britannia bridge is

[1] A description of several large plate girders can be found in the paper by L. Karner, *Pub. Intern. Assoc. Bridge and Structural Eng.*, vol. 1, 1932, p. 297

[2] See, for instance, the paper by F. E. Turneaure, *J. Western Soc. Eng.*, vol. 12, p. 788, 1907.

[3] See William Fairbairn, "Conway and Britannia Tubular Bridges," 1849

of the tube type with a rectangular cross section. The larger tubes have a span of 450 ft. and cross-sectional dimensions of 27 by 16 ft. As this was an unusually large structure for that time, it was decided to make experiments with models to determine the safe dimensions of the tube and the most favorable distribution of material. After a considerable amount of preliminary experimenting, it was decided to test large models, one-sixth the linear dimensions of the intended bridge. The sides of these model tubes consisted of sheets 3 ft. 9 in. deep and only 0.1 in. thick. The first experiments showed that at a comparatively small load undulations in the sides appeared which formed angles of about 45° with the line of the bottom.

It was evident, from these experiments, that the tension throughout the bottom and the compression throughout the top stood in the relation of action and reaction to each other, the diagonal strain in the sides being the medium of communication.

A diagonal wave of puckering clearly exposed the line of severest strain. It was evident that the sides were exposed to unfair strain from the change of shape consequent on the tendency of the top and bottom to come together, the plates being strong enough, if they could but be kept in shape; and it was therefore determined, in this experiment, to modify the construction of the sides. This was done by the addition of pillars of angle-iron throughout, of the whole height of the sides, riveted to them, having the effect of stiffening them, and at the same time of keeping the top and bottom in place. They were prototypes of the T-iron pillars used in the large tubes.

Further experiments illustrated the importance of the pillars in the sides, for, with a small addition of metal to the weight of the tube, the top and bottom remained precisely the same as before, while the ultimate strength was increased considerably. From these experiments it was learned that "as the depth of a web increased, the precautions requisite for maintaining the sides in shape become very formidable." The T-irons, gussets and stiffening plates for this purpose in one of the Britannia tubes weigh 215 tons, or upward of one-third of the whole weight of the sides.

The experimental tubes were submitted to a concentrated load at the middle and the shearing force was constant along the length of the span. In the design of the actual bridge it was taken into account that the maximum shearing force diminishes toward the middle, and the web was taken $\frac{1}{2}$ in. thick in the middle portion and $\frac{5}{8}$ in. thick at the ends.

Some experimental work on plate girders was also done at that time.[1] The thickness of the web of the model girder was $\frac{1}{4}$ in. throughout; the over-all depth was 10 ft. at the center, and 6 ft. at the ends, and the distance between the bearings was 66 ft. The girder failed by buckling of the web. Later on the girder was repaired and the vertical web stiffened by the addition of angle-iron pillars at each joint in the vertical plates of the web. In this way the strength of the girder was considerably increased and finally it failed at a larger load by a simultaneous collapse of the top and the bottom.

Further experiments with plate girders were made by a Belgian engineer, Houbotte.[2] Two plate girders, 1.50 m. in span length, 0.5 cm. in thickness of the web, and 30 cm. and 49 cm. in depth, were tested. Loaded at the middle, both these girders failed by buckling of the web, which had no stiffeners. The girder of larger depth failed at smaller load although its section modulus was twice as great as that of the girder with smaller depth.

More recently some work with plate girders has been done by Professor W. E. Lilly.[3] A plate girder of the following dimensions was constructed: depth $9\frac{1}{2}$ in.; length, 5 ft. 3 in. The flanges were made up of two plates 2 by $\frac{3}{8}$ in., and two angles $1\frac{1}{4}$ by $1\frac{1}{4}$ by $\frac{1}{4}$ in. The framework of the girder was made in separate halves and was bolted together to the web. This construction allowed different thicknesses of web to be used in the experiments. A large number of tests were then carried out with different thicknesses of the web and spacing of stiffeners.

Applying the load at the middle the wave formation in the web was obtained.

It was found that the wave-length of the wave formation is nearly independent of the thickness, if the stiffeners are of great strength compared with the web. The angle of inclination of the wave depends upon the distance apart of the stiffeners and the depth of the girder. The stiffeners prevent the formation of the waves, and severe local stresses are set up

[1] CLARK, EDWIN, "Britannia and Conway Tubular Bridges," London, 1850.

[2] HOUBOTTE, M., *Der Civilingenieur*, vol. 4, 1856.

[3] LILLY, W. E., *Engineering*, vol. 83, p. 136, 1907. See also his book "The Design of Plate Girders and Columns," 1908.

around the ends of the stiffeners, causing a crumpling up of this part of the web.

Experiments with a plate girder of a larger size were made in this country by Professor Turneaure.[1] The principal conclusions of these experiments were: (1) The stresses in web plates with stiffeners, when stressed within the elastic limit, agree closely with the theoretical stresses; and as a necessary result the axial stresses in vertical stiffeners, not subjected to local loads, are practically zero. (2) The elastic limit strength of a web plate without stiffeners is about twice the ultimate strength given by Euler's column formula applied to a diagonal column element (see p. 409).

Fig. 222.

A series of tests on rolled I-beams and built-up plate girders has been made by H. F. Moore and W. M. Wilson.[2] One example of a tested plate girder with a buckled web is shown in Fig. 222. These experimenters came to the conclusion "that the ability to resist buckling of thin webs without intermediate stiffeners had been underestimated" and "that it may be safe to build girders without intermediate stiffeners if the ratio of the unsupported width to the thickness of the web exceeds 60. However, it is necessary to decrease the working stress allowable in the web as this ratio becomes greater."

From the experiments made it may be seen that a plate girder can transmit the shearing force to the bearings in two different ways: (1) If the load is not sufficient to produce wave formation, the web of the girder transmits the shearing force by working in shear. (2) In the case of larger loads, which produce wave formation, one part of the shearing force is transmitted by shear-

---

[1] *Loc. cit.*, p. 409.

[2] Moore, H. F., University of Illinois Bulletin 68, 1913. Also H. F. Moore and W. M. Wilson, University of Illinois Bulletin 86, 1916.

ing stresses in the web, as before, and the other part as in a truss, in which the web plate is working as ties and the stiffeners as struts. The magnitude of the load at which wave formation begins depends on the thickness of the web and on the spacing and dimensions of stiffeners. In the case of a sufficient thickness of the web and a satisfactory stiffening, a plate girder can carry the total load for which it is designed without any buckling of the web. We usually have such proportions in bridges. On the other hand there are constructions with very thin webs which buckle at the very beginning of loading and the total load is practically transmitted as in a truss. We have examples of such girders in airplane construction.[1]

Although buckling of the web does not mean an immediate failure of the girder, the dimensions in the case of bridges are usually taken so as to eliminate buckling under service conditions. A common procedure is to adopt a certain value of the working stress in shear and on this basis to decide upon the web thickness. Then the spacing of stiffeners is determined so as to enable the web to transmit shearing stresses without buckling. Observing that in railway girders the total load varies approximately as the span, and assuming the ratio of the depth to the span to be constant, it may be seen that the above procedure would result in nearly the same thickness for all spans. Assuming that this thickness is satisfactory for small bridges, it certainly will be insufficient for larger spans and some increase in the thickness for eliminating the possibility of buckling of the web becomes necessary. This is provided for in some specifications. For instance, American Railway Engineering Association specifications require that the thickness of the web shall be not less than $\frac{1}{20}\sqrt{h}$, where h represents the distance between the flanges in inches.

Another limitation for thickness is usually obtained from the consideration of corrosion and from the fact that too thin plates, if deep and long, are very awkward to handle. The $\frac{3}{8}$-in. thickness is usually considered as the least thickness permissible to provide against corrosion and insure a satisfactory handling of material during construction and shipping.

---

[1] WAGNER, H., *Z. Flugtech. Motorluftsch.*, vol. 20, p. 200, 1919. See also *Eng. News*, vol. 40, p. 154, 399, 1899.

To obtain any rational basis for the design, it is necessary to make a study of the elastic stability of thin webs.   In discussing buckling of the web we must consider three cases: (1) Near the supports the shearing force is the most important factor and the part of the web between two stiffeners may be considered as a rectangular plate subjected to the action of uniform shear (Fig. 223*a*).   (2) At the middle of the span the shearing stresses can be neglected in comparison with normal stresses.   Then the part of the web between two stiffeners is in condition of pure

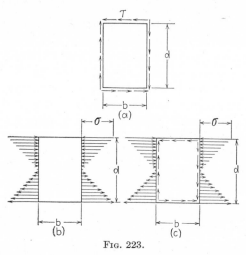

Fig. 223.

bending represented in Fig. 223*b*.   (3) In the intermediate cross sections there is a combination of normal and shearing forces such as shown in Fig. 223*c*.   These three cases have been discussed in Arts. 66 and 67.

In application of the theoretical formulas obtained, we begin with the determination of the thickness of the web at the middle of the span, where only bending stresses need be taken into consideration.   Since a long rectangular plate submitted to bending subdivides at buckling into comparatively short waves (see Table 36), the constraint due to the vertical stiffeners usually will be negligible and we can assume

$$\sigma_{cr} = 23.9 \frac{\pi^2 E}{12(1 - \nu^2)} \frac{h^2}{d^2}. \qquad (h)$$

From this formula the required value of the ratio of the thickness of the web to its depth[1] can be calculated for any value of σ_{cr}. To eliminate any possibility of buckling of the web under service conditions, the value of σ_{cr} must be larger than the maximum bending stress in the web. In choosing the necessary factor of safety we proceed here differently than in the case of plates of compression members. In the case of columns any local buckling of the plates usually means a complete failure of the structure, and it was recommended in our previous discussion to take for plates such proportions that no buckling will occur below the yield-point stress. In the case of plate girders, however, buckling of the web does not represent any immediate danger to the structure, but simply indicates that the web no longer takes its full share of compressive bending stresses. Under such circumstances it seems reasonable to use a lower factor of safety.

Let us consider the case of structural carbon steel with a yield-point stress equal to 34,000 lb. per square inch. Taking 16,000 lb. per square inch as a basic tensile stress in this case, we have a factor of safety equal to $2\frac{1}{8}$. This factor not only covers the possibility of the action of some increased loads but also takes care of any stress concentration due to rivets and sharp changes in cross section and also any fatigue effect due to fluctuation of stresses. In considering the stability of web plates, the local stress concentration and fatigue effects should be disregarded. Also taking into consideration that any constraint at the flanges and at the stiffeners is neglected in formula (h), it seems logical to take a factor of safety against buckling lower than $2\frac{1}{8}$. We suggest taking it equal to 1.5. Then, assuming that the maximum stress of 16,000 lb. per square inch is obtained by deducting rivet holes, which may constitute 15 per cent of the flange area, we substitute for σ_{cr} in formula (h) the value of $16,000 \cdot 0.85 \cdot 1.5 = 20,400$ lb. per square inch. In this way we obtain, with $E = 30 \cdot 10^6$ lb. per square inch and $\nu = 0.3$

$$\frac{d}{h} = \sqrt{23.9 \frac{\pi^2 E}{12(1 - \nu^2)16,000 \cdot 0.85 \cdot 1.5}} \approx 180. \qquad (i)$$

In existing plate girders this ratio sometimes is larger than 180,

---

[1] In this discussion the resistance furnished by the flange angles to buckling of the web is neglected and the web is considered as a simply supported rectangular plate of width d, where d is the distance between the inner surfaces of the flanges.

which indicates that a smaller factor of safety than 1.5 is used. If $d/h = 200$, this factor is about 1.25.

Considering now the stiffening of the web by ribs, let us determine first the limiting value of the ratio d/h at which such stiffening will not be necessary except, of course, at the points of application of heavy concentrated loads. In such case the portions of the web between these loads can be considered as rectangular plates which, near the supports, will be submitted principally to the action of shearing stresses. Neglecting the constraint at the flanges and assuming that the plate is long, we take for the critical value of shearing stresses Eq. (216). Then

$$\tau_{cr} = 5.35 \frac{\pi^2 E}{12(1 - \nu^2)} \frac{h^2}{d^2}. \qquad (j)$$

Substituting for τ_{cr} the yield-point stress,[1] we obtain the limiting value for the ratio d/h. Taking again structural steel with $\sigma_{Y.P.} = 34,000$ lb. per square inch and assuming that

$$\tau_{Y.P.} = 0.58\sigma_{Y.P.},$$

we obtain

$$\frac{d}{h} = \sqrt{\frac{5.35\pi^2 E}{12(1 - \nu^2)\tau_{Y.P.}}} \approx 86. \qquad (k)$$

For materials with higher values of the yield-point stress we will get from (k) smaller values for the ratio d/h. Taking, for instance, silicon steel with $\tau_{Y.P.} = 26,000$ lb. per square inch and nickel steel with $\tau_{Y.P.} = 29,000$ lb. per square inch, we obtain $d/h = 75$ and $d/h = 71$, respectively.

In calculating the required distances between the stiffeners near the supports, we consider a portion of the web between two stiffeners as a simply supported plate of length equal to depth d and of width b equal to the distance between the axes of the stiffeners.[2] For calculating critical values of shearing stress we use the curve in Fig. 189. Then

$$\tau_{cr} = \left(5.35 + 4\frac{b^2}{d^2}\right)\frac{\pi^2 E}{12(1 - \nu^2)} \frac{h^2}{b^2}. \qquad (l)$$

---

[1] Since buckling of the web does not mean an immediate failure of the girder, we use Eq. (j) up to the yield-point stress, neglecting some permanent set of the material in the regions of transition between the proportional limit and the yield point.

[2] We assume that the distance between stiffeners is smaller than the depth d.

Taking again a factor of safety equal to 1.5, we obtain

$$\frac{b}{h} = \frac{1.16}{\sqrt{0.415\dfrac{\tau}{E} - \dfrac{h^2}{d^2}}}, \qquad (m)$$

where τ is the gross shearing stress in the panel at the support.

As a numerical example, let us apply formulas (i) and (m) to plate girders of depths 6 ft. and 10 ft., respectively. Considering the case $d = 6$ ft., and assuming $d/h = 180$, we find $h = 0.40$ in. and we take the web thickness as $\frac{7}{16}$ in. Assuming now a working stress in shear of $\tau = 10,000$ lb. per square inch, we obtain from Eq. (m) $b/h = 115$ and $b = 50.3$ in.

Considering the case $d = 10$ ft., and assuming $d/h = 180$, we find $h = 0.67$ in. and take $h = \frac{11}{16}$ in. Then, from Eq. (m), for $\tau = 10,000$ lb. per square inch, we obtain $b/h = 113$ and $b = 77.7$ in. Applying to the same examples the specifications of the American Railway Engineering Association, we find, for $d = 6$ ft., $h = \frac{1}{20}\sqrt{d} = 0.424$ in. and take $h = \frac{7}{16}$ in. The distance between stiffeners, for the working stress $\tau = 10,000$ lb. per square inch, is $b = \dfrac{h}{40}(12,000 - \tau) = 50h = 22$ in. In this case the formulas (i) and (m) give the same thickness of the web and a somewhat larger distance between stiffeners than is obtained by using the A.R.E.A. specifications. In the case $d = 10$ ft., the A.R.E.A. specifications give $h = \frac{9}{16}$ in. and the distance between stiffeners $b = 6$ ft. The formulas (i) and (m) give for this case a somewhat greater thickness of the web and a larger distance between the stiffeners.

When the thickness of the web and the distance between the stiffeners at the supports are determined, some intermediate panels can be considered and the stability of the web can be checked by using the curves shown in Fig. 194.

For determining the required flexural rigidity of stiffeners, Tables 43 and 44 should be used. The values of γ are represented by curves[1] in Fig. 224. It is seen that, in the case of three panels, the required γ for the two intermediate stiffeners is larger than in the case of two panels, and γ should increase somewhat when the number of panels increases. Assuming that in all practical cases the required rigidity will not be larger than twice that given by Table 43, we arrive at the following values of the required moment of inertia of the cross section of the stiffeners for various depths and thicknesses of web and for a stiffener spacing of $b = 5$ ft.

[1] Note that in the figure notation $\gamma = B/Db$ is used. Hence values for γ given in Table 43 must be multiplied by 2 and the values of Table 44 by 3.

TABLE 50.—REQUIRED MOMENT OF INERTIA FOR STIFFENERS

	$d = 60$ in.	$d = 80$ in.	$d = 96$ in.	$d = 120$ in.
	$b/d = 1$ $\gamma = 3.30$	$\frac{3}{4}$ 11.6	$\frac{5}{8}$ 25.2	$\frac{1}{2}$ 60.
$h = \frac{3}{8}$ in. $h = \frac{7}{16}$ in. $h = \frac{1}{2}$ in. $h = \frac{9}{16}$ in.	$I = \begin{cases} 0.96 \text{ in.}^4 \\ 1.52 \text{ in.}^4 \\ 2.27 \text{ in.}^4 \\ 3.23 \text{ in.}^4 \end{cases}$	3.36 in.⁴ 5.34 in.⁴ 8.00 in.⁴ 11.4 in.⁴	7.30 in.⁴ 11.6 in.⁴ 17.3 in.⁴ 24.7 in.⁴	17.4 in.⁴ 27.6 in.⁴ 41.3 in.⁴ 58.8 in.⁴

It is seen that for smaller depth the calculated cross-sectional moment of inertia is much smaller than that which is actually

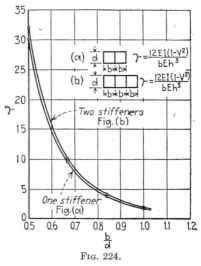

FIG. 224.

used. For larger depth the calculated values of I approach the usual proportions. For instance, in the case of $d = 10$ ft., the stiffener, following the American rule,[1] consists of two angles 6 by $3\frac{1}{2}$ by $\frac{3}{8}$ in. The moment of inertia for this stiffener for $h = \frac{9}{16}$ in. is $I = 62.5$ in.⁴, which is close to the value 58.8 in.⁴ given in the table above.

[1] See J. A. L. Waddell, "Bridge Engineering," p. 1670, New York, 1916.

CHAPTER VIII

BENDING OF THIN SHELLS

76. Deformation of an Element of a Shell.—Let $ABCD$ (Fig. 225) represent an infinitely small element cut out from a shell by two pairs of adjacent planes normal to the middle surface of the shell and containing its principal curvatures. Taking the coordinate axes x and y tangent at O to the lines of principal curvatures and the axis z normal to the middle surface, as shown in the figure, we denote by r_x and r_y the radii of principal curvatures in the xz- and yz-planes, respectively. The thickness of the shell, which is assumed constant, we denote by h.

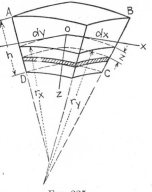

FIG. 225.

In considering bending of the shell, we assume that linear elements such as AD and BC, which are normal to the middle surface of the shell, remain straight and become normal to the deformed middle surface of the shell. Let us begin with a simple case in which, during bending, the lateral faces of the element $ABCD$ rotate only with respect to their lines of intersection with the middle surface. If r'_x and r'_y are the values of the radii of curvature after deformation, the unit elongations of a thin lamina at a distance z from the middle surface (see Fig. 225) are

$$\epsilon_x = -\frac{z}{1 - \dfrac{z}{r_x}}\left(\frac{1}{r'_x} - \frac{1}{r_x}\right); \qquad \epsilon_y = -\frac{z}{1 - \dfrac{z}{r_y}}\left(\frac{1}{r'_y} - \frac{1}{r_y}\right). \quad (a)$$

If, in addition to rotation, the lateral sides of the element are displaced parallel to themselves, owing to stretching of the middle surface, and if the corresponding unit elongations of the

419

middle surface in the x- and y-directions are denoted by ϵ_1 and ϵ_2, respectively, the elongation ϵ_x of the lamina considered above, as seen from Fig. 226, is

$$\epsilon_x = \frac{l_2 - l_1}{l_1}.$$

Substituting

$$l_1 = ds\left(1 - \frac{z}{r_x}\right); \qquad l_2 = ds(1 + \epsilon_1)\left(1 - \frac{z}{r'_x}\right),$$

we obtain

$$\epsilon_x = \frac{\epsilon_1}{1 - \dfrac{z}{r_x}} - \frac{z}{1 - \dfrac{z}{r_x}}\left[\frac{1}{(1 - \epsilon_1)r'_x} - \frac{1}{r_x}\right]. \qquad (b)$$

In the same manner, for elongation in the y-direction

$$\epsilon_y = \frac{\epsilon_2}{1 - \dfrac{z}{r_y}} - \frac{z}{1 - \dfrac{z}{r_y}}\left[\frac{1}{(1 - \epsilon_2)r'_y} - \frac{1}{r_y}\right]. \qquad (c)$$

In our further discussion the thickness h of the shell will be always assumed small in comparison with the radii of curvature. In such a case the quantities z/r_x and z/r_y can be neglected in comparison with unity. We will neglect also the effect of the elongations ϵ_1 and ϵ_2 on the curvature. Then, instead of expressions (b) and (c), we obtain

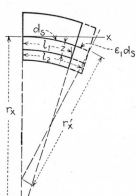

Fig. 226.

$$\left.\begin{aligned} \epsilon_x &= \epsilon_1 - z\left(\frac{1}{r'_x} - \frac{1}{r_x}\right) = \epsilon_1 - \chi_x z; \\ \epsilon_y &= \epsilon_2 - z\left(\frac{1}{r'_y} - \frac{1}{r_y}\right) = \epsilon_2 - \chi_y z, \end{aligned}\right\} \quad (247)$$

where χ_x and χ_y are the changes of curvature. Using these expressions for the components of strain of a lamina and assuming that there are no normal stresses between laminae ($\sigma_z = 0$), the following expressions for the components of stress are obtained:

$$\left.\begin{array}{l} \sigma_x = \dfrac{E}{1 - \nu^2}[\epsilon_1 + \nu\epsilon_2 - z(\chi_x + \nu\chi_y)]; \\[3mm] \sigma_y = \dfrac{E}{1 - \nu^2}[\epsilon_2 + \nu\epsilon_1 - z(\chi_y + \nu\chi_x)]. \end{array}\right\} \tag{248}$$

On each side of the element *ABCD* the corresponding forces can be replaced by a normal force applied at the centroid of the side and by a bending moment. Since the thickness of the shell is very small, the lateral sides of the element can be considered as rectangles; hence the resultant forces will act in the middle surface of the shell. Using for these resultant forces and for the bending moments per unit length the same notations as in the case of plates (see Arts. 55 and 56), we obtain[1]

$$\left.\begin{array}{l} N_x = \displaystyle\int_{-\frac{h}{2}}^{+\frac{h}{2}} \sigma_x \, dz = \dfrac{Eh}{1 - \nu^2}(\epsilon_1 + \nu\epsilon_2); \\[4mm] N_y = \displaystyle\int_{-\frac{h}{2}}^{+\frac{h}{2}} \sigma_y \, dz = \dfrac{Eh}{1 - \nu^2}(\epsilon_2 + \nu\epsilon_1), \end{array}\right\} \tag{249}$$

and also

$$\left.\begin{array}{l} M_x = \displaystyle\int_{-\frac{h}{2}}^{+\frac{h}{2}} z\sigma_x \, dz = -D(\chi_x + \nu\chi_y); \\[4mm] M_y = \displaystyle\int_{-\frac{h}{2}}^{+\frac{h}{2}} z\sigma_y \, dz = -D(\chi_y + \nu\chi_x), \end{array}\right\} \tag{250}$$

where D has the same meaning as in the case of plates [see Eq. (175)] and denotes the *flexural rigidity* of the shell.

A more general case of deformation of the element in Fig. 225 is obtained if we assume that, in addition to normal stresses, shearing stresses also are acting on the lateral sides of the element. Using the same notations as in the case of plates and considering that on the side normal to the x-axis the components of shearing stress are τ_{xy} and τ_{xz}, we obtain for the resultant forces and for the torsional moment

$$Q_x = \int_{-\frac{h}{2}}^{+\frac{h}{2}} \tau_{xz}\, dz; \quad N_{xy} = \int_{-\frac{h}{2}}^{+\frac{h}{2}} \tau_{xy}\, dz; \quad M_{xy} = -\int_{-\frac{h}{2}}^{+\frac{h}{2}} z\tau_{xy}\, dz. \tag{251}$$

[1] The positive directions of moments and forces are the same as shown in Figs. 160 and 166 for bending of plates.

In the same manner, for the side normal to the y-axis, we obtain

$$Q_y = \int_{-\frac{h}{2}}^{+\frac{h}{2}} \tau_{yz} \, dz; \qquad N_{yx} = N_{xy} = \int_{-\frac{h}{2}}^{+\frac{h}{2}} \tau_{xy} \, dz;$$

$$M_{yx} = -M_{xy} = \int_{-\frac{h}{2}}^{+\frac{h}{2}} z\tau_{xy} \, dz. \tag{252}$$

The relation between the shearing stress τ_{xy} and the twisting of the element $ABCD$ (Fig. 225) can be established exactly in the same manner as in the case of an element cut out from a plate (see p. 292); in this way we obtain

$$\tau_{xy} = -2Gz\chi_{xy}; \qquad M_{xy} = D(1 - \nu)\chi_{xy}, \tag{253}$$

where χ_{xy} takes the place of $\partial^2 w/\partial x \, \partial y$ in the case of a plate and represents the twist of the element $ABCD$ during bending of the shell, so that $\chi_{xy} \, dx$ is the rotation[1] of the edge BC relative to Oz with respect to the x-axis.

If, in addition to twist, there is a shearing strain γ in the middle surface of the shell, we obtain

$$\tau_{xy} = (\gamma - 2z\chi_{xy})G; \quad N_{xy} = \int_{-\frac{h}{2}}^{+\frac{h}{2}} \tau_{xy} \, dz = \frac{\gamma hE}{2(1 + \nu)};$$

$$M_{xy} = -\int_{-\frac{h}{2}}^{+\frac{h}{2}} \tau_{xy}z \, dz = D(1 - \nu)\chi_{xy}. \tag{254}$$

Thus assuming that during bending of a shell the linear elements normal to the middle surface remain straight and become normal to the deformed middle surface, we can express the resultant forces N_x, N_y and N_{xy} and the moments M_x, M_y and M_{xy} in terms of six quantities: the three components of strain ϵ_1, ϵ_2 and γ of the middle surface of the shell and the three quantities χ_x, χ_y and χ_{xy} representing the changes of curvature and the twist of the middle surface.

The strain energy of a deformed shell consists of two parts: (1) the strain energy due to bending, and (2) strain energy due to stretching of the middle surface. For the first part of this energy we can use Eq. (199). Substituting in it the

---

[1] Rotations with respect to x-, y-, and z-axes are taken positive in conformance with the right-hand screw rule.

changes of curvatures χ_x, χ_y and χ_{xy}, instead of curvatures $\partial^2 w/\partial x^2$, $\partial^2 w/\partial y^2$ and $\partial^2 w/\partial x\ \partial y$, we obtain

$$V_1 = \tfrac{1}{2}D\int\int[(\chi_x + \chi_y)^2 - 2(1 - \nu)(\chi_x\chi_y - \chi^2_{xy})]dA, \quad (255)$$

where the integration should be extended over the entire surface of the shell.

That part of the energy due to stretching of the middle surface is

$$V_2 = \int\int\tfrac{1}{2}(N_x\epsilon_1 + N_y\epsilon_2 + N_{xy}\gamma)dA$$

or, by using Eqs. (249) and (254),

$$V_2 = \frac{Eh}{2(1 - \nu^2)}\int\int\left[(\epsilon_1 + \epsilon_2)^2 - 2(1 - \nu)\left(\epsilon_1\epsilon_2 - \frac{1}{4}\gamma^2\right)\right]dA. \quad (256)$$

The total energy of deformation is obtained by adding together expressions (255) and (256). Applications of these expressions in discussing bending and buckling of shells will be shown later.

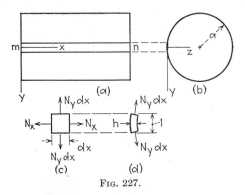

Fig. 227.

77. Symmetrical Deformation of a Circular Cylindrical Shell.—

There are many practical cases in which the load acting on a cylindrical shell is symmetrically distributed with respect to the axis of the cylinder. A tube submitted to the action of uniformly distributed internal pressure, a vertical cylindrical reservoir containing a liquid or a rotating drum submitted to the action of centrifugal forces are examples of such symmetrical loading. Since in these cases all points of the middle surface of the shell, lying in the same cross section perpendicular to the axis of symmetry, have the same displacements, it is sufficient to consider one elemental strip mn (Fig. 227), of unit width,[1] cut out from the shell by two axial[2] sections. An element dx of this strip (Fig. 227c) is submitted to the action of forces N_x and $N_y\,dx$ in the middle surface of the shell and of a force $q\,dx$ normal to the surface, where q is the intensity of the load acting on the shell. Also there will be bending moments acting on the sides of the element.

Let us assume that the forces N_x are constant, *i.e.*, that the cylindrical shell is submitted to the action of a uniform axial tension or compression. The forces N_y will depend on the radial displacements of the points of the strip during deformation of the shell. Denoting these displacements in the z-direction by w, we find that the strain of the middle surface of the shell in the circumferential direction is $-w/a$, where a is the radius of the middle surface of the shell. By using Eqs. (249) we obtain

$$N_x = \frac{Eh}{1-\nu^2}\left(\epsilon_1 - \nu\frac{w}{a}\right); \qquad N_y = \frac{Eh}{1-\nu^2}\left(-\frac{w}{a} + \nu\epsilon_1\right),$$

from which

$$N_y = \nu N_x - \frac{w}{a}Eh. \tag{a}$$

Considering bending of the strip mn, the forces (a) give a component in the radial direction (Fig. 227d), the magnitude of which per unit length is

$$\frac{N_y}{a} = \frac{1}{a}\left(\nu N_x - \frac{w}{a}Eh\right).$$

Owing to curvature of the strip in the xz-plane, the longitudinal forces N_x also give a radial component, the magnitude of which is

$$N_x\frac{d^2w}{dx^2}.$$

Summing up all transverse loads per unit length of the strip, we obtain

$$q + \frac{1}{a}\left(\nu N_x - \frac{w}{a}Eh\right) + N_x\frac{d^2w}{dx^2}, \tag{b}$$

[1] This width will be assumed as very small in comparison with the radius a and the cross section of the strip will be considered rectangular.

[2] This term will be used hereafter to designate a section through the axis of the cylinder.

and the differential equation for the deflection of the strip is

$$D \frac{d^4 w}{dx^4} = q + \frac{1}{a}\nu N_x - \frac{w}{a^2}Eh + N_x \frac{d^2 w}{dx^2}. \qquad (257)$$

The quantity D is taken for the flexural rigidity of the strip since distortion of the cross section is prevented by the action of adjacent strips.

If the load q and the forces N_x are given, the deflection of the shell is found from Eq. (257). Application of this equation in studying buckling of shells will be shown later (see Art. 81).

78. Inextensional Deformation of a Circular Cylindrical Shell.[1]—In the discussion of deformations of a circular ring (Art. 39), it was pointed out that a simplification in the analysis can be obtained if the extension of the center line of the ring may be neglected. The same kind of simplification can be obtained also in the case of *inextensional* deformation of a circular cylindrical shell. Let us consider the limitations that must be imposed on the displacements of the points of the middle surface of the

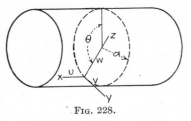

Fig. 228.

shell in order to have inextensional deformation. Taking the origin of coordinates at any point in the middle surface of the shell, directing the axes as shown in Fig. 228, and denoting by u, v and w the components of the displacement of that point, the condition that there is no stretching of the middle surface in the x-direction is

$$\epsilon_1 = \frac{\partial u}{\partial x} = 0. \qquad (a)$$

The condition of inextensibility in the circumferential direction will be written as in the case of a ring [see Eq. (b), p. 208]

$$\epsilon_2 = \frac{\partial v}{a\,\partial \theta} - \frac{w}{a} = 0. \qquad (b)$$

The condition that there is no shearing strain in the middle surface is

$$\gamma = \frac{\partial u}{a\,\partial \theta} + \frac{\partial v}{\partial x} = 0, \qquad (c)$$

which is the same as in the case of small deflection of plates except that $a\,d\theta$ takes the place of dy. The three conditions (a), (b) and (c) will be satisfied by taking for the components of displacement the same expressions

[1] The theory of inextensional deformations of shells is due to Lord Rayleigh, *Proc. London Math. Soc.*, vol. 13, 1881, and *Proc. Roy Soc., London*, vol. 45, 1889.

as in the case of a circular ring (see Art. 39). These components can be put in the following form:

$$
\left.
\begin{aligned}
u_1 &= 0; \\
v_1 &= \sum_{n=1}^{\infty} a(a_n \cos n\theta - a'_n \sin n\theta); \\
w_1 &= -\sum_{n=1}^{\infty} na(a_n \sin n\theta + a'_n \cos n\theta),
\end{aligned}
\right\} \tag{d}
$$

where a is the radius of the middle surface of the shell, θ the central angle, and a_n and a'_n constants which must be calculated for each particular case of loading. The displacements (d) represent the case in which all cross sections of the shell deform identically. On these displacements we can superpose displacements which vary along the length of the cylinder and which are given by the series

$$
\left.
\begin{aligned}
u_2 &= -\sum_{n=1}^{\infty} \frac{a}{n}(b_n \sin n\theta + b'_n \cos n\theta); \\
v_2 &= x\sum_{n=1}^{\infty}(b_n \cos n\theta - b'_n \sin n\theta); \\
w_2 &= -x\sum_{n=1}^{\infty} n(b_n \sin n\theta + b'_n \cos n\theta).
\end{aligned}
\right\} \tag{e}
$$

It can be readily proved that these expressions also satisfy the conditions of inextensibility. Then the general expressions for displacemends in inextensional deformation of a cylindrical shell are

$$
u = u_1 + u_2; \qquad v = v_1 + v_2; \qquad w = w_1 + w_2. \tag{f}
$$

In calculating inextensional deformations of a cylindrical shell under the action of a given system of forces, it is advantageous to use the expression for strain energy of bending [Eq. (255)]. The changes of curvature χ_x, χ_y and χ_{xy}, which enter in this expression, can be calculated as follows: the quantity χ_x representing the change of curvature in the direction of the generator is equal to zero since the generators, as seen from expressions (d) and (e), remain straight. The quantity χ_y, representing the change of curvature of the circumference, can be determined as in the case of a ring (see Art. 38) and we obtain

$$
\chi_y = \frac{1}{a^2}\left(w + \frac{\partial^2 w}{\partial \theta^2}\right)
$$

or, by using condition (b),

$$
\chi_y = \frac{1}{a^2}\left(\frac{\partial v}{\partial \theta} + \frac{\partial^2 w}{\partial \theta^2}\right). \tag{g}
$$

In calculating twist we note that an element of a generator, during deformation, rotates[1] with respect to the y-axis through an angle equal to $-\partial w/\partial x$ and with respect to z-axis through an angle equal to $\partial v/\partial x$. Considering now a similar element of a generator at a circumferential distance $a\,d\theta$ from the first one, we see that its rotation about the y-axis, corresponding to displacement w, is

$$-\frac{\partial w}{\partial x} - \frac{\partial^2 w}{\partial \theta\, \partial x}\, d\theta. \tag{h}$$

Rotation of the same element in the plane tangent to the shell is

$$\frac{\partial v}{\partial x} + \left[\frac{\partial(\partial v/\partial x)}{\partial \theta} \right] d\theta.$$

Owing to the central angle $d\theta$ between the two elements, the latter rotation has a component with respect to the y-axis equal to

$$-\frac{\partial v}{\partial x}\, d\theta. \tag{i}$$

From the results (h) and (i) we conclude that the total angle of twist between the two elements under consideration is

$$-\left(\frac{\partial^2 w}{\partial \theta\, \partial x} + \frac{\partial v}{\partial x} \right) d\theta.$$

Hence

$$\chi_{xy} = \frac{1}{a}\left(\frac{\partial^2 w}{\partial \theta\, \partial x} + \frac{\partial v}{\partial x} \right). \tag{j}$$

Substituting the calculated changes of curvatures in expression (255) for the strain energy of bending[2] and using for displacements expressions (f), we finally obtain for the total energy of deformation of a cylindrical shell of length $2l$ (Fig. 229) the following expression:

$$V = \pi D l \sum_{n=2}^{\infty} \frac{(n^2 - 1)^2}{a^3} \left\{ n^2 \left[a^2(a^2{}_n + a'^2{}_n) + \frac{1}{3}l^2(b^2{}_n + b'^2{}_n) \right] + \right.$$
$$\left. 2(1 - \nu)a^2(b^2{}_n + b'^2{}_n) \right\}. \tag{258}$$

This expression does not contain a term with $n = 1$ since, as was pointed out in considering the deformation of a circular ring (Art. 39), the corresponding displacements are the same as for a rigid body and do not contribute to the strain energy.

Let us now apply the above expression for V in calculating the deformation produced in a cylindrical shell by two equal and opposite forces P acting along a diameter at a distance c from the middle (Fig. 229). These forces produce work only on radial displacements w of their points of application and, since the terms with coefficients a_n and b_n in the expressions for

---

[1] In determining the sign of rotation the right-hand screw rule is used.

[2] The energy of deformation due to stretching of the middle surface of the shell is zero in this case, since the deformation is assumed inextensional.

w_1 and w_2 [see Eqs. (d) and (e)] vanish at these points, only terms with coefficients a'_n and b'_n will enter in the expressions for deformation. By using the principle of virtual displacements, the equations for calculating coefficients a'_n and b'_n become

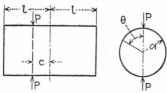

FIG. 229.

$$\frac{\partial V}{\partial a'_n}\delta a'_n = -na\delta a'_n(1 + \cos n\pi)P;$$

$$\frac{\partial V}{\partial b'_n}\delta b'_n = -nc\delta b'_n(1 + \cos n\pi)P.$$

Substituting expression (258) for V, we obtain, for the case where n is an even number,

$$a'_n = -\frac{a^2P}{n(n^2 - 1)^2\,\pi Dl};$$

$$b'_n = -\frac{ncPa^3}{(n^2 - 1)^2\,\pi Dl\left[\dfrac{n^2l^2}{3} + 2(1 - \nu)a^2\right]}.$$

If n is an odd number, we obtain

$$a'_n = b'_n = 0.$$

Substituting the values of a'_n and b'_n in expressions (f) and also putting $a_n = b_n = 0$, rapidly convergent series for displacements u, v and w are obtained. Although these expressions do not satisfy rigorously the conditions at the free edges of the cylindrical shell, the displacements calculated

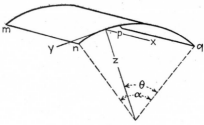

FIG. 230.

are in good agreement with experiments,[1] provided the thickness h of the shell is small in comparison with the radius a. The same method also can be used sometimes in calculating deformations of a portion of a cylindrical shell cut out from a complete cylinder of radius a by two axial sections making an angle α with one another (Fig. 230). Taking, for instance,

[1] Such experiments were made at the University of Michigan by I. A. Wojtaszak with brass tubes having a diameter of 6 in., a thickness of $\frac{1}{16}$ in. and lengths of 30 in. and 24 in. Deflection curves drawn for the generator for which $\theta = 90°$ (Fig. 229) deviated only slightly from straight lines, found by substituting a'_n and b'_n (found above) in the equation for the displacement w given by (f).

for the displacements the series

$$u = -\sum \frac{\alpha a b_n}{\pi n} \sin \frac{n\pi\theta}{\alpha}$$

$$v = \sum a a_n \cos \frac{n\pi\theta}{\alpha} + x \sum b_n \cos \frac{n\pi\theta}{\alpha}$$

$$w = -\sum \frac{n\pi}{\alpha} a a_n \sin \frac{n\pi\theta}{\alpha} - x \sum \frac{n\pi}{\alpha} b_n \sin \frac{n\pi\theta}{\alpha}$$

we obtain an inextensional deformation such that the displacements u and w and also the bending moments vanish along the edges mn and pq.

79. General Case of Deformation of a Cylindrical Shell.[1]—To establish the differential equations for the displacements u, v and w (Fig. 228) which define the deformation of a shell, we proceed as in the case of plates and begin with the equations of

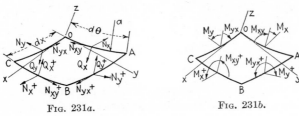

Fig. 231a.   Fig. 231b.

equilibrium of an element cut out from the cylindrical shell by two adjacent axial sections and by two adjacent sections perpendicular to the axis of the cylinder. The corresponding element of the middle surface of the shell, after deformation, is shown in Figs. 231a and 231b. In Fig. 231a the resultant forces, discussed in Art. 76, are shown. Before deformation the axes x, y and z at any point of the middle surface had the directions of the generator, the tangent to the circumference and the normal to the middle surface of the shell, respectively. After deformation, which is assumed very small, these directions are slightly changed and we take the z-axis normal to the deformed middle surface, the x-axis in the direction of a tangent to the generator, which may become curved, and the y-axis perpendicular to the xz-plane. The directions of the resultant forces will also be slightly changed accordingly, and these changes must be considered in writing the equations of equilibrium of the element $OABC$.

[1] A general theory of bending of thin shells has been developed by A. E. H. Love in his book on "Elasticity," 4th ed., Chap. 24, p. 515, 1927.

Let us begin by establishing formulas for angular displacements of the sides BC and AB with respect to the sides OA and OC of the element, respectively. In these calculations we consider displacements u, v and w as very small, calculate the angular motions produced by each of these displacements and obtain the resultant angular displacement by superposition. We begin with the rotation of the side BC with respect to the side OA. This rotation can be resolved into three component rotations with respect to the x-, y- and z-axes. Rotations of the sides OA and BC with respect to the x-axis are due to displacements v and w. Since displacements v represent motion of the sides OA and BC in circumferential directions (see Fig. 228) and a is the radius of the middle surface of the cylinder, the corresponding rotation of the side OA, with respect to the x-axis, is v/a and that of the side BC is

$$\frac{1}{a}\left(v + \frac{\partial v}{\partial x}\,dx\right).$$

Thus, owing to displacements v, the relative angular motion of BC with respect to AO about the x-axis is

$$\frac{1}{a}\,\frac{\partial v}{\partial x}\,dx. \qquad (a)$$

Owing to displacements w, the side OA rotates with respect to the x-axis by the angle $\partial w/a\,\partial\theta$ and the side BC by the angle

$$\frac{\partial w}{a\,\partial\theta} + \frac{\partial}{\partial x}\left(\frac{\partial w}{a\,\partial\theta}\right)dx.$$

Thus, because of displacements w, the relative angular displacement is

$$\frac{\partial}{\partial x}\left(\frac{\partial w}{a\,\partial\theta}\right)dx. \qquad (b)$$

Summing up (a) and (b), the relative angular displacement about the x-axis of the side BC with respect to the side OA is

$$\frac{1}{a}\left(\frac{\partial v}{\partial x} + \frac{\partial^2 w}{\partial x\,\partial\theta}\right)dx. \qquad (c)$$

The rotation about the y-axis of the side BC with respect to the side OA is due to bending of generators in axial planes and is equal to[1]

$$-\frac{\partial^2 w}{\partial x^2}\, dx. \qquad (d)$$

The rotation about the z-axis of the side BC with respect to the side OA is due to bending of the generators in tangent planes and is equal to

$$\frac{\partial^2 v}{\partial x^2}\, dx. \qquad (e)$$

The formulas (c), (d) and (e) give the three components of rotation of the side BC with respect to the side OA.

Let us establish now the corresponding formulas for the angular displacement of the side AB with respect to the side OC. Owing to curvature of the cylindrical shell, the initial angle between these lateral sides of the element $OABC$ is $d\theta$. However, because of displacements v and w, this angle will be changed and rotation of the lateral side OC with respect to the x-axis becomes

$$\frac{v}{a} + \frac{\partial w}{a\, \partial \theta}. \qquad (f)$$

The corresponding rotation for the lateral side AB is

$$\frac{v}{a} + \frac{\partial w}{a\, \partial \theta} + \frac{\partial}{\partial \theta}\left(\frac{v}{a} + \frac{\partial w}{a\, \partial \theta}\right)d\theta.$$

Hence, instead of the initial angle $d\theta$, we must take

$$d\theta + d\theta\left(\frac{\partial v}{a\, \partial \theta} + \frac{\partial^2 w}{a\, \partial \theta^2}\right). \qquad (g)$$

In calculating the angle of rotation about the y-axis of the side AB with respect to the side OC, we use for twist expression (j) of the previous article (see p. 427); then the required angular displacement is

$$-\left(\frac{\partial^2 w}{\partial \theta\, \partial x} + \frac{\partial v}{\partial x}\right)d\theta. \qquad (h)$$

Rotation about the z-axis of the side AB with respect to OC is due to displacements v and w. Owing to displacement v,

---

[1] The signs of angular displacements with respect to coordinate axes x, y and z are taken in accordance with the right-hand screw rule.

the angle of rotation of the side OC is $\partial v/\partial x$ and that of the side AB is

$$\frac{\partial v}{\partial x} + \frac{\partial}{a\,\partial\theta}\left(\frac{\partial v}{\partial x}\right)a\,d\theta,$$

so that the relative angular displacement is

$$\frac{\partial}{a\,\partial\theta}\left(\frac{\partial v}{\partial x}\right)a\,d\theta. \tag{i}$$

Because of displacement w, the side AB rotates in the axial plane by the angle $\partial w/\partial x$. The component of this rotation with respect to the z-axis is

$$-\frac{\partial w}{\partial x}\,d\theta. \tag{j}$$

Summing up (i) and (j), the relative angular displacement about the z-axis of the side AB with respect to the side OC is

$$\left(\frac{\partial^2 v}{\partial\theta\,\partial x} - \frac{\partial w}{\partial x}\right)d\theta. \tag{k}$$

Having the above formulas[1] for the angles, we may now obtain the three equations of equilibrium of the element $OABC$ (Fig. 231a) by projecting all forces on the x-, y- and z-axes. Beginning with those forces parallel to the resultant forces N_x and N_{yx}, and projecting them on the x-axis, we obtain $(\partial N_x/\partial x)dx\,a\,d\theta$ and $(\partial N_{yx}/\partial\theta)d\theta\,dx$. Owing to the angle of rotation given by expression (k), the forces parallel to N_y give in the x-direction a component

$$-N_y\left(\frac{\partial^2 v}{\partial\theta\,\partial x} - \frac{\partial w}{\partial x}\right)d\theta\,dx.$$

Because of the rotation given by expression (e), the forces parallel to the resultant forces N_{xy} give in the x-direction a component

$$-N_{xy}\frac{\partial^2 v}{\partial x^2}\,dx\,a\,d\theta.$$

Finally, owing to the angles given by expressions (d) and (h), the forces parallel to Q_x and Q_y give in the x-direction the components

[1] These formulas can be readily obtained for a cylindrical shell from the general formulas given by A. E. H. Love, *op. cit.*, p. 523, 1927.

$$-Q_x \frac{\partial^2 w}{\partial x^2} \, dx \, a \, d\theta - Q_y\left(\frac{\partial^2 w}{\partial \theta \, \partial x} + \frac{\partial v}{\partial x}\right)d\theta \, dx.$$

Regarding external forces acting on the element, we assume that there is only a normal pressure of intensity q, the projection of which on the x-axis is zero.

Summing up all the projections calculated above, we obtain

$$\frac{\partial N_x}{\partial x} \, dx \, a \, d\theta + \frac{\partial N_{yx}}{\partial \theta} \, d\theta \, dx - N_y\left(\frac{\partial^2 v}{\partial \theta \, \partial x} - \frac{\partial w}{\partial x}\right)d\theta \, dx -$$

$$N_{xy} \frac{\partial^2 v}{\partial x^2} \, dx \, a \, d\theta - Q_x \frac{\partial^2 w}{\partial x^2} \, dx \, a \, d\theta - Q_y\left(\frac{\partial^2 w}{\partial \theta \, \partial x} + \frac{\partial v}{\partial x}\right)d\theta \, dx = 0.$$

In the same manner, two other equations of equilibrium can be written. After simplification, all three equations can be put in the following form:

$$\left.\begin{array}{l} a\,\dfrac{\partial N_x}{\partial x} + \dfrac{\partial N_{yx}}{\partial \theta} - aQ_x\dfrac{\partial^2 w}{\partial x^2} - aN_{xy}\dfrac{\partial^2 v}{\partial x^2} - Q_y\left(\dfrac{\partial v}{\partial x} + \dfrac{\partial^2 w}{\partial x \, \partial \theta}\right) - \\[2mm] \hspace{4cm} N_y\left(\dfrac{\partial^2 v}{\partial x \, \partial \theta} - \dfrac{\partial w}{\partial x}\right) = 0; \\[4mm] \dfrac{\partial N_i}{\partial \theta} + a\,\dfrac{\partial N_{xy}}{\partial x} + aN_x\dfrac{\partial^2 v}{\partial x^2} - Q_x\left(\dfrac{\partial v}{\partial x} + \dfrac{\partial^2 w}{\partial x \, \partial \theta}\right) + \\[2mm] \hspace{2cm} N_{yx}\left(\dfrac{\partial^2 v}{\partial x \, \partial \theta} - \dfrac{\partial w}{\partial x}\right) - Q_y\left(1 + \dfrac{\partial v}{a \, \partial \theta} + \dfrac{\partial^2 w}{a \, \partial \theta^2}\right) = 0; \\[4mm] a\,\dfrac{\partial Q_x}{\partial x} + \dfrac{\partial Q_y}{\partial \theta} + N_{xy}\left(\dfrac{\partial v}{\partial x} + \dfrac{\partial^2 w}{\partial x \, \partial \theta}\right) + aN_x\dfrac{\partial^2 w}{\partial x^2} + \\[2mm] N_y\left(1 + \dfrac{\partial v}{a \, \partial \theta} + \dfrac{\partial^2 w}{a \, \partial \theta^2}\right) + N_{yx}\left(\dfrac{\partial v}{\partial x} + \dfrac{\partial^2 w}{\partial x \, \partial \theta}\right) + qa = 0. \end{array}\right\} \quad (259)$$

In the derivation of these equations the change in size of the element due to stretching of the middle surface was not considered. In the solution of problems of stability a further refinement is sometimes introduced and the strains ϵ_1 and ϵ_2 of the middle surface are taken into account in writing the equations of equilibrium of the element. Since ϵ_1 and ϵ_2 are small quantities expressed by the derivatives of the displacements u, v and w [see Eqs. (261)], they must be introduced only in such terms of Eqs. (259) which are not multiplied by the derivatives of the displacements. Considering, for instance, the case of buckling of a cylindrical shell under lateral pressure (Art. 83), we will find that the stress resultant N_y is very large in comparison with the other stress resultants; thus $N_y(1 + \epsilon_1)$ should be introduced, instead of N_y, in the second and the third of Eqs. (259) and $q(1 + \epsilon_1)(1 + \epsilon_2)$ should be substituted for q in the third equation to take into account the stretching of the middle surface. In the case of buckling of a cylindrical shell under torsion (Art. 90), the stress resultants N_{xy} and N_{yx} become the most important; considering the effect of stretching of the middle surface, $N_{yx}(1 + \epsilon_1)$ and $N_{xy}(1 + \epsilon_2)$ instead of N_{yx} and N_{xy} should be substituted in the first and second of Eqs. (259). This question of taking account of stretching of the middle surface will be discussed later in considering particular problems.

Considering now the three equations of moments with respect to the x-, y- and z-axes (Fig. 231b), and again taking into consideration the small angular displacements of the sides BC and AB with respect to OA and OC, respectively, we obtain the following equations:

$$
\left.
\begin{aligned}
& a\,\frac{\partial M_{xy}}{\partial x} - \frac{\partial M_y}{\partial \theta} - aM_x\,\frac{\partial^2 v}{\partial x^2} - M_{yx}\!\left(\frac{\partial^2 v}{\partial x\,\partial \theta} - \frac{\partial w}{\partial x}\right) + aQ_y = 0; \\[2mm]
& \frac{\partial M_{yx}}{\partial \theta} + a\,\frac{\partial M_x}{\partial x} + aM_{xy}\,\frac{\partial^2 v}{\partial x^2} - M_y\!\left(\frac{\partial^2 v}{\partial x\,\partial \theta} - \frac{\partial w}{\partial x}\right) - aQ_x = 0; \\[2mm]
& M_x\!\left(\frac{\partial v}{\partial x} + \frac{\partial^2 w}{\partial x\,\partial \theta}\right) + aM_{xy}\,\frac{\partial^2 w}{\partial x^2} + M_{yx}\!\left(1 + \frac{\partial v}{a\,\partial \theta} + \frac{\partial^2 w}{a\,\partial \theta^2}\right) - \\[2mm]
& \qquad\qquad M_y\!\left(\frac{\partial v}{\partial x} + \frac{\partial^2 w}{\partial x\,\partial \theta}\right) + a(N'_{xy} - N_{yx}) = 0.
\end{aligned}
\right\} \tag{260}
$$

By using the first two of these equations we can eliminate Q_x and Q_y from Eqs. (259) and obtain in this way three equations containing the resultant forces N_x, N_y and N_{xy} and the moments M_x, M_y and M_{xy}. By using the formulas of Art. 76, all these quantities can be expressed in terms of the three strain components ϵ_1, ϵ_2 and γ of the middle surface and the three curvature changes χ_x, χ_y and χ_{xy}, all of which are represented in terms of the displacements u, v and w as follows (see Art. 78):

$$
\left.
\begin{aligned}
& \epsilon_1 = \frac{\partial u}{\partial x}; \qquad \epsilon_2 = \frac{\partial v}{a\,\partial \theta} - \frac{w}{a}; \qquad \gamma = \frac{\partial u}{a\,\partial \theta} + \frac{\partial v}{\partial x}; \\[2mm]
& \chi_x = \frac{\partial^2 w}{\partial x^2}; \quad \chi_y = \frac{1}{a^2}\!\left(\frac{\partial v}{\partial \theta} + \frac{\partial^2 w}{\partial \theta^2}\right); \quad \chi_{xy} = \frac{1}{a}\!\left(\frac{\partial v}{\partial x} + \frac{\partial^2 w}{\partial x\,\partial \theta}\right).
\end{aligned}
\right\} \tag{261}
$$

Thus we finally obtain the three differential equations for determining the displacements u, v and w.

80. Symmetrical Deformation of a Spherical Shell.—Let us assume that the vertical diameter is the axis of symmetry of the deformation of a spherical shell (Fig. 232) and let us consider an element $OABC$ cut out from the shell by two meridional sections an angle $d\psi$ apart and by two conical surfaces normal to the meridians and inclined to the axis of symmetry by the angles θ and $\theta + d\theta$. Taking the x- and y-axes as tangents at O to the meridian and to the parallel circle, respectively, and the z-axis in the radial direction, as shown in the figure, we denote

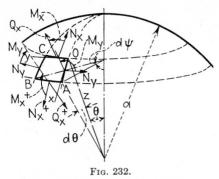

Fig. 232.

the corresponding components of the displacement at O by u, v and w. In the case of a symmetrical deformation, $v = 0$ and u and w are functions of the angle θ only. Between the meridional faces OA and BC of the element there is a small angle $d\psi$ which may be obtained by rotating the meridional plane OA with respect to the x- and z-axes by the angles $d\psi \sin \theta$ and $d\psi \cos \theta$, respectively. The angle between the lateral faces OC and AB of the element is equal to $d\theta$ and the direction of the face AB is obtained by rotation of the face OC with respect to the y-axis by the angle[1] $-d\theta$. By using these initial values of the angles between the faces of the element $OABC$ and by denoting the resultant forces and the moments as shown in the figure, the differential equations of equilibrium of the element can be readily written.

In the case of symmetrical deformation we have only three equations to consider: projections of forces on the x- and z-axes

---

[1] The right-hand screw rule is used in determining the sign of rotation.

and moments of forces with respect to the y-axis. Projecting all forces on the x-axis and assuming that any external load is normal to the shell, we obtain

$$\left(N_x + \frac{\partial N_x}{\partial \theta}\, d\theta\right) a \sin\,(\theta + d\theta)\, d\psi - N_x a \sin\theta\, d\psi -$$

$$N_y a\, d\theta \cos\theta\, d\psi - Q_x a \sin\theta\, d\psi\, d\theta = 0.$$

In the same manner the other two equations of equilibrium can be written. After simplification the three equations of equilibrium become

$$\left.\begin{array}{c} \dfrac{\partial N_x}{\partial \theta} + (N_x - N_y)\cot\theta - Q_x = 0; \\[2mm] \dfrac{\partial Q_x}{\partial \theta} + Q_x \cot\theta + N_x + N_y + qa = 0; \\[2mm] \dfrac{\partial M_x}{\partial \theta} + (M_x - M_y)\cot\theta - Q_x a = 0, \end{array}\right\} \qquad (262)$$

where q is the intensity of the external load. These equations should be used in investigating deformation of a spherical shell under the action of a normal load symmetrically distributed with respect to a diametral axis.

In writing the equations of equilibrium for the case of the buckled surface of a shell, which is assumed symmetrical with respect to a diametral axis, small changes of the angles between the faces of an element such as $OABC$, due to deformation, should be taken into account. Considering the change of the angle between the faces OC and AB of the element, we conclude from the assumed symmetry of deformation that there will be rotation only with respect to the y-axis. This angle of rotation for the face OC is $\dfrac{u}{a} + \dfrac{dw}{a\, d\theta}.$ Thus the angle between the faces OC and AB after deformation becomes

$$d\theta + \frac{d}{d\theta}\left(\frac{u}{a} + \frac{dw}{a\, d\theta}\right) d\theta. \qquad (a)$$

Considering now the change of the angle between the faces AO and BC, we observe that, owing to symmetry of deformation, these faces rotate only in their own planes by the angle

$$-\left(\frac{u}{a} + \frac{dw}{a\, d\theta}\right).$$

Such a rotation in the plane of the face BC has components with respect to the x- and z-axes equal to

$$\left(\frac{u}{a} + \frac{dw}{a\,d\theta}\right)\cos\theta\,d\psi \quad \text{and} \quad -\left(\frac{u}{a} + \frac{dw}{a\,d\theta}\right)\sin\theta\,d\psi,$$

respectively. Thus, after deformation, the direction of the face BC with respect to the face AO can be obtained by the rotation of the face AO with respect to the x- and z-axes through the angles

$$\sin\theta\,d\psi + \left(\frac{u}{a} + \frac{dw}{a\,d\theta}\right)\cos\theta\,d\psi \qquad (b)$$

and

$$\cos\theta\,d\psi - \left(\frac{u}{a} + \frac{dw}{a\,d\theta}\right)\sin\theta\,d\psi, \qquad (c)$$

respectively.

Using the angles given by expressions (a), (b) and (c), instead of the initial angles $d\theta$, $\sin\theta\,d\psi$ and $\cos\theta\,d\psi$, the equations of equilibrium of the element $OABC$ become

$$\left. \begin{aligned} &\frac{dN_x}{d\theta} + (N_x - N_y)\cot\theta - Q_x + N_y\left(\frac{u}{a} + \frac{dw}{a\,d\theta}\right) - \\ &\hspace{4cm} Q_x\left(\frac{d^2w}{a\,d\theta^2} + \frac{w}{a}\right) = 0; \\ &\frac{dQ_x}{d\theta} + Q_x\cot\theta + N_x + N_y + qa + N_x\left(\frac{d^2w}{a\,d\theta^2} + \frac{du}{a\,d\theta}\right) \\ &\hspace{2.5cm} + N_y\left(\frac{u}{a} + \frac{dw}{a\,d\theta}\right)\cot\theta = 0; \\ &\frac{dM_x}{d\theta} + (M_x - M_y)\cot\theta - Q_x a + M_y\left(\frac{u}{a} + \frac{dw}{a\,d\theta}\right) = 0. \end{aligned} \right\} \quad (263)$$

Eliminating Q_x from these equations, we obtain two equations containing N_x, N_y, M_x, M_y. All these quantities can be expressed in terms of the displacements u and w by using Eqs. (249) and (250) of Art. 76. The quantities ϵ_1 and ϵ_2, entering in Eqs. (249), can be readily determined from geometrical considerations. In this case they are

$$\epsilon_1 = \frac{du}{a\,d\theta} - \frac{w}{a}; \qquad \epsilon_2 = \frac{u\cos\theta}{a\sin\theta} - \frac{w}{a}. \qquad (d)$$

By using expressions (*a*) and (*b*), we obtain for the changes of curvature

$$\chi_x = \frac{d^2w}{a^2\,d\theta^2} + \frac{du}{a^2\,d\theta}; \qquad \chi_y = \left(\frac{u}{a^2} + \frac{dw}{a^2\,d\theta}\right)\cot\theta. \qquad (e)$$

With these values of ϵ_1, ϵ_2, χ_x and χ_y we obtain finally, from Eqs. (263), two equations containing only u and w. The application of these equations in discussing stability of a compressed spherical shell will be shown in Art. 91.

CHAPTER IX

BUCKLING OF SHELLS

81. Symmetrical Buckling of a Cylindrical Shell under the Action of Uniform Axial Compression.—If a cylindrical shell is uniformly compressed in the axial direction, buckling symmetrical with respect to the axis of the cylinder (Fig. 233) may occur at a certain value of the compressive load.[1] The critical value of the compressive force N_{cr} per unit length of the edge of the shell can be obtained by using the energy method. As long as the shell remains cylindrical, the total strain energy is the energy of axial compression. However, when buckling begins, we must consider, in addition to axial compression, the strain of the middle surface in the circumferential direction and also bending of the shell. Thus the strain energy of the shell is increased; at the critical value of the load this increase in energy must be equal to the work done by the compressive load as the cylinder shortens owing to buckling.

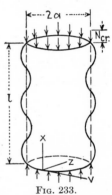

Fig. 233.

We assume for radial displacements during buckling the expression

$$w = -A \sin \frac{m\pi x}{l}, \qquad (a)$$

where l is the length of the cylinder. The strain ϵ_1 and ϵ_2 in the axial and circumferential directions after buckling will be found from the condition that the axial compressive force during buckling remains constant. Using for the axial strain before buckling the notation

---

[1] See author's paper in *Z. Math. Physik*, vol. 58, p. 378, 1910. See also R. Lorenz, *Z. Ver. deut. Ing.*, vol. 52, p. 1766, 1908, and *Physik. Z.*, vol. 13, p. 241, 1911.

$$\epsilon_0 = -\frac{N_{cr}}{Eh},\qquad(b)$$

where h is the thickness of the shell, we obtain

$$\epsilon_1 + \nu\epsilon_2 = (1 - \nu^2)\epsilon_0.$$

Observing that

$$\epsilon_2 = -\nu\epsilon_0 - \frac{w}{a} = -\nu\epsilon_0 + \frac{A}{a}\sin\frac{m\pi x}{l},\qquad(c)$$

we find

$$\epsilon_1 = \epsilon_0 - \nu\frac{A}{a}\sin\frac{m\pi x}{l}.\qquad(d)$$

The change of curvature in the axial plane is

$$\chi_x = \frac{\partial^2 w}{\partial x^2} = A\frac{m^2\pi^2}{l^2}\sin\frac{m\pi x}{l}.\qquad(e)$$

Substituting expressions (c), (d) and (e) in Eqs. (255) and (256) for strain energy, and noting that, owing to symmetry of deformation,

$$\gamma = \chi_y = \chi_{xy} = 0,$$

we find for the increase of strain energy during buckling the following expression:

$$\Delta V = -2\pi hE\nu\epsilon_0\int_0^l A\sin\frac{m\pi x}{l}\,dx + \frac{\pi A^2Ehl}{2a} + A^2\frac{\pi^4m^4}{2l^4}\pi al D.\qquad(f)$$

The work done by compressive forces during buckling is

$$\Delta T = 2\pi N_{cr}\left(\nu\int_0^l A\sin\frac{m\pi x}{l}\,dx + \frac{a}{4}A^2\frac{m^2\pi^2}{l}\right),\qquad(g)$$

where the first term in the parenthesis is due to the change $\epsilon_1 - \epsilon_0$ of the axial strain and the second term is due to bending of generators given by Eq. (a). Equating expressions (f) and (g), we obtain

$$\sigma_{cr} = \frac{N_{cr}}{h} = D\left(\frac{m^2\pi^2}{hl^2} + \frac{E}{a^2D}\frac{l^2}{m^2\pi^2}\right).\qquad(h)$$

Assuming that there are many waves formed along the length of the cylinder during buckling, and considering σ_{cr} as a continuous function of $m\pi/l$, the minimum value of expression (h) is

$$\sigma_{cr} = \frac{2}{ah}\sqrt{EDh} = \frac{Eh}{a\sqrt{3(1 - \nu^2)}},\qquad(264)$$

and occurs at

$$\frac{m\pi}{l} = \sqrt[4]{\frac{Eh}{a^2D}}.$$

Thus the length of half-waves into which the shell buckles, for $\nu = 0.3$, is

$$\frac{l}{m} = \pi\sqrt[4]{\frac{a^2D}{Eh}} = \pi\sqrt[4]{\frac{a^2h^2}{12(1-\nu^2)}} \approx 1.72\sqrt{ah}. \qquad (265)$$

It is seen that the results obtained for the symmetrical buckling of a cylindrical shell are similar to those obtained for buckling of a bar in an elastic medium (see Art. 21) and the discussion given there regarding the number of waves for the bar can be applied here also. It is seen also that a symmetrical buckling, which we are considering, may occur within the elastic limit only in the case of very thin shells. Taking, for instance, a steel shell with $E = 30 \cdot 10^6$ lb. per square inch, $\sigma_{\text{P.L.}} = 60,000$ lb. per square inch and $\nu = 0.3$, we find from Eq. (264) that $a/h = 303$ and from Eq. (265) we conclude that the length of half-waves is less than one-tenth of the radius, also that for cylinders whose length is not smaller than the diameter the number of half-waves is larger than 20. Our assumption that m is a large number is accurate enough in such cases.

Instead of the energy method the differential equation for symmetrical deflection of a cylindrical shell (257) can be used in calculating the critical load. In applying this equation we take $q = 0$ and measure the displacement w, not from the unstrained middle surface of the shell as was assumed in the derivation of the equation, but from the middle surface after uniform compression is applied. This requires that we replace w in Eq. (257) by $w + \dfrac{\nu N_x a}{Eh}$ and consider N_x positive, when it is compression. Then the differential equation for symmetrical buckling of a cylindrical shell becomes

$$D\frac{d^4w}{dx^4} + N_x\frac{d^2w}{dx^2} + Eh\frac{w}{a^2} = 0. \qquad (266)$$

Substituting for w the previous expression (a) and equating to zero the coefficient of $\sin\dfrac{m\pi x}{l}$, we obtain from this equation the critical stress given by expression (h).

When the shell is not very thin and buckling occurs at a stress that is beyond the proportional limit, the critical load may be obtained again from Eq. (266), it being necessary only to introduce in the expression for the flexural rigidity D the reduced modulus E_r instead of E[1]. Then, proceeding as before, we obtain from Eq. (266)

$$\sigma_{cr} = \frac{\sqrt{EE_r}h}{a\sqrt{3(1 - \nu^2)}}.$$ (267)

By taking a series of values for σ_{cr} and determining the values of E_r from the compression-test diagram (see Art. 29), the corresponding values of the ratio a/h can be calculated from Eq. (267).

In the case of buckling beyond proportional limit, the expression for the length of a half-wave becomes

$$\frac{l}{m} = \pi\sqrt[4]{\frac{a^2h^2}{12(1 - \nu^2)}}\sqrt[4]{\frac{E_r}{E}} \approx 1.72\sqrt{ah}\sqrt[4]{\frac{E_r}{E}}.$$ (268)

Thus the length of waves becomes shorter for buckling beyond proportional limit.

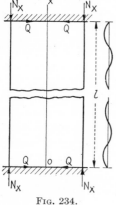

Fig. 234.

If we assume that the mechanical properties of the material beyond the proportional limit are the same in the axial and circumferential directions (see p. 388) and if we introduce E_r instead of E in the first and the third terms of Eq. (266), we find that

$$\sigma_{cr} = \frac{E_r h}{a\sqrt{3(1 - \nu^2)}}$$ (269)

and that beyond the proportional limit the length of waves remains unchanged.

In experimenting with cylindrical shells, the compression is usually applied by the rigid blocks of the testing machine and lateral expansion of the shell is prevented by friction. Then, instead of a stability problem, we have a problem involving the simultaneous action of compressive and bending forces as shown in Fig. 234.[2]

[1] The value of E in the last term on the left side of Eq. (266) is assumed unchanged.

[2] This problem of simultaneous compression and bending has been discussed by L. Föppl, *Sitzungsb. math.-physik. Klasse bayer. Akad. Wiss.*, *München*, 1926, p. 27, and by J. W. Geckeler, *Z. angew. Math. Mech.*, vol. 8, p. 341, 1928.

Assuming that the compressive stress is smaller than the critical stress given by Eq. (266) and using the notation

$$\frac{N_x}{N_{cr}} = z,$$

the general solution of Eq. (266) can be put in the following form:

$$w = C_1 e^{\alpha x} \sin (\beta x + \gamma_1) + C_2 e^{-\alpha x} \sin (\beta x + \gamma_2), \qquad (i)$$

where

$$\alpha = \sqrt{1 - z}\sqrt[4]{\frac{Eh}{4a^2D}}; \qquad \beta = \sqrt{1 + z}\sqrt[4]{\frac{Eh}{4a^2D}}$$

and where C_1, C_2, γ_1 and γ_2 are four constants of integration which are to be determined in each particular case from the conditions at the edges. Assuming that the edges are simply supported, we have

$$\frac{\partial^2 w}{\partial x^2} = 0 \qquad \text{for} \qquad x = 0 \qquad \text{and} \qquad x = l; \qquad (j)$$

$$w = \frac{\nu N_x a}{Eh} \qquad \text{for} \qquad x = 0 \qquad \text{and} \qquad x = l. \qquad (k)$$

The second of these conditions states that the friction forces Q suppress entirely the lateral expansion of the shell at the edges. If the cylinder is not short and the load is not close to its critical value, we can put, in the general solution (i), $C_1 = 0$,[1] when considering the end $x = 0$ of the cylinder. Then we obtain a deflection in the form of waves which are rapidly damped out owing to the presence of the factor $e^{-\alpha x}$. The length of waves is

$$L = \frac{2\pi}{\beta} = \frac{2\pi}{\sqrt{1 + z}}\sqrt[4]{\frac{4a^2D}{Eh}}. \qquad (l)$$

This length is somewhat larger than that obtained for the case of buckling [Eq. (265)] and approaches the latter when z approaches unity. When the load approaches its critical value and z approaches unity, the factor $e^{-\alpha x}$ approaches unity also. The waves are no longer rapidly damped out; we cannot treat the edge conditions separately for each end and must consider all four constants in the expression (i). The deflection form is as shown in Fig. 234. The maximum deflection increases rapidly as the load approaches its critical value and failure occurs owing to yielding of the material at the crests of the waves nearest to the blocks of the testing machine. When the first half-wave, due to plastic deformation, flattens out, the second half-wave begins to grow rapidly, and so on. We finally get the kind of deformation shown in the photograph[2] (Fig. 235). Such deformation is usually obtained with thicker tubes in which buckling occurs beyond the proportional limit. In the case of thin tubes, buckling which is non-symmetrical with respect to the axis usually occurs (see Art. 85).

82. Inextensional Forms of Bending of Cylindrical Shells Due to Instability.—If the edges of a uniformly axially compressed cylindrical shell are

[1] See "Strength of Materials," vol. 2, p. 402, 1930.

[2] The photograph is taken from Geckeler's paper, *loc. cit.*, p. 442.

free to move laterally, an inextensional form of lateral bending may occur. Using expressions (e) of Art. 78 (see p. 426), we take the following displacements[1] for buckling:

$$u = -\sum_{n=2}^{\infty} \frac{a}{n} b_n \sin (n\theta + \beta_n);$$

$$v = x \sum_{n=2}^{\infty} b_n \cos (n\theta + \beta_n);$$

$$w = -x \sum_{n=2}^{\infty} n b_n \sin (n\theta + \beta_n).$$

(a)

The critical value of compressive forces N_{cr} can be obtained now by using

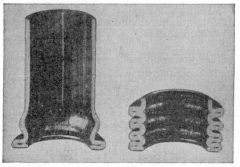

Fig. 235.

the energy method. During deformation as given by expressions (a) the strain energy of the shell increases by the amount [see Eq. (255), p. 423]

$$\Delta V = \pi Dl \sum_{n=2}^{\infty} b^2{}_n \frac{(n^2-1)^2}{a^3} \left[\frac{n^2 l^2}{3} + 2(1-\nu)a^2 \right].$$

(b)

In calculating the work done by compressive forces during bending, we note that, owing to displacements (a), the generators of the cylindrical shell become inclined to the x-axis by the angle

$$\frac{1}{x}\sqrt{v^2 + w^2}.$$

Then the work done is

$$\Delta T = N_{cr}\frac{l}{2}\int_0^{2\pi} \frac{v^2 + w^2}{x^2} a\, d\theta = \frac{\pi}{2} al N_{cr} \sum_{n=2}^{\infty} b^2{}_n (1 + n^2).$$

(c)

[1] The coefficients b_n in these expressions are equal to $\sqrt{b^2{}_n + (b'{}_n)^2}$ of Art. 78 and $\tan \beta_n = b'{}_n/b_n$.

Equating this work to the increase in strain energy (b), we obtain

$$N_{cr} = \frac{2D}{a^4} \frac{\displaystyle\sum_{n=2}^{\infty} b^2{}_n (n^2 - 1)^2 \left[\frac{n^2 l^2}{3} + 2(1 - \nu)a^2 \right]}{\displaystyle\sum_{n=2}^{\infty} b^2{}_n (1 + n^2)}.$$

The smallest value of N_{cr} is obtained by taking only one term, with $n = 2$, in the series, *i.e.*, by assuming that the cross section of the shell flattens to an elliptical shape. Then

$$\sigma_{cr} = \frac{N_{cr}}{h} = \frac{2D}{a^4 h} \frac{9}{5} \left[\frac{4}{3} l^2 + 2(1 - \nu)a^2 \right] = \frac{3Eh^2}{10(1 - \nu^2)a^2} \left[\frac{4}{3} \frac{l^2}{a^2} + 2(1 - \nu) \right].$$

It may be seen that this critical stress is smaller than that obtained for a symmetrical form of buckling [Eq. (264)] provided only that the ratio l/a is not very large.[1]

83. Buckling of a Cylindrical Shell under the Action of Uniform External Lateral Pressure.—In discussing buckling of a uniformly compressed circular ring (Art. 41), it was pointed out that the formula for the critical load obtained for a ring can be applied also in the case of cylindrical shells with free edges submitted to a uniform lateral pressure. The same formula can be applied also in the case of a shell with some constraint at the edges if the length of the shell is so large that the stiffening effect of any constraint at the edges can be neglected. If the length of a cylinder is not very large in comparison with its diameter, we can no longer disregard the end conditions, and in calculating the intensity of lateral pressure at which buckling occurs[2] we must have recourse to the general equations of deformation of a cylindrical shell (Art. 79). Considering Eqs. (259), we assume that in the case of uniform lateral pressure all resultant forces, except N_y, are small and we neglect the terms containing the products of these resultants with the derivatives of the displacements u, v and w. In this manner we obtain

[1] See writer's paper, *loc. cit.*, p. 439.
[2] The first investigations of this kind were made by R. Lorenz, *Physik. Z.*, vol. 13, p. 241, 1911, and R. V. Southwell, *Phil. Mag.*, vol. 25, p. 687, 1913, and *Phil. Trans. Roy. Soc., London*, series A, vol. 213, p. 187, 1914. A more accurate formula for the critical load was developed by R. v. Mises, *Z. Ver. deut. Ing.*, vol. 58, p. 750, 1914.

$$a\frac{\partial N_x}{\partial x} + \frac{\partial N_{yx}}{\partial \theta} - N_y\left(\frac{\partial^2 v}{\partial x\,\partial \theta} - \frac{\partial w}{\partial x}\right) = 0;$$

$$\frac{\partial N_y}{\partial \theta} + a\frac{\partial N_{xy}}{\partial x} - Q_y = 0; \qquad\qquad\quad (a)$$

$$a\frac{\partial Q_x}{\partial x} + \frac{\partial Q_y}{\partial \theta} + N_y\left(1 + \frac{\partial v}{a\,\partial \theta} + \frac{\partial^2 w}{a\,\partial \theta^2}\right) + qa = 0.$$

In Eqs. (260) we assume that bending and twisting moments are small and we neglect the products of these moments with the derivatives of the displacements u, v and w. Then the first two of these equations give

$$Q_x = \frac{\partial M_{yx}}{a\,\partial \theta} + \frac{\partial M_x}{\partial x};$$

$$Q_y = \frac{\partial M_y}{a\,\partial \theta} - \frac{\partial M_{xy}}{\partial x}. \qquad (b)$$

Substituting in Eqs. (a), we obtain

$$a\frac{\partial N_x}{\partial x} + \frac{\partial N_{yx}}{\partial \theta} - N_y\left(\frac{\partial^2 v}{\partial x\,\partial \theta} - \frac{\partial w}{\partial x}\right) = 0;$$

$$\frac{\partial N_y}{\partial \theta} + a\frac{\partial N_{xy}}{\partial x} - \frac{\partial M_y}{a\,\partial \theta} + \frac{\partial M_{xy}}{\partial x} = 0;$$

$$\frac{\partial^2 M_{yx}}{\partial x\,\partial \theta} + \frac{a\,\partial^2 M_x}{\partial x^2} + \frac{\partial^2 M_y}{a\,\partial \theta^2} - \frac{\partial^2 M_{xy}}{\partial x\,\partial \theta} + \qquad\qquad (c)$$

$$N_y\left(1 + \frac{\partial v}{a\,\partial \theta} + \frac{\partial^2 w}{a\,\partial \theta^2}\right) + qa = 0.$$

A particular solution of Eqs. (c) is obtained by assuming that under the action of uniform external pressure the circular cylindrical shell remains circular and undergoes only a uniform compression in the circumferential direction so that

$$v = 0; \qquad w = \frac{a^2 q}{Eh};$$

$$N_x = 0; \qquad N_y = -qa; \qquad M_x = M_y = M_{xy} = 0.$$

In discussing buckling of the shell we shall consider only small deflections from this uniformly compressed form of equilibrium, so that N_y in Eqs. (c) will differ but little from the value $-qa$, and we can put

$$N_y = -qa + N'_y,$$

where N'_y is a small change in the resultant force $-qa$ corresponding to small displacements u, v and w from the uniformly compressed cylindrical form of the shell.

We shall take into account also stretching of the middle surface of the shell during buckling and substitute $N_y(1 + \epsilon_1)$ and $q(1 + \epsilon_1)(1 + \epsilon_2)$ for N_y and q, respectively, in the second and third of Eqs. (c). Observing then that

$$\epsilon_1 = \frac{\partial u}{\partial x}; \qquad \epsilon_2 = \frac{\partial v}{a\,\partial \theta} - \frac{w}{a},$$

we represent Eqs. (c) in the following form

$$a\frac{\partial N_x}{\partial x} + \frac{\partial N_{yx}}{\partial \theta} + qa\left(\frac{\partial^2 v}{\partial x\,\partial \theta} - \frac{\partial w}{\partial x}\right) = 0;$$

$$\frac{\partial N'_y}{\partial \theta} + a\frac{\partial N_{xy}}{\partial x} - \frac{\partial M_y}{a\,\partial \theta} + \frac{\partial M_{xy}}{\partial x} = 0; \qquad (d)$$

$$\frac{\partial^2 M_{yx}}{\partial x\,\partial \theta} + a\frac{\partial^2 M_x}{\partial x^2} + \frac{\partial^2 M_y}{a\,\partial \theta^2} - \frac{\partial^2 M_{xy}}{\partial x\,\partial \theta} + N'_y - q\left(w + \frac{\partial^2 w}{\partial \theta^2}\right) = 0.$$

By using the formulas of Art. 76 and Eqs. (261) we express now all resultant forces and moments in terms of the displacements u, v and w. Substituting such expressions in Eqs. (d) and using the notations

$$\frac{qa(1 - \nu^2)}{Eh} = \phi \qquad \text{and} \qquad \frac{h^2}{12a^2} = \alpha, \qquad (e)$$

we obtain

$$a^2\frac{\partial^2 u}{\partial x^2} + \frac{1 + \nu}{2}\frac{a\,\partial^2 v}{\partial x\,\partial \theta} - \nu a\frac{\partial w}{\partial x} + a\phi\left(\frac{\partial^2 v}{\partial x\,\partial \theta} - \frac{\partial w}{\partial x}\right) +$$

$$\frac{1 - \nu}{2}\frac{\partial^2 u}{\partial \theta^2} = 0;$$

$$\frac{1 + \nu}{2}\frac{a\,\partial^2 u}{\partial x\,\partial \theta} + \frac{1 - \nu}{2}a^2\frac{\partial^2 v}{\partial x^2} + \frac{\partial^2 v}{\partial \theta^2} - \frac{\partial w}{\partial \theta} + \alpha\left[\frac{\partial^2 v}{\partial \theta^2} + \right.$$

$$\left. \frac{\partial^3 w}{\partial \theta^3} + a^2\frac{\partial^3 w}{\partial x^2\,\partial \theta} + a^2(1 - \nu)\frac{\partial^2 v}{\partial x^2}\right] = 0; \qquad (f)$$

$$a\nu\frac{\partial u}{\partial x} + \frac{\partial v}{\partial \theta} - w - \alpha\left[\frac{\partial^3 v}{\partial \theta^3} + (2 - \nu)a^2\frac{\partial^3 v}{\partial x^2\,\partial \theta} + a^4\frac{\partial^4 w}{\partial x^4} + \right.$$

$$\left. \frac{\partial^4 w}{\partial \theta^4} + 2a^2\frac{\partial^4 w}{\partial x^2\,\partial \theta^2}\right] = \phi\left(w + \frac{\partial^2 w}{\partial \theta^2}\right).$$

Thus the problem of determining the critical value of the lateral pressure is reduced to solving the above three differential equations and satisfying the boundary conditions. If the edges of the shell are simply supported, the boundary conditions require that w and $\partial^2 w/\partial x^2$ become zero at the ends. Assuming that the length of the cylinder is l and that x is measured from the middle cross section of the shell, we obtain a solution of Eqs. (f) satisfying the boundary conditions by taking for the displacements during buckling the following expressions:

$$\left.\begin{aligned} u &= A \sin n\theta \sin \frac{\pi x}{l}; \\ v &= B \cos n\theta \cos \frac{\pi x}{l}; \\ w &= C \sin n\theta \cos \frac{\pi x}{l}, \end{aligned}\right\} \qquad (g)$$

which show that during buckling the generators of the shell deflect to one half-wave of a sine curve while the circumference is subdivided into $2n$ half-waves. At the ends the displacements w and the derivative $\partial^2 w/\partial x^2$ both are zero, which represents the conditions of simply supported edges.

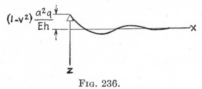

Fɪɢ. 236.

In actual cases the edges of the shell will usually be fastened to the supports before the uniform load q is applied; thus, in addition to uniform compression of the shell, assumed in our discussion, local bending at the edges will be produced. Assuming that the supports are absolutely rigid, the local bending will be of the type shown in Fig. 236. From the discussion of Art. 81 we conclude that the deflection curve of a generator is

$$w = \frac{a^2 q}{Eh}(1 - \nu^2)e^{-\beta x} \cos \beta x,$$

where

$$\beta = \sqrt[4]{\frac{3(1 - \nu^2)}{a^2 h^2}}.$$

It has a wavy form in which the waves are rapidly damped out. The length of waves is

$$L = \frac{2\pi}{\beta} = 4.90\sqrt{ah}.$$

In the case of thin shells, h is small in comparison with a and the wave length is usually much smaller than the radius, so that for a cylinder, the length of which is several times its radius, bending at the edges may be considered as a local factor that has no serious effect on the magnitude of the critical load. In the same manner, in the case of built-in edges, bending produced in the shell by bending moments M_x can be discussed and it can be shown that for longer cylinders there will not be much difference in the critical loads for simply supported or for built-in edges.

Substituting expressions (g) for the displacements in Eqs. (f) and using the notation $\lambda = \pi a/l$, the following equations are obtained:

$$A\left(-\lambda^2 - \frac{1-\nu}{2}n^2\right) + B\left(\frac{1+\nu}{2}n\lambda + n\lambda\phi\right) + C(\nu + \phi)\lambda = 0;$$

$$A\left(\frac{1+\nu}{2}n\lambda\right) - B\left[\frac{1-\nu}{2}\lambda^2 + n^2 + n^2\alpha + \alpha(1-\nu)\lambda^2\right] -$$
$$C(n + \alpha n^3 + \alpha n\lambda^2) = 0; \quad (h)$$
$$A(\nu\lambda) - B[n + \alpha n^3 + (2-\nu)\alpha n\lambda^2] - C[1 + \alpha\lambda^4 + \alpha n^4 +$$
$$2\alpha n^2\lambda^2 + \phi(1 - n^2)] = 0.$$

These equations can be satisfied by putting A, B and C equal to zero, which corresponds to a uniformly compressed circular form of equilibrium of the shell. A buckled form of equilibrium becomes possible only if Eqs. (h) yield for A, B and C solutions different from zero; this requires that the determinant of these equations becomes zero. In this manner the equation for determining the critical load is obtained. This equation has the form

$$\phi(D + E\alpha + F\phi) = G + H\alpha + K\alpha^2, \quad (i)$$

in which D, E, . . . have the following meanings:

$$D = (1 - n^2)(n^2 + \lambda^2)^2 - \nu\lambda^4;$$

$$E = (1 - n^2)\left(n^2 + \frac{2\lambda^2}{1 - \nu}\right)[n^2 + (1 - \nu)\lambda^2] + \frac{1 + 3\nu}{1 - \nu}n^4\lambda^2 +$$
$$\frac{2 + 3\nu - \nu^2}{1 - \nu}n^2\lambda^4 - \frac{2\nu n^2\lambda^2}{1 - \nu} - 2\nu\lambda^4 - \frac{1 + \nu}{1 - \nu}n^2\lambda^2(\lambda^2 + n^2)^2;$$

$$F = -\frac{1 + \nu}{1 - \nu}(1 - n^2)n^2\lambda^2;$$

$$G = -(1 - \nu^2)\lambda^4;$$

$$H = -(n^2 + \lambda^2)^4 + 2n^2\left(n^2 + \frac{3 - \nu}{2}\lambda^2\right)[n^2 + (2 + \nu)\lambda^2] -$$
$$[n^2 + (1 - \nu)\lambda^2][n^2 + 2(1 + \nu)\lambda^2];$$
$$K = -\lambda^4(n^2 + \lambda^2)[n^2(1 - \nu) + 2\lambda^2].$$

After omitting the small terms, which have very little effect on the magnitude of the critical pressure, and substituting for α, ϕ and λ their expressions, Eq. (i) can be put in the following form:[1]

$$\frac{(1 - \nu^2)q_{cr}a}{Eh} = \frac{1 - \nu^2}{(n^2 - 1)\left(1 + \dfrac{n^2l^2}{\pi^2a^2}\right)^2} + \frac{h^2}{12a^2}\left(n^2 - 1 + \frac{2n^2 - 1 - \nu}{1 + \dfrac{n^2l^2}{\pi^2a^2}}\right). \quad (270)$$

When the shell is very long, l/a is a large number; neglecting, in

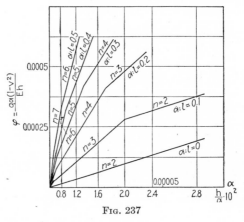

Fig. 237

Eq. (270), the terms containing the square of this ratio in the denominator, we obtain

$$q_{cr} = \frac{Eh^3(n^2 - 1)}{12a^3(1 - \nu^2)},$$

which, with $n = 2$, coincides with our previous result [see Eq. (125), p. 220]. In calculating the critical load for shorter cylinders, using our previous notations (e), Eq. (270) represents a linear relation between the quantities α and ϕ. For a given value of l/a, a chosen value of the number n and with α and ϕ as coordinates, we obtain a straight line. By taking $n = 2, 3, 4, \ldots$, a system of lines is obtained which, for each value of a/l, forms a broken line. Several such lines are shown in Fig. 237.

[1] This is the equation obtained by R. v. Mises, *loc. cit.*, p. 445.

Having these lines, the magnitude of the critical load can be readily determined in each particular case. It is seen that the number of waves n, into which the shell buckles, increases as the length and the thickness of the shell decrease.

The results of calculations, by using Eq. (270), can be represented in another way by taking as abscissas the values of the ratio l/a and as ordinates the quantities $(1 - \nu^2)a\dfrac{q_{cr}}{Eh}$. Then,

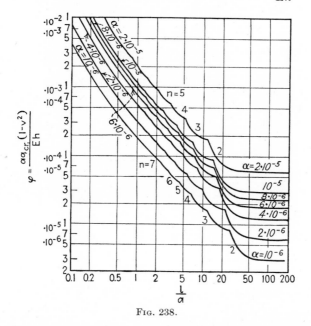

Fig. 238.

for each value of $h^2/12a^2$, a line is obtained which is formed by portions of curves constructed for various values of n. Several lines of this kind are shown in Fig. 238.[1] This manner of representation of the results is similar to that used before in discussing buckling of plates (see Art. 63). It is seen that for shorter tubes the critical load increases rapidly as the ratio l/a decreases. For long tubes, say for $l/a > 50$, the critical load

[1] These curves are taken from "Statik und Dynamik der Schalen," by W. Flügge. They are calculated by using an equation which is somewhat different from Eq. (270) and by taking $\nu = \frac{1}{6}$. Calculations show that the difference between the results obtained from the two equations mentioned is small and can be disregarded in practical applications.

does not depend on the length and is equal to the value given by Eq. (125) as derived for the case of an infinitely long tube.

The results obtained from Eq. (270) represent the correct values of the critical load only as long as the calculated compressive stresses are within the elastic region. Beyond the proportional limit Eq. (270) gives exaggerated values for q_{cr}; to obtain satisfactory results the reduced modulus E_r, instead

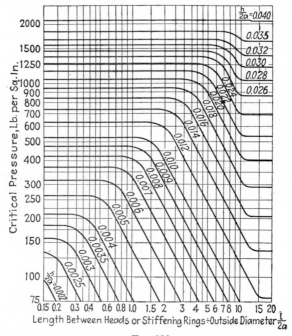

Fig. 239.

of E, should be used. When the compressive stress approaches the yield-point stress, the value of E_r decreases rapidly so that the load producing a yield-point stress must be considered as the ultimate load for materials with a pronounced yield point.

In the case of steel cylindrical shells, the curves given in Fig. 239 can be used[1] for determining the critical value of the load or for determining the necessary thickness of the wall, if the ratio of length to diameter $l/2a$ is given and if a suitable factor of safety is chosen. The right portion of these curves is calculated by using Eq. (270) and by taking $E = 30 \cdot 10^6$ lb. per square inch and $\nu = 0.3$. On the left side we have a system of parallel

[1] These curves have been prepared by the A.S.M.E. Research Committee on the Strength of Vessels under External Pressure, December, 1933.

lines corresponding to compressive stresses equal to the yield-point stress, which in this case was taken very low—26,000 lb. per square inch. Analogous curves can be constructed for any other material.

These curves can be used, not only in the case of shells with simply supported edges, but also in the case of built-in edges, since the manner of edge constraint is not of much influence on q_{cr}, and again in the case of a long shell stiffened by rings, provided the flexural rigidity of these rings is such that they can carry the lateral load alone without buckling. In such case l is the distance between rings.

The case in which a cylindrical shell with supported edges has some initial curvature is also of practical importance. One particular case of this kind has been discussed by H. M. Westergaard.[1]

A considerable number of experiments have been made with buckling of cylindrical shells under lateral uniform pressure.[2] One of the newest experimental series of this kind, together with a comparison of the experimental results with the theory developed by R. V. Southwell,[3] is given in the paper by G. Cook.[4] These experiments show that Southwell's theory, considering buckling of shorter tubes into a number of lobes, is in better agreement with experiments than the older formula developed by Carman,[5] which states that the critical pressure for shorter tubes is

$$q_{cr} = \frac{L}{l}(q_{cr})_0.$$

In this formula l is the length of the tube, L is the so-called critical length, which by Carman is assumed equal to six diameters of the tube, and $(q_{cr})_0$ is the critical pressure for an infinitely long tube.

84. Buckling of a Cylindrical Shell under the Action of Uniform Axial Pressure.

—Although the case of symmetrical buckling of an axially compressed cylindrical shell has been discussed before (see Art. 81), we will consider here a more general case by using Eqs. (259) and (260).[6] Assuming in this case that all resultant forces except N_x (Fig. 233) are very small and neglecting the products of these forces with the derivatives of the displacements u, v and w, which are also small, we obtain from Eqs. (259)

[1] *Reports 4th Intern. Cong. Appl. Mech.*, p. 274, 1934. See also the paper by R. D. Johnson presented before the Engineering Institute of Canada, Feb. 9, 1935.

[2] A bibliography on this subject has been published by Gilbert Cook, *Brit Assoc. Advancement Sci., Repts.*, Birmingham, 1913.

[3] *Loc. cit.*, p. 445.

[4] See *Phil. Mag.*, 6th series, vol. 28, p. 51, 1914.

[5] *Phys. Rev.*, vol. 21, p. 381, 1905.

[6] See R. Lorenz, *loc. cit.*, p. 445; R. V. Southwell, *Phil. Trans. Roy. Soc., London*, series A, vol. 213, p. 187, 1914. See also writer's paper, *Bull. Electrotech. Inst.*, St. Petersburg, vol. 11, 1914. From the latter paper the following discussion is taken.

$$a\frac{\partial N_x}{\partial x} + \frac{\partial N_{yx}}{\partial \theta} = 0;$$

$$\frac{\partial N_y}{\partial \theta} + a\frac{\partial N_{xy}}{\partial x} + aN_x\frac{\partial^2 v}{\partial x^2} - Q_y = 0; \qquad (a)$$

$$a\frac{\partial Q_x}{\partial x} + \frac{\partial Q_y}{\partial \theta} + aN_x\frac{\partial^2 w}{\partial x^2} + N_y = 0.$$

From Eqs. (260), neglecting the products of moments and derivatives of the displacements u, v and w, we obtain

$$Q_x = \frac{\partial M_x}{\partial x} + \frac{\partial M_{yx}}{a\ \partial \theta};$$

$$Q_y = \frac{\partial M_y}{a\ \partial \theta} - \frac{\partial M_{xy}}{\partial x}. \qquad (b)$$

Substituting these in Eqs. (a), the three equations of equilibrium for buckling of an axially compressed cylindrical shell become

$$a\frac{\partial N_x}{\partial x} + \frac{\partial N_{yx}}{\partial \theta} = 0;$$

$$\frac{\partial N_y}{\partial \theta} + a\frac{\partial N_{xy}}{\partial x} + aN_x\frac{\partial^2 v}{\partial x^2} + \frac{\partial M_{xy}}{\partial x} - \frac{\partial M_y}{a\ \partial \theta} = 0; \qquad (c)$$

$$aN_x\frac{\partial^2 w}{\partial x^2} + N_y + a\frac{\partial^2 M_x}{\partial x^2} + \frac{\partial^2 M_{yx}}{\partial x\ \partial \theta} + \frac{\partial^2 M_y}{a\ \partial \theta^2} - \frac{\partial^2 M_{xy}}{\partial x\ \partial \theta} = 0.$$

All resultant forces and moments entering in these equations can be expressed in terms of displacements u, v and w [see definitions of Art. 76 and Eqs. (261)], the positive directions of which are shown in Fig. 228. By taking compressive stress as positive and using the notations

$$\frac{h^2}{12a^2} = \alpha; \qquad \frac{N_x(1-\nu^2)}{Eh} = \phi, \qquad (d)$$

we finally obtain the following equations:

$$\frac{\partial^2 u}{\partial x^2} + \frac{1+\nu}{2a}\frac{\partial^2 v}{\partial x\ \partial \theta} - \frac{\nu}{a}\frac{\partial w}{\partial x} + \frac{1-\nu}{2}\frac{\partial^2 u}{a^2\ \partial \theta^2} = 0;$$

$$\frac{1+\nu}{2}\frac{\partial^2 u}{\partial x\ \partial \theta} + \frac{a(1-\nu)}{2}\frac{\partial^2 v}{\partial x^2} + \frac{\partial^2 v}{a\ \partial \theta^2} - \frac{\partial w}{a\ \partial \theta} +$$

$$\alpha\left[\frac{\partial^2 v}{a\ \partial \theta^2} + \frac{\partial^3 w}{a\ \partial \theta^3} + a\frac{\partial^3 w}{\partial x^2\ \partial \theta} + a(1-\nu)\frac{\partial^2 v}{\partial x^2}\right] - a\phi\frac{\partial^2 v}{\partial x^2} = 0; \qquad (271)$$

$$-a\phi\frac{\partial^2 w}{\partial x^2} + \nu\frac{\partial u}{\partial x} + \frac{\partial v}{a\ \partial \theta} - \frac{w}{a} - \alpha\left[\frac{\partial^3 v}{a\ \partial \theta^3} +\right.$$

$$\left. (2-\nu)a\frac{\partial^3 v}{\partial x^2\ \partial \theta} + a^3\frac{\partial^4 w}{\partial x^4} + \frac{\partial^4 w}{a\ \partial \theta^4} + 2a\frac{\partial^4 w}{\partial x^2\ \partial \theta^2}\right] = 0.$$

These equations will be satisfied by assuming

$$v = 0; \qquad \frac{\nu \, \partial u}{\partial x} = \frac{w}{a} = \text{const.} \qquad (e)$$

This solution represents the cylindrical form of equilibrium in which the compressed shell expands uniformly in the lateral direction.

Another solution is obtained by assuming that $v = 0$ and that u and w are functions of x only. In this manner we obtain the case of buckling symmetrical with respect to the axis of the cylinder which was discussed in Art. 81.

Considering now the general solution of Eqs. (271), we assume that u, v, and w in these equations represent very small displacements from the cylindrical compressed form of equilibrium discussed above [Eqs. (e)]. With the origin of coordinates at one end of the shell, and using, as before, the notations a and l for the radius and length of the shell, respectively, we take the solution of Eqs. (271) in the following form

$$\left. \begin{array}{l} u = A \sin n\theta \cos \dfrac{m\pi x}{l}; \\[2ex] v = B \cos n\theta \sin \dfrac{m\pi x}{l}; \\[2ex] w = C \sin n\theta \sin \dfrac{m\pi x}{l}, \end{array} \right\} \qquad (f)$$

which assumes that during buckling the generators of the shell subdivide into m half-waves and the circumference into $2n$ half-waves. At the ends we have

$$w = 0 \qquad \text{and} \qquad \frac{d^2 w}{dx^2} = 0,$$

which are the conditions of simply supported edges. The results obtained in this way can be used also for other edge conditions since these conditions have only a small effect on the magnitude of the critical load if the length of the cylinder is not small (say $l > 2a$).[1]

Substituting expressions (f) in Eqs. (271) and using the notation

---

[1] Experiments show that the effect of edge conditions remains small also for shorter cylinders; see L. H. Donnell's paper in *Trans. Am. Soc. Mech. Eng.*, vol. 56, p. 795, 1934.

$$\frac{m\pi a}{l} = \lambda, \qquad (g)$$

we obtain the following equations:

$$\left.\begin{array}{l} A\left(\lambda^2 + \dfrac{1-\nu}{2}n^2\right) + B\dfrac{n(1+\nu)\lambda}{2} + C\nu\lambda = 0; \\[2ex] A\dfrac{n(1+\nu)\lambda}{2} + B\left[\dfrac{(1-\nu)\lambda^2}{2} + n^2 + \alpha(1-\nu)\lambda^2 + \right. \\[2ex] \left. \qquad \alpha n^2 - \lambda^2\phi\right] + C[n + \alpha n(n^2 + \lambda^2)] = 0; \\[2ex] A\nu\lambda + Bn\{1 + \alpha[n^2 + (2-\nu)\lambda^2]\} + C[1 - \lambda^2\phi + \\[1ex] \qquad\qquad \alpha(\lambda^2 + n^2)^2] = 0. \end{array}\right\} \qquad (h)$$

Equating the determinant of these equations to zero and neglecting small quantities of higher order containing α^2 and ϕ^2 as factors, we obtain

$$\phi = \frac{R}{S}, \qquad (i)$$

where

$$R = (1 - \nu^2)\lambda^4 + \alpha[(n^2 + \lambda^2)^4 - (2 + \nu)(3 - \nu)\lambda^4 n^2 + \\ 2\lambda^4(1 - \nu^2) - \lambda^2 n^4(7 + \nu) + \lambda^2 n^2(3 + \nu) + n^4 - 2n^6]$$

and

$$S = \lambda^2\left\{(n^2 + \lambda^2)^2 + \frac{2}{1-\nu}\left(\lambda^2 + \frac{1-\nu}{2}n^2\right)[1 + \alpha(n^2 + \lambda^2)^2] - \\ \frac{2\nu^2\lambda^2}{1-\nu} + \frac{2\alpha}{1-\nu}\left(\lambda^2 + \frac{1-\nu}{2}n^2\right)[n^2 + (1 - \nu)\lambda^2]\right\}.$$

Experiments show (see Fig. 242) that thin cylindrical shells under compression usually buckle into short longitudinal waves so that λ^2 is a large number. Then, by keeping only the first term in the brackets of the numerator R and the first term in the denominator S, we can represent expression (i) in the following simplified form:

$$\phi = \alpha\frac{(n^2 + \lambda^2)^2}{\lambda^2} + \frac{(1 - \nu^2)\lambda^2}{(n^2 + \lambda^2)^2}. \qquad (272)$$

For $n = 0$, Eq. (272) coincides with Eq. (h), Art. 81, which was obtained for the symmetrical type of buckling.

We obtain the smallest value of expression (272) when

$$\frac{(n^2 + \lambda^2)^2}{\lambda^2} = \sqrt{\frac{1 - \nu^2}{\alpha}} = \frac{2a}{h}\sqrt{3(1 - \nu^2)}, \qquad (j)$$

in which case Eq. (272) gives

$$\phi = 2\sqrt{\alpha(1 - \nu^2)},$$

and, by using notations (d),

$$\sigma_{cr} = \frac{N_{cr}}{h} = \frac{Eh}{a\sqrt{3(1 - \nu^2)}}. \qquad (k)$$

This shows that in this case the critical stress does not depend on the length l of the cylinder; it is of the same magnitude as in the case of symmetrical buckling. The number of lobes into which the circumference subdivides during buckling remains indefinite as long as we consider λ^2 and n^2 as large numbers and determine the minimum value of expression (272) by treating it as a continuous function of $(n^2 + \lambda^2)^2/\lambda^2$. For any value of λ^2 smaller than $2a\sqrt{3(1 - \nu^2)}/h$ we find, from Eq. (j), the corresponding value of n^2.

In the case of shorter cylinders we cannot assume that λ is varying continuously; some additional discussion of expression (272) is necessary. If the cylindrical shell is so short that

$$\left(\frac{\pi a}{l}\right)^2 > \frac{2a}{h}\sqrt{3(1 - \nu^2)},$$

there will be formed during buckling only one half-wave in the axial direction and the smallest value of expression (272) is obtained by taking $n = 0$. That is, in such a case the form of buckling of the shell is symmetrical with respect to the axis of the cylinder. By taking the length of the cylinder shorter and shorter, we shall find that the second term in expression (272) becomes smaller and smaller in comparison with the first; by neglecting it we obtain, with $n = 0$,

$$\phi = \alpha\lambda^2,$$

from which, by using notations (d), we obtain

$$\sigma_{cr} = \frac{\pi^2 E h^2}{12(1 - \nu^2)l^2}. \qquad (l)$$

This is Euler's formula for an elemental strip.

When the length of the cylinder is such that $(\pi a/l)^2$ is somewhat smaller than $2a\sqrt{3(1-\nu^2)}/h$, we will continue to have one half-wave in the axial direction but n will no longer be zero and several lobes will appear along the circumference. The number of lobes, making expression (272) a minimum, will increase with the length of the cylinder up to the limit when two half-waves in the axial direction will be formed and the form of buckling again becomes symmetrical with respect to the axis. With further increase of the length, circumferential lobes again appear, and so on. For longer cylinders there will be only a small fluctuation in the critical value of compressive stress between two consecutive values of λ, and we can assume that this stress always remains equal to that found for a long cylinder with symmetrical buckling.

This discussion is of practical interest only in the case of very small values of the ratio h/a, in which case the critical stress (k) is below the proportional limit of the material. For thicker tubes failure will occur owing to yielding of the material rather than instability.

In the case of long cylindrical shells, we may expect generators to buckle into long waves. In such case the quantity λ may become small. Neglecting in the numerator of expression (i) all terms containing products of α with powers of λ higher than the second, and in the denominator all powers of λ higher than the second, we can represent this expression in the following form:

$$\phi = \frac{(1 - \nu^2)\lambda^4 + \alpha\{(n^4 - n^2)^2 + \lambda^2[4n^6 - (7 + \nu)n^4 + (3 + \nu)n^2]\}}{\lambda^2 n^2(n^2 + 1)} \quad (m)$$

By taking $n = 1$, we obtain from this expression

$$\phi = \frac{1 - \nu^2}{2}\lambda^2$$

or, by using notations (d),

$$\sigma_{cr} = \frac{\pi^2 E a^2}{2l^2}.$$

This is Euler's formula for a strut, since $a^2/2$ is the square of the radius of gyration for the cross section of a thin tube. For $n = 1$ the cross sections remain circular (see p. 209) and the tube buckles as a strut.

For $n > 1$, neglecting additional small terms in expression (m), we obtain

$$\phi = \frac{(1 - \nu^2)\lambda^2}{n^2(n^2 + 1)} + \frac{\alpha n^2(n^2 - 1)^2}{\lambda^2(n^2 + 1)}. \quad (n)$$

The value of λ^2, which makes this expression a minimum, is

$$\lambda^2 = \frac{\sqrt{\alpha}n^2(n^2 - 1)}{\sqrt{1 - \nu^2}} = \frac{hn^2(n^2 - 1)}{2a\sqrt{3(1 - \nu^2)}} \quad (o)$$

and the corresponding value of the critical stress, from expression (m), is

$$\sigma_{cr} = \frac{Eh}{a\sqrt{3(1 - \nu^2)}} \frac{n^2 - 1}{n^2 + 1}. \qquad (p)$$

This stress is smaller than that obtained for symmetrical buckling and its smallest value, for $n = 2$, is

$$\sigma_{cr} = \frac{3}{5} \frac{Eh}{a\sqrt{3(1 - \nu^2)}}. \qquad (273)$$

As may be seen from expression (o), this buckling is characterized by comparatively long waves in the axial direction.[1]

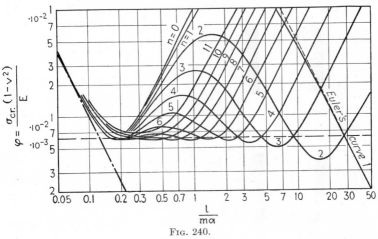

Fig. 240.

If the ratio h/a is given, $i.e.$, if α is known, we can, by using expression (i) and choosing a value for n representing the number of lobes of the buckled shell, obtain a curve representing the relation between λ and ϕ. Several curves[2] of this kind are shown in Fig. 240. The logarithmic values of $l/ma = \pi/\lambda$ are taken as abscissas and the logarithmic values of $\phi = \sigma_{cr}(1 - \nu^2)/E$ are taken as ordinates. On the left side the curves approach, asymptotically, the inclined line representing the condition of buckling of a strip [Eq. (l)]. On the right side the curves are limited by the curve $n = 1$ representing buckling of the shell as a strut. It is seen that for shorter cylindrical shells the critical values of the compressive stress are always close to the value calculated for a symmetrical buckling of a long cylindrical shell, indicated in the figure by the dotted horizontal line. For longer cylindrical shells, buckling into

---

[1] These waves were indicated by R. V. Southwell, *loc. cit.*, p. 453.

[2] These curves are taken from Flügge's book, *loc. cit.* p. 451. They are calculated for $\alpha = h^2/12a^2 = 10^{-5}$ and $\nu = \frac{1}{6}$ from an expression slightly different from the expression (i).

long waves with a comparatively small number of lobes [Eq. (p)] may occur at a stress which is smaller than that for a symmetrical buckling.

Noting the fact that a complete cylindrical shell submitted to uniform axial compression subdivides into a large number of small waves, it can be concluded that in the case of a non-circular cylindrical shell buckling will start in those portions of the shell where the curvature is the smallest. For instance, in the case of a cylindrical tube of an elliptical cross section, buck-

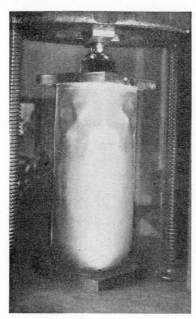

ling will begin at the ends of the minor axis of the ellipse and an ap_ proximate value for the critical stress is obtained by substituting in formula (k) the larger radius of curvature instead of the radius a of a circular cylinder.

85. Experiments with Cylindrical Shells in Axial Compression.—From the discussion of the previous article it is seen that only in the case of very thin shells will buckling occur within the elastic range in which the theoretical formulas can be applied. In structural engineering such thin shells are not used and quite naturally practically all the early experiments were made with comparatively thick tubes which fail, if longi-

Fig. 241.

tudinally compressed, owing to yielding of the material and not to buckling.[1] Only in recent times, in connection with applications of thin shells in airplane structures, have experiments with very thin cylindrical shells under axial pressure been made.[2] Figure 241 shows

---

[1] The first experiments with buckling of tubes were made by W. Fairbairn, "Conway and Menai Tubular Bridges," London, 1849; also E. Clark, "Britannia and Conway Tubular Bridges," London, 1850.

[2] The first experiments of this kind and the comparison with theoretical formulas were made by Andrew Robertson, *Proc. Roy. Soc., London*, series A, vol. 121, p. 558, 1928. In this country extensive experiments with thin cylindrical shells have been made by E. E. Lundquist, *Nat. Advisory Comm. Aeronautics Rept.* 473, and by L. H. Donnell, *Trans. Am. Soc. Mech. Eng.*, vol. 56, 1934. The results given in our discussion are taken from the latter paper.

a thin cylindrical shell in a compression-testing machine. To realize a central application of the load, steel balls are used as shown. The edges of the shell are welded to the end plates. Owing to this additional constraint the edges are stiffened and buckling usually occurs at some distance from the ends.

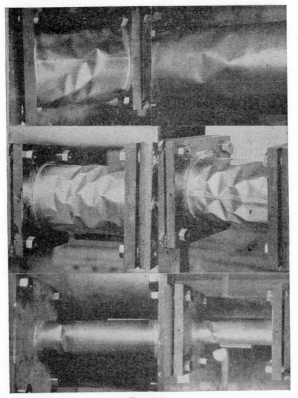

Fig. 242.

Several examples of buckling of thin cylindrical shells of steel and brass are shown in Fig. 242. As should be expected from the theory, shells of such proportion as shown in the figure buckle in comparatively small waves. Usually the length of these waves in the axial and circumferential directions is about the same.

The results obtained in these experiments are shown in Fig. 243. The ratios of the radius to the wall thickness a/h are taken as abscissas and the ratios of the ultimate compressive stress to the stress $Eh/[a\sqrt{3(1 - \nu^2)}]$ calculated for short waves are taken as ordinates. The results obtained on duralumin shells (Lundquist's tests) are denoted with crosses and those on steel and brass shells (Donnell's tests) with circles. It is seen that in all cases failure has occurred at a stress much lower than the theory predicts. In not one case was the ultimate stress

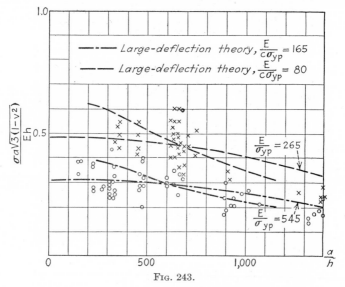

Fig. 243.

more than 60 per cent of the theoretical. It is clearly seen that the ratio of the ultimate stress to the theoretical decreases as the ratio a/h increases, *i.e.*, the discrepancy between experiment and theory is larger for thinner shells. To explain this discrepancy L. H. Donnell advanced[1] a theory which takes into account the initial displacements from the ideal cylindrical surface and investigated bending of the shell due to this initial imperfection, assuming that deflections are not small. He assumed also that the shells collapse when yielding of the material begins. Taking initial displacements in the form of waves of equal length in the axial and circumferential directions in combination with waves of buckling symmetrical with respect to the axis,[2] Donnell found that the ultimate load, for a given

[1] See L. H. Donnell's paper, *loc. cit.*, p. 460.

[2] Donnell has chosen such a combination from a consideration of the energy of deformation. It should be noted that waves symmetrical with

value of the ratio $E/(\sigma_{\text{Y.P.}}\sqrt{12(1 - \nu^2)})$, can be represented as a function of the radius-thickness ratio a/h. The corresponding curves calculated for duralumin shells $E/(\sigma_{\text{Y.P.}}\sqrt{12(1 - \nu^2)}) = 165$ and for steel and brass shells $E/(\sigma_{\text{Y.P.}}\sqrt{12(1 - \nu^2)})) = 80$ are shown in Fig. 243 by dotted lines.[1] It may be seen that there is a satisfactory agreement between these curves and the test results.

On the basis of the existing experimental data, Donnell developed an empirical formula for calculating the ultimate strength of cylindrical shells under axial compression. This formula takes into consideration the ratios a/h and $E/\sigma_{\text{Y.P.}}$ and gives

$$\sigma_{\text{ult.}} = E\frac{0.6\dfrac{h}{a} - 10^{-7}\dfrac{a}{h}}{1 + 0.004\dfrac{E}{\sigma_{\text{Y.P.}}}} \tag{274}$$

For the shells tested, with $E/\sigma_{\text{Y.P.}} = 545$ for steel and brass and $E/\sigma_{\text{Y.P.}} = 265$ for duralumin, the curves representing this formula are also shown in Fig. 243.

86. Bent or Eccentrically Compressed Cylindrical Shells.—In the discussion of Art. 84 it was always assumed that the force compressing the shell is centrally applied and that the resultant force N_x is constant. If the compressive force is applied with some eccentricity, we obtain a combined compression and bending of a cylindrical shell. Denoting by θ the angle that an axial plane makes with the plane in which bending occurs, the resultant forces N_x in the axial direction are no longer constant and can be represented by the formula[2]

$$N_x = -(N_0 + N_1 \cos \theta), \tag{a}$$

in which N_0/h is the uniform compressive stress and N_1/h is the maximum compressive stress due to bending. Then the maximum compressive stress is

---

respect to the axis always are present owing to constraint at the ends preventing lateral expansion of the shell during compression.

[1] Letter c is used for $\sqrt{12(1 - \nu^2)}$ in the figure. Two steeper curves of the figure are here considered.

[2] N_x is taken here positive if tension.

$$\sigma = \frac{1}{h}(N_0 + N_1). \tag{b}$$

Considering Eqs. (271) of Art. 84 and noting that N_x is no longer constant, it is seen that we cannot use, as a solution of these equations, the expressions (f) of Art. 84 (see p. 455) but must have recourse to the more general expressions

$$\left.\begin{aligned} u &= \cos\frac{m\pi x}{l}\sum_{0}^{\infty}A_n\cos n\theta; \\[2mm] v &= \sin\frac{m\pi x}{l}\sum_{0}^{\infty}B_n\sin n\theta; \\[2mm] w &= \sin\frac{m\pi x}{l}\sum_{0}^{\infty}C_n\cos n\theta, \end{aligned}\right\} \tag{c}$$

which imply that in a circumferential direction we have no longer simple sinusoidal waves, and that a more complicated form of buckling occurs. Because of the presence of the infinite series, the calculation of the critical value of the maximum compressive stress (b) becomes much more complicated than before. This calculation[1] shows that we can get a satisfactory approximation and are on the safe side by assuming, for any ratio N_0/N_1, that buckling occurs when the maximum compressive stress becomes equal to the critical stress calculated for symmetrical buckling. Thus

$$\frac{1}{h}(N_0 + N_1)_{cr} = \frac{Eh}{a\sqrt{3(1 - \nu^2)}}. \tag{d}$$

In Fig. 244 a comparison of exact and approximate values of the critical stresses is shown for the particular case where

$$\alpha = \frac{h^2}{12a^2} = 10^{-6}; \qquad \nu = \frac{1}{6}.$$

The quantities $N_0(1 - \nu^2)/Eh$ are plotted as abscissas and $N_1(1 - \nu^2)/Eh$ as ordinates. The results of exact calculations

---

[1] Such calculations have been made by W. Flügge, *Ingenieur-Archiv*, vol. 3, p. 463, 1932.

are given by the full line, and the results obtained by using Eq. (d) are shown by the dotted line. It is seen that for pure bending ($N_0 = 0$) the exact solution gives for the critical com-

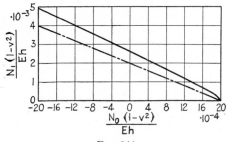

Fig. 244.

pressive stress a value which is about 30 per cent higher than that obtained from Eq. (d).

An interesting case of instability of a thin cylindrical shell in bending has been discussed by Brazier.[1] It is known that

Fig. 245.

in the bending of thin curved tubes a flattening of the cross sections takes place and such tubes are more flexible than would be expected from the usual theory of curved bars.[2] This

---

[1] BRAZIER, L. G., *Proc. Roy. Soc.*, London, series A, vol. 116, p. 104, 1927. More rigorously the same question has been discussed by E. Chwalla, *Z. angew. Math. Mech.*, vol. 13, p. 48, 1933.

[2] KÁRMÁN, TH. V., *Z. Ver. deut. Ing.*, vol. 55, 1911, and the writer, *Trans. Am. Soc. Mech. Eng.*, vol. 45, p. 135, 1923.

phenomenon of flattening occurs also in the case of initially straight cylinders, where it is due to curvature produced by bending. During bending the cross section becomes more and more oval until a point is reached at which the resistance to bending starts to decrease, after which, of course, complete collapse takes place. Such type of failure occurs in comparatively thick tubes made of a material with a low modulus, such

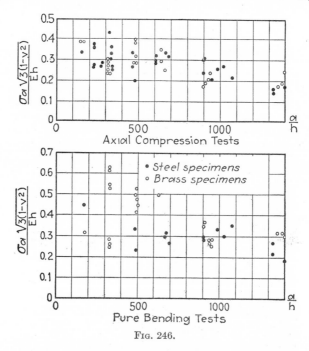

Fig. 246.

as rubber tubes, and in thick metal tubes stressed above the yield point. For thin metal tubes with built-in edges, such as used, for instance, in previously described experiments, failure always occurred as a result of buckling in small waves of the same kind as in the case of uniformly compressed cylindrical shells. Several examples of failure under bending are shown in Fig. 245. In Fig. 246 the results of Donnell's axial-compression and bending tests[1] on thin tubes of steel

---

[1] *Loc. cit.*, p. 460. A similar series of tests with thin cylindrical shells of duralumin has been made by E. E. Lundquist, *Nat. Advisory Comm. Aeronautics Tech. Notes* 479, Washington, 1933.

and brass are given. The ratios a/h are taken as abscissas and the ratios of the maximum compressive stress (b) to the stress $Eh/a\sqrt{3(1-\nu^2)}$ for a symmetrical buckling are taken as ordinates. The results show exactly the same decrease of σ_{cr} with the increase of a/h as are shown by the axially loaded specimens. The values found for σ_{cr} are about 1.4 times those found in axial-compression tests for all values of a/h.

87. Axial Compression of Curved Sheet Panels.—In the case of a cylindrical shell supported along two generators and along two circular edges normal to the axis of the cylinder and uniformly compressed in the direction of generators (Fig. 247), the same method as in the case of a circular cylindrical tube axially compressed (Art. 84) can be used[1] in calculating critical stresses. If β is the central angle of the shell, a the radius and l the length in the direction of generators, then, with coordinate axes directed as shown

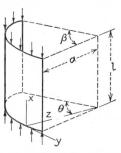

FIG. 247.

in the figure, we can satisfy the boundary conditions by taking for the displacements during buckling of the shell the following expressions:

$$
\left.
\begin{aligned}
u &= A \sin \frac{n\pi\theta}{\beta} \cos \frac{m\pi x}{l}; \\[4pt]
v &= B \cos \frac{n\pi\theta}{\beta} \sin \frac{m\pi x}{l}; \\[4pt]
w &= C \sin \frac{n\pi\theta}{\beta} \sin \frac{m\pi x}{l}.
\end{aligned}
\right\}
\qquad (a)
$$

It may be seen that the radial displacements w and the bending moments become zero along the edges of the shell, *i.e.*, for $x = 0$ and $x = l$ and for $\theta = 0$ and $\theta = \beta$, as is required for simply supported edges.[2] Substituting expressions (a) in Eqs. (271) (see p. 454), we obtain three homogeneous linear equations, and the equation for determining the critical value of the com-

---

[1] This problem has been discussed by the writer in "Theory of Elasticity," vol. 2, p. 395, St. Petersburg, 1916.

[2] Note that v is not zero along the generators $\theta = 0$ and $\theta = \beta$ and that there are some circumferential displacements in the planes tangent to the middle surface of the shell. This corresponds to the case when the edges of the shell are supported in V-grooves with some clearance.

pressive stress is obtained, as before, by equating to zero the
determinant of these equations. This equation is similar to
Eq. (*i*) (see p. 456) obtained for cylindrical tubes, the only
change being that the quantity $n\pi/\beta$ takes the place of the
quantity n. If the central angle β is not small and the length l
is of the same order of magnitude as βa, we can expect the shell
to buckle into a large number of circumferential and longitudinal
waves. Then by using notations (g) of Art. 84 and Eq. (272),
we obtain for calculating critical stresses the following equation:

$$\phi = \alpha \frac{\left(\dfrac{n^2\pi^2}{\beta^2} + \lambda^2\right)^2}{\lambda^2} + \frac{(1 - \nu^2)\lambda^2}{\left(\dfrac{n^2\pi^2}{\beta^2} + \lambda^2\right)^2}, \tag{275}$$

from which we can conclude, as before in the case of thin cylindrical tubes, that the critical stress is the same as for the case of
buckling of a tube into a form symmetrical with respect to the
axis of the cylinder, and we can take

$$\sigma_{cr} = \frac{Eh}{a\sqrt{3(1 - \nu^2)}}. \tag{b}$$

If the angle β is very small, the conditions of buckling of the
shell will approach those of a longitudinally compressed rectangular plate; the critical value of the compressive stress is obtained
by taking $n = 1$ in Eq. (275). Then

$$\phi = \alpha \frac{\left(\dfrac{\pi^2}{\beta^2} + \lambda^2\right)^2}{\lambda^2} + \frac{(1 - \nu^2)\lambda^2}{\left(\dfrac{\pi^2}{\beta^2} + \lambda^2\right)^2}. \tag{c}$$

As the radius a of the shell becomes larger and larger, λ increases
also and for a very large value of a we can omit the second term
in expression (c). Then we obtain

$$\phi = \alpha \frac{\left(\dfrac{\pi^2}{\beta^2} + \lambda^2\right)^2}{\lambda^2} = \alpha\left(\frac{\pi^2}{\beta^2\lambda} + \lambda\right)^2. \tag{d}$$

The smallest value of this expression occurs when

$$\lambda = \frac{\pi}{\beta}, \qquad \text{or} \qquad \frac{l}{m} = \beta a,$$

i.e., when the length of longitudinal half-waves is equal to the width of the curved panel.   Then

$$\phi = 4\frac{\alpha\pi^2}{\beta^2}.$$

Noting that

$$\phi = \frac{(1 - \nu^2)\sigma_{cr}}{E} \quad \text{and} \quad \alpha = \frac{h^2}{12a^2},$$

we obtain

$$\sigma_{cr} = \frac{\pi^2 E h^2}{3(1 - \nu^2)(\beta a)^2}. \tag{e}$$

This is the same value of the critical stress that we obtain for long rectangular plates.

Keeping both terms in expression (*c*), we find that it becomes a minimum for

$$\frac{\left(\dfrac{\pi^2}{\beta^2} + \lambda^2\right)^2}{\lambda^2} = \sqrt{\frac{1 - \nu^2}{\alpha}} \tag{f}$$

if

$$\beta a \geqq 2\pi \sqrt[4]{\frac{a^2 h^2}{12(1 - \nu^2)}}, \tag{g}$$

i.e., if the circumferential dimension of the panel is at least equal to twice the half-wave length for symmetrical buckling of the shell.   Then

$$\phi = 2\sqrt{\alpha(1 - \nu^2)}.$$

By substituting for ϕ its value $(1 - \nu^2)\sigma_{cr}/E$, we again obtain for the critical stress the value given by expression (*b*). It indicates that, for any value of the width βa of the curved panel satisfying condition (*g*), we can find from (*f*) such a length l/m of longitudinal half-waves that the critical stress becomes equal to that found before for symmetrical buckling of a thin tube. This value should be used in design of curved panels uniformly compressed along the generators.

If the circumferential dimension of the shell is smaller than that required by (*g*), expression (*c*) becomes a minimum if

$$\lambda^2 = \frac{\pi^2}{\beta^2}.$$

This means that for a considerable length l such a narrow shell like a long narrow compressed plate, will subdivide during buckling into squares. From Eq. (c) the magnitude of the critical stress in such a case is

$$\sigma_{cr} = \frac{\pi^2 E h^2}{3(1 - \nu^2)(a\beta)^2} + \frac{E\beta^2}{4\pi^2}. \tag{276}$$

The first term on the right side gives the stress calculated as for a plate and the second term gives the increase of the critical stress due to curvature of the shell.

Experiments with axial compression of cylindrical panels show[1] that formula (b), which can be put in the form

$$\sigma_{cr} = 0.6E\frac{h}{a}, \tag{277}$$

is in satisfactory agreement with test results providing the axial and circumferential dimensions of the panel are about equal and the central angle β is small, say $\beta < \frac{1}{2}$. With an increase of this angle, σ_{cr} diminishes; for $\beta > 2$ it is only about half of what we obtain from formula (277) and approaches the value given by experiments on thin cylindrical tubes (Art. 85).

If β is very small the conditions for buckling of a cylindrical shell approach those of buckling of plane panels, and an increase in the ultimate load, similar to that discussed in the case of buckling of plates (Art. 73), should be considered.

88. Buckling of a Stiffened Cylindrical Shell under Axial Compression.— If a cylindrical shell is stiffened by equidistant longitudinal and circumferential ribs, its stability can be discussed in the same manner as that of a stiffened plate (see p. 380). The ribs can be replaced by equivalent increases in flexural and torsional rigidities and in thickness of the wall. Thus the problem is reduced to that of investigation of the buckling of a non-isotropic shell.[2] To describe the elastic properties of such a shell, we introduce the following notations:

[1] A large number of such experiments with simply supported duralumin curved panels have been made by J. S. Newell and W. H. Gale; see A Report on Aircraft Materials Research at the Massachusetts Institute of Technology, 1931–1932. Some experimental data are given in the paper by S. C. Redshaw, *Aeronautical Research Committee Reports and Memoranda* 1565, 1933.

[2] The differential equations for this problem have been established by W. Flügge, *Ingenieur-Archiv*, vol. 3, p. 463, 1932. Calculations of critical loads have been made by Dji-Djüän Dschou in a dissertation made under the direction of Professor H. Wagner, *Luftfahrt-Forschung*, vol. 11, p. 223, 1935.

$h_x = h + \dfrac{A_x}{d_x}$, the equivalent thickness of the shell in the axial direction, which
is obtained by adding to the thickness h of the wall the cross-sectional
area A_x of the longitudinal ribs divided by the distance d_x between
these ribs.

$h_y = h + \dfrac{A_y}{d_y}$, the equivalent thickness of the wall in the circumferential
direction.

I_x, the moment of inertia of the cross section of a longitudinal rib together
with the corresponding portion of the wall and taken with respect to
the centroidal axis of this combined cross section.

I_y, the same quantity for circumferential ribs.

EI_{xy}, the average torsional rigidity per unit width of a strip cut out from the
shell in the axial direction.

EI_{yx}, the same quantity for a strip taken in the circumferential direction.

The torsional rigidities[1] EI_{xy} and EI_{yx} are usually small in comparison
with flexural rigidities EI_x and EI_y and in many cases can be neglected.
We introduce also notations for the following ratios:

$$r = \frac{h}{h_x}; \qquad s = \frac{h_y}{h_x}; \qquad (a)$$

$$k_x = \frac{I_x}{a^2 h_x}; \qquad k_y = \frac{I_y}{a^2 h_x}; \qquad k_{xy} = \frac{I_{xy} + I_{yx}}{a^2 h_x}. \qquad (b)$$

In the case of an unstiffened shell the following relation should be used:

$$r = s = 1;$$
$$I_x = I_y = \frac{1}{2}(I_{xy} + I_{yx}) = \frac{h^3}{12(1 - \nu^2)}.{}^{2} \qquad (c)$$

Using notations (a) and (b), the equations of equilibrium, similar to Eqs.
(271) for an unstiffened shell, can be written. With the origin of coordinates
at one end of the shell, and using, as before, the notations a and l for the
radius and length of the shell, respectively, and θ for the central angle, we
can take the solution of the equations of equilibrium for simply supported
edges in the same form as for an unstiffened shell and assume for displacements the following expressions:

$$\left.\begin{array}{l} u = A \sin n\theta \cos \dfrac{m\pi x}{l}; \\[2mm] v = B \cos n\theta \sin \dfrac{m\pi x}{l}; \\[2mm] w = C \sin n\theta \sin \dfrac{m\pi x}{l}, \end{array}\right\} \qquad (d)$$

[1] These torsional rigidities can be obtained experimentally by twisting a
rectangular plate which has a stiffening equivalent (1) to the longitudinal
and (2) to the circumferential stiffening of the shell.

[2] The quantity $Eh^3/12(1 - \nu^2)$, instead of $Eh^3/12(1 + \nu)$, is taken here
for torsional rigidity to bring the equations developed for a stiffened shell in
coincidence with those for an unstiffened shell.

which indicate that the shell subdivides during buckling into m half-waves in the axial direction and into $2n$ half-waves in the circumferential direction. Substituting these expressions in the equations of equilibrium, we arrive at three homogeneous equations linear in A, B and C; the equation for calculating the critical value of the axial compressive stress is obtained by equating to zero the determinant of these three linear equations.

In cases where k_{xy} is smaller than $1.4k_x$ and also in cases where the shell is stiffened only in the circumferential direction, the equation for calculating critical stresses can be written in the following simplified form:[1]

$$\frac{\sigma}{E} = \lambda^2 k_x + n^2 k_{xy} + \frac{n^4}{\lambda^2}k_y + \frac{\lambda^2}{\dfrac{\lambda^4}{s} + \dfrac{2}{r}\lambda^2 n^2 + n^4}, \qquad (278)$$

where, as before, $\lambda = m\pi a/l$.

For an unstiffened shell, by using relations (c), this equation reduces to

$$\frac{\sigma}{E} = \frac{(\lambda^2 + n^2)^2}{\lambda^2}\frac{h^2}{12(1 - \nu^2)a^2} + \frac{\lambda^2}{(\lambda^2 + n^2)^2},$$

which is the same as Eq. (272) obtained previously.

In using Eq. (278) it is necessary, in each particular case, to find for λ and n values that make the right side of the equation a minimum. If there is a possibility of having many waves in the axial and circumferential directions, we consider the expression (278) as a continuous function of λ and n. Then we find for its minimum the following value

$$\sigma = 2E\sqrt{\frac{r(k_{xy} + 2\beta^2{}_1 k_y)}{2(1 + r\beta^2{}_1)}}, \qquad (279)$$

in which

$$\beta_1 = \frac{n}{\lambda} = \frac{l}{m}:\frac{\pi a}{n}, \qquad (e)$$

i.e., β_1 represents the ratio of the lengths of longitudinal and circumferential waves into which the shell subdivides during buckling. If k_{xy} is small in comparison with k_x or k_y, which is usually the case for a stiffened shell, we can take as a satisfactory approximation

$$\beta^2{}_1 = \frac{sk_x - \dfrac{rk_{xy}}{2}}{k_y - \dfrac{rk_{xy}}{2}} = \frac{h_y I_x - \dfrac{h}{2}(I_{xy} + I_{yx})}{h_x I_y - \dfrac{h}{2}(I_{xy} + I_{yx})}. \qquad (f)$$

If this expression becomes negative, it indicates that the assumption of many waves in the axial and circumferential directions is not satisfied, and some other assumption regarding the number of waves should be made. Substituting expression (f) for $\beta^2{}_1$ in formula (279) and neglecting the term with k_{xy}, which is considered as small, we obtain for the critical stress the following expression:

[1] The case where the cylinder is so long that buckling as for a column may occur is excluded from consideration here.

$$(\sigma_{cr})_0 = \frac{2E}{ah_x}\sqrt{\frac{I_x I_y}{\dfrac{I_x}{h_x} + \dfrac{I_y h_x}{h h_y}}}. \tag{280}$$

Assuming that there is stiffening only in the axial direction and considering I_y as small in comparison with I_x, we obtain from (280)

$$(\sigma_{cr})_0 = \frac{2E}{ah_x}\sqrt{h_x I_y} = \frac{E}{\sqrt{3(1-\nu^2)}}\frac{h}{a}\sqrt{\frac{h}{h_x}}. \tag{281}$$

In the same manner, if there is stiffening only in the circumferential direction, we obtain

$$(\sigma_{cr})_0 = \frac{E}{\sqrt{3(1-\nu^2)}}\frac{h}{a}\sqrt{\frac{h_y}{h}}. \tag{282}$$

The last two formulas indicate that, if there is buckling into many waves in the axial and circumferential directions, stiffening of the shell in only one direction increases the critical load as obtained for an unstiffened shell [see Eq. (b), Art. 87] in the ratio $\sqrt{h_x/h}$ or $\sqrt{h_y/h}$. Thus, in such cases, the effect of stiffening is small and a better result is obtained by adding the material of the stiffeners to the thickness of the wall.

Formulas (278), (279) and (280) developed for a full cylindrical shell can be used also for a cylindrical panel with simply supported edges if several waves are produced in the axial and circumferential directions during buckling of the panel. To decide whether this condition is satisfied, we use the equation[1]

$$\frac{1}{\lambda^2_1} = \sqrt{(k_x + \beta^2_1 k_{xy} + \beta^4_1 k_y)\left(\frac{1}{s} + \frac{2\beta^2_1}{r} + \beta^4_1\right)}, \tag{g}$$

in which β_1 is given by formula (f) and the other quantities by notations (a) and (b). This equation gives the value of λ at which expression (278) becomes a minimum and determines the length of half-waves in the axial direction. Substituting this value of λ in Eq. (e), the number n and the length of circumferential half-waves are obtained. If the lengths of both axial and circumferential half-waves are smaller than the corresponding dimensions of the curved panel, formula (280) should be used for determining the critical stress. If one or both half-waves become larger than the corresponding dimensions of the shell, one of the following three cases is possible: (1) several half-waves only in the circumferential direction; (2) several half-waves only in the axial direction; (3) only one half-wave in each direction. For the last case the critical stress is obtained from Eq. (278) by substituting in it

$$\lambda = \frac{\pi a}{l}; \qquad n \approx \frac{\pi}{\beta},$$

where β is the central angle of the panel and l its length. Cases (1) and (2) require additional investigations, and we limit ourselves here to giving only some final results.[2]

[1] This equation should be used also in the case of full cylindrical shells.

[2] These cases are treated with necessary detail in the paper by D. D. Dschou, *loc. cit.*, p. 470.

If there are several waves only in the circumferential direction, as is usually the case with longitudinal stiffeners only, the critical stress can be calculated from the equation

$$\sigma_{cr} = \sigma_e + \gamma \frac{E}{h} \sqrt{\frac{I_y}{h_x}}, \qquad (283)$$

in which

$$\sigma_e = \frac{\pi^2 E I_x}{h_x l^2}$$

represents the critical stress for one longitudinal rib, together with the corresponding portion of the wall, calculated as for a strut, and γ is a numerical factor, the values of which are given in Fig. 248. For the case of an

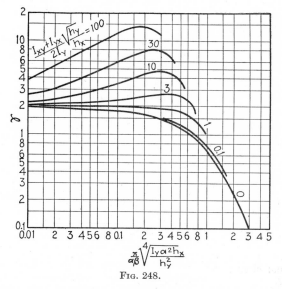

Fig. 248.

unstiffened shell, the abscissas in the figure represent the ratio of the half-wave length for a symmetrical buckling of a full cylindrical shell [see Eq. (265), p. 441] to the circumferential dimension of the panel. The factor γ is obtained in this case from the curve for which

$$\frac{I_{xy} + I_{yx}}{2I_y} \sqrt{\frac{h_y}{h_x}} = 1.$$

It may be seen that, if the circumferential dimension of the panel is not very small, the value of the factor γ is about equal to 2 and the second term in formula (283) is close to the value (b) obtained in the previous article (p. 468). The first term of the same formula is very small as long as the length l is of the same order as the radius a.

If there is only longitudinal stiffening of the shell, the formula (283) can be replaced by the simple expression

$$\sigma_{cr} = \sigma_e + (\sigma_{cr})_0, \qquad (284)$$

in which $(\sigma_{cr})_0$ is given by formula (280).

In the case of circumferential stiffening only, the critical stress is

$$\sigma_{cr} = \sigma_e \left[1 + \frac{(\sigma_{cr})^2{}_0}{4\sigma^2{}_e} \right]. \qquad (285)$$

If there are several waves only in the axial direction (case 2), the critical value of compressive stresses is given by the formula

$$\sigma_{cr} = \mu \sqrt{\sigma^2{}_1 + \sigma^2{}_2} + \frac{\pi^2 E(I_{xy} + I_{yx})}{h_x(a\beta)^2}, \qquad (286)$$

in which

$$\sigma_1 = \frac{2E}{ah_x} \sqrt{\frac{I_x I_y}{\dfrac{I_x}{h_x} + \dfrac{I_y}{h_y}}}; \qquad \sigma_2 = \frac{2\pi^2 E}{h_x(a\beta)^2} \sqrt{I_x I_y}$$

and μ is a numerical factor which does not differ much from unity and which can be taken from the curves in Fig. 249.

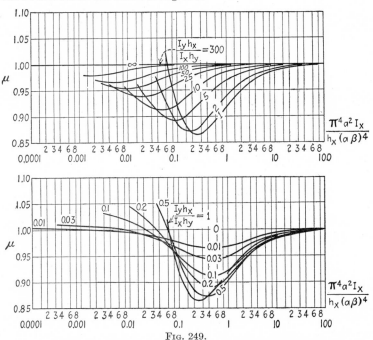

Fig. 249.

Calculations show that, in the case of shorter cylinders, longitudinal stiffening is much more efficient than circumferential stiffening.

89. Buckling of a Cylindrical Shell under Combined Axial and Uniform Lateral Pressure.—There are cases in machine design and shipbuilding in which thin cylindrical shells are submitted to the simultaneous action of axial compression and uniform lateral pressure. Under the action of such forces the shell may retain its cylindrical form, but at certain critical values of the pressures this form of equilibrium may become unstable and the shell may buckle.[1] If u, v and w denote, as before, small displacements from the compressed cylindrical form during buckling of the shell, the three differential equations of equilibrium for determining these displacements can be written by using Eqs. (f) (Art. 83) for the case of lateral pressure and Eqs. (271) for the case of axial compression of the shell. Using notations

$$\frac{qa(1-\nu^2)}{Eh} = \phi_1 \quad \text{and} \quad \frac{N_x(1-\nu^2)}{Eh} = -\phi_2, \qquad (a)$$

these equations become

$$a^2\frac{\partial^2 u}{\partial x^2} + \frac{1+\nu}{2}\frac{a\,\partial^2 v}{\partial x\,\partial\theta} - \nu a\frac{\partial w}{\partial x} + a\phi_1\left(\frac{\partial^2 v}{\partial x\,\partial\theta} - \frac{\partial w}{\partial x}\right) +$$
$$\frac{1-\nu}{2}\frac{\partial^2 u}{\partial\theta^2} = 0;$$

$$\frac{1+\nu}{2}\frac{a\,\partial^2 u}{\partial x\,\partial\theta} + \frac{1-\nu}{2}a^2\frac{\partial^2 v}{\partial x^2} + \frac{\partial^2 v}{\partial\theta^2} - \frac{\partial w}{\partial\theta} + \alpha\left[\frac{\partial^2 v}{\partial\theta^2} + \frac{\partial^3 w}{\partial\theta^3} + \right.$$
$$\left. a^2\frac{\partial^3 w}{\partial x^2\,\partial\theta} + a^2(1-\nu)\frac{\partial^2 v}{\partial x^2}\right] - a^2\phi_2\frac{\partial^2 v}{\partial x^2} = 0; \qquad (b)$$

$$\nu a\frac{\partial u}{\partial x} + \frac{\partial v}{\partial\theta} - w - \alpha\left[\frac{\partial^3 v}{\partial\theta^3} + (2-\nu)a^2\frac{\partial^3 v}{\partial x^2\,\partial\theta} + a^4\frac{\partial^4 w}{\partial x^4} + \right.$$
$$\left. \frac{\partial^4 w}{\partial\theta^4} + 2a^2\frac{\partial^4 w}{\partial x^2\,\partial\theta^2}\right] = \phi_1\left(w + \frac{\partial^2 w}{\partial\theta^2}\right) + \phi_2 a^2\frac{\partial^2 w}{\partial x^2}.$$

Assuming that the edges of the shell are simply supported, we use for displacements the same expressions as in the case of an axially compressed shell (Art. 84) and take

$$\left.\begin{aligned} u &= A\sin n\theta\cos\frac{m\pi x}{l}; \\[4pt] v &= B\cos n\theta\sin\frac{m\pi x}{l}; \\[4pt] w &= C\sin n\theta\sin\frac{m\pi x}{l}. \end{aligned}\right\} \qquad (c)$$

[1] This problem has been solved by R. v. Mises, "Stodola-Festschrift," p. 418, Zürich, 1929. It was also discussed by K. v. Sanden and F. Tölke, *Ingenieur-Archiv*, vol. 3, p. 24, 1932, and by W. Flügge, *Ingenieur-Archiv*, vol. 3, p. 463, 1932.

Substituting these expressions in Eqs. (b), we obtain for A, B and C three homogeneous linear equations. The equation for calculating the critical values of pressures is obtained by equating to zero the determinant of these equations. After simplifications this equation can be put in the following form:[1]

$$C_1 + C_2\alpha = C_3\phi_1 + C_4\phi_2, \qquad (d)$$

in which

$C_1 = (1 - \nu^2)\lambda^4;$

$C_2 = (\lambda^2 + n^2)^4 - 2[\nu\lambda^6 + 3\lambda^4 n^2 + (4 - \nu)\lambda^2 n^4 + n^6] +$
$$2(2 - \nu)\lambda^2 n^2 + n^4;$$

$C_3 = n^2(\lambda^2 + n^2)^2 - (3\lambda^2 n^2 + n^4);$

$C_4 = \lambda^2(\lambda^2 + n^2)^2 + \lambda^2 n^2;$

$$\alpha = \frac{h^2}{12a^2}; \qquad \lambda = \frac{m\pi a}{l}. \qquad (e)$$

If the dimensions of the shell are given and if certain values are assumed for the numbers m and $2n$, which indicate, respectively, the number of half-waves in the axial direction and in the circumferential direction, Eq. (d) represents a certain linear relation between the quantities ϕ_1 and ϕ_2, determining external pressures. Taking ϕ_1 and ϕ_2 as rectangular coordinates, a straight line is defined by Eq. (d). If we keep m constant and give to n the values 2, 3, 4, . . . , a system of such straight lines is obtained. The portions of these lines which for a given abscissa have the smallest ordinates form a broken line which can be used for determining the critical values of pressures. In Fig. 250 such lines are constructed[2] for the case where $\alpha = 10^{-5}$, $\nu = \frac{1}{6}$ and for various values of λ.

Taking the points of intersection of these lines with the horizontal axis ($\phi_2 = 0$), we obtain the critical values of ϕ_1 when lateral pressures alone are acting. It is seen that ϕ_1 and the critical pressure increase as λ increases. This indicates that in the case of lateral pressure acting alone $m = 1$, i.e., the buckled shell has one half-wave in the axial direction and the critical pressure increases as the length of the cylinder decreases. The number of waves in the circumferential direction, indicated

[1] The equation is given in this form in the paper by W. Flügge, *loc. cit.* Flügge uses a system of equations slightly different from Eqs. (b), but this difference affects only terms of minor importance in the final equation.

[2] This figure is taken from the paper by W. Flügge, *loc. cit.*, p. 276.

on the sides of the polygons, also increases as the length of the cylinder becomes shorter. These conclusions coincide with statements previously made in Art. 83.

Taking the points of intersection of the same polygons with the vertical axis ($\phi_1 = 0$), we obtain the critical values of ϕ_2 providing axial pressure alone is acting.

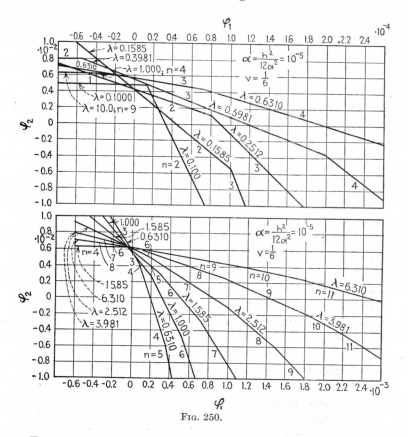

Fig. 250.

For any given value of the ratio $\phi_1 : \phi_2$ we draw through the origin a straight line with the slope ϕ_1/ϕ_2. The points of intersection of this line with the polygons determine the corresponding critical values of ϕ_1 and ϕ_2. It is seen that any axial pressure makes the critical value of the lateral pressure decrease; any lateral pressure produces a decrease in the critical value of the axial pressure.

The most common case is that of a cylindrical shell with closed ends submitted to the action of a uniform external pressure. In this case

$$\phi_2 = \tfrac{1}{2}\phi_1.$$

Assuming that the shell is thin and keeping only the principal terms in Eq. (d), we obtain for this case the following simplified formula for the critical value of the lateral pressure:[1]

$$q_{cr} = \frac{Eh}{a}\,\frac{1}{n^2 + \tfrac{1}{2}(\pi a/l)^2}\left\{\frac{1}{[n^2(l/\pi a)^2 + 1]^2} + \frac{h^2}{12a^2(1 - \nu^2)}\left[n^2 + \left(\frac{\pi a}{l}\right)^2\right]^2\right\}. \quad (287)$$

The values of n which make this expression a minimum and which must be used in calculating q_{cr} should be taken from Fig. 251,

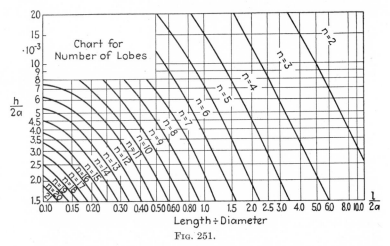

Chart for Number of Lobes

Length ÷ Diameter

Fig. 251.

in which the ratios of the length l to the diameter $2a$ are taken as abscissas and the ratios of the thickness of the wall to the diameter as ordinates.[2]

It may be seen from the figure that the number of circumferential lobes into which the shell buckles increases as the length and thickness of the cylinder decrease. Experiments

[1] This simplified formula has been given by R. v. Mises, *loc. cit.*, p. 476.

[2] This figure is taken from the paper by D. F. Windenburg and C. Trilling, *Trans. Am. Soc. Mech. Eng.*, vol. 56, p. 819, 1934. Note that numbers on vertical axis are multiplied by 10^{-3}.

made with thin shells, which buckle within the elastic region of the material, are in satisfactory agreement with the theory.[1]

The case of buckling of a cylindrical shell stiffened by equidistant circumferential rings also has been investigated.[2] Replacing the rings by equivalent increases in the circumferential direction of the flexural rigidity of the shell and of the thickness of the wall, and using the equation for nonisotropic shells, we obtain, for calculating critical pressures, an equation similar to Eq. (d). If EI_y is the flexural rigidity of one ring, together with the corresponding portion of the wall of the cylinder,[3] and b is the distance between the rings, we use EI_y/b instead of $Eh^3/12(1 - \nu^2)$ in considering bending in the circumferential direction; we also use the equivalent thickness $h_y = h + \dfrac{A_y}{b}$ instead of h in considering the circumferential compression. Using the notations

$$\frac{I_y(1 - \nu^2)}{bha^2} = \alpha_1 \quad \text{and} \quad \frac{h_y(1 - \nu^2)}{h} = s, \qquad (f)$$

the equation for determining the critical values of pressures becomes

$$C_1 + C_2\alpha + C_3\alpha_1 = C_4\phi_1 + C_5\phi_2, \qquad (g)$$

in which α, ϕ_1 and ϕ_2 have the same meaning as before [see notations (a) and (e)] and the coefficients C_1, C_2, . . . are as follows:

$C_1 = s\lambda^4;$
$C_2 = \lambda^6(\lambda^2 + 2n^2) + s\lambda^2n^2[2(\lambda^2 - 1)^2 + 2(n^2 - 1)^2 + 5\lambda^2n^2 - 2];$
$C_3 = (n^2 - 1)^2[\lambda^4 + s(2\lambda^2 + n^2)n^2];$
$C_4 = \lambda^4n^2 + s(2\lambda^2 + n^2)n^4 - s(3\lambda^2 + n^2)n^2;$
$C_5 = \lambda^6 + s\lambda^2n^2(2\lambda^2 + n^2 + 1).$

Again for given dimensions of the shell and ribs and for assumed values for m and n we obtain a straight line giving the relation between ϕ_1 and ϕ_2. Keeping m constant and taking $n = 2, 3, \cdots$, polygons similar to those shown in Fig. 250 can be obtained and the critical pressure can be calculated.

90. Buckling of a Cylindrical Shell Subjected to Torsion.—In the case of buckling of a cylindrical shell under the action of torque applied at the ends, the resultant shearing force N_{xy} becomes of preponderant importance. Taking this into account,

---

[1] Some experimental results are given in the paper by H. E. Saunders and D. F. Windenburg, *Trans. Am. Soc. Mech. Eng.*, vol. 54, p. 263, 1932, and in the paper by D. F. Windenburg and C. Trilling, *loc. cit.*, p. 479. See also the paper by T. Tokugawa, *Proc. World Eng. Cong.*, Tokyo, vol. 29, p. 249, 1929.

[2] W. Flügge, *loc. cit.*, p. 476; Sanden and Tölke, *loc. cit.*, p. 476.

[3] It is assumed here that the cross section of the ring is symmetrical with respect to the middle surface of the shell, *i.e.*, half of the ring is projecting inside the shell.

the general equations of equilibrium (259) can be put in the following simplified form:[1]

$$a\frac{\partial N_x}{\partial x} + \frac{\partial N_{yx}}{\partial \theta} - aN_{xy}\frac{\partial^2 v}{\partial x^2} = 0;$$

$$\frac{\partial N_y}{\partial \theta} + a\frac{\partial N_{xy}}{\partial x} + N_{yx}\left(\frac{\partial^2 v}{\partial x\,\partial\theta} - \frac{\partial w}{\partial x}\right) - Q_y = 0; \qquad (a)$$

$$a\frac{\partial Q_x}{\partial x} + \frac{\partial Q_y}{\partial \theta} + (N_{xy} + N_{yx})\left(\frac{\partial v}{\partial x} + \frac{\partial^2 w}{\partial x\,\partial\theta}\right) + N_y = 0.$$

We substitute in these equations

$$N_{xy} = N_{yx} = \frac{M}{2\pi a^2} + N'_{xy},$$

where M is the applied torque, $M/2\pi a^2$ is the resultant shearing force due to this torque, and N'_{xy} is the small change in this force due to buckling. We take into consideration also the stretching of the middle surface during buckling and substitute $N_{yx}(1 + \epsilon_1)$ and $N_{xy}(1 + \epsilon_2)$ instead of N_{yx} and N_{xy} in the second terms of the first and the second equations of the system (a). Then, neglecting the products of the derivatives of N'_{xy} with the displacements u, v and w, we obtain

$$a\frac{\partial N_x}{\partial x} + \frac{\partial N'_{yx}}{\partial \theta} + \frac{M}{2\pi a^2}\left(\frac{\partial^2 u}{\partial x\,\partial\theta} - a\frac{\partial^2 v}{\partial x^2}\right) = 0;$$

$$\frac{\partial N_y}{\partial \theta} + a\frac{\partial N'_{xy}}{\partial x} + 2\frac{M}{2\pi a^2}\left(\frac{\partial^2 v}{\partial x\,\partial\theta} - \frac{\partial w}{\partial x}\right) - Q_y = 0;$$

$$a\frac{\partial Q_x}{\partial x} + \frac{\partial Q_y}{\partial \theta} + N_y + 2\frac{M}{2\pi a^2}\left(\frac{\partial v}{\partial x} + \frac{\partial^2 w}{\partial x\,\partial\theta}\right) = 0.$$

Substituting in these equations [see Art. 76 and Eqs. (261), p. 434],

$$N_x = \frac{Eh}{1 - \nu^2}\left[\frac{\partial u}{\partial x} + \frac{\nu}{a}\left(\frac{\partial v}{\partial\theta} - w\right)\right];$$

$$N_y = \frac{Eh}{1 - \nu^2}\left[\nu\frac{\partial u}{\partial x} + \frac{1}{a}\left(\frac{\partial v}{\partial\theta} - w\right)\right];$$

[1] Here, as before, u, v and w are small displacements from the cylindrical form of equilibrium of the twisted shell. The products of all moments and all forces, except N_{xy}, with the derivatives of u, v and w are neglected.

$$N'_{xy} = \frac{Eh}{2(1 + \nu)}\left(\frac{\partial v}{\partial x} + \frac{1}{a}\frac{\partial u}{\partial \theta}\right);$$

$$M_x = -\frac{Eh^3}{12(1 - \nu^2)}\left[\frac{\partial^2 w}{\partial x^2} + \frac{\nu}{a^2}\left(\frac{\partial^2 w}{\partial \theta^2} + \frac{\partial v}{\partial \theta}\right)\right];$$

$$M_y = -\frac{Eh^3}{12(1 - \nu^2)}\left[\nu\frac{\partial^2 w}{\partial x^2} + \frac{1}{a^2}\left(\frac{\partial^2 w}{\partial \theta^2} + \frac{\partial v}{\partial \theta}\right)\right];$$

$$M_{xy} = \frac{Eh^3}{12(1 + \nu)a}\left(\frac{\partial v}{\partial x} + \frac{\partial^2 w}{\partial x \partial \theta}\right),$$

and using the notations

$$\alpha = \frac{h^2}{12a^2}; \qquad \phi = \frac{M(1 - \nu^2)}{2\pi a^2 Eh} = \frac{\tau(1 - \nu^2)}{E}, \qquad (b)$$

we obtain

$$a^2\frac{\partial^2 u}{\partial x^2} + \frac{1 - \nu}{2}\frac{\partial^2 u}{\partial \theta^2} + \frac{a(1 + \nu)}{2}\frac{\partial^2 v}{\partial x \partial \theta} - \nu a\frac{\partial w}{\partial x} +$$
$$\phi a\left(\frac{\partial^2 u}{\partial x \partial \theta} - a\frac{\partial^2 v}{\partial x^2}\right) = 0;$$

$$\frac{\partial^2 v}{\partial \theta^2} + \frac{a^2(1 - \nu)}{2}\frac{\partial^2 v}{\partial x^2} + \frac{a(1 + \nu)}{2}\frac{\partial^2 u}{\partial x \partial \theta} - \frac{\partial w}{\partial \theta} + \alpha\left[\frac{\partial^2 v}{\partial \theta^2} + \right.$$
$$\left. a^2(1 - \nu)\frac{\partial^2 v}{\partial x^2} + a^2\frac{\partial^3 w}{\partial x^2 \partial \theta} + \frac{\partial^3 w}{\partial \theta^3}\right] + \phi a\left(\frac{\partial^2 v}{\partial x \partial \theta} - \frac{\partial w}{\partial x}\right) = 0; \qquad (c)$$

$$\frac{\partial v}{\partial \theta} + a\nu\frac{\partial u}{\partial x} - w - \alpha\left[a^4\frac{\partial^4 w}{\partial x^4} + 2a^2\frac{\partial^4 w}{\partial x^2 \partial \theta^2} + \frac{\partial^4 w}{\partial \theta^4} + \right.$$
$$\left. (2 - \nu)a^2\frac{\partial^3 v}{\partial x^2 \partial \theta} + \frac{\partial^3 v}{\partial \theta^3}\right] + 2\phi a\left(\frac{\partial v}{\partial x} + \frac{\partial^2 w}{\partial x \partial \theta}\right) = 0.$$

Thus the problem of buckling of a cylindrical shell under the action of torque is reduced to the integration of these three equations.[1] There is a substantial difference between these equations and those which we have had previously in discussing lateral or axial compression of a cylinder. The difference lies in the fact that in the same equation we encounter both odd and even orders of derivatives of a displacement with respect to the same independent variable. This indicates that we can no longer satisfy the equations by using solutions in the form of products of sines or cosines, which means physically that there

[1] The first investigation of buckling of cylindrical shells under torsion is due to E. Schwerin; see *Reports Intern. Cong. App. Mech.*, Delft, 1924, and also *Z. angew. Math. Mech.*, vol. 5, p. 235, 1925.

are no generators which remain straight during buckling and which form a system of straight nodal lines for a buckled surface. In the case of torsion we may expect nodal lines of helical form and this condition will be fulfilled if we take for the displacements the following expressions:

$$
\left.\begin{aligned}
u &= A \cos\left(\frac{\lambda x}{a} - n\theta\right); \\
v &= B \cos\left(\frac{\lambda x}{a} - n\theta\right); \\
w &= C \sin\left(\frac{\lambda x}{a} - n\theta\right),
\end{aligned}\right\} \tag{d}
$$

where, as before, a is the radius of the cylinder, l its length, n the number of waves in the circumferential direction and

$$
\lambda = \frac{m\pi a}{l}.
$$

The corresponding form of buckling has n circumferential waves which spiral along the cylinder; the pitch L of the corresponding helical lines is found from the condition

$$
\frac{\lambda L}{a} = 2\pi n,
$$

from which

$$
L = \frac{2a\pi n}{\lambda}.
$$

Regarding conditions at the ends, we assume first that the cylinder is so long that constraints at the edges do not affect greatly the magnitude of the critical stress and can therefore be disregarded. Substituting expressions (d) in Eqs. (c), we obtain

$$
-A\left(\lambda^2 + \frac{1-\nu}{2}n^2 - \lambda n\phi\right) + B\left(\frac{1+\nu}{2}\lambda n + \lambda^2\phi\right) - C\nu\lambda = 0;
$$

$$
A\frac{1+\nu}{2}\lambda n - B\left[n^2(1+\alpha) + \frac{1-\nu}{2}\lambda^2(1+2\alpha) - 2\phi\lambda n\right] + Cn\left(1 + \alpha n^2 + \alpha\lambda^2 - 2\phi\frac{\lambda}{n}\right) = 0; \tag{e}
$$

$$
A\lambda n - Bn\left[1 + \alpha n^2 + (2-\nu)\lambda^2\alpha - 2\phi\frac{\lambda}{n}\right] + C[1 + \alpha(\lambda^2 + n^2)^2 - 2\phi\lambda n] = 0.
$$

These three homogeneous linear equations can yield for A, B and C solutions different from zero only if their determinant is zero. Equating the determinant to zero and neglecting[1] terms containing α^2, $\alpha\phi$, α^3, ϕ^2 and ϕ^3, we find

$$\phi = \frac{R}{S}, \qquad (f)$$

where

$$R = \lambda^4(1 - \nu^2) + \alpha[2\lambda^4(1 - \nu^2) + (\lambda^2 + n^2)^4 + (3 + \nu)\lambda^2 n^2 - (2 + \nu)(3 - \nu)\lambda^4 n^2 - (7 + \nu)\lambda^2 n^4 - 2n^6 + n^4]$$

and

$$S = 2\lambda n^5 - 2\lambda n^3 + 4\lambda^3 n^3 - 2\lambda^3 n + 2\lambda^5 n.$$

Taking for m and n certain integers, the corresponding value of ϕ can be calculated from this expression.

We begin with $n = 1$. In this case, as may be seen from expressions (d), a cross section of the tube remains circular and moves, during buckling, only in its plane (see p. 209). For $n = 1$, expression (f) becomes

$$\phi = \frac{\lambda^4(1 - \nu^2) + \alpha\lambda^4[\lambda^4 + 4\lambda^2 + (2 + \nu)(1 - \nu)]}{2\lambda^3(\lambda^2 + 1)}. \qquad (g)$$

Neglecting, in the numerator, the terms with the factor α as very small, we obtain

$$\phi = \frac{\lambda(1 - \nu^2)}{2(\lambda^2 + 1)}. \qquad (h)$$

To obtain such buckling within the elastic limit, ϕ must be very small [see notation (b)]; hence λ must also be small[2] and we neglect λ^2 in comparison with unity. Then

$$\phi = \tfrac{1}{2}\lambda(1 - \nu^2). \qquad (i)$$

We obtain the smallest value for λ when, during buckling, the cylinder forms only one complete wave in the axial direction, *i.e.*, from expressions (d), when

---

[1] From notations (b) it may be seen that α and ϕ are small quantities since buckling within the elastic limit may occur only in the case of very thin shells so that h^2/a^2 is very small. τ/E is also very small.

[2] The case of buckling which we are considering requires large value for l/a; thus large values of λ are excluded from this discussion.

$$\frac{\lambda l}{a} = 2\pi \qquad \text{and} \qquad \lambda = \frac{2\pi a}{l}. \tag{j}$$

Substituting in (i), we obtain

$$\phi = \frac{\pi a(1 - \nu^2)}{l}$$

and, by using notation (b),

$$M_{cr} = \frac{2\pi^2 a^3 E h}{l}. \tag{288}$$

Noting that $2\pi a^3 h$ is the polar moment of inertia of the cross section of the tube, we find that the result obtained is in complete agreement with Greenhill's solution obtained for a sideways buckling of a long thin rod under torsion (Art. 31, p. 167).

If we take $n = 2$ in expression (f), we obtain

$$\phi = \frac{\lambda^4(1 - \nu^2) + \alpha[\lambda^8 + 16\lambda^6 + \lambda^4(74 - 4\nu + 2\nu^2) + \lambda^2(156 - 12\nu) + 144]}{4(\lambda^5 + 7\lambda^3 + 12\lambda)}. \tag{k}$$

By taking $\lambda = 1$ in this expression, we obtain a very high value for ϕ. Much smaller values can be obtained by assuming λ very small or very large. Calculations show that the first of these two assumptions gives smaller values for ϕ. Adopting this assumption and retaining only the important terms in expression (k), we obtain

$$\phi = \frac{\lambda^4(1 - \nu^2) + 144\alpha}{48\lambda}. \tag{l}$$

We now determine λ from the condition that ϕ becomes a minimum. Then

$$\frac{\partial \phi}{\partial \lambda} = \frac{3\lambda^2(1 - \nu^2)}{48} - \frac{3\alpha}{\lambda^2} = 0,$$

from which

$$\lambda = \sqrt[4]{\frac{48\alpha}{1 - \nu^2}} = \sqrt{\frac{2h}{a\sqrt{1 - \nu^2}}}.$$

Substituting in Eq. (l), we obtain

$$\phi = 2\sqrt[4]{\frac{1 - \nu^2}{3}}\alpha^{\frac{3}{4}}$$

and, by using notations (b),

$$M_{cr} = \frac{\pi\sqrt{2}E}{3(1 - \nu^2)^{\frac{3}{4}}}\sqrt{ah^5}$$

and

$$\tau_{cr} = \frac{M_{cr}}{2\pi a^2 h} = \frac{E}{3\sqrt{2}(1 - \nu^2)^{\frac{3}{4}}}\left(\frac{h}{a}\right)^{\frac{3}{2}} \tag{289}$$

Calculations with $n > 2$ always give[1] for τ_{cr} values larger than those we have just obtained with $n = 2$. Thus formula (289) must always be used in calculating critical stresses for a long cylindrical shell in twist.

In the case of shorter cylinders the conditions at the ends can no longer be disregarded and the problem of determining critical stress becomes more complicated. The general procedure will be as follows: We consider Eq. (f) as an equation of eighth degree in λ. Assuming certain values for ϕ, α and n, we find eight roots $\lambda_1, \lambda_2, \ldots, \lambda_8$ of this equation and, substituting them in expressions (d), we obtain eight corresponding elementary solutions. By superposing these solutions, the expressions for the displacements become

$$\left.\begin{aligned}
u &= \sum_{i=1}^{8} A_i \cos\left(\frac{\lambda_i x}{a} - n\theta\right); \\
v &= \sum_{i=1}^{8} B_i \cos\left(\frac{\lambda_i x}{a} - n\theta\right); \\
w &= \sum_{i=1}^{8} C_i \sin\left(\frac{\lambda_i x}{a} - n\theta\right).
\end{aligned}\right\} \tag{m}$$

Regarding the constants A_i, B_i, C_i it should be noted that for any root λ_i of Eq. (f) we obtain definite ratios for A_i/C_i and B_i/C_i from Eqs. (e). Thus there are only eight independent constants in expressions (m). For determining these constants we have eight boundary conditions, four at each end of the cylinder. Assuming, for instance, that the ends are simply supported, we have for each end

[1] Such calculations have been made by E. Schwerin, loc. cit., p. 482, and by W. Flügge. loc. cit., p. 459.

$$u = v = w = \frac{\partial^2 w}{\partial x^2} + \nu \frac{\partial^2 w}{a^2 \, \partial \theta^2} = 0. \qquad (n)$$

In the case of clamped edges, we have at each end

$$u = v = w = \frac{\partial w}{\partial x} = 0. \qquad (o)$$

Substituting expressions (m) in the boundary conditions, we obtain eight linear homogeneous equations. Equating to zero the determinant of these equations, we finally obtain an equation from which can be calculated the length l of the cylinder, to which the assumed values of ϕ, α and n correspond. Repeating such calculations for a considerable number of assumed values of ϕ, α and n, curves representing critical stresses as functions of the geometrical dimensions of the shell can be constructed.

Such calculations, however, would require an immense amount of work; to make the problem less intricate, several simplifications[1] have been proposed by L. H. Donnell. In the first two equations of the system (c) he omits all terms containing α or ϕ as a factor. In the third equation of the same system he retains only such terms with factors α or ϕ which contain the derivatives of w. In this manner Eq. (f) is also considerably simplified. Further simplification is introduced in the boundary conditions by omitting the requirement that $u = 0$ at the ends of the shell. Then the rest of the end conditions can be satisfied by keeping only four terms in the summations in expressions (m) and by replacing the simplified Eq. (f) of eighth degree in λ with an approximate equation of the fourth degree. In such a manner the boundary conditions and the determinant for calculating the critical stress are brought to the same form as in the problem of buckling of an infinitely long strip under shear, as discussed by Southwell and Skan.[2] As a result of all these simplifications, Donnell finally succeeds in presenting in a very simple form the relation between the critical stress and the proportions of the shell. He gives for short and moderately long shells the following formulas:

$$(1 - \nu^2) \frac{\tau_{cr}}{E} \frac{2}{h^2} = 4.6 + \sqrt{7.8 + 1.67 \left(\sqrt{1 - \nu^2 \frac{l^2}{2ha}} \right)^{\frac{3}{2}}} \qquad (290)$$

[1] DONNELL, L. H., *Nat. Advisory Comm. Aeronautics Rept.* 479, 1933.
[2] *Loc. cit.*, p. 360.

for clamped edges, and

$$(1 - \nu^2)\frac{\tau_{cr}}{E}\frac{l^2}{h^2} = 2.8 + \sqrt{2.6 + 1.40\left(\sqrt{1 - \nu^2}\frac{l^2}{2ah}\right)^{\frac{3}{2}}} \quad (291)$$

for simply supported edges.

To check these formulas some 50 tests were made, the results of which, together with those obtained by other experimenters,[1] are plotted in Fig. 252. It may be seen that all tests give values for the failure stress somewhat lower than the values of critical

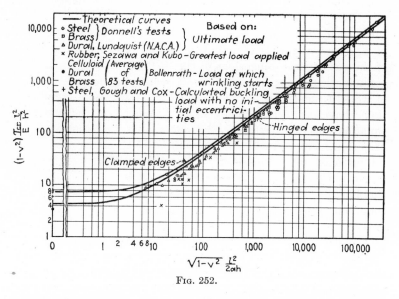

Fig. 252.

stress calculated from theoretical formulas. Donnell assumes that this discrepancy is due chiefly to unavoidable defects in actual tubes and also to the fact that it is impossible to attain a true clamped edge in practice.

For longer cylinders, namely, where

$$\frac{1}{\sqrt{1 - \nu^2}}\frac{l^2h}{(2a)^3} > 7.8 \text{ for clamped edges}$$

---

[1] See E. E. Lundquist, *Nat. Advisory Comm. Aeronautics Tech. Notes* 427, 1932; Katsutada Sezawa and Kei Kubo, *Tokyo Imp. Univ.*, Report 76, vol. 6, 1931. The experiments by F. Bollenrath and by Gough and Cox refer to buckling of flat strips, *loc. cit.*, p. 403.

and

$$\frac{1}{\sqrt{1-\nu^2}} \frac{l^2 h}{(2a)^3} > 5.5 \text{ for simply supported edges,}$$

it is recommended to use, in calculating critical stresses, formulas developed previously for very long cylinders.

Regarding the number of waves formed in the circumferential direction during buckling of tubes, the experiments are in very satisfactory agreement with the simplified theory.

Fig. 253.

Figure 253 represents the machine used by Donnell in his torsion and also combined torsion and bending and torsion and compression tests. The three types of load are applied by three conveniently located cranks. The amount of the load is read directly on the dial gauges. Figure 254 shows a cylindrical shell buckled under torsion.

The case of combined torsion and compression or tension of a thin cylindrical shell is of great practical interest; to get some information regarding critical stresses under such conditions, a considerable number of experiments have been made by using the above-mentioned machine.[1] The results of one series of such tests are plotted in Fig. 255. The coordinates

[1] See paper by F. J. Bridget, C. C. Jerome and A. B. Vosseller, *Trans. Am. Soc. Mech. Eng.*, vol. 56, p. 569, 1934.

are the ratios σ/σ_0 and τ/τ_0, where σ_0 and τ_0 are the critical stresses for compression and torsion when acting separately and where σ and τ are the critical stresses for combined loading. The full line averaging the experimental results is, in this case, a cubic parabola.

Fig. 254.

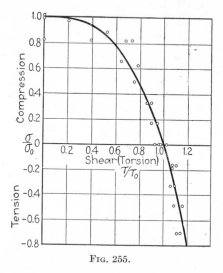

Fig. 255.

The case of buckling of a portion of a cylindrical shell bounded by two generators and two sections perpendicular to the axis of the cylinder has been discussed by T. E. Schunck.[1] The critical value of the shearing stress has been calculated for one particular case by using the strain-energy method.

[1] SCHUNCK, T. E., *Ingenieur-Archiv*, vol. 4, p. 394, 1933.

91. Buckling of Uniformly Compressed Spherical Shells.—If a spherical shell is submitted to uniform external pressure, it may retain its spherical form and undergo only a uniform compression. The magnitude of the uniform compressive stress in this case is

$$\sigma = \frac{qa}{2h}, \qquad (a)$$

where q is the pressure per unit area of the middle surface; a the radius of the sphere and h the thickness of the shell. If the pressure increases beyond a certain limit, the spherical form of equilibrium of the compressed shell may become unstable and buckling then occurs.[1] In calculating the critical value of pressure at which buckling occurs, we assume that the buckled surface is symmetrical with respect to a diameter of the sphere and we use Eqs. (263) derived for the case of symmetrical deformation of a symmetrically loaded shell. In the derivation of equations for the buckled surface of the sphere, we proceed as before and assume that the quantities u, v and w (Fig. 232) represent components of small displacements during buckling from the compressed spherical form. Then N_x and N_y in Eqs. (263) differ but little from the uniform compressive forces $qa/2$, and we can put

$$N_x = -\frac{qa}{2} + N'_x \qquad \text{and} \qquad N_y = -\frac{qa}{2} + N'_y, \qquad (b)$$

where N'_x and N'_y are the resultant forces due to small displacements u, v and w. Substituting these expressions in Eqs. (263), using[2] $q(1 + \epsilon_1 + \epsilon_2)$ instead of q and neglecting small terms such as products of N'_x, N'_y and Q_x with the derivatives of u, v and w, we obtain

---

[1] The buckling of spherical shells has been discussed by R. Zoelly, Dissertation, Zürich, 1915, and E. Schwerin, *Z. angew. Math. Mech.*, vol. 2, p. 81, 1922. A general solution of the problem, considering also unsymmetrical buckling, has been given by A. Van der Neut, Dissertation, Delft, 1932.

[2] This accounts for a small change of pressure on an element of the surface due to stretching of the surface. The corresponding terms in the equations are very small and could be neglected. We keep them only to bring the calculations into agreement with existing derivations in which the above-mentioned stretching of the surface has been considered.

$$\left.\begin{array}{l} \dfrac{dN'_x}{d\theta} + (N'_x - N'_y)\cot\theta - Q_x - \dfrac{qa}{2}\left(\dfrac{u}{a} + \dfrac{dw}{a\,d\theta}\right) = 0; \\[2mm] \dfrac{dQ_x}{d\theta} + Q_x\cot\theta + N'_x + N'_y + qa\left(\dfrac{du}{a\,d\theta} + \dfrac{u}{a}\cot\theta - \dfrac{2w}{a}\right) \\[2mm] \qquad - \dfrac{qa}{2}\left(\dfrac{du}{a\,d\theta} + \dfrac{d^2w}{a\,d\theta^2}\right) - \dfrac{qa}{2}\cot\theta\left(\dfrac{u}{a} + \dfrac{dw}{a\,d\theta}\right) = 0; \\[2mm] \dfrac{dM_x}{d\theta} + (M_x - M_y)\cot\theta - Q_x a = 0. \end{array}\right\} \quad (c)$$

Eliminating Q_x from the first two equations by the use of the third one and substituting in these equations (see p. 437)

$$N'_x = \frac{Eh}{1-\nu^2}\left[\frac{du}{a\,d\theta} - \frac{w}{a} + \nu\left(\frac{u\cot\theta}{a} - \frac{w}{a}\right)\right];$$

$$N'_y = \frac{Eh}{1-\nu^2}\left[\frac{u\cot\theta}{a} - \frac{w}{a} + \nu\left(\frac{du}{a\,d\theta} - \frac{w}{a}\right)\right];$$

$$M_x = -\frac{D}{a^2}\left[\frac{du}{d\theta} + \frac{d^2w}{d\theta^2} + \nu\left(u + \frac{dw}{d\theta}\right)\cot\theta\right];$$

$$M_y = -\frac{D}{a^2}\left[\left(u + \frac{dw}{d\theta}\right)\cot\theta + \nu\left(\frac{du}{d\theta} + \frac{d^2w}{d\theta^2}\right)\right],$$

we obtain for determining u and w two equations which, with the notations

$$\alpha = \frac{D(1-\nu^2)}{a^2 Eh} = \frac{h^2}{12a^2}; \qquad \phi = \frac{qa(1-\nu^2)}{2Eh}, \qquad (d)$$

can be represented in the following form:

$$(1+\alpha)\left[\frac{d^2u}{d\theta^2} + \cot\theta\,\frac{du}{d\theta} - (\nu + \cot^2\theta)u\right] - (1+\nu)\frac{dw}{d\theta} +$$
$$\alpha\left[\frac{d^3w}{d\theta^3} + \cot\theta\frac{d^2w}{d\theta^2} - (\nu + \cot^2\theta)\frac{dw}{d\theta}\right] - \phi\left(u + \frac{dw}{d\theta}\right) = 0; \quad (e)$$

$$(1+\nu)\left(\frac{du}{d\theta} + u\cot\theta - 2w\right) + \alpha\left[-\frac{d^3u}{d\theta^3} - 2\cot\theta\,\frac{d^2u}{d\theta^2} + \right.$$
$$(1+\nu+\cot^2\theta)\frac{du}{d\theta} - \cot\theta(2-\nu+\cot^2\theta)u - \frac{d^4w}{d\theta^4} -$$
$$\left. 2\cot\theta\frac{d^3w}{d\theta^3} + (1+\nu+\cot^2\theta)\frac{d^2w}{d\theta^2} - \cot\theta(2-\nu+\cot^2\theta)\frac{dw}{d\theta}\right] -$$
$$\phi\left(-u\cot\theta - \frac{du}{d\theta} + 4w + \cot\theta\,\frac{dw}{d\theta} + \frac{d^2w}{d\theta^2}\right) = 0. \quad (f)$$

We begin with Eq. (e) which can be simplified by omitting α in comparison with unity in the first factor.[1] We note also that the expressions in the brackets become identical if we replace u with $dw/d\theta$. Thus a simplification can be obtained if we introduce a new variable ψ by putting

$$u = \frac{d\psi}{d\theta}. \tag{g}$$

Equation (e) then becomes

$$\frac{d^3\psi}{d\theta^3} + \cot\theta\frac{d^2\psi}{d\theta^2} - (\nu + \cot^2\theta)\frac{d\psi}{d\theta} - (1+\nu)\frac{dw}{d\theta} +$$
$$\alpha\left[\frac{d^3w}{d\theta^3} + \cot\theta\frac{d^2w}{d\theta^2} - (\nu + \cot^2\theta)\frac{dw}{d\theta}\right] - \phi\left(\frac{d\psi}{d\theta} + \frac{dw}{d\theta}\right) = 0.$$

Using the symbol H for the operation

$$\frac{d^2(\cdots)}{d\theta^2} + \cot\theta\frac{d(\cdots)}{d\theta} + 2(\cdots), \tag{h}$$

this equation can be written as follows:

$$\frac{d}{d\theta}[H(\psi) + \alpha H(w) - (1+\nu)(\psi + w) - \alpha(1+\nu)w -$$
$$\phi(\psi + w)] = 0.$$

In this equation the fourth term, containing the factor α, can be neglected in comparison with the third. Integrating the equation after this simplification, and assuming the constant of integration equal to zero,[2] we obtain

$$H(\psi) + \alpha H(w) - (1+\nu)(\psi + w) - \phi(\psi + w) = 0. \tag{i}$$

Proceeding in the same manner with Eq. (f), we obtain

$$\alpha HH(\psi + w) - (1+\nu)H(\psi) - (3+\nu)\alpha H(w) +$$
$$2(1+\nu)(\psi + w) + \phi[-H(\psi) + H(w) + 2(\psi + w)] = 0. \tag{j}$$

Thus the investigation of buckling of a spherical shell reduces to the integration of the two Eqs. (i) and (j).

[1] From notation (d) it is seen that α is a very small quantity since buckling within the elastic limit may occur only in the case of very thin shells where h/a is small.

[2] From Eq. (g) it is seen that an addition of a constant to ψ does not affect the value of u.

We can solve these equations by using spherical functions of the order zero, one, two, . . . , which are[1]

$$P_0\,(\cos\theta) = 1;\quad P_1\,(\cos\theta) = \cos\theta;\quad P_2\,(\cos\theta) = \tfrac{1}{4}(3\cos 2\theta + 1);$$
$$P_3\,(\cos\theta) = \tfrac{1}{8}(5\cos 3\theta + 3\cos\theta);\quad P_4\,(\cos\theta) = \tfrac{1}{64}(35\cos 4\theta +$$
$$20\cos 2\theta + 9);$$

. . . .

$$P_n\,(\cos\theta) = 2\frac{1\cdot 3\cdot 5\;\cdots\;(2n-1)}{2^n\cdot n!}\Bigg[\cos n\theta +$$
$$\frac{1}{1}\frac{n}{2n-1}\cos(n-2)\theta + \frac{1\cdot 3}{1\cdot 2}\frac{n(n-1)}{(2n-1)(2n-3)}\cos(n-4)\theta +$$
$$\frac{1\cdot 3\cdot 5}{1\cdot 2\cdot 3}\frac{n(n-1)(n-2)}{(2n-1)(2n-3)(2n-5)}\cos(n-6)\theta + \cdots\Bigg]. \quad (k)$$

All these functions satisfy the equation[2]

$$\frac{d^2 P_n}{d\theta^2} + \cot\theta\,\frac{dP_n}{d\theta} + n(n+1)P_n = 0. \quad (l)$$

Hence, performing the operation indicated in (h), we obtain

$$H(P_n) = -\lambda_n P_n, \quad (m)$$
where
$$\lambda_n = n(n+1) - 2 \quad (n)$$
and
$$HH(P_n) = \lambda^2_n P_n. \quad (o)$$

Proceeding with spherical functions as we did before with trigonometric functions and using series, we obtain general expressions for any symmetrical buckling of a spherical shell by assuming

$$\left.\begin{aligned}\psi &= \sum_{n=0}^{\infty} A_n P_n;\\ w &= \sum_{n=0}^{\infty} B_n P_n.\end{aligned}\right\} \quad (p)$$

Substituting these expressions in Eqs. (i) and (j) and using Eqs. (m) and (o), we obtain

[1] Numerical tables and graphs of these functions can be found in E. Jahnke and F. Emde, "Funktionentafeln mit Formeln und Kurven," Berlin, 1933.

[2] Spherical functions are discussed by W. E. Byerly, "Fourier Series and Spherical Harmonics," 1893.

$$\sum_{n=0}^{\infty} \{A_n[\lambda_n + (1 + \nu) + \phi] + B_n[\alpha\lambda_n + (1 + \nu) + \phi]\}P_n = 0;$$

$$\sum_{n=0}^{\infty} \{A_n[\alpha\lambda^2_n + (1 + \nu)(\lambda_n + 2) + \phi(\lambda_n + 2)] +$$
$$B_n[\alpha\lambda^2_n + (3 + \nu)\alpha\lambda_n + 2(1 + \nu) - \phi(\lambda_n - 2)]\}P_n = 0.$$

The series on the left sides of these equations can vanish only if each term by itself vanishes. Thus we obtain for each value of n the following two homogeneous equations:

$$A_n[\lambda_n + (1 + \nu) + \phi] + B_n[\alpha\lambda_n + (1 + \nu) + \phi] = 0;$$
$$A_n[\alpha\lambda^2_n + (1 + \nu)(\lambda_n + 2) + \phi(\lambda_n + 2)] + B_n[\alpha\lambda^2_n +$$
$$(3 + \nu)\alpha\lambda_n + 2(1 + \nu) - \phi(\lambda_n - 2)] = 0. \quad (q)$$

Buckling of the shell becomes possible if these equations, for some value of n, yield for A_n and B_n a solution different from zero, which requires that the determinant of these equations becomes equal to zero. In this manner we obtain the following equation for calculating the critical value of the external pressure:[1]

$$(1 - \nu^2)\lambda_n + \alpha\lambda_n[\lambda^2_n + 2\lambda_n + (1 + \nu)^2] - \phi\lambda_n[\lambda_n +$$
$$(1 + 3\nu)] = 0. \quad (r)$$

One solution of this equation is

$$\lambda_n = 0.$$

The corresponding value of n, from Eq. (n), is

$$n = 1$$

and from the first of Eqs. (q) we conclude that

$$A_1 = -B_1.$$

The corresponding displacements, from Eqs. (p), are

$$u = \frac{d\psi}{d\theta} = -A_1 \sin \theta;$$
$$w = -A_1 \cos \theta.$$

They represent a displacement of the sphere as a rigid body of the amount A_1 along the axis of symmetry.

[1] The quantities α and ϕ are very small and are neglected in comparison with unity in the derivation of this equation.

To get displacements corresponding to buckling of the shell, we must assume in Eq. (r) that λ_n is different from zero. Then

$$\phi = \frac{(1 - \nu^2) + \alpha[\lambda^2{}_n + 2\lambda_n + (1 + \nu)^2]}{\lambda_n + (1 + 3\nu)}. \qquad (s)$$

For any value of n we can calculate ϕ, and by using notation (d) we obtain the corresponding value of the external pressure. To find the smallest value of ϕ and q at which buckling may occur, we consider expression (s) as a continuous function of λ_n and determine its minimum from the condition that

$$\frac{d\phi}{d\lambda_n} = 0.$$

This gives, after neglecting small terms,

$$\lambda^2{}_n + 2(1 + 3\nu)\lambda_n - \frac{1 - \nu^2}{\alpha} = 0$$

and, approximately,

$$\lambda_n = -(1 + 3\nu) + \sqrt{\frac{1 - \nu^2}{\alpha}}. \qquad (t)$$

Substituting in (s), we obtain

$$\phi_{\text{min.}} = 2\sqrt{(1 - \nu^2)\alpha} - 6\nu\alpha.$$

By using notations (d),

$$q_{cr} = \frac{\phi_{\text{min.}}.2Eh}{a(1 - \nu^2)} = \frac{2Eh}{a(1 - \nu^2)}\left(\sqrt{\frac{1 - \nu^2}{3}}\frac{h}{a} - \frac{\nu h^2}{2a^2}\right)$$

or, by neglecting the second term in the parenthesis,

$$q_{cr} = \frac{2Eh^2}{a^2\sqrt{3(1 - \nu^2)}}, \qquad (292)$$

and from Eq. (a)

$$\sigma_{cr} = \frac{Eh}{a\sqrt{3(1 - \nu^2)}}. \qquad (293)$$

This stress has the same magnitude as the critical stress for an axially compressed cylindrical shell of radius a and of thickness h [see Eq. (k), p. 457].

In the above derivation a continuous variation of λ_n has been assumed. But λ_n is defined from Eq. (n) in which n is an integer. Hence, to get a more accurate value for σ_{cr}, two adjacent integers, as obtained from Eq. (n), instead of the value (t), should be substituted in Eq. (s) and the value of λ_n which gives the smaller value for ϕ_n should be used in calculating critical stresses. From Eq. (t) it may be seen that λ_n is a large number; hence the numbers n are also large and the result of this more accurate calculation of σ_{cr} will differ but little from that given by formula (293).

Until now we have considered only symmetrical buckling of the shell, but a more general investigation shows[1] that, owing to symmetry of the uniformly compressed spherical shell with respect to any diameter, Eq. (s), derived on the assumption of symmetry, gives all possible values of ϕ_{cr} and that formula (293) always can be used for calculating the critical stress.

[1] See paper by A. Van der Neut, *loc. cit.*, p. 491; also W. Flügge, *loc. cit.*, p. 459.

APPENDIX

TABLE I.—TABLES OF FUNCTIONS $\phi(u)$, $\psi(u)$, $\chi(u)$

$$\phi(u) = \frac{3}{u}\left(\frac{1}{\sin 2u} - \frac{1}{2u}\right); \qquad \psi(u) = \frac{3}{2u}\left(\frac{1}{2u} - \frac{1}{\tan 2u}\right)$$

$$\chi(u) = \frac{3(\tan u - u)}{u^3}$$

$2u = kl$	$\phi(u)$	$\Delta\phi$	$\psi(u)$	$\Delta\psi$	$\chi(u)$	$\Delta\chi$	$2u = kl$
0	1.0000	....	1.0000	....	1.0000	....	0
0.5	1.0300	....	1.0171	....	1.0256	....	0.5
1.00	1.1304	....	1.0737	....	1.1113	....	1.00
		0.0151		0.0085		0.0128	
1.05	1.1455		1.0822		1.1241		1.05
		0.0162		0.0090		0.0138	
1.10	1.1617		1.0912		1.1379		1.10
		0.0175		0.0097		0.0148	
1.15	1.1792		1.1009		1.1527		1.15
		0.0187		0.0105		0.0159	
1.20	1.1979		1.1114		1.1686		1.20
		0.0201		0.0111		0.0170	
1.25	1.2180		1.1225		1.1856		1.25
		0.0216		0.0120		0.0183	
1.30	1.2396		1.1345		1.2039		1.30
		0.0232		0.0128		0.0196	
1.35	1.2628		1.1473		1.2235		1.35
		0.0250		0.0137		0.0210	
1.40	1.2878		1.1610		1.2445		1.40
		0.0268		0.0147		0.0226	
1.45	1.3146		1.1757		1.2671		1.45
		0.0288		0.0158		0.0243	
1.50	1.3434		1.1915		1.2914		1.50
		0.0310		0.0169		0.0260	
1.55	1.3744		1.2084		1.3174		1.55
		0.0334		0.0182		0.0281	
1.60	1.4078		1.2266		1.3455		1.60
		0.0361		0.0196		0.0303	
1.65	1.4439		1.2462		1.3758		1.65
		0.0391		0.0211		0.0327	
1.70	1.4830		1.2673		1.4085		1.70
		0.0422		0.0228		0.0353	
1.75	1.5252		1.2901		1.4438		1.75
		0.0458		0.0246		0.0383	
1.80	1.5710		1.3147		1.4821		1.80
		0.0498		0.0267		0.0416	
1.85	1.6208		1.3414		1.5237		1.85

TABLE I.—TABLES OF FUNCTIONS $\phi(u)$, $\psi(u)$, $\chi(u)$.—(Continued)

$2u = kl$	$\phi(u)$	$\Delta\phi$	$\psi(u)$	$\Delta\psi$	$\chi(u)$	$\Delta\chi$	$2u = kl$
1.85	1.6208		1.3414		1.5237		1.85
		0.0542		0.0290		0.0452	
1.90	1.6750		1.3704		1.5689		1.90
		0.0593		0.0316		0.0493	
1.95	1.7343		1.4020		1.6182		1.95
		0.0650		0.0345		0.0540	
2.00	1.7993		1.4365		1.6722		2.00
		0.0137		0.0073		0.0114	
2.01	1.8130		1.4438		1.6836		2.01
		0.0140		0.0074		0.0117	
2.02	1.8270		1.4512		1.6953		2.02
		0.0143		0.0075		0.0118	
2.03	1.8413		1.4587		1.7071		2.03
		0.0145		0.0077		0.0121	
2.04	1.8558		1.4664		1.7192		2.04
		0.0148		0.0078		0.0123	
2.05	1.8706		1.4742		1.7315		2.05
		0.0152		0.0080		0.0126	
2.06	1.8858		1.4822		1.7440		2.06
		0.0154		0.0082		0.0128	
2.07	1.9012		1.4904		1.7568		2.07
		0.0156		0.0083		0.0130	
2.08	1.9168		1.4987		1.7698		2.08
		0.0161		0.0084		0.0134	
2.09	1.9329		1.5071		1.7832		2.09
		0.0165		0.0087		0.0135	
2.10	1.9494		1.5158		1.7967		2.10
		0.0168		0.0088		0.0139	
2.11	1.9661		1.5246		1.8106		2.11
		0.0170		0.0090		0.0141	
2.12	1.9831		1.5336		1.8247		2.12
		0.0174		0.0091		0.0145	
2.13	2.0005		1.5427		1.8392		2.13
		0.0179		0.0094		0.0147	
2.14	2.0184		1.5521		1.8539		2.14
		0.0182		0.0095		0.0150	
2.15	2.0366		1.5616		1.8689		2.15
		0.0186		0.0097		0.0154	
2.16	2.0552		1.5713		1.8843		2.16
		0.0189		0.0100		0.0157	
2.17	2.0741		1.5813		1.9000		2.17
		0.0194		0.0101		0.0160	
2.18	2.0935		1.5914		1.9160		2.18
		0.0198		0.0104		0.0163	
2.19	2.1133		1.6018		1.9323		2.19
		0.0203		0.0106		0.0168	
2.20	2.1336		1.6124		1.9491		2.20
		0.0207		0.0109		0.0172	
2.21	2.1543		1.6233		1.9663		2.21
		0.0211		0.0110		0.0174	
2.22	2.1754		1.6343		1.9837		2.22
		0.0218		0.0114		0.0179	
2.23	2.1972		1.6457		2.0016		2.23

TABLE I.—TABLES OF FUNCTIONS $\phi(u)$, $\psi(u)$, $\chi(u)$.—*(Continued)*

$2u = kl$	$\phi(u)$	$\Delta\phi$	$\psi(u)$	$\Delta\psi$	$\chi(u)$	$\Delta\chi$	$2u = kl$
2.23	2.1972		1.6457		2.0016		2.23
		0.0222		0.0115		0.0183	
2.24	2.2194		1.6572		2.0199		2.24
		0.0227		0.0118		0.0187	
2.25	2.2421		1.6690		2.0386		2.25
		0.0232		0.0122		0.0192	
2.26	2.2654		1.6812		2.0578		2.26
		0.0237		0.0124		0.0197	
2.27	2.2891		1.6936		2.0775		2.27
		0.0244		0.0126		0.0201	
2.28	2.3135		1.7062		2.0976		2.28
		0.0249		0.0130		0.0205	
2.29	2.3384		1.7192		2.1181		2.29
		0.0257		0.0133		0.0211	
2.30	2.3641		1.7325		2.1392		2.30
		0.0262		0.0136		0.0216	
2.31	2.3902		1.7461		2.1608		2.31
		0.0269		0.0140		0.0222	
2.32	2.4171		1.7601		2.1830		2.32
		0.0277		0.0143		0.0227	
2.33	2.4448		1.7744		2.2057		2.33
		0.0283		0.0147		0.0233	
2.34	2.4731		1.7891		2.2290		2.34
		0.0291		0.0150		0.0239	
2.35	2.5022		1.8041		2.2529		2.35
		0.0298		0.0154		0.0245	
2.36	2.5320		1.8195		2.2774		2.36
		0.0305		0.0159		0.0251	
2.37	2.5625		1.8354		2.3025		2.37
		0.0314		0.0162		0.0259	
2.38	2.5939		1.8516		2.3284		2.38
		0.0323		0.0167		0.0266	
2.39	2.6262		1.8683		2.3550		2.39
		0.0334		0.0171		0.0272	
2.40	2.6596		1.8854		2.3822		2.40
		0.0339		0.0177		0.0281	
2.41	2.6935		1.9031		2.4103		2.41
		0.0352		0.0181		0.0288	
2.42	2.7287		1.9212		2.4391		2.42
		0.0362		0.0186		0.0296	
2.43	2.7649		1.9398		2.4687		2.43
		0.0372		0.0191		0.0306	
2.44	2.8021		1.9589		2.4993		2.44
		0.0382		0.0197		0.0313	
2.45	2.8403		1.9786		2.5306		2.45
		0.0395		0.0203		0.0324	
2.46	2.8798		1.9989		2.5630		2.46
		0.0406		0.0209		0.0334	
2.47	2.9204		2.0198		2.5964		2.47
		0.0420		0.0215		0.0343	
2.48	2.9624		2.0413		2.6307		2.48
		0.0432		0.0222		0.0355	
2.49	3.0056		2.0635		2.6662		2.49

TABLE I.—TABLES OF FUNCTIONS $\phi(u)$, $\psi(u)$, $\chi(u)$.—(*Continued*)

$2u = kl$	$\phi(u)$	$\Delta\phi$	$\psi(u)$	$\Delta\psi$	$\chi(u)$	$\Delta\chi$	$2u = kl$
2.49	3.0056		2.0635		2.6662		2.49
		0.0446		0.0229		0.0365	
2.50	3.0502		2.0864		2.7027		2.50
		0.0461		0.0236		0.0378	
2.51	3.0963		2.1100		2.7405		2.51
		0.0475		0.0243		0.0389	
2.52	3.1438		2.1343		2.7794		2.52
		0.0493		0.0252		0.0403	
2.53	3.1931		2.1595		2.8197		2.53
		0.0506		0.0260		0.0415	
2.54	3.2437		2.1855		2.8612		2.54
		0.0526		0.0269		0.0431	
2.55	3.2963		2.2124		2.9043		2.55
		0.0545		0.0278		0.0445	
2.56	3.3508		2.2402		2.9488		2.56
		0.0564		0.0288		0.0461	
2.57	3.4072		2.2690		2.9949		2.57
		0.0585		0.0298		0.0478	
2.58	3.4657		2.2988		3.0427		2.58
		0.0605		0.0309		0.0495	
2.59	3.5262		2.3297		3.0922		2.59
		0.0628		0.0321		0.0513	
2.60	3.5890		2.3618		3.1435		2.60
		0.0652		0.0332		0.0533	
2.61	3.6542		2.3950		3.1968		2.61
		0.0678		0.0345		0.0554	
2.62	3.7220		2.4295		3.2522		2.62
		0.0705		0.0359		0.0575	
2.63	3.7925		2.4654		3.3097		2.63
		0.0734		0.0373		0.0599	
2.64	3.8659		2.5027		3.3696		2.64
		0.0762		0.0388		0.0623	
2.65	3.9421		2.5415		3.4319		2.65
		0.0797		0.0404		0.0650	
2.66	4.0218		2.5819		3.4969		2.66
		0.0829		0.0422		0.0677	
2.67	4.1047		2.6241		3.5646		2.67
		0.0867		0.0439		0.0707	
2.68	4.1914		2.6680		3.6353		2.68
		0.0906		0.0460		0.0739	
2.69	4.2820		2.7140		3.7092		2.69
		0.0946		0.0479		0.0771	
2.70	4.3766		2.7619		3.7863		2.70
		0.0991		0.0502		0.0808	
2.71	4.4757		2.8121		3.8671		2.71
		0.1038		0.0527		0.0846	
2.72	4.5795		2.8648		3.9517		2.72
		0.1090		0.0551		0.0888	
2.73	4.6885		2.9199		4.0405		2.73
		0.1144		0.0579		0.0932	
2.74	4.8029		2.9778		4.1337		2.74
		0.1204		0.0608		0.0980	
2.75	4.9233		3.0386		4.2317		2.75

TABLE I.—TABLES OF FUNCTIONS $\phi(u)$, $\psi(u)$, $\chi(u)$.—*(Continued)*

$2u = kl$	$\phi(u)$	$\Delta\phi$	$\psi(u)$	$\Delta\psi$	$\chi(u)$	$\Delta\chi$	$2u = kl$
2.75	4.9233		3.0386		4.2317		2.75
		0.1266		0.0641		0.1032	
2.76	5.0499		3.1027		4.3349		2.76
		0.1336		0.0675		0.1087	
2.77	5.1835		3.1702		4.4436		2.77
		0.1410		0.0712		0.1148	
2.78	5.3245		3.2414		4.5584		2.78
		0.1491		0.0752		0.1213	
2.79	5.4736		3.3166		4.6797		2.79
		0.1579		0.0797		0.1285	
2.80	5.6315		3.3963		4.8082		2.80
		0.1675		0.0844		0.1362	
2.81	5.7990		3.4807		4.9444		2.81
		0.1780		0.0897		0.1448	
2.82	5.9770		3.5704		5.0892		2.82
		0.1894		0.0955		0.1540	
2.83	6.1664		3.6659		5.2432		2.83
		0.2021		0.1017		0.1643	
2.84	6.3685		3.7676		5.4075		2.84
		0.2160		0.1088		0.1757	
2.85	6.5845		3.8764		5.5832		2.85
		0.2315		0.1164		0.1881	
2.86	6.8160		3.9928		5.7713		2.86
		0.2486		0.1251		0.2020	
2.87	7.0646		4.1179		5.9733		2.87
		0.2676		0.1346		0.2174	
2.88	7.3322		4.2525		6.1907		2.88
		0.2890		0.1452		0.2348	
2.89	7.6212		4.3977		6.4255		2.89
		0.3131		0.1573		0.2543	
2.90	7.9343		4.5550		6.6798		2.90
		0.3402		0.1709		0.2763	
2.91	8.2745		4.7259		6.9561		2.91
		0.3710		0.1862		0.3012	
2.92	8.6455		4.9121		7.2573		2.92
		0.4061		0.2039		0.3298	
2.93	9.0516		5.1160		7.5871		2.93
		0.4466		0.2241		0.3625	
2.94	9.4982		5.3401		7.9496		2.94
		0.4933		0.2474		0.4004	
2.95	9.9915		5.5875		8.3500		2.95
		0.5478		0.2747		0.4446	
2.96	10.5393		5.8622		8.7946		2.96
		0.6117		0.3066		0.4964	
2.97	11.1510		6.1688		9.2910		2.97
		0.6876		0.3446		0.5579	
2.98	11.8386		6.5134		9.8489		2.98
		0.7785		0.3901		0.6315	
2.99	12.6171		6.9035		10.4804		2.99
		0.8886		0.4451		0.7209	
3.00	13.5057		7.3486		11.2013		3.00
		1.0238		0.5127		0.8304	
3.01	14.5295		7.8613		12.0317		3.01

TABLE I.—TABLES OF FUNCTIONS $\phi(u)$, $\psi(u)$, $\chi(u)$.—(*Continued*)

$2u = kl$	$\phi(u)$	$\Delta\phi$	$\psi(u)$	$\Delta\psi$	$\chi(u)$	$\Delta\chi$	$2u = kl$
3.01	14.5295		7.8613		12.0317		3.01
		1.1924		0.5970		0.9671	
3.02	15.7219		8.4583		12.9988		3.02
		1.4063		0.7040		1.1405	
3.03	17.1282		9.1623		14.1393		3.03
		1.6834		0.8426		1.3651	
3.04	18.8116		10.0049		15.5044		3.04
		2.0513		1.0265		1.6633	
3.05	20.8629		11.0314		17.1677		3.05
		2.5547		1.2782		2.0711	
3.06	23.4176		12.3096		19.2388		3.06
		3.2684		1.6350		2.6498	
3.07	26.6860		13.9446		21.8886		3.07
		4.3300		2.1659		3.5103	
3.08	31.0160		16.1105		25.3989		3.08
		6.0084		3.0051		4.8712	
3.09	37.0244		19.1156		30.2701		3.09
		8.8990		4.4503		7.2138	
3.10	45.9234		23.5659		37.4839		3.10
		14.5332		7.2675		11.7808	
3.11	60.4566		30.8334		49.2647		3.11
		27.9956		13.9987		22.6930	
3.12	88.4522		44.8321		71.9577		3.12
		76.2965		38.1491		61.8440	
3.13	164.7487		82.9812		133.8017		3.13
		1034.4142		517.2088		838.4545	
3.14	1199.1629		600.1900		972.2562		3.14
		∞		∞		∞	
3.15	−227.1668		−112.9747		−183.8716		3.15
		123.4092		61.7055		100.0325	
3.16	−103.7576		−51.2692		−83.8391		3.16
		36.5228		18.2624		29.6049	
3.17	−67.2348		−33.0068		−54.2342		3.17
		17.5035		8.7527		14.1884	
3.18	−49.7313		−24.2541		−40.0458		3.18
		10.2713		5.1365		8.3263	
3.19	−39.4600		−19.1176		−31.7195		3.19
		6.7537		3.3778		5.4750	
3.20	−32.7063		−15.7398		−26.2445		3.20
		4.7787		2.3903		3.8742	
3.21	−27.9276		−13.3495		−22.3703		3.21
		3.5593		1.7807		2.8858	
3.22	−24.3683		−11.5688		−19.4845		3.22
		2.7541		1.3779		2.2330	
3.23	−21.6142		−10.1909		−17.2515		3.23
		2.1940		1.0980		1.7790	
3.24	−19.4202		−9.0929		−15.4725		3.24
		1.7890		0.8954		1.4507	
3.25	−17.6312		−8.1975		−14.0218		3.25
		1.4865		0.7443		1.2057	
3.26	−16.1447		−7.4532		−12.8161		3.26
		1.2548		0.6284		1.0178	
3.27	−14.8899		−6.8248		−11.7983		3.27

TABLE I.—TABLES OF FUNCTIONS $\phi(u)$, $\psi(u)$, $\chi(u)$.—(*Concluded*)

$2u = kl$	$\phi(u)$	$\Delta\phi$	$\psi(u)$	$\Delta\psi$	$\chi(u)$	$\Delta\chi$	$2u = kl$
3.27	−14.8899		−6.8248		−11.7983		3.27
		1.0733		0.5376		0.8707	
3.28	−13.8166		−6.2872		−10.9276		3.28
		0.9285		0.4652		0.7533	
3.29	−12.8881		−5.8220		−10.1743		3.29
		0.8111		0.4066		0.6581	
3.30	−12.0770		−5.4154		−9.5162		3.30
		4.6522		2.3367		3.7784	
3.40	−7.4248		−3.0787		−5.7378		3.40
		2.0479		1.0354		1.6681	
3.50	−5.3769		−2.0433		−4.0697		3.50
		1.1477		0.5861		0.9389	
3.60	−4.2292		−1.4572		−3.1308		3.60
		0.7302		0.3785		0.6016	
3.70	−3.4990		−1.0787		−2.5292		3.70
		0.5029		0.2659		0.4179	
3.80	−2.9961		−0.8128		−2.1113		3.80
		0.3647		0.1981		0.3070	
3.90	−2.6314		−0.6147		−1.8043		3.90
		0.2744		0.1544		0.2349	
4.00	−2.3570		−0.4603		−1.5694		4.00
		0.2116		0.1248		0.1854	
4.10	−2.1454		−0.3355		−1.3840		4.10
		0.1662		0.1038		0.1498	
4.20	−1.9792		−0.2317		−1.2342		4.20
		0.1317		0.0887		0.1237	
4.30	−1.8475		−0.1430		−1.1105		4.30
		0.1046		0.0778		0.1036	
4.40	−1.7429		−0.0652		−1.0069		4.40
		0.0826		0.0696		0.0881	
4.50	−1.6603		0.0044		−0.9188		4.50
		0.0641		0.0638		0.0757	
4.60	−1.5962		0.0682		−0.8431		4.60
		0.0810		0.1169		0.1235	
4.80	−1.5152		0.1851		−0.7196		4.80
		0.0238		0.1124		0.0962	
5.00	−1.4914		0.2975		−0.6234		5.00
		0.0568		0.1520		0.0938	
5.25	−1.5482		0.4495		−0.5296		5.25
		0.1964		0.1975		0.0733	
5.5	−1.7446		0.6470		−0.4563		5.5
		0.4898		0.3277		0.0589	
5.75	−2.2344		0.9747		−0.3974		5.75
		1.5111		0.8268		0.0482	
6.0	−3.7455		1.8015		−0.3492		6.0
		25.3412		12.7331		0.0404	
6.25	−29.0867		14.5346		−0.3088		6.25
		∞		∞		0.0048	
2π	± ∞		± ∞		−0.3040		2π
		∞		∞		0.0295	
6.5	4.1490		−2.0242		−0.2745		6.5

AUTHOR INDEX

B

Back, G., 400, 401
Bairstow, L., 134
Basquin, O. H., 191
Bauschinger, I., 170, 184
Bergmann, S., 360, 384, 404
Biezeno, C. G., 165, 167, 236
Blasius, H., 138
Bleich, F., 21, 181, 386
Bollenrath, F., 403, 488
Boobnov, J. G., 105, 350
Born, M., 73
Boussinesq, J., 206
Brazier, L. G., 465
Bridget, F. J., 340, 402, 489
Broszko, M., 160
Brunner, J., 58
Bryan, G. H., 220, 313, 327, 367
Bulgakov, B. V., 224
Byerly, W. E., 24, 494

C

Čališev, K., 346
Carman, A. P., 453
Chwalla, E., 45, 58, 59, 226, 227, 349, 389, 465
Clark, E., 411, 460
Clausen, 138
Clebsch, A., 73, 299, 305
Collignon, E., 73
Considère, A., 157, 170, 171, 175
Cook, G., 453
Coulomb, 170
Cox, H. L., 399, 403, 488

D

Dinnik, A. N., 118, 133, 134, 137, 139, 230, 242, 248, 249, 255

Domke, O., 73
Dondorff, J., 115
Donnell, L. H., 396, 397, 455, 460, 462, 463, 466, 487, 488, 489
Dschou, D. D., 470, 473

E

Eichinger, A., 389
Elwitz, E., 131, 157
Emde, F., 71, 247, 368, 494
Engesser, F., 86, 92, 140, 143, 157, 158, 160
Euler, L., 64, 115, 133

F

Fairbairn, W., 409, 460
Faxen, O. H., 365
Federhofer, K., 242, 243, 248, 249, 250
Fleming, R., 269
Flügge, W., 451, 459, 464, 470, 476, 477, 480, 486, 497
Föppl, A., 183, 259
Föppl, L., 442
Forsyth, A. R., 116, 135
Frandsen, P. M., 186
Franke, A., 131, 135
Fuller, C. E., 185
Funk, P., 86

G

Gaber, E., 227
Gale, W. H., 470
Galerkin, B., 371
Geckeler, J. W., 442, 443
Gehler, W., 161, 180
Gibb, H. M., 408
Gibbons, H. B., 105, 107

507

SUBJECT INDEX

A

Allowable stress in columns, based on critical stress diagram, 180
under combined axial and lateral load, 36
diagram for, 182
magnification factor for determining, 182
Angles of rotation at ends of compressed bar, 13
Anisotropic (*see* Non-isotropic plates)
Anticlastic surface, 289
Application of buckling formulas for plates, 404
Approximate calculation of critical loads, energy method, 78, 252, 325, 439
graphical method, 87, 131
successive approximations, 84
Arches, flat parabolic, buckling of, 226
with small curvature, buckling of, 230
uniformly compressed circular, buckling of, 225
Average compressive stress at yielding for, initially curved column, 44
short bars eccentrically loaded, 42
slender bars eccentrically loaded, 42

B

Batten-plate column, critical load of, 145
design of, 196
rigorous formula for buckling of, 155

Bending, of bars, under the action of axial and lateral loads, 1
with built-in ends, 14
with circular axis, 204
by couples at the ends, 11
initially curved, 31
on many supports, 17
principle of superposition in, 7
beyond proportional limit, 45
by several lateral loads, 6
by uniform lateral load, 8
use of trigonometric series in, 23
combined with compression beyond proportional limit, 51
by couples, of plates, 287
of prismatical bars, 11
of plates, combined with tension or compression, 302
by distributed lateral load, 294
pure, 287
with small initial curvature, 319
strain energy of, 305
pure (*see* Pure bending)
of thin shells, 419
Bessel's functions, application of, in buckling of columns under distributed axial loads, 115
in lateral buckling of beams, 247
Bimetallic strip, buckling of, 236
Body forces, in bending of plates, 305
Boundary conditions of plates, 298
Buckling load (*see* Critical load)
Buckling, of bars, with built-in ends, 67
continuous, 96, 100
with distributed axial loads, 115
on elastic foundation, 108
with elastically built-in ends, 90
fundamental case of, 67